COBALT

Its Chemistry, Metallurgy, and Uses

Edited by
ROLAND S. YOUNG
Consulting Chemical Engineer
Victoria, B. C.

American Chemical Society
Monograph Series

REINHOLD PUBLISHING CORPORATION
New York
CHAPMAN & HALL, LTD., *London*

Library of Congress Catalog Card Number: 60-53328

Photocomposed by The Science Press, Inc., Lancaster, Pa.

Printed in the United States of America
THE GUINN CO., INC.
New York 14, N. Y.

GENERAL INTRODUCTION

American Chemical Society's Series of Chemical Monographs

By arrangement with the Interallied Conference of Pure and Applied Chemistry, which met in London and Brussels in July, 1919, the American Chemical Society was to undertake the production and publication of Scientific and Technologic Monographs on chemical subjects. At the same time it was agreed that the National Research Council, in cooperation with the American Chemical Society and the American Physical Society, should undertake the production and publication of Critical Tables of Chemical and Physical Constants. The American Chemical Society and the National Research Council mutually agreed to care for these two fields of chemical progress. The American Chemical Society named as Trustees, to make the necessary arrangements of the publication of the Monographs, Charles L. Parsons, secretary of the Society, Washington, D. C.; the late John E. Teeple, then treasurer of the Society, New York; and the late Professor Gellert Alleman of Swarthmore College. The Trustees arranged for the publication of the ACS Series of (a) Scientific and (b) Technological Monographs by the Chemical Catalog Company, Inc. (Reinhold Publishing Corporation, successor) of New York.

The Council of the American Chemical Society, acting through its Committee on National Policy, appointed editors (the present list of whom appears at the close of this sketch) to select authors of competent authority in their respective fields and to consider critically the manuscripts submitted.

The first Monograph of the Series appeared in 1921. After twenty-three years of experience certain modifications of general policy were indicated. In the beginning there still remained from the preceding five decades a distinct though artibrary differentiation between so-called "pure science" publications and technologic or applied science literature. By 1944 this differentiation was fast becoming nebulous. Research in private enterprise had grown apace and not a little of it was pursued on the frontiers of knowledge. Furthermore, most workers in the sciences were coming to see the artificiality of the separation. The methods of both groups of workers are the same. They employ the same instrumentalities, and frankly recognize that their objectives are common, namely, the search for new knowledge for the service of man. The officers of the Society therefore combined the two editorial Boards in a single Board of twelve representative members

iii

Also in the beginning of the Series, it seemed expedient to construe rather broadly the definition of a Monograph. Needs of workers had to be recognized. Consequently among the first hundred Monographs appeared works in the form of treatises covering in some instances rather broad areas. Because such necessary works do not now want for publishers, it is considered advisable to hew more strictly to the line of the Monograph character, which means more complete and critical treatment of relatively restricted areas, and, where a broader field needs coverage, to subdivide it into logical subareas. The prodigious expansion of new knowledge makes such a change desirable.

These Monographs are intended to serve two principal purposes: first, to make available to chemists a thorough treatment of a selected area in form usable by persons working in more or less unrelated fields to the end that they may correlate their own work with a larger area of physical science discipline; second, to stimulate further research in the specific field treated. To implement this purpose the authors of Monographs are expected to give extended references to the literature. Where the literature is of such volume that a complete bibliography is impracticable, the authors are expected to append a list of references critically selected on the basis of their relative importance and significance.

PREFACE

This new book replaces the former monograph No. 108 entitled simply "Cobalt," written entirely by the present Editor.

The substantial rise in world production of cobalt in recent years has been accompanied by an increasing interest in the properties and applications of this metal and its compounds by workers in many fields of science and technology.

This new monograph is written for two classes of readers: (1) The chemist, or other scientific worker, who has occasion to work with cobalt and wants accurate, up-to-date, and complete information; (2) the chemist or metallurgist who wishes to browse through this field in the hope of adding to his general knowledge or acquiring ideas which may be applicable to his own sphere of work.

In the preparation of this reference book we have attempted not only to summarize the newer developments in cobalt, but also to include many chapters where experience has indicated that treatment of the subject would be appreciated. We have been fortunate in securing the cooperation of specialists who have contributed a number of chapters.

The Editor is indebted to many individuals and organizations for information, and trusts that in all instances appropriate acknowledgment has been given. Special mention should be made of the assistance obtained from Mr. H. L. Talbot, whose extensive experience as consulting metallurgical engineer has been of great value, and from Dr. G. R. Lusby, whose translations of Russian work have been very helpful.

To those who kindly offered comments and suggestions for improvement, the Editor is deeply grateful. It is our hope that the present edition will experience the benefit of constructive criticism from its readers.

Victoria, B. C.   R. S. YOUNG
December, 1960

v

CONTENTS

Chapter 1
HISTORICAL AND GENERAL

In the sixteenth century, the term *kobold*, probably derived from the Greek κοβαλοι, mischievous goblins, was applied to certain ores in the Hartz Mountains which, when roasted, not only failed to yield copper but emitted troublesome and dangerous fumes from the associated arsenic. Modifications of this local designation soon spread over Europe, and the alchemical literature of that period has references to kobolt, cobalt, etc. We cannot be certain, however, that these terms, in all cases, referred to cobalt, since a good deal of confusion over cobalt, zinc and arsenic minerals was exhibited even by that scholarly Renaissance expositor of mining and metallurgy, Georgius Agricola.[1]

When cobalt ores were roasted to eliminate most of the sulfur and arsenic, they yielded a mixture of crude cobalt oxide and sand, called *zaffre*. Fusion of the latter with potassium carbonate, or occasionally with glass, produced *smalt*, essentially a potash silica glass colored blue with cobalt. For a long time, the alchemists believed the color was due to arsenic or bismuth, but in 1742 Brandt showed that the effect was derived from a new demi-metal, *cobalt rex*. About 1780, Bergman and others studied the properties of cobalt and established its elemental character.[8]

In the latter part of the seventeenth century, invisible inks attracted considerable attention, and it was inevitable that the color changes of cobalt salts should be utilized for this purpose. In 1705, a colorless solution of bismuthiferous cobalt was used to give a green color on heating. For a long time, the color phenomena in these impure products were alleged to be caused by the presence of other metals, but finally the effects were correctly attributed to cobalt.

Although the beginning of cobalt chemistry and metallurgy may be said to date from the middle of the sixteenth century, the element has been found in some ancient blue glazes and glasses. A few statuettes have revealed that a cobalt-base coloring agent was used by the Egyptians about 1300 B.C., and perhaps much earlier, but the blue of most old Egyptian glazes was due to copper. The blue of some early specimens of Persian glass beads, dating from about 2250 B.C., is due to cobalt; the element is also found in some specimens of ancient Roman and Venetian blue glass. It is certain that cobalt was used in pottery of Persia and Syria in the early centuries of the Christian Era. The use of cobalt blue in China has been authenticated for at least as early as the T'ang Dynasty—618-906 A.D. Since ores of copper are more abundant and widely distributed on the earth's surface than those of cobalt, it is not surprising that most of the ancient blue glasses and glazes were colored with copper compounds.

Toward the close of the nineteenth century, the small world output of cobalt, derived chiefly from various German, Norwegian and Hungarian deposits which had been worked for very long periods, was greatly augmented by the development of oxidized cobalt ores in New Caledonia. The latter deposits were discovered by Garnier in 1864, and the mines were opened about ten years later. New Caledonia remained the principal source of cobalt for some years until the silver-cobalt ores of Ontario, Canada were exploited, around 1903. It is probable that in the period 1880-1905, New Caledonia furnished about 100,000 tons of ore averaging 3.0-3.5 per cent Co.[10] In 1958, after a lapse of nearly half a century, New Caledonia reappeared in world cobalt production statistics.

The rich arsenide ores around the town of Cobalt in northern Ontario yielded a rapid increase in production from 16 tons of cobalt in 1904 to a maximum of 1,553 in 1909, thereafter declining to 337 in 1917.[2,3]. Canadian production in the period 1920-1940 ranged from about 150 to 550 tons per annum, depending on world economic conditions. During and immediately following World War II, the Canadian output of cobalt was low; in recent years, however, it has shown a steady increase as a recovered by-product of the nickel industry, and Canada is once again one of the principal world producers.

About 1920, Union Minière du Haut Katanga began to extract cobalt from their copper-cobalt ores of Katanga province in the Belgian Congo, and in 1926 became the leading world producer. The Belgian Congo still retains this position by a wide margin.

With the opening of the great copper deposits of Northern Rhodesia, around 1930, it was found that cobalt occurred in a small but fairly constant concentration in the copper ores of one producer, Rhokana Corporation Limited, at Nkana. Since then, Northern Rhodesia has held, in most years, second or third place in cobalt production. In 1953, Northern Rhodesia united with Southern Rhodesia and Nyasaland to form the Federation of Rhodesia and Nyasaland; subsequently, statistical data have been included under the latter designation. Since the only cobalt produced in the Federation comes from Northern Rhodesia, however, and this territory retains a large measure of local autonomy as a distinct political unit, the familiar name of Northern Rhodesia will continue to be used throughout this book, except in a few statistical tables.

In 1933, the cobalt deposits of French Morocco, which had been discovered some years previously, yielded 40 tons of cobalt. Output increased rapidly to 793 tons in 1938, placing this country in third position as a cobalt producer. In recent years, Morocco has fallen behind Canada and the United States in cobalt output, but it still remains one of the few important producers.

Around 1936, Finland entered the ranks with the development, at Outokumpu, of cupriferous pyrite containing about 0.18–0.19 per cent Co. An output of 276 short tons was reported for 1938, but in the war years production statistics became unreliable or unavailable. In recent years, pyrite concentrates from Finland have been sent to West Germany for recovery of metal values, and this cobalt appears in German production statistics lumped together with that derived from other sources. Taking the figures given in the United Nations Statistical Yearbooks for contained cobalt in the cupriferous pyrite mined in Finland, and assuming only a 40–50 per cent over-all recovery, it is evident that Finland has been for some years an important primary producer.

Before 1940, scarcely any cobalt was mined in the United States. In that year, an output was recorded of 64 tons which by 1945 had increased tenfold. After the war, production continued at the lower rate of 250–450 tons per annum; since 1954, however, there has been a steady increase under the stimulus of industrial and strategic demands.

The principal smaller producers include:

(1) *Australia.* A small but steady annual output of about 10 tons of cobalt has been reported for many years, as a by-product of lead-zinc mining.

(2) *Burma.* Between World War I and II Burma yielded cobalt in two forms—approximately 0.5 per cent Co in a copper-lead matte; up to 7 per cent Co in a copper-nickel speiss. Since 1941 no output has been recorded.

(3) *Japan.* Under the stress of war, production of cobalt rose from 1 ton in 1942 to 17 in 1944, declined to 7 in 1947 and has been virtually nil since then.

(4) Small and spasmodic output has been reported from *Bolivia, Chile, Italy, Mexico* and *Sweden.*

Prior to 1914, scarcely any cobalt metal was produced in the world, the oxide being the marketable form of the element. About this time, several factors were responsible for the development of methods designed to produce the metal: the war created a demand for research into ferrous alloying metals; the Canadian government sponsored a comprehensive investigation by Kalmus and associates into the properties and uses of cobalt to aid the rapidly-growing Canadian mining operations.[4,5,6,7] Another influence was the increasing interest in an alloy which had been developed a few years earlier by Elwood Haynes in the United States. Called "Stellite," it contained approximately 75 per cent cobalt and 25 per cent chromium, and possessed unusual hardness, toughness, and corrosion resistance. In 1916,

TABLE 1.1. WORLD PRODUCTION OF

(Mainly from U.S. Bureau

	1936	1937	1938	1939	1940	1941	1942	1943	1944	1945	1946
Australia			22	14	13	14	15	17	10	11	12
Belgian Congo	782	1,697	1,708	1,234	2,656	2,513	1,818	2,270	2,061	3,086	2,369
Burma	236	323	262	252	240	80					
Canada	444	253	229	366	397	131	42	88	18	54	37
*Finland			276								768
Japan							1	3	17	12	8
Morocco	409	640	793	749	364	72	3	238	268	108	207
New Caledonia											
†Rhodesia and Nyasaland, Federation of	508	974	1,182	1,761	1,348	716	1,007	1,039	1,078	963	608
United States					64	261	331	381	279	640	253
Estimated Total	2,400	3,900	4,600	4,400	5,100	3,800	3,300	4,100	3,800	5,200	3,900

* Total cobalt content of cupriferous pyrite mined as copper ore.
† In 1953, Northern Rhodesia united with Southern Rhodesia and Nyasaland to form the Federation of Rhodesia and Nyasaland. Statistical data in publications prior to this date would be listed under Northern Rhodesia.

when Canada provided 90 per cent of the cobalt, the world output of oxide was approximately 400 tons and of cobalt metal 165 tons.

Before World War I, most of the world's cobalt was utilized by ceramic and glass industries as oxide for glazing and coloring china, pottery, porcelain and glass. After the war, increasing proportions were used in tool steels and permanent magnets, and for other alloying purposes in the metal industries. Although it was first shown about 1910 that an addition of 5 per cent cobalt to a high-speed steel containing 18 per cent tungsten and 6 per cent chromium improved the tool performance greatly, it was some years before such additions became general in the tool steel industry.

Cobalt now enters into many other fields which will be discussed in detail in later chapters, such as ground coat frit, driers, electroplating, catalysis, cemented carbides, magnets, high temperature alloys, glass-to-metal seals, radiography, radioactive tracers and animal nutrition. On the whole, the demand for, and production of, cobalt parallels industrial progress of the world, particularly in the metallurgical sphere.

World production of cobalt during the period 1936–1958 is given in Table 1.1. In recent years, six countries have supplied most of the world's cobalt: the Belgian Congo, Canada, the Federation of Rhodesia and Nyasaland, Finland, Morocco and the United States. Production has increased from about 4,600 tons in 1938 to 6,800 in 1948, and to 14,600 tons in 1958. About three-quarters of the output comes from the continent of Africa, and more than three-quarters of the cobalt mined is eventually used in the metallic state.

Table 1.2 gives the present distribution of cobalt among the arts and in-

COBALT, BY COUNTRIES, IN SHORT TONS

Mines *Minerals Yearbooks*)

1947	1948	1949	1950	1951	1952	1953	1954	1955	1956	1957	1958
9	11	10	11	9	12	12	12	12	12	13	13
3,926	4,763	4,852	5,673	6,298	7,530	9,125	9,490	9,443	10,019	8,945	7,166
287	773	310	292	476	711	801	1,126	1,659	1,758	1,961	1,261
900	1,241	1,091	1,031	1,230	1,438	1,297	1,316	1,377	1,494		
7											
234	244	230	463	750	1,100	661	811	834	710	500	1,021
											143
463	404	443	739	747	645	746	1,199	741	1,205	1,583	1,774
338	290	337	330	378	483	439	719	926	1,269	1,651	2,012
5,800	6,800	6,600	7,900	9,800	11,100	12,500	14,400	14,700	15,900	15,900	14,600

TABLE 1.2. CONSUMPTION OF COBALT IN THE UNITED STATES IN 1958 BY USES IN POUNDS OF CONTAINED COBALT

(From U.S. Bureau of Mines *Minerals Yearbook*, 1958)

	lb	%
METALLIC		
High-speed steel	88,000	1.0
Other steel	100,000	1.3
Permanent magnet alloys	2,340,000	31.0
Cutting and wear-resisting materials	161,000	2.1
High-temperature, high-strength alloys	2,193,000	29.1
Alloy hard-facing rods and materials	361,000	4.8
Cemented carbides	148,000	2.0
Other, including alloys for radio and X-ray tubes, glass-to-metal seals, surveyors' tapes, watch springs, dental and surgical uses, etc.	252,000	3.3
Total metallic	5,643,000	74.8
NON-METALLIC, EXCLUSIVE OF SALTS AND DRIERS		
Ground coat frit	457,000	6.1
Pigments	251,000	3.3
Catalysts and other uses	161,000	2.1
Total non-metallic	869,000	11.5
SALTS AND DRIERS		
Lacquers, varnishes, paints, inks, pigments, enamels, glazes, feed, electroplating, etc.	1,030,000	13.7
Grand total	7,542,000	

dustries in the United States, as well as the consumption for a recent typical year. About one-third was used in high-temperature alloys, roughly another third in magnet alloys; the remainder was divided among eight other major categories of applications.

The range of raw materials used and cobalt products formed by refiners and processors in the United States is given in Tables 1.3 and 1.4.

TABLE 1.3. REFINERS OR PROCESSORS OF COBALT IN THE UNITED STATES IN 1958

(Courtesy U.S. Bureau of Mines)

Refiner or Processor	Location of Plant	Cobalt Product* Made	Cobalt Raw Material* Used
Allied Chemical and Dye Corp., General Chemical Div.	Marcus Hook, Pa.	B,D	A
Baker Chemical Co., J. T.	Phillipsburg, N.J.	B,D	A
Carlisle Chemical Works Inc.	Reading, Ohio	E	A,D
Carlisle Chemical Works Inc., Advance Solvents and Chem. Div.	New Brunswick, N.J.	E	A,D
Calera Mining Co.	Garfield, Utah	A	F
Ceramic Color and Chemical Mfg. Co.	New Brighton, Pa.	C,D	A
Chase Chemical Corp.	Pittsburgh, Pa.	E	C
Ferro Chemical Corp.	Bedford, Ohio	C,D,E	A,C
Hall Chemical Co.	Wickcliffe, Ohio	B,C,D	A,G
Harshaw Chemical Co.	Cleveland, Ohio Gloucester, N.J.	C,D,E	A
Mallinckrodt Chemical Works	St. Louis, Mo.	D	A,D
McGean Chemical Co.	Cleveland, Ohio	C,D,E	A
Metallurgical Resources Inc.	Newburgh, N.Y.	...	F,A
Mooney Chemicals Inc.	Cleveland, Ohio	E	A
National Lead Co.	Fredericktown, Mo.	A	F
Nuodex Products Co.	Elizabeth, N.J.	E	A,C
	Long Beach, Calif.	E	...
Pyrites Company, The	Wilmington, Del.	A,B,C	F
Shepherd Chemical Co.	Cincinnati, Ohio	D,E	A,C,D,G
Sherwin-Williams Co.	Chicago, Ill.	E	A,C
Standard Oil Co. of California	Richmond, Calif.	E	A
Stresen-Reuter Inc., Frederick A.	Bensenville, Ill.	C,D,E	A,C
Troy Chemical Co.	Newark, N.J.	E	A
Vitro Rare Metals Co.	Cannonsburg, Pa.	B,C,D	G
Whitmoyer Laboratories Inc.	Myerstown, Pa.	D	A,C
Witco Chemical Co.	Chicago, Ill.	C,E	A

*Code: A, metal; B, oxide; C, hydrate; D, salts; E, driers; F, concentrate; G, scrap.

TABLE 1.4. COBALT CONSUMED BY REFINERS OR PROCESSORS
IN THE UNITED STATES IN 1958 IN POUNDS OF
CONTAINED COBALT*

(From U.S. Bureau of Mines *Minerals Yearbook*, 1958)

	lb
Alloy and concentrate	4,645,000
Metal	999,000
Hydrate	57,000
Carbonate	...
Purchased scrap	250,000
Other	56,000

*Total consumption is not shown because the metal, hydrate and carbonate
originated from alloy and concentrate.

Imports of cobalt into the United States, according to classes and countries, for the year 1958 are given in Table 1.5. Although such statistics may exhibit wide fluctuations from year to year, the example from the largest consumer of cobalt serves to illustrate how cobalt enters into international trade.

Production of various forms of cobalt by refiners and processors in the United States is given in Table 1.6, and the forms in which cobalt enters into consumption in this country are given in Table 1.7.

Since 1925, cobalt has not suffered the violent price changes which an al-

TABLE 1.5. COBALT IMPORTED FOR CONSUMPTION IN THE
UNITED STATES IN 1958, BY CLASSES AND COUNTRIES

(From U.S. Bureau of Mines *Minerals Yearbook*, 1958)

	Metal, lb	Oxide, gross wt, lb	Salts and Compounds, gross wt, lb
Belgian Congo	10,295,000		
Belgium	2,054,000	773,000	
Canada	1,065,000	64,000	
France	25,000		
Germany, West	713,000		
Norway	737,000		
Rhodesia and Nyasaland, Federation of	817,000		
United Kingdom	13,000		
Total in pounds	15,719,000	837,000	234,000
Value in dollars	30,995,000	1,116,000	145,000

TABLE 1.6. FORMS OF COBALT PRODUCED BY REFINERS AND PROCESSORS IN THE UNITED STATES IN 1958

(From U.S. Bureau of Mines *Minerals Yearbook*, 1958)

Form	Production	
	Gross wt, lb	Cobalt Content, lb
Metal	3,702,000	3,638,000
Oxide	292,000	202,000
Hydrate	227,000	116,000
Salts		
Acetate	112,000	26,000
Carbonate	297,000	138,000
Sulfate	479,000	107,000
Other	262,000	62,000
Driers	11,252,000	649,000
Total	16,623,000	4,938,000

teration in economic conditions brings to most base metals. In the thirties, the leading Belgian, British, Canadian, Finnish and French producers agreed to control the orderly marketing of their products and maintain a uniform price. The advent of war terminated this agreement; since then, the quoted price of the dominant producer, Union Minière du Haut Katanga, has become the established world price. Table 1.8 gives the price changes of cobalt on the New York metal market over a period of years, for metal of 97–99 per cent purity.

In recent years, compilation of statistics in the cobalt industry has been facilitated by a more rapid release of information by governments and corporations. Special tribute should be given to the staff of the Branch of Ferrous Metals and Ferroalloys, U. S. Bureau of Mines, who have for many years prepared the excellent chapters on cobalt in the U. S. Bureau of

TABLE 1.7. FORMS OF COBALT CONSUMED IN THE UNITED STATES IN 1958

(From U.S. Bureau of Mines *Minerals Yearbook*, 1958)

Form	Consumption	
	lb	%
Metal	5,403,000	71.6
Oxide	754,000	10.0
Purchased scrap	355,000	4.7
Salts and driers	1,030,000	13.7
Total	7,542,000	

TABLE 1.8. PRICES OF COBALT, 1925–1959

	Price per lb under 100 lb
1925–1937	$2.50
1938–1940	1.92
1941–1944	2.11
1945–1946	1.57
1947–1948	1.72
1949–1950	1.87
1951–1952	2.40
1953–1956	2.60
1957–1958	2.00
1959	1.75

Mines *Minerals Yearbooks*,[12] as well as interim statistical reports and surveys on this metal.[11]

It is regrettable that statistics on cobalt production are not forthcoming from the Soviet Union. The Russian monograph on cobalt, published in 1949,[9] gives a good survey of the entire subject, and includes some interesting work of Russian investigators on the chemistry and metallurgy of this metal. It omits, however, detailed information on the extractive practices in Russia, and we can only surmise that this country is probably self-sufficient in regard to cobalt.

Since both short ton and metric ton are used in reference to cobalt, a little confusion may arise in the interpretation of data where the unit has not been specified. In the present edition of this book, the word ton, unless otherwise designated, refers to the short ton.

In 1956, cobalt information bureaus, supported by an international association of cobalt producers, were established as Centre d'Information du Cobalt, 35 Rue des Colonies, Bruxelles, and Cobalt Information Center, Battelle Memorial Institute, 505 King Avenue, Columbus 1, Ohio. The function of these bureaus, as with other metal trade associations, is to encourage new uses for cobalt by the promotion of research, the distribution of literature and the provision of technical assistance to users.

The world reserves of cobalt are large, for it is found in small quantities and recovered in the extensive nickel orebodies of Canada, and in the huge copper deposits of the Belgian Congo and Northern Rhodesia. In addition, the largest source of cobalt has been virtually untouched—the small percentages of this element present in the enormous nickel-containing laterite deposits of Celebes, Cuba, New Caledonia and other countries. At Nicaro and Moa Bay, Cuba, a promising start has been made on the extraction of cobalt from the nickel in these deposits—a beginning which in time will undoubtedly stimulate development in similar areas.

References

1. Agricola, G., "De Re Metallica," translated from the first Latin edition of 1556 by H. C. Hoover and L. H. Hoover, London, The Mining Magazine, 1912.
2. Drury, C. W., "Cobalt—Its Occurrence, Metallurgy, Uses and Alloys," *Rept. Ontario Bur. Mines*, **27,** Part III, 31–69 (1918).
3. Jones, R. J., "Cobalt in Canada," *Can. Dept. Mines, Mines Branch* No. 847, (1954).
4. Kalmus, H. T., "Preparation of Metallic Cobalt by Reduction of Oxide," Ottawa, Can. Dept. Mines, (1916).
5. —, "Physical Properties of Metallic Cobalt," Ottawa, Can. Dept. Mines, (1916).
6. Kalmus, H. T., and Blake, K. B., "The Magnetic Properties of Cobalt and Ferro Cobalt," Ottawa, Can. Dept. Mines, (1917).
7. Kalmus, H. T., Harper, C. H., and Savell, W. L., "Electroplating with Cobalt," Can. Dept. Mines Rept., 334 (1915).
8. Mellor, J. W., "A Comprehensive Treatise on Inorganic and Theoretical Chemistry," Vol. XIV, London, Longmans, Green & Co., 1935.
9. Perel'man, F. M., Zvorykin, A. Y., and Gudima, N. V., "Kobal't," *Akad. Nauk S.S.S.R.*, 1949.
10. Perrault, R., "Le Cobalt," Paris, Dunod, 1946.
11. U. S. Bureau of Mines, *Materials Survey*, "Cobalt," Washington, D. C., 1952.
12. —, *Minerals Yearbooks*, Washington, D. C., 1935–1958.

Chapter 2
OCCURRENCE OF COBALT

Although cobalt is not one of the abundant elements it is nevertheless quite widely diffused in nature. It occurs in rocks, sea water, mineral waters, coal, meteorites, the sun and stellar atmospheres, soils, plants and animals. Traces of cobalt have been observed in many ores of iron, nickel, copper, silver, bismuth, antimony, manganese and zinc. Goldschmidt[21] postulated that the greater part of the earth's cobalt is concentrated in the iron core and that only small quantities are left in silicate rocks.

In oxides and silicates, where bonding is principally the result of electrostatic attraction between oppositely charged ions, a reasonably accurate prediction of isomorphous substitutions can be made by consideration of ionic radii. Substitution is usually possible if the ionic radii of the elements are within 15 per cent of one another. The ionic radius of Co^{++} (0.72 Å) is close to those of Cu^{++} (0.72), Fe^{++} (0.74), Fe^{+++} (0.64), Mn^{++} (0.80), Mg^{++} (0.65), Ni^{++} (0.69) and Zn^{++} (0.74). In sulfides, bonding is chiefly the covalent type wherein the atoms are held by mutual sharing of electrons. The covalent or atomic radius of Co (1.32Å) is not far from those of Cu (1.35), Fe (1.23), Mn (1.29), Ni (1.39) and Zn (1.31), but it is not possible to predict with accuracy isomorphous substitution in sulfides on the basis of covalent radii.

It has been suggested[12] that most trace elements, or at least significant quantities, do not occupy regular lattice sites but occur on growth surfaces, imperfections, dislocations and various interfaces within the crystal. Adsorption would thereby be responsible for the fixation during crystal growth of such trace elements as cobalt.

The distribution of cobalt is influenced by the solubility of the metal in natural waters, and its precipitation with changes in pH and other conditions. From the little, and often conflicting, data in the literature on solubility and precipitation it is very difficult to compare cobalt with similar metals such as iron or nickel, and to correlate these results with geological processes. Furthermore, chemical data in these fields are based on pure water or single salt solutions, and both solubility and precipitation are often markedly affected by the presence of other ions in solution. The solubility, in grams per liter of distilled water at 20°C, is as follows: $Co(OH)_3$, 0.00318; $Ni(OH)_2$, 0.0127; $Fe(OH)_2$, 0.006; $Fe(OH)_3$, 0.00015.[62] Such values, however, cannot be readily projected to natural processes of unknown valence states and salt concentrations. The approximate hydrogen ion concentrations at which hydroxides are precipitated have been tabulated.[29] Expressed as pH, they are: Fe^{+++} 2.3; Al 4.2; Zn, Cu and Fe^{++} 5.5; Pb 6; Ni 6.7; Co 6.8; Mn 8.5; Mg 10.5 and Ca 12.4.

Mason[44] pointed out that the high potential required to convert bivalent cobalt to trivalent in acid solution indicates that the mineral stainierite, a hydrated cobaltic oxide, is deposited from alkaline solution for which the oxidation potential is much lower. Iron is readily oxidized to the trivalent state in alkaline and mildly acid conditions; cobalt requires a much higher potential even in alkaline solution, and in acid solution the potential lies high above the oxygen electrode. Nickel does not form trivalent compounds but a dioxide is known, the formation of which even in alkaline solution requires a potential above that of the oxygen electrode. This behavior is reflected in natural occurrences: the common form of iron in supergene deposits is hydrated ferric oxide; stainierite is found only where conditions have been strongly oxidizing, and the higher form of nickel is not known to occur as a mineral.

ROCKS

The classic calculations of Clarke and his associates[9] indicated that the igneous rocks of the earth's surface contained about 0.001 per cent Co compared with 0.020 per cent Ni. In recent years, others have given slightly different quantities and ratios in the earth's crust. Lundegardh[41] quotes Co 0.004 per cent and Ni 0.01 per cent; Mason[45] cites Co 0.002 per cent and Ni 0.008 per cent.

Much less is known about the occurrence and distribution of cobalt in rocks than of most other important metals. In general, cobalt may be found in rocks to the extent of about 0.2–250 ppm.[85]

There are several principal geologic processes which give concentrations of cobalt.

Magmatic Differentiation

Magmatic differentiation, which produces basic or ultrabasic rocks, appears to concentrate cobalt along with nickel, chromium and some other elements.

Certain types of basic rocks, particularly norite, are associated with concentrations of iron, nickel and copper sulfides. Usually cobalt is present in a ratio of 1 Co:20–40 Ni. Hydrothermal activity as well as magmatic segregation were probably important in the origin of such deposits. The average concentration of cobalt in Sudbury norite has been reported as

30 ppm, and Stonehouse[66] concluded that the cobalt content of the rock did not vary with relation to the mineralized zone.

Nickel[48] observed variations in the iron and cobalt content of biotite which could be correlated with the development of pyrite in the schist. This indicated that the metallic elements in the pyrite were most likely derived from the wallrock biotite. The distribution of cobalt, nickel and manganese in co-existing biotite and pyrite is a measure of their relative sulphophile character, cobalt being the most sulphophile. The ratios $\frac{\% \text{ metal in pyrite}}{\% \text{ metal in biotite}}$ ranged from 25 to >600 for Co, 0.89 to 2.75 for Ni, and 0.005 to 0.023 for Mn.

Some contact metamorphic deposits associated with basic igneous rocks contain cobaltiferous pyrite and chalcopyrite in large masses of magnetite, as at Cornwall, Pa.

Usually the cobalt content of rocks which crystallize first from a molten magma is higher than that of rocks which solidify last. Wager and Mitchell[75] found that a gabbro picrite, the first rock to crystallize in a series, contained 100 ppm. cobalt, while a granophyre had only 4 ppm. The same workers later observed[77] that in passing from basalt to oligoclase andesite, in Hawaii, cobalt dropped from 30 to 5 ppm. Lundegardh[40] reported that in an intrusive complex, peridotite, the first rock to crystallize, had 200 ppm cobalt, while microcline granite, the last to solidify, contained only 0.5 ppm. Verification of the concentration of cobalt in early crystallizing fractions has been reported by Nockolds and Mitchell,[49] and Wager and Mitchell.[76]

Vogt[74] pointed out that cobalt enters predominantly into ferromagnesian silicates such as olivine, pyroxene and amphiboles on crystallization of the original magma. Thus the gabbroic and peridotitic rocks are enriched in cobalt, and very little is left for granitic rocks, perhaps less than 0.00005 per cent. Gold-quartz veins, representing the ultimate residual product of the high-silica magmas, carry only a trace of cobalt. The element is almost entirely absent in tin and contact iron deposits.

A study of American igneous rocks by Sandell and Goldich[61] established that cobalt was low in granites, varying from 0.5 to 5 ppm as compared with 26–45 ppm in the diabases. They found that the metal varies linearly with magnesia, and the ratio Co:MgO is approximately 0.00066. According to these workers, this value may be used to predict the cobalt content of common igneous rocks with a fair degree of accuracy.

Nockolds and Mitchell,[49] however, in a study of some Caledonian plutonic rocks, found that the cobalt:magnesia ratio was highly variable and lacked a definite trend. They reported the presence of cobalt in minerals of a diorite as follows (in ppm): plagioclase 15, hypersthene 100, augite 70, and biotite 50. Wager and Mitchell[76] observed the occurrence of cobalt in minerals from an olivine-free gabbro in ppm: pyroxene 60, magnetite 80 and ilmenite 100. Various investigators have found a low level of this metal in limestones, varying from 0.2 to 12.5 ppm. Cobalt has been reported to be below 2 ppm in perthite pegmatites,[28] and to be present in hornblende 8–173, biotite 11–102, garnets 4–43 and chlorites 8–197.[12]

Cobalt has been determined in a number of samples of dunites and olivine-rich inclusions in basaltic rocks.[59] The low cobalt content, usually amounting to 5–10 per cent of the nickel, was (in percentages): olivines, 0.015–0.02; enstatites, 0.004–0.008; chromium diopsides, 0.004–0.005; chromium spinels and chromites, 0.008–0.02.

Hydrothermal Activity

Hydrothermal activity has probably formed the largest number of cobalt deposits. Some of these contain enough cobalt, usually associated with one or more other metals, to be minable as originally formed, as at Blackbird, Idaho; others have been concentrated to an adequate degree by weathering, like some of the Katanga deposits; still others yield cobalt as a by-product from the extraction of other metals, as in Northern Rhodesia. Some of the deposits are fissure fillings; others are replacements of the country rock. Common gange minerals are quartz, carbonate and mica.

Some cobalt occurs in a number of large deposits, formed mostly by replacement of schistose rocks, in which the principal mineral is either pyrite or pyrrhotite. Such deposits may contain appreciable chalcopyrite, as does the Outokumpu deposit in Finland.

Another type of hydrothermal deposit is the silver-cobalt-nickel ore found at Cobalt, Ontario and many other places. Sometimes these deposits contain pitchblende, the best known examples occurring in the Erzegebirge region of Germany and Czechoslovakia, and at Great Bear Lake in Canada.

Chemical Weathering

Chemical weathering is responsible for important concentrations of cobalt. Although ultrabasic rocks such as serpentine, pyroxenite and dunite do not contain cobalt in commercial quantities, the soil formed from them after extensive weathering and leaching, especially under tropical conditions causing lateritization, has concentrations of iron, manganese, nickel and cobalt.[72] Manganese and cobalt accumulate fairly close to the surface; nickel silicate works down to a lower level. Cobalt in amount between 0.04 and 1 per cent accompanies this nickel silicate.

In the vast nickel-containing laterites of Celebes, Cuba, New Caledonia and other countries, cobalt is usually richest in the upper layers where nickel is leanest. At Nicaro, for instance, a typical limonite might have 1.31 per cent Ni and 0.07 per cent Co, while the underlying serpentine may show 1.61 per cent Ni and 0.03 per cent Co. Other ores, such as hematites, may have 0.80 per cent Ni and 0.12 per cent Co. De Vletter[11] has shown that cobalt values in the iron ore of Nicaro usually increase with depth, reaching a peak near the transition zone into serpentine ore. He suggests that some cobalt goes into solution in higher parts of the iron ore profile, to be redeposited in the lower part where more magnesium is present. This concentration occurs on a higher level than that of nickel because the solubility of cobalt under existing conditions is much less than that of nickel, and cobalt is redeposited earlier. Caillère, Henin and Esquevin[8] have prepared cobalt-bearing analogues of antigorite and saponite. The cobalt content and the proportion of antigorite were highest at low pH conditions of 5–5.5, while saponite preponderated at the higher pH of 8.5–9.

Cobalt is found in concentrations of manganese oxide in chert or quartz portions of originally calcareous rock. Such manganese oxide concentrations were formed during long periods of weathering and leaching of sedimentary carbonate rocks which contained small amounts of manganese and cobalt when deposited. Moving ground water may have helped to concentrate these metals. Cobalt is found in the manganese nodules of the ocean, a typical sample containing 0.4 per cent Co and 33 per cent Mn.[9]

The occurrence has been recorded of 0.5–5 per cent Co in lithiophorite, a hydrous lithium-manganese aluminate,[55] and a maximum of 0.002 per cent Co in Arkansas bauxites.[22]

Concentration of Cobalt in Organic Matter

Some coal ashes have shown an enrichment ratio of cobalt in coal ash to earth's crust of 2.4, which is of the same order as that of iron (1.9) and nickel (3.6). It has been suggested that if the present coal ash is representative of the original living plant ash, analyses of the former should indicate the optimum concentration for maximum plant growth.[26]

MINERALS

The important cobalt minerals are sulfides, arsenides and oxidized compounds. As a sulfide, cobalt occurs with copper as carrollite ($CuCo_2S_4$), the principal source of the metal in Northern Rhodesia and one of increasing importance in the Belgian Congo, and as linnaeite or siegenite (Co_3S_4) in the Mississippi Valley lead-zinc deposits. Cobalt substitutes for nickel in many of the minerals in Sudbury and similar copper-nickel-iron sulfide ore-bodies.

The principal cobalt arsenides mined in Canada, the United States, Morocco and a few other localities are smaltite and safflorite ($CoAs_2$), skutterudite ($CoAs_3$), and the cobalt sulfo-arsenide, cobaltite ($CoAsS$). Oxidized cobalt minerals include asbolite ($CoO \cdot 2MnO_2 \cdot 4H_2O$), found in New Caledonia and in similar lateritic nickel deposits, and heterogenite ($CoO \cdot 2Co_2O_3 \cdot 6H_2O$), the principal cobalt mineral of the Belgian Congo. Minor oxides are stainierite ($Co_2O_3 \cdot H_2O$), sphaerocobaltite ($CoCO_3$) and erythrite ($3CoO \cdot As_2O_5 \cdot 8H_2O$).

The following cobalt minerals have been described:[10,27,47,51,64,65]

Alloclasite, (Fe, Co) (As, Bi) S, with part of the cobalt replaced by iron.
Annabergite, $(Co, Ni)_3 (AsO_4)_2 \cdot 8H_2O$
Asbolite, an impure mixture of manganese and other oxides, containing 3–27 per cent cobalt. An example is $CoO \cdot 2MnO_2 \cdot 4H_2O$
Badenite, (Co, Ni, Fe) (As, Bi)$_3$
Bieberite, $CoSO_4 \cdot 7H_2O$
Bismuth skutterudite, (Fe, Co) (As, Bi, Sb)$_3$
Bismuto-smaltite, Co(As, Bi)$_2$
Bravoite, (Co, Ni, Fe)S$_2$
Cabrerite, $(Ni, Mg, Co)_3(AsO_4)_2 \cdot H_2O$
Carrollite, $CuCo_2S_4$
Cattierite, (Co, Ni, Fe)S$_2$, (88.1:3.8:8.6) or (87.5:6.7:5.8)
Cobaltite, CoAsS
Cobaltomenite, $CoSeO_3 \cdot 2H_2O$
Cornetite, $Cu_3P_2O_8 \cdot 3Cu(OH)_2$, frequently containing cobalt
Cuproasbolite, hydroxide of cobalt, copper and manganese
Danaite, (Co, Fe)AsS
Dzhulukulite, (Co, Ni)AsS
Erythrite, $3CoO \cdot As_2O_5 \cdot 8H_2O$
Ferrocobaltite, $FeAsS \cdot nCoAsS$
Forbesite, $H_2(Ni, Co)_2(AsO_4)_2 \cdot 8H_2O$
Gersdorffite, (Ni, Fe, Co)AsS
Glaucodite, (Co, Fe)AsS
Hauchecornite, $(Ni, Co)_7(S, Sb, Bi)_8$
Hengleinite, (Co, Ni, Fe)S$_2$
Heterogenite, $CoO \cdot 2Co_2O_3 \cdot 6H_2O$ or $CoO \cdot 3Co_2O_3 \cdot CuO \cdot 7H_2O$
Heubachite, $3(Co, Ni, Fe)_2O_3 \cdot 4H_2O$
Jaipurite, CoS
Kerzinite, a peat containing nickel silicate and cobalt
Keweenawite, $(Cu, Co, Ni)_2As$
Koeltigite, $(Cu, Co, Ni)_3(AsO_4)_2 \cdot 8H_2O$
Lavendulane, an arsenate of cobalt and copper
Lebeckite, $8CuO \cdot Co_2O_3 \cdot 2Mn_2O_3 \cdot 8H_2O$

Ledouxite, $(Cu, Co, Ni)_4As$

Linnaeite, Co_3S_4, where cobalt may be replaced partially by nickel, copper or iron

Lusakite, a cobalt-bearing silicate $8(RO \cdot Al_2SiO_5)$.

Maucherite, $(Ni, Co)_3As_2$

Mohawkite, $(Cu, Co, Ni)_3As$

Nickel skutterudite, $(Ni, Co)As_3$

Penroseite, $2PbSe_2 \cdot 3CuSe \cdot 5(Ni, Co)Se_2$

Petzite, $(Ag_2, Al_2, Fe, Co) (Te, As)$

Polydymite, $(Co, Ni, Fe)_4S_5$

Rammelsbergite, $(Ni, Co)As_2$

Remingtonite, a hydrated cobalt carbonate

Roselite, $(Ca, Co, Mg)_3As_2O_8 \cdot 2H_2O$

Safflorite, $(Fe, Co)As_2$ or $CoAs_2$

Schulzenite, $2CoO \cdot Co_2O_3 \cdot CuO \cdot 4H_2O$

Siegenite, $(Fe, Co, Ni)_3S_4$

Skutterudite, $CoAs_3$

Smaltite, $CoAs_2$

Sphaerocobaltite, $CoCO_3$

Stainierite, $(Co, Al, Fe)_2O_3 \cdot H_2O$

Sychnodymite, $(Co, Cu)_4S_5$

Tilkerodite, a lead selenide containing cobalt

Transvaalite, $Co_2O_3 \cdot nH_2O$

Tricuite, hydroxide of cobalt and colloidal copper

Vaesite, $(Co, Ni, Fe)S_2$, $(7.2:88.0:4.8)$ or $(-:98.0:2.0)$

Villamaninite, $(Cu, Ni, Co, Fe) (S, Se)_2$

Violarite, $(Ni, Fe, Co)_3S_4$

Willyamite, $CoS_2 \cdot NiS_2 \cdot CoSb_2 \cdot NiSb_2$

Winklerite, $2Co_2O_3 \cdot Ni_2O_3 \cdot 2H_2O$

A mineral having the approximate atomic formula $Co_{3.0}Ni_{2.0}Cu_{3.5}Se_{9.5}$ has been reported from the Goldfields district of Saskatchewan.[58]

PRINCIPAL COBALT MINERALS

Cobalt Sulfides

Carrollite. Carrollite is a steel-gray mineral with a hardness of 5.5, a specific gravity of 4.85 and a theoretical formula of $CuCo_2S_4$, containing 20.53 per cent Cu, 38.06 per cent Co and 41.41 per cent S. Analyses of selected specimens of carrollite at Rhokana Corporation have yielded results very close to the theoretical formula, for example 20.62 per cent Cu, 37.90 per cent Co and 41.14 per cent S, with 0.20 per cent iron and a trace of silica.

Linnaeite. There are several linnaeites found in the Belgian Congo, the Mississippi Valley lead-zinc deposits, and elsewhere, having the general formula Co_3S_4, where cobalt may to some extent be replaced by nickel, copper or iron. It is a mineral of hardness 5 and specific gravity 4.65, and has been found to contain up to 48.7 per cent Co.

Siegenite. This is usually represented as $(Co, Ni)_3S_4$, although iron may also be present. It is found in the cobaltiferous deposits near Fredericktown in the southern Missouri lead district. The mineral has a hardness of 5, a specific gravity of 4.8 and may contain up to 26 per cent Co.

Cobalt Arsenides

Smaltite. Smaltite $(CoAs_2)$ is the principal cobalt arsenide and is an important mineral of American, Canadian and Moroccan arsenide ores. It is often associated with silver, as in the Cobalt district of Ontario; or with gold, as in Morocco. This gray mineral has a metallic luster, a hardness of 6, a specific gravity of 6.5, a cubic structure and a theoretical cobalt content of 28.2 per cent.

Safflorite. Safflorite $(CoAs_2)$ is found associated with smaltite in arsenide deposits of Canada, the United States, Morocco and other parts of the world. In contrast to smaltite it crystallizes in the orthorhombic system, and possesses a hardness of 5 and a specific gravity of 7.2. Russian workers have found that of the cobalt-nickel arsenides safflorite is the most resistant to oxidation and to solution in sulfuric acid.[82,83]

Skutterudite. This mineral $(CoAs_3)$, like smaltite, crystallizes in the cubic system but has a cobalt content of only 20.8 per cent. It has a hardness of 6 and a specific gravity of 6.5. In Morocco, the deposits at depth are smaltite–skutterudite, with native gold in quantities ranging from 3 to 300 g/metric ton.[54]

Cobalt Sulfo-arsenides

Cobaltite. Cobaltite $(CoAsS)$ is found in the Cobalt district of Ontario, the Blackbird region of Idaho, Australia, Burma and many other localities. It is a grayish mineral with a metallic luster, has a hardness of 6 and a specific gravity of 6.3, and when pure contains 35.5 per cent Co.

Oxidized Cobalt Minerals

Asbolite. This term designates an impure mixture of manganese and cobalt oxides $(CoO \cdot 2MnO_2 \cdot 4H_2O)$ in which the cobalt content may vary from 3 to 27 per cent. The hardness of the mineral is only 1 or 2 and the specific gravity about 1.1. Asbolite, the principal cobalt mineral of New Caledonia, is also found in small quantities in Northern Rhodesia.

Heterogenite. This cobalt mineral is generally represented as $CoO \cdot$

$2Co_2O_3 \cdot 6H_2O$, but it often contains a little copper, and occasionally nickel and iron. It is of great economic importance since it is one of the principal cobalt minerals of the Belgian Congo. It has a hardness of 4, a specific gravity of about 3.5 and may contain up to 57 per cent Co.

Sphaerocobaltite. This mineral ($CoCO_3$) is found in the Belgian Congo and to a very small extent in Northern Rhodesia. When pure, it contains 49.6 per cent Co.

Stainierite. Stainierite is usually represented as $Co_2O_3 \cdot H_2O$, although aluminum and iron may also be present as oxides. It is found among the oxidized cobalt minerals of the Belgian Congo and in other countries. Orcel, Henin and Caillère[50] have indicated from X-ray and differential thermal studies that stainierite is cobaltous hydroxide rather than hydrated oxide.

Erythrite. Erythrite ($3CoO \cdot As_2O_5 \cdot 8H_2O$), an oxidation product of cobalt arsenide minerals, varies in color from pale crimson to orange-red. Its hardness is 2, specific gravity 3 and cobalt content, when pure, 29.5 per cent.

OCCURRENCE OF COBALT IN SULFIDES

The distribution of cobalt among sulfide minerals is a matter of considerable economic importance. Cobalt, though a siderophilic element, is also markedly concentrated in sulfides. Fleischer[18] has ably summarized the data in the literature on the minor element content of a number of important sulfides. Cobalt has been reported in a few samples of galena but may actually be present in associated pyrite or other minerals. In sphalerite and wurtzite, about half of the 429 samples examined contained cobalt, ranging approximately from 10 to 3000 ppm. Some of the cobalt reported may be in chalcopyrite, or in admixed pyrite or arsenopyrite, but probably a portion of the cobalt is present in the sphalerite itself. There does not seem to be a relationship between cobalt and iron content, and there is very little correlation of cobalt content with temperature of formation. In 88 samples of chalcopyrite, one-fifth contained cobalt, varying from 10 to 2000 ppm.

Pyrite from sulfide ore deposits usually contains appreciable amounts of cobalt; the content of the latter and the Co:Ni ratio seem to be characteristic of the individual deposit. Of 1097 samples reported by Fleischer, 87 per cent contained cobalt, ranging from less than 10 ppm to over 2.5 per cent. Pyrite of sedimentary origin usually has an appreciably lower cobalt content (less than 100 ppm) than pyrite of hydrothermal origin which is far more variable and has a cobalt content ranging from traces to over 1 per cent. Pyrite from high temperature deposits is generally high in cobalt.

In metamorphosed sulfide deposits, cobalt has been reported to increase with increased metamorphism; higher cobalt contents have been observed in samples from slate or sericite than in samples from quartz. Other workers, however, have concluded that the effect of the type of wall rock is slight. The pyrite group apparently forms an isostructural series with pyrite (FeS_2), vaesite (NiS_2) and cattierite (CoS_2) as end members, while bravoite $[(Co, Ni, Fe)S_2]$ is intermediate.[33]

From his experience in Northern Rhodesia and other parts of the world, Mr. H. L. Talbot concludes that in bornite or chalcocite copper ores the cobalt mineral may be either carrollite or linnaeite. In chalcopyrite-pyrite ores, however, linnaeite alone is present, associated only with pyrite in which it is finely disseminated.

In 252 pyrrhotite samples examined by Fleischer, about two-thirds contained cobalt, ranging from 10 to 8500 ppm. Part of the cobalt is probably present as intergrown or exsolved pentlandite. Cobalt was present in most of the arsenopyrites analyzed, ranging from 10 ppm to 3.3 per cent, with nearly one-fourth containing more than 1 per cent.

Few analyses of coexisting ore minerals are available, but they indicate that in pyrite-pyrrhotite, cobalt tends to concentrate in pyrite, nickel in pyrrhotite, and that the order of decreasing cobalt content is arsenopyrite, pyrite, pyrrhotite, chalcopyrite.

A study of the relation of minor element content of serpentines to their geological origin has shown that minerals from ultrabasic rocks are significantly richer in cobalt as well as nickel, chromium and scandium than those from metamorphic limestone and related rocks.[15]

Several investigators have examined the relation between the cobalt content of sulfide minerals and depth in orebodies. Auger[3] reported that the cobalt content of chalcopyrite increased with depth at Noranda, the cobalt content of pyrite decreased, and that of pyrrhotite increased until it finally equalled the concentration in pyrite. In the gold-quartz veins of Hollinger, cobalt does not show the decrease with depth observed in the massive pyrite orebodies of Noranda. On the other hand, Hawley[25] found that in three out of four Canadian mines the only consistent variation in composition of pyrite with depth was a slight increase in cobalt.

Fryklund and Harner[19] could not establish a significant variation in either cobalt or nickel analyses, or Co:Ni ratios with respect to position in the ore shoot. They concluded that the cobalt and nickel content of pyrrhotite is not affected by wall rock, temperature or chemical composition of major constituents of veins. Caution was advised in regard to the determination of relative temperature conditions in ore shoots by means of studies of minor elements, chiefly because it seemed unlikely that equilibrium conditions were present.

MAJOR COBALT DEPOSITS

Belgian Congo

Most of the copper-cobalt deposits in Katanga Province are in sedimentary rocks, essentially dolomitic in character, called the "Série des Mines." Several types of cobaltiferous ores are mined and subjected to varying extraction techniques by Union Minière du Haut Katanga. Some are local enrichments in cobalt of cobalt-bearing copper ores; others are copper and cobalt-bearing formations from which some of the copper has been leached out by weathering. Small quantities of high-grade oxidized cobalt ores containing 5 per cent Cu and 7–8 per cent Co are sent directly to the electric smelting plant. Other oxidized cobalt ores containing 2 per cent Cu and 2 per cent Co are concentrated before smelting. The large oxidized copper deposits, chiefly malachite, which, up to the present, have furnished the bulk of Union Minière's copper output, may contain 5–6 per cent Cu and 0.3–0.4 per cent Co. Many oxidized cobalt minerals are found in the above deposits, the principal ones being heterogenite, stainierite, sphaerocobaltite, cornetite, tricuite, asbolite and cuproasbolite.

In recent years, Union Minière has proceeded with the development of the lower deposits of sulfide ores in their western mines, centered around the new hydro-metallurgical plants of Kolwezi. The ore containing copper sulfide minerals, principally chalcocite with minor amounts of bornite and chalcopyrite, has 5 per cent Cu, together with 0.1–0.2 per cent Co as carrollite.

In 1952, the U. S. Bureau of Mines and the Geological Survey estimated reserves of recoverable cobalt in the Belgian Congo at 450 million pounds.[72]

Northern Rhodesia

In Northern Rhodesia, cobalt occurs almost entirely as carrollite and linnaeite. An oxidized fraction, which appears to be asbolite and sphaerocobaltite, forms a very small and varying proportion of the cobalt in the mill feed of Rhokana Corporation. In chalcocite or bornite ores, the cobalt mineral is chiefly carrollite; in chalcopyrite-pyrite, as in the South Orebody of Rhokana, only linnaeite finely disseminated in the pyrite, is present.

At Nkana, carrollite is closely associated with copper minerals throughout the sediments of the ore horizon; it is not evenly distributed, however, and the cobalt content of the ore varies from a trace to over 3 per cent, with an average of 0.25 per cent in the Nkana North and South Orebodies and 0.07 per cent in the Mindola Orebody. This has given Rhokana concentrator, in recent years, an average mill feed varying from 0.13 to 0.19 per cent Co.

Where the cobalt content is low, around 0.07 per cent, it appears to be fairly evenly distributed throughout the ore; where it is high, around 0.50 per cent, the carrollite tends to be concentrated in the porous sandstone and cherty ore, the two upper members of the ore horizon, and to some extent in the lowest part of the argillite which forms the hanging wall.

Microscopic examination has shown that carrollite generally occurs as finely disseminated grains with cubic outlines. It appears to be one of the early ore minerals, older than chalcopyrite and bornite which cut and replace it.

Chibuluma Mines, Ltd., one of the copper properties of the Selection Trust Group, has reported ore reserves of 9,982,000 short tons averaging 4.98 per cent Cu and 0.19 per cent Co, as of July 1, 1959. The cobalt mineral is chiefly linnaeite.

In 1952, the U. S. Bureau of Mines and the Geological Survey estimated reserves of recoverable cobalt in Northern Rhodesia at 225 million pounds.[72]

Morocco

The cobalt deposits of this territory, which was formerly called French Morocco, are the property of La Société Minière de Bou-Azzer et du Graara; they lie in a rocky desert region in the south of the Atlas Mountains, about 250 kilometers east of the port of Agadir. The deposits of cobalt and nickel are found in veins at or near the contact of serpentine and diorite rocks. The gangue is principally carbonate. Smaltite, skutterudite and safflorite are the main cobalt minerals; niccolite and other nickel-arsenic minerals are also present. Gold, varying from 3 to 300 g/metric ton, is found in smaltite-skutterudite minerals. Silver is found in varying quantities but always less than 50 g/ton. Perrault[54] reported an analysis of a smaltite-skutterudite mineral as follows (in per cent): Co 12.8, Ni 4.0, Fe 5.5, As 74.0, S 1.9 and insoluble 0.6. In general, the commercial ore of Morocco does not have nickel or iron exceeding 20 per cent of the cobalt, although some deposits have more nickel than cobalt.

Reserves have been estimated roughly at 23 million pounds of recoverable cobalt.

Canada

Cobalt is found in Canada in two major types of deposits, the silver-cobalt-arsenic minerals of the Temiskaming district of Ontario, and the copper-nickel minerals of Sudbury, Ontario, Lynn Lake, Manitoba, and Thompson, Manitoba. There are a number of small producers around the town of Cobalt in the Temiskaming district;[6,24,35,57,60] mineralization includes native silver and bismuth, argentite, smaltite, cobaltite, erythrite, niccolite, safflorite, skutterudite, glaucodite and mispickel. In the veins, the arsenide of nickel and cobalt may fill the whole vein, or may be distributed in calcite or dolomite gangue. Lindgren[39] maintains that calcite gangue was the earliest mineral, and that it was replaced by all arsenides, sulfo-salts and native metals.

In various parts of Canada, a number of small deposits have been reported, usually arsenides, where cobalt is associated with gold. Cobalt in the pyrite of many Canadian gold mines has been reported to range from 0.02 to 0.1 per cent, with a Co:Ni ratio of 1:2.[25] At Great Bear Lake, cobalt occurs with silver and pitchblende in a gangue of quartz and rhodochrosite.[34] In fact, it was the stain of cobalt bloom on the rocks of Echo Bay at Great Bear Lake, recorded by two government geologists in 1900, that led to the discovery and development, many years later, of this important uranium deposit.

The copper-nickel ores of the International Nickel Company of Canada, and Falconbridge Nickel Mines Ltd., in the Sudbury district, contain about 3 to 5 parts of cobalt for every 100 parts of nickel. Cobalt substitutes for nickel in many of the minerals in Sudbury ores, while minor quantities of cobalt also occur in minerals of the cobaltite-gersdorffite isomorphous series. Essentially the same type of mineralization occurs in the Lynn Lake deposits of Sherritt Gordon Mines Ltd. and the Thompson property of International Nickel in northern Manitoba.

Canadian reserves of recoverable cobalt have been estimated at 260 million pounds;[72] however the Manitoba deposits would increase this total considerably.

United States

At Cornwall, Pa., cobalt has been obtained since 1941 as a by-product of iron ore mined by the Bethlehem Cornwall Corporation. The deposit, essentially 50 per cent magnetite, also contains about 3.5 per cent pyrite which carries cobalt to the extent of about 1.5 parts for every 100 of pyrite. The original ore, therefore, has only about 0.05 per cent Co.

At Fredericktown, Mo., some of the galena deposits are associated with pyrite, chalcopyrite and siegenite. An example has been published (in percentages): Pb 2.29; Cu 1.43; Ni 0.46; Co 0.28. These complex ores have been described by Fine et al.[17] and by Lutjen.[42] The ores of the southern part of the Lead Belt district of southeast Missouri have been known to contain cobalt since 1818, and small quantities of cobalt and nickel were produced in 1857. The St. Louis Smelting and Refining Division of the National Lead Company has been recovering this cobalt for some years.

In the Blackbird district of Idaho, ore deposits contain chalcopyrite, cobaltite, safflorite, pyrite and pyrrhotite. Mineralizing solutions apparently had their source in early Tertiary magma which also provided the accompanying bodies of gabbro and lamprophyre.[2,56] Mineral associations suggest relatively high temperatures, particularly when cobaltite was deposited. The early-stage solutions apparently carried the cobalt directly from its magmatic source, but the cobalt contained in the second-stage solutions was probably obtained by solution of the previously deposited cobaltite. Calera Mining Co., a subsidiary of Howe Sound Co., upgrades the cobalt from about 0.7 per cent in the ore to 15 per cent in a concentrate, before shipping the latter to the refinery at Garfield, Utah.[13]

Bunker Hill Zinc Plant at Kellogg, Idaho recovers a few thousand pounds of cobalt a year from its sludge.[70]

Other occurrences of cobalt in the United States have been investigated extensively by the Bureau of Mines, such as the Goodsprings area in Nevada where 0.5–0.75 per cent occurs as stainierite and heterogenite in a number of small deposits.[63]

Kaiser, Herring and Rabbitt[32] noted the presence of cobalt in a variety of American rocks, ores, mill and smelter products, ranging (in percentages of CoO) from 0.4 in coarse manganese concentrate; 0.2 in gold table and jig concentrate, and manganese tailings; 0.1 in concentrates of copper and zinc to 0.01 or lower in tungsten tailings and various copper products.

Vhay[72] has made a complete survey of the occurrence of cobalt in the United States, placing the reserves of recoverable cobalt at 85 million pounds.

Finland

The cupriferous pyrite ore of Outokumpu contains the following (in percentages): Cu 4–4.5, Fe 27, S 26, Zn 1, Co 0.18–0.19, Ni 0.1, As trace and SiO_2 39, with 1 and 12 g/ton, respectively, of gold and silver. Reserves of recoverable cobalt have been estimated at 50 million pounds.

Cuba

From laterite ore containing 1.36 per cent Ni and 0.13 per cent Co, Moa Bay Mining Co., a subsidiary of Freeport Sulphur Co., produces a nickel-cobalt concentrate which is sent to a pressure refining plant near New Orleans.

At Nicaro, the reserves quoted are about 28 million tons carrying (in percentages) Ni 1.45, Co 0.075, Cr 1.5 and Fe 36–37. In the initial operation of this plant, cobalt was not recovered.

The nickel-cobalt resources of Cuba have been described by McMillan and Davis.[46]

MINOR COBALT DEPOSITS

Australia

Cobalt has been reported from many districts in Australia in a variety of forms: sulfide, arsenide and oxide, associated with other metals. The deposits are all small, and most of the Australian output has been obtained from the purification of electrolytic zinc solutions derived from lead-zinc ores.[81]

Brazil

Manganese-iron-oxide pebbles containing 1-2 per cent Co occur in the ferruginous clay overlying the nickel-silicate deposits near São José do Tocantins, Goiaz. The nickel deposits themselves carry 2-4 per cent Ni and 0.2-0.4 per cent Co.[52]

Burma

The lead-zinc-copper orebodies of Bawdwin Mine contain (in percentages) about 25 Pb, 15 Zn, 1 Cu, less than 1 each of Ni and Co, and 20 oz Ag/ton. It is not known what reserves are left, since the properties have not been operated since World War II.

Celebes

The extensive nickel-silicate deposits of Celebes, in Indonesia, contain 2-3 per cent Ni and carry about 0.05 per cent Co.

Chile

A number of cobalt deposits have been reported in Chile, small shipments having been made intermittently for nearly a century.

Germany

Virtually no cobalt ore is mined in Germany, yet this country is listed in world statistics as an important producer. The output is obtained from two sources: roasted pyrites from Finland, Spain, Sweden, Norway and other countries; cobalt-containing residues of customs smelters and refineries.

New Caledonia

The nickel-silicate ores of New Caledonia, which may contain about 2 per cent Ni and 0.05 per cent Co, are irregularly overlain by nodules of asbolite having the variable composition (in percentages): Co 1-8, Mn 7-21, Fe 7-18, SiO_2 20-50 and CaO + MgO 0-10.

Uganda

The copper-cobalt property of Kilembe Mines Ltd., in western Uganda, began the production of concentrates in 1956. The ore averages 2.25 per cent Cu and 0.2 per cent Co, and anticipated annual output is about 16 million pounds of copper and 1.1 million pounds of cobalt. Reserves are quoted at 48 million pounds of recoverable cobalt. Linnaeite is the principal cobalt mineral.

U.S.S.R.

Russian workers[53] have reported that cobalt is recovered from the following types of deposit:

> Copper-nickel ores where the ratio of Co:Ni is about 1:25–50
> Iron ores
> Copper ores
> Arsenides of cobalt and other metals
> Nickel silicates
> Cobalt-manganese deposits

Statistics on concentrations, output and reserves are not available.

A description of an important copper-nickel-cobalt-arsenic mineral deposit in the Altai-Sayan faulted area has been published.[69]

WATERS

The presence of cobalt has been reported in a few waters. A sulfate water from Southern Tyrol contains 13.8 ppm cobalt, probably derived from arsenical pyrite;[9] another sulfate water from a Montana mine contains 4.6 ppm cobalt.[9] A strongly acid water from a mine shaft in Australia has 310 ppm cobalt.[9]

An alum spring in Virginia, cited by Clarke, analyzed 0.2 ppm cobalt. In Japan, springs rich in iron and of the acidic alum vitriol type contain 1–6 $\gamma Co/l$.[68] No cobalt was found in neutral or alkaline springs. A procedure has been outlined for determining radioactive cobalt in river water.[14] Malyuga[43] gave 2.1×10^{-7} per cent or 0.0021 ppm for the abundance of cobalt in surface waters, and a ratio of Co:Ni:Cu of 1:2.7:5 for sea water.

Goldberg,[20] noting the occurrence of cobalt in sea water (0.0001 ppm) compared with nickel (0.0005) and copper (0.004 ppm), indicated that nickel and copper might be positively charged and cobalt negatively charged in this medium.

Variations have been observed in the cobalt content of sea water, and in the ratio of cobalt to nickel and copper. Such variations are probably inevitable since many sea areas are no doubt influenced by land drainage and the rock composition of the shore. Black and Mitchell[5] found 0.3 γ/l, or parts per billion, of cobalt in sea water samples from the English Channel and off the Scottish coast. The nickel content of these samples ranged from 1.5 to 6 γ/l, while copper was <3000 γ/l. Black and Mitchell noted that these values were higher than those previously recorded in the literature (in γ/l): Co 0.1, Ni 0.5 and Cu 4. Ishibashi[31] reported the following concentrations in sea water off the coast of Japan: Co 0.38–0.67 and Ni 0.7–0.8. Vinogradov,[73] in his extensive compilations on the composition of marine organisms, gives the following values for sea water: Co 1, Ni 3 and Cu 20.

Krauskopf[37] observed that the concentration of cobalt in sea water is caused neither by precipitation of sulfides nor by adsorption. Organic reactions are responsible for removal of cobalt, but its enrichment in sediments is less marked and less consistent than that of nickel and vanadium. The principal ions present are probably Co^{++}, $CoCl^+$ and perhaps $Co(OH)^+$.

The little data on the occurrence of cobalt in natural waters, indicating a range of from 0.0001 to 13.8 ppm,[85] should be supplemented to provide more information on this subject.

METEORITES AND OTHER OCCURRENCES

Cobalt as metal or oxide is found in meteorites, but to a much less extent than nickel, being nearly always below 1 per cent. Brown and Patterson[7] reported that the average silicate phase of stony meteorites contained (in percentages): NiO 0.50 and CoO 0.027, whereas the averages for iron meteorites were Ni 8.59 and Co 0.63, and for the metal phase of stony meteorites Ni 10.59 and Co 0.70. For various stony meteorites, Wahl[78] reported cobalt contents varying from 0.07 to 1.63 per cent, compared with nickel ranging from 1.25 to 25.81 per cent. The metallic phase of the Nortonite meteor had 0.37 per cent Co and 5.82 per cent Ni, while the stony phase had 0.005 per cent CoO and 0.43 per cent NiO.[4]

West Virginia coal ash has been reported to contain 0.046 per cent NiO and 0.012 per cent CoO, the latter element occurring to about the same extent as Ge, Hg, Mo and W.[26] Kimberlites have been found to contain 30–80 ppm cobalt,[86] Chilean nitrate of soda contains 2–6 ppm,[84] and oyster shells 1 ppm as compared with nickel (30 ppm) and copper (33 ppm).

Tatsumoto found that 31 red clays from the Sea of Japan contained 4–30 ppm cobalt, averaging 13.9; and that 22 samples of blue mud and other deposits contained 0.4–30 ppm cobalt, averaging 11.1.[67]

Soils

The occurrence and distribution of cobalt in soils, and the interrelationships of this element in soils, plants and animals are fully discussed in Chapter 15.

IDENTIFICATION OF COBALT MINERALS

Chemical Identification

   Dry Method. Cobalt compounds give a blue bead with borax or sodium metaphosphate in both the oxidizing and reducing flames of the blow pipe. Prolonged heating in the reducing flame minimizes the interference from iron or manganese, but reduces the cobalt to a gray metal similar in appearance to nickel.

   On the charcoal stick, cobalt compounds give gray metallic cobalt which can be removed by means of a magnetized knife blade, placed on filter paper, moistened with HCl and dried. Cobalt gives a blue color to the paper.

   Wet Method. Much more positive and satisfactory identification is made by the following qualitative chemical determinations.

   (1) To a small quantity of the sample dissolved in acids add 2–3 ml of 70 per cent ammonium acetate solution, 1–2 ml of 50 per cent tartaric acid solution, 10 ml of 60 per cent ammonium thiocyanate, 5 ml. of 20 per cent sodium thiosulfate solution, 3 ml of 10 per cent sodium phosphate solution and 10 ml of a mixture of 3 parts amyl alcohol to 1 part ether. Transfer to a small separatory funnel and shake thoroughly. If cobalt is present the upper layer will be blue; since no other common element will interfere, the color can be detected when only 0.2 γ of cobalt are present.

   (2) Nitroso-R-salt is a very sensitive indicator for cobalt, but requires the removal of copper. Dissolve a small quantity of the unknown sample in HCl or H_2SO_4; dilute to appropriate volume; remove copper and other group 2 metals with H_2S. Boil off the latter; add 1 g of sodium acetate and 2 ml of 0.5 per cent solution of nitroso-R-salt in water. Boil. Add 2–5 ml HNO_3, and boil for a minute or two to destroy any red color which is also produced by iron. If cobalt is present, a permanent red color, not affected by boiling with HNO_3, is produced. A detectable red develops if cobalt is present in only 5 ppm. For qualitative work no other element is apt to interfere enough to mask the red color.

   (3) Feigl and Goldstein[16] have proposed a specific test for cobalt using the p-nitrophenylhydrazone of diacetylmonoxime in ethyl alcohol. When this reagent is added to ammoniacal solutions of the amine-forming metals Pd, Ag, Cu, Ni and Co, only the cobalt gives a violet color. Interference from copper and nickel can be avoided by the addition of KCN. The limit of identification is 0.1 γ of Co; the dilution limit is 1 in 500,000. If the mineral is brought into solution by acid or fusion treatment, made ammoniacal, and the insoluble hy-

droxides removed by filtration, the filtrate is ready for the test with this reagent.

Microchemical Identification

It is difficult to differentiate carrollite from pyrite under the microscope. Dr. J. F. Vaes,[71] of the Union Minière du Haut Katanga, found a modification of the contact print method of Gutzeit[23] and Hiller[30] satisfactory. He covered a polished section of carrollite with filter paper moistened with dilute HCl, and passed a current from a car battery through the mineral and paper. After drying, the paper showed a faint pink color, indicating the presence of cobalt chloride. When a drop of copper mercuric thiocyanate was added to the dry paper, a blue diffuse spot surrounded by a red aureole was immediately formed. The blue color was due to cobalt, the red to traces of iron in the mineral or reagents.

Gutzeit uses gelatin-impregnated paper from which the silver has been dissolved by sodium thiosulfate, and 5 per cent KCN solution. After electrographic attack at 8 volts for 30 seconds, a direct orange print of co-balticyanide is obtained. Nitroso-R-salt in sodium acetate solution gives a red print with cobalt, iron, copper and other metals, but brief washing in 2:1 HNO_3 destroys the red color of other metals while that of cobalt remains unchanged.

The Geological Survey and Museum of London suggest treatment of the polished section with a drop of 5 per cent mercuric chloride. Most carrollites show a brown, iridescent stain, while pyrite is unaffected. Some carrollites, however, give a negative reaction to this test.

The following microchemical test is of greater diagnostic value: With a needle, dig out a few grains of the mineral from the polished section under a microscope. Decompose the mineral with 1:1 HNO_3; leach the residue with a drop of 5 per cent potassium mercuric thiocyanate in water. Copper precipitates as yellowish-green prisms and moss-like clumps, whereas cobalt precipitates separately as indigo-blue prisms. If only pyrite is present, the drop of potassium mercuric thiocyanate would merely turn red without forming a precipitate.

It has been found at Rhokana Corporation that an experienced microscopist can make a fair differentiation between pyrite and carrollite by giving the briquetted sample a minimum of polishing. Carrollite polishes more readily than pyrite, and the scarred appearance of the latter serves to distinguish it from carrollite.

GEOCHEMICAL PROSPECTING

In recent years, chemical analyses for small quantities of metals in waters, soils and vegetation have been carried out in many parts of the world to assist in the search for underground orebodies. Many procedures have been adapted for rapid, approximate determinations under field conditions, and geochemical prospecting is firmly established as one of the valuable tools in geological exploration. Cobalt has shared with other base metals in the extensive literature on methods and results in this sphere.

Koehler, Hostetler and Holland[36] concluded that techniques of cobalt determination in soil were applicable to locating orebodies where mineralization extends to the bedrock surface in geologic settings similar to those of the Cobalt district of Ontario. Warren and Delavault[79] reported that the cobalt content of trees and shrubs growing above cobalt ore in several parts of Canada is 1–3 ppm in dry plant, 50–300 in ash. This appears to be 10–100 times the amount encountered in vegetation from non-mineralized areas. The procedure used was as follows: the sample was dissolved in HCl, evaporated to dryness, taken up in dilute HCl; Rochelle salt, hydroxylamine hydrochloride and ammonia were added. To this solution, 2-nitroso-1-naphthol in acetone and toluene were added, the test tube was shaken, and the yellow color of the supernatant toluene layer compared with standards containing 0.2–4 γ of cobalt.

The field method used by the U. S. Geological Survey in geochemical prospecting for cobalt has been described.[38] The procedure is suitable for determining 10–400 ppm Co in soils and rocks. It consists of fusion, careful adjustment of acidity to prevent interference of iron and to assure complete precipitation of cobalt with 2-nitroso-1-naphthol in a chromograph, and comparison of the color of the confined spot with standards. A modification of this field method is carried out by extraction with CCl_4 of the colored complex formed by cobalt with 2-nitroso-1-naphthol, addition of cyanide to prevent interference from Cu, Ni and excess naphthol, and comparison of the resulting pink color in CCl_4 solution with a series of standards.[1]

Webb and Tooms[80] reported that the background content of cobalt in soil and stream sediments in unmineralized areas of Northern Rhodesia was in the range of 3–12 ppm, while values up to 160 ppm were recorded in the vicinity of mineralized ground.

References

1. Almond, H., "Determination of Traces of Cobalt in Soils," *Anal. Chem.,* **25,** 166–7 (1953).
2. Anderson, A. L., "Cobalt Mineralization in the Blackbird District, Lemhi County, Idaho," *Econ. Geol.,* **42,** 22–46 (1947).
3. Auger, P. E., "Zoning and District Variations of the Minor Elements in Pyrite of Canadian Gold Deposits," *Econ. Geol.,* **36,** 401–23 (1941).

4. Beck, C. W., and LaPaz, L., "The Nortonite Fall and its Mineralogy," *Am. Mineralogist,* **36,** 45–59 (1951).

5. Black, W. A. P., and Mitchell, R. L., "Trace Elements in the Common Brown Algae and in Sea Water," *J. Marine Biol. Assoc. United Kingdom,* **30,** 575–84 (1952).

6. Bridges, R. W., "The Metallurgy of Canadian Cobalt Ores," *Can. Mining J.,* **37,** No. 2, 48–50 (1916).

7. Brown, H., and Patterson, C., "The Composition of Meteoritic Matter. I. The Composition of the Silicate Phase of Stony Meteorites," *J. Geol.* **55,** 405–11 (1947). II. "The Composition of Iron Meteorites and of the Metal Phase of Stony Meteorites," *Ibid* 508–10 (1947).

8. Caillère, S., Henin, S., and Esquevin, J., "Synthesis of Cobaltiferous Clays," *Clay Minerals Bull.,* **3,** 232–7 (1958). *Chem. Abst.,* **53,** 9915 (1959).

9. Clarke, F. W., "The Data of Geochemistry," *U. S. Geol. Surv., Bull.,* 616 (1916).

10. Dana, E. S., and Ford, W. E., "Textbook of Mineralogy," New York, John Wiley and Sons, Inc., 1932.

11. DeVletter, D. R., "How Cuban Nickel Ore was Formed—A Lesson in Laterite Genesis," *Eng. Mining J.,* **156,** No. 10, 84–7, 178 (1955).

12. DeVore, G. W., "The Role of Adsorption in the Fractionation and Distribution of the Elements," *J. Geol.,* **63,** 159–90 (1955).

13. Douglas, E. B., "Mining and Milling Cobalt Ore," *Mining Eng.,* **8,** 280–3 (1956).

14. Duncan, J. F., Johns, T. F., Johnson, K. B. D., McKay, H. A. C., Maton, W. R. E., Pike, E. W. A., and Walton, G. N., "The Estimation of Radioactive Strontium, Barium, Cobalt, and Iodine in River Water," *J. Soc. Chem. Ind.,* **69,** 25–9 (1950).

15. Faust, G. T., Murata, K. J., and Fahey, J. J., "Relation of Minor Element Content of Serpentines to Their Geological Origin," *Geochim. et Cosmochim. Acta.,* **10,** 316–20 (1956).

16. Feigl, F., and Goldstein, D., "A Specific Test for Cobalt," *Analyst,* **81,** 709–10 (1956).

17. Fine, M. M., Brown, W. E., Vahrenkamp, G. J., and Knickerbocker, R. G., "Concentration of the Complex Copper-Lead-Cobalt-Nickel Ores of Southeast Missouri," *Mining Eng.,* **3,** 602–4 (1951).

18. Fleischer, M., "Minor Elements in Some Sulfide Minerals," *Econ. Geol.* **Fiftieth Anniv. Vol.,** 970–1024 (1955).

19. Fryklund, V. C., Jr., and Harner, R. S., "Comments on Minor Elements in Pyrrhotite," *Econ. Geol.,* **50,** 339–44 (1955).

20. Goldberg, E. D., "Marine Geochemistry. 1. Chemical Scavengers of the Sea," *J. Geol.,* **62,** 249–65 (1954).

21. Goldschmidt, V. M., "The Principles of Distribution of Chemical Elements in Minerals and Rocks," *J. Chem. Soc.,* **1937,** 655–73 (1937).

22. Gordon, M., and Murata, K. J., "Minor Elements in Arkansas Bauxite," *Econ. Geol.,* **47,** 169–79 (1952).

23. Gutzeit, G., "Determination and Localization of Metallic Minerals by the Contact Print Method," *Am. Inst. Mining Met. Engrs. Tech. Publs.,* **1457,** 1–13 (1942).

24. Harris, A. C., "Metallurgy of the Ores from Cobalt, Ontario," *Eng. Mining J.,* April 8, 1916.

25. Hawley, J. E., "Spectrographic Studies of Pyrite in Some Eastern Canadian Gold Mines," *Econ. Geol.,* **47,** 260–304 (1952).

26. Headlee, A. J. W., and Hunter, R. G., "Elements in Coal Ash and Their Industrial Significance," *Ind. Eng. Chem.,* **45,** 548–51 (1953).

27. Hey, M. H., "Chemical Index of Minerals," London, British Museum (Natural History), 1950.

28. Higazy, R. A., "Observations on the Distribution of Trace Elements in the Perthite Pegmatites of the Black Hills, South Dakota," *Am. Mineralogist,* **38,** 172–90 (1953).

29. Hillebrand, W. F., Lundell, G. E. F., Bright, H. A., and Hoffman, J. I., "Applied Inorganic Analysis," New York, John Wiley and Sons, Inc., 1953.

30. Hiller, T., "Contribution a l'étude des mineraux opaques par la méthode des empreintes: Perfectionnements apportés à la technique d'attaque electrolytique," *Compt. rend. soc. phys. et hist. nat. Genève,* **52,** 119–25 (1935).

31. Ishibashi, M., "Minute Elements in Sea Water," *Records Oceanog. Works Japan* [*N.S.*], **1,** No. 1, 88–93 (1953). *Chem. Abst.,* **48,** 6175 (1954).

32. Kaiser, E. P., Herring, B. F., and Rabbitt, J. C., "Minor Elements in Some Rocks, Ores, and Mill and Smelter Products," *U. S. Geol. Surv., T.E.,* 1–415 (1954).

33. Kerr, P. F., "Cattierite and Vaesite: Two New Co-Ni Minerals From the Belgian Congo," *Am. Mineralogist,* **30,** 483–97 (1945).

34. Kidd, D. F., and Haycock, M. H., "Mineragraphy of the Ores of Great Bear Lake," *Bull. Geol. Soc. Amer.,* **46,** 879–960 (1935).

35. Knight, C. W., "Geology of the Mine Workings of Cobalt and South Lorrain Silver Areas," *Rept. Ont. Dept. Mines,* (1932).

36. Koehler, G. F., Hostetler, P. B., and Holland, H. D., "Geochemical Prospecting at Cobalt, Ontario," *Econ. Geol.,* **49,** 378–88 (1954).

37. Krauskopf, K. B., "Factors Controlling the Concentration of Thirteen Rare Metals in Sea Water," *Geochim. et. Cosmochim. Acta.,* **9,** 1–32 B (1957).

38. Lakin, H. W., Almond, H., and Ward, F. N., "Compilation of Field Methods Used in Geochemical Prospecting by the U. S. Geological Survey," *U. S. Geol. Surv. Circ.,* 161 (1952).

39. Lindgren, W., "Mineral Deposits," New York, McGraw-Hill Book Co., Inc., 1933.

40. Lundegardh, P. H., "Distribution of Vanadium, Chromium, Cobalt, and Nickel in Eruptive Rocks," *Nature,* **155,** 753 (1945).

41. —, "The Geochemistry of Chromium, Cobalt, Nickel, and Zinc," *Sveriges Geol. Undersokn, Arsbok Ser. C Avhandl och Uppsa,* No. 513 **43,** No. 11 (1951). *Chem. Abst.,* **45,** 88 (1951).

42. Lutjen, G. P., "Cobalt at Fredericktown," *Eng. Mining J.,* **154,** No. 12, 72–6 (1953).

43. Malyuga, D. P., "The Content of Cobalt, Nickel, Copper and Other Iron Family Elements in Black Sea Deposits," *Akad. Nauk S.S.S.R.,* **67,** 1057–60 (1949). *Chem. Abst.,* **44,** 496 (1950).
44. Mason, B., "Oxidation and Reduction in Geochemistry," *J. Geol.,* **57,** 62–72 (1949).
45. —, "Principles of Geochemistry," New York, John Wiley and Sons, Inc., 1952.
46. McMillan, W. D., and Davis, H. W., "Nickel-Cobalt Resources of Cuba," *U.S. Bur. Mines Rept. Invest.,* 5099 (1955).
47. Mellor, J. W., "A Comprehensive Treatise on Inorganic and Theoretical Chemistry," **XIV,** London, Longmans, Green and Co., Ltd., 1935.
48. Nickel, E. H., "The Distribution of Iron, Manganese, Nickel, and Cobalt Between Co-existing Pyrite and Biotite," *Am. Mineralogist,* **39,** 494–503 (1954).
49. Nockolds, S. R., and Mitchell, R. L., "The Geochemistry of Some Caledonian Plutonic Rocks. A Study in the Relationship Between Major and Trace Elements of Igneous Rocks and their Minerals," *Trans. Roy. Soc. Edinburgh,* **61,** 533–75 (1948).
50. Orcel, J., Heinin, S., and Caillère, S., "Properties of Stainierite," *Bull. soc. franç. minéral. et crist.,* **81,** 189–94 (1958). *Chem. Abst.* **53,** 7867 (1959).
51. Palache, C., Berman, H., and Frondel, C., "Dana's System of Mineralogy." Seventh Edition. Vol. 1, Vol. II, New York, John Wiley and Sons, Inc., 1944.
52. Pecora, W. T., and Barbosa, A. L. M., "Deposits of Nickel and Cobalt of São José do Tocantins, State of Goias, Brazil," *Ministerio agr. Dept. nacl. produção mineral,* Div. fomento produção mineral, Bol., **64,** 15–69 (1944). *Chem. Abst.* **41,** 3023 (1947).
53. Perel'man, F. M., Zvorykin, A. Y., and Gudima, N. V., "Kobal't," *Akad. Nauk S.S.S.R.,* 1949.
54. Perrault, R., "Le Cobalt," Paris, Dunod, 1946.
55. Pierce, W. G., "Cobalt-Bearing Manganese Deposits of Alabama, Georgia, and Tennessee," *U. S. Geol. Surv., Bull.,* No. 940-J. (1944).
56. Reed, G. C., and Herdlick, J. A., "Blackbird Cobalt Deposits, Lemhi County, Idaho," *U. S. Bur. Mines Rept. Invest.,* 4012 (1947).
57. Reid, F. D., Denny, J. J., and Hutchinson, R. H., "Mining and Metallurgical Practice in Treatment of Silver Ores at Cobalt," *33rd. Rept. Ontario Dept. Mines* (1922).
58. Robinson, S. C., and Brooker, E. J., "A Cobalt-Nickel-Copper Selenide From the Goldfields District, Saskatchewan," *Am. Mineralogist,* **37,** 542–4 (1952).
59. Ross, C. S., Foster, M. D., and Myers, A. T., "Origin of Dunites and of Olivine-Rich Inclusions in Basaltic Rock," *Am. Mineralogist,* **39,** 693–737 (1954).
60. Sampson, E., and Hriskevich, M. E., "Cobalt-Arsenic Minerals Associated with Aplites, at Cobalt, Ontario," *Econ. Geol.,* **52,** 60–75 (1957).
61. Sandell, E. B., and Goldich, S. S., "The Rarer Metallic Constituents of Some American Igneous Rocks," *J. Geol.,* **51,** 99–115, 167–89 (1943).
62. Seidell, A., "Solubilities of Inorganic and Metal Organic Compounds," Vol. 1, 3rd. Ed., New York, D. Van Nostrand Co. Inc., 1940.

63. Shelton, F. K., "Metallurgical Treatment of Cobalt Ores from the Goodsprings Mining District, Nevada," *U. S. Bur. Mines Rept. Invest.* 3836 (1946).
64. Shishkin, N. N., "Dzhulukulite, a New Cobalt Mineral," *Doklady Akad. Nauk S.S.S.R.,* **121,** 724–6 (1958). *Chem. Abst.* **53,** 133 (1959).
65. Short, M. N., "Microscopic Determination of the Ore Minerals," *U. S. Geol. Surv., Bull.,* 914 (1940).
66. Stonehouse, H. B., "An Association of Trace Elements and Mineralization at Sudbury," *Am. Mineralogist,* **39,** 452–74 (1954).
67. Tatsumoto, M., "Chemical Investigations of Deep-Sea Deposits. XXII. Cobalt and Nickel in Sea Deposits," Nippon Kagaku Zassi, **78,** 38–42 (1957). *Chem. Abst.,* **52,** 8871 (1958).
68. Torii, T., "Occurrence of Cobalt in Mineral Springs of Japan," *J. Chem. Soc. Japan, Pure Chem. Sect.,* **76,** 707–10 (1955). *Chem. Abst.,* **50,** 11569 (1956).
69. Unksov, V. A., "Types of the Copper-Nickel-Cobalt-Arsenic Mineralization in the Altai-Sayan Faulted Area," Zapiski Vsesoyuz. Mineral. Obshchestva **87,** 554–66 (1958). *Chem. Abst.,* **53,** 2955 (1959).
70. U. S. Bureau of Mines, *Minerals Yearbooks,* Washington, D. C., 1935–58.
71. Vaes, J. F., Personal communication, 1943.
72. Vhay, J. S., "Cobalt Resources," U. S. Bureau Mines Materials Survey, Cobalt, Chapter VI, (1952).
73. Vinogradov, A. P., "The Elementary Chemical Composition of Marine Organisms," New Haven, Sears Foundation for Marine Research, 1953.
74. Vogt, J. H. L., "Magmas and Igneous Ore Deposits," *Econ. Geol.,* **21,** 207–33, 309–32, 469–97 (1926).
75. Wager, L. R., and Mitchell, R. L., "Preliminary Observations on the Distribution of Trace Elements in the Rocks of the Skaergaard Intrusion, Greenland," *Mining Mag.* **26,** 283–96 (1943).
76. —, "The Distribution of Trace Elements During Strong Fractionation of Basic Magma—A Further Study of the Skaergaard Intrusion, East Greenland," *Geochim. et Cosmochim. Acta.,* **1,** 129–208 (1951).
77. —, "Trace Elements in a Suite of Hawaiian Lavas," *Geochim. et Cosmochim. Acta.,* **3,** 217–23 (1953).
78. Wahl, W., "The Statement of Chemical Analyses of Stony Meteorites and the Interpretation of the Analyses in Terms of Minerals," *Mineral. Mag.* **24,** 416–26 (1950).
79. Warren, H. V., and Delavault, R. E., "Biogeochemical Prospecting for Cobalt," *Trans. Roy. Soc. Can.,* **IV, 51,** 33–7 (1957).
80. Webb, J. S., and Tooms, J. S., "Geochemical Drainage Reconnaissance for Copper in Northern Rhodesia," *Trans. Inst. Mining and Met.* **68,** 125–44 (1958).
81. Woodward, O. H., "A Review of the Broken Hill Lead-Silver-Zinc Industry," *Proc. Australasian Inst. Mining & Met.,* New Ser., No. 119, Part 1 (1940).
82. Yakhontova, L. K., "Experimental Study of the Oxidation of Cobalt and Nickel Arsenides in Solutions Containing Oxygen and Carbon Dioxide," *Geokhimiya,* **1958,** 70–80. *Chem. Abst.,* **52,** 15351 (1958).
83. —, Bukina, A. N., and Raudonis, P. A., "Solubility of Some Cobalt-Nickel

Arsenides in a Sulfuric Acid Medium," *Zapiski Vsesoyuz. Mineralog. Obsh-chestva,* **87,** 23–30 (1958). *Chem. Abst.,* **52,** 10811 (1958).

84. Young, R. S., "Cobalt Content of Chilean Nitrate of Soda," *Research,* **4,** 392 (1951).

85. —, "The Geochemistry of Cobalt," *Geochim. et Cosmochim. Acta.,* **13,** 28–41 (1957).

86. —, Benfield, D. A., and Strachan, K. G. A., "Cobalt in Kimberlites," *Am. Mineralogist,* **39,** 143–4 (1954).

Chapter 3
EXTRACTIVE METALLURGY OF COBALT

In reducing ore to refined metal, few base metals exhibit such a diversity of extractive metallurgical operations as cobalt. Depending on its original state—arsenide, oxide or sulfide—one may encounter gravity, magnetic and flotation concentrating operations; blast, reverberatory and electric furnace practices; roasting; leaching at normal or elevated temperatures and pressures with water, acid or ammoniacal solutions; chemical precipitation by solids, liquids or gases, with accompanying purification and filtration; electrolysis; and many methods of pyrometallurgical and hydrometallurgical oxidation and reduction.

The metallurgy of cobalt may be considered under the following headings:

(1) Belgian Congo operations

Owing to the variation in cobalt content and the type of mineralization of its ores, several distinct processes are employed by Union Minière du Haut Katanga.[67]

(2) Northern Rhodesia practice

The low content of cobalt sulfide in copper ores has resulted in the continuous evolution of recovery methods in this territory.

(3) Arsenide deposits of Morocco, Canada, the United States and other countries

(a) The high grade and associated nickel and silver of most of these ores dictate an initial pyrometallurgical treatment followed by conventional leaching and purification processes.

(b) For cobaltite concentrates from Idaho, newer techniques of acid leaching under pressure and hydrogen reduction in ammoniacal solution are employed at the Garfield plant of the Calera Mining Co.

(4) By-product of nickel refining

(a) Some of the small quantity of cobalt occurring in the nickel sulfide ores of the Sudbury area eventually appears in the electrolytic refineries of International Nickel and Falconbridge.

(b) A portion of the nickel oxide output of International Nickel is refined at Clydach, Wales by the carbonyl process, and cobalt is recovered from the residues of this operation.

36

(c) Cobalt is recovered at Sherritt Gordon Mines Ltd. by pressure hydrogen reduction in ammoniacal solution following the removal of copper and nickel from leachates obtained by pressure ammonia treatment of nickel-copper-cobalt concentrates.

(d) The nickel ores of Moa Bay, Cuba, will undergo acid leaching, precipitation of nickel and cobalt as a sulfide concentrate, and ultimate extraction of these metals by selective hydrogen reduction of sulfate solutions.

(e) Ammonia leaching of nickeliferous laterites dissolves a large part of the associated cobalt.

(5) Pyrite

In Finland, Sweden, Spain and many other countries, pyrite containing small quantities of cobalt and other metals is mined and sent to Germany and other industrial nations for the production of sulfuric acid. For some ores, the cobalt content of the roasted residue is high enough to warrant recovery by hydrometallurgical processes before sending the iron to the blast furnace. In the United States, cobalt has been extracted in this way for many years from the pyrite associated with the Cornwall magnetite deposit.

(6) By-product of lead production

(a) Cobalt, together with nickel, occurs in the ores of the southern part of the Lead Belt district of southeast Missouri. For some years, these metals have been recovered at the St. Louis Smelting and Refining Division of the National Lead Company.

(b) Before World War II, the lead mines of Burma furnished about 0.3–0.8 per cent Co in a copper-lead matte, and 3–4 per cent Co in a nickel-copper speiss, delivered to European refineries. The properties have been inactive since then.

BELGIAN CONGO

Production of Crude Cobalt Alloy

Local enrichments of cobalt in several copper mines of the Union Minière provide the following sources of feed for the electric smelting plant at Jadotville, where four furnaces yield a capacity of 4,400 tons of contained cobalt in alloy per annum. These cobalt ores, chiefly heterogenite, stainierite, asbolite, etc., are all oxidized.

(a) High grade cobalt ores, containing 5 per cent Cu and 7–8 per cent Co, are sent directly to the electric furnaces.

(b) Some cobalt ores having little copper are found in argillaceous schists, and simple washing serves to concentrate them.

(c) Certain copper-cobalt ores with a relatively low copper content are concentrated by palm oil flotation to give, for example, a product having 8–9 per cent Co and 10 per cent Cu.

In all cases, lump ore and coarse concentrates above 3/8 in. are charged directly to the electric furnace. Fines, on the other hand, are first sintered on a Dwight-Lloyd machine with fine coke or coal amounting to about 10 per cent of their weight.

The natural products listed above as feed for electric furnaces are supplemented by a copper refinery slag containing about 15 per cent Co.

The cobalt-containing feed, together with about 50 per cent lump lime and 15 per cent coke, is charged to the electric furnaces. The latter operate at a voltage of 120 and a current of 5000–5500 amp, and are provided with continuous electrodes. Power consumption is about 12,000 kwh/ton of cobalt in alloy.

The products of electric furnace reduction are slag and two alloys. The slag, containing about 0.3 per cent Cu and 0.4 per cent Co, is run through a water-cooled slag hole. The copper, the cobalt, a large part of the iron, and some silicon in the charge are reduced to their metallic state, becoming two alloys. The white alloy, which is the lighter, usually contains 15 per cent Cu, 42 per cent Co, 39 per cent Fe and 1.6–2 per cent Si; the heavier red alloy has about 89 per cent Cu, 4.5 per cent Co and 4 per cent Fe. These alloys are tapped together into a ladle but discharged separately—the red alloy by tapping the bottom of the ladle, the white alloy by pouring from the lip. The white alloy is cast into ingots or granulated into shot in a stream of water; the red is sent to the copper refinery furnace and the resultant slag, containing about 15 per cent Co, is returned to the electric furnace charge. By adjusting the quantity and size of coke in the electric furnace charge, the silicon in the white alloy is kept above 1.5 per cent, permitting separation of the two alloys in the ladle.

The white alloy from the Congo is sent to Belgium for refining. The relative importance of alloy production in the cobalt operations of Union Minière will gradually decline, as the reserves of high grade ore diminish, in favor of the more flexible production of electrolytic cobalt as a by-product of copper leaching plants.

The process for refining Congo copper-cobalt-iron alloy is essentially similar to that described for alloys from Northern Rhodesia.[6] Until recent years, the cobalt output from this latter territory was sent in alloy form to Canadian or British refineries.

In these alloys, about 8–10 per cent of the copper is in solid solution with the cobalt-iron phase, the remainder being precipitated as free copper. The first treatment step, digestion of the alloy with hot 20 per cent sulfuric acid, produces a solution of cobaltous and ferrous sulfates which carries the copper in finely-divided form in suspension. The acidity is reduced with lime, and a little iron powder is added to re-precipitate any copper which may have dissolved as a result of aeration in the digestion vessel. The copper residue is filtered off, washed and sent to a smelter.

The filtrate is oxidized by sodium chlorate in the presence of additional sulfuric acid. Lime is added to precipitate iron as a basic ferric sulfate; the latter is removed, together with calcium sulfate, by filtration. Sodium carbonate is added to the filtrate of hot cobalt sulfate to precipitate a basic carbonate of cobalt. The latter is dried and calcined to crude cobalt oxide in a rotary hearth furnace. Sodium sulfate and lime are removed from this cobalt oxide by successive leaching with hot water and agitation, followed by leaching with ammonium chloride, filtering and washing. The pure cobalt oxide is either marketed as such, or reduced to metallic rondels or powder.

In the production of rondels, first about 4 per cent dextrin is mixed with the cobalt oxide which is then granulated and sprinkled with stearic acid. The granulated material is fed into a tabletting machine; the resulting briquettes are packed in saggars with charcoal and placed in a reduction furnace. The compacted cobalt rondels are separated from the unconsumed charcoal by sieving, and are polished with sawdust in a tumbling barrel.

If cobalt metal powder is desired, trays of cobalt oxide are passed at regular intervals into a long, rectangular-tube muffle furnace provided with valves which seal the heating chamber from the atmosphere. Hydrogen is circulated around the electrically heated furnace, and temperature and gas flow are adjusted to yield the desired particle size.

For permanent magnets the carbon content of cobalt must be low; sometimes a further decarburizing step is required after normal refining treatment. If so, molten cobalt may be maintained for a time in an atmosphere of carbon dioxide, or the latter may be bubbled through the cobalt bath.[18]

Alternative methods for removing nickel from cobalt solutions have been described. Iron sulfide containing an excess of metallic iron[16], or finely divided iron and sulfur[65] are added to the sulfate or chloride solution, at a pH of around 5, to precipitate NiS and leave a cobalt-rich solution. The sulfidizing cementation of nickel from cobaltiferous solutions has become established commercially in certain cases where it is necessary to reduce the Ni:Co ratio from around 10 Ni:100 Co to 0.5 or even 0.01 Ni:100 Co. Elemental sulfur is used with metallic iron or, preferably, cobalt; however, Na_2S or NaHS may also be added to the cobalt solution. In the presence of sulfur or a sulfide, nickel is preferentially precipitated; the result is a mixed sulfide precipitate of nickel and cobalt, and a solution enriched in cobalt.

Another reducing agent, such as hydrogen or an electrolytic depolarizer, may replace the cementing metal in this reaction. Sulfidizing cementation has been practiced at the Société Générale Métallurgique de Hoboken and at the Congo operations of Union Minière du Haut Katanga.

Production of Electrolytic Cobalt

At present, the main sources of copper in the Belgian Congo are the oxidized deposits, chiefly malachite, containing 5 per cent Cu and 0.2–0.3 per cent Co. At Kolwezi they are concentrated with hydrolyzed palm oil, in a pulp dispersed with sodium carbonate and sodium silicate, to about 27 per cent Cu and 1 per cent Co; then they are sent to the Jadotville leaching and electro-winning plant.

Cobalt oxides are soluble in sulfuric acid only in the presence of a reducing agent. The latter is furnished by the ferrous sulfate formed in copper electrolysis. The reactions $Fe_2(SO_4)_3 + Cu \rightarrow 2FeSO_4 + CuSO_4$ and $2FeSO_4 + Co_2O_3 + 3H_2SO_4 \rightarrow 2CoSO_4 + Fe_2(SO_4)_3 + 3H_2O$ indicate that conditions for complete solution of cobalt oxides by the acid used to dissolve copper concentrates may be maintained, if necessary, by the addition of iron or copper to the leach solution. Since cobalt is not deposited in the copper electrolysis circuit, it accumulates in solution to an equilibrium point where the quantity of cobalt eliminated with the washed gangue of the copper leach section is equal to the quantity of cobalt dissolved. In other words, all the soluble cobalt is found in the solution accompanying the gangue eliminated from the copper circuit after washing.

These dilute pulps, which are the starting point for electrolytic cobalt production, contain (in g/l): Cu 16–20, Co 6–10, Fe 0.6–0.9, Zn 0.2–0.4, Mn 1.2–1.6, Ni 0.03–0.08, Al_2O_3 1.2–1.4, P_2O_5 2–3, MgO 5–6 and H_2SO_4 5–6. They are treated with a lime slurry to bring the pH to 3.5–3.8, precipitating iron, phosphorus and aluminum. The pulp passes to a series of thickeners; from there the solution goes to electrolytic cells for de-copperizing, the solids to a series of countercurrent washing thickeners. Solution from the latter is returned to the primary thickeners while the solids go to waste.

The first de-copperizing by electrolysis, at high current densities with vigorous air agitation, lowers the copper content to about 1 g/l. The solution is treated with lime slurry to bring the pH to 5–5.5, the pulp is thickened, and the solids are returned to the stage of initial lime treatment. The solution, reduced to about 0.2 g/l copper, is carried to beds of annealed cobalt granules where the last traces of copper are removed.

Further addition of lime slurry in agitation machines now produces a cobalt precipitate which is feed for the cobalt electrolysis cells. It contains (in per cent): Co 16–18, Ni 0.1–0.2, Cu 0.01–0.02, Zn 0.3–0.5, Mn 1.5–2, Fe

0.1–0.15, CaO 19–22, MgO 4–18 and S 12–14. Mild steel cathodes and lead anodes are employed.

Use of a pulp containing cobalt hydroxide in suspension, and vigorous air agitation of the electrolyte maintain a high pH (around 5.8) in the electrolysis cells. A little ammonium sulfate is added to improve the buffering and conductivity of the system. The usual composition of the electrolyte is (in g/l): Co 10, Ni 0.2, Mn 5, Zn 0.1, Cu 0.002, MgO 40, $(NH_4)_2SO_4$ 5, CaO saturation. Power consumption is about 6.5 kwh/kilo of cobalt at a current density of 500 amp/sq meter; electrolyte temperature is 55–58° C. The solids suspended in the spent electrolyte are dissolved, with the addition of H_2SO_4, thickened, filtered and washed; the cake is discarded and the solutions returned to the circuit.

The cathode deposit normally contains the following (in percentages): Co 92–94, Ni 0.25–0.30, Zn 1–1.8, Fe 0.05–0.1, Mn 0.1–0.3, Cu 0.01–0.02 and S 0.1–0.3. These deposits, after being stripped from the cathode, are melted in an electric furnace under slightly oxidizing conditions. Zinc is volatilized at the outset and the last traces are removed by agitation with poles. Manganese is scorified at the same time. Sulfur is removed with lime and calcium carbide. A jet of oxygen on the surface of the bath reacts with combined carbon derived from electrodes or calcium carbide. Finally, the bath is deoxidized with silicon-cobalt, aluminum or silicon-calcium, and the product granulated into shot by pouring it into a stream of water.

The granules are dried, polished in a sawdust barrel and screened to remove minus 3 mm diameter. The usual composition is (in percentages): Co 99.1, Ni 0.5, Fe 0.2, Cu 0.01, Zn 0.01, Al 0.02, Si 0.07, Mn 0.01, S 0.02 and C 0.02.

Treatment of Sulfide Ores in the Belgian Congo

Union Minière commenced, in 1959, to mine some mixed sulfide and oxide copper ores which underlie the surface deposits of malachite. The sulfide copper minerals are chalcocite with minor quantities of bornite and chalcopyrite; the cobalt mineral is carrollite. These lower sulfide deposits are, like the copper oxide ores of the Belgian Congo, rich by world standards, running 5 per cent Cu and 0.1–0.2 per cent Co.

The mixed ores are finely ground; the sulfides are floated by conventional frothers and xanthate collectors. The malachite is then floated, after superficial sulfidization with an alkaline sulfhydrate sulfide and collection with xanthate. The malachite concentrate is sent to the leach plant as usual. The sulfide concentrate, running 45 per cent Cu, 1–3 per cent Co, 12 per cent S and 1–2 per cent Fe, is subjected to a sulfating roast at 675–700° C in a Fluosolids reactor to give the most favorable temperature for sulfating copper without decomposing the cobalt sulfate which forms at a lower temperature. About half of the small quantity of iron present is not sulfated and remains insoluble in the subsequent leach.

Leaching with dilute sulfuric acid yields about 95 per cent of both the copper and the cobalt in the concentrate. The leached solutions are electrolyzed for copper; cobalt is recovered from the spent electrolyte by essentially the same steps outlined above for the recovery from oxidized ores. The new hydrometallurgical plants of Kolwezi-Luilu will produce initially, per annum, 100,000 tons of electrolytic copper and 3,500 tons of electrolytic cobalt.

NORTHERN RHODESIA

Rhokana Corporation Limited

Cobalt has been recovered for many years from the large copper mining operations of Rhokana Corporation Limited, a Northern Rhodesian producer located at Nkana, where small quantities of carrollite are associated with the copper ores. Two concentrates are made by (1) floating the bulk of the copper in a high lime circuit with a minimum addition of conventional frothing and collecting agents, and (2) by greatly increasing the addition of flotation reagents, and re-circulating various pulps to produce a "cobalt" concentrate. Since the flotation properties of carrollite closely resemble those of pyrite, its flotation is suppressed by lime in the initial copper circuit. Additional reagents and further flotation treatment overcome the depressant effect of lime, and carrollite is recovered with the balance of the copper minerals in a "cobalt" concentrate.

For a number of years the "cobalt" concentrate, which contained very much more copper than cobalt, was smelted in separate reverberatory furnaces and converters. The converter slag, which might contain 5-10 per cent Co, was granulated, mixed with coke and smelted in electric arc furnaces to produce a copper-cobalt-iron alloy. The latter, containing 12–15 per cent Cu, 37–43 per cent Co and 40–50 per cent Fe, was granulated and shipped overseas for refining.

During this period of operating, although the nickel content of Rhokana mill feed was extremely small (less than 1/100 that of cobalt), more nickel than cobalt was consistently found in blister and electrolytic copper, and in tank house solutions and slimes. This illustrates the greater affinity of cobalt for oxygen, and its more complete removal in smelter slagging operations. Tichenor[64], noting that the rate of oxidation of cobalt at 500-800° C in oxygen was 25 times greater than that of nickel, accepted the view that cobalt oxide near the oxygen interface has a much larger proportion of ca-

tion vacancies than the corresponding nickel oxide. He attributes this difference to the higher oxygen content of cobalt oxide under equilibrium conditions rather than to differences in rates of ionization of oxygen.

In the earlier years of operation, the copper in the ore was mainly derived from bornite, and the cobalt grade was higher, giving an iron:cobalt
ratio in the concentrate of 3–4:1. Pyrometallurgical treatment was reasonably satisfactory and gave a low production cost for cobalt as a by-product
from the copper smelting operations.

After the war, mining development resulted in an increased proportion of
chalcopyrite and pyrite in the ore, and high smelting losses unavoidable
when a concentrate with a high iron:cobalt ratio is treated. The extensive
laboratory and pilot plant investigations which were then instituted to de-
vise a process for acid leaching of matte, or roasting and leaching of concentrates, followed, in both cases, by eventual production of electrolytic
cobalt, have been summarized by Talbot and Hepker.[63] Roasting and
aqueous leaching of the cobalt concentrate was finally selected as the commercial process, and the output of electrolytic cobalt commenced in 1953.
By 1957, virtually the entire cobalt production from Rhokana was obtained
in the form of electrolytic cobalt. Operations have been described by Talbot
and Chapman.[62]

The cobalt concentrate, which may contain 25 per cent Cu, 17 per cent
Fe and 3.5–4 per cent Co, is given a stage sulfatizing roast in six 8-hearth
Nichols-Herreshoff downdrafted furnaces. Cobalt is converted from oxide
to sulfate at 680–710° C in the lower sections; copper sulfate formed at
lower temperatures is decomposed to cupric oxide, and the iron after de-
sulfidizing in the early stages of roasting remains as Fe_2O_3. As a net result
of the roasting operation, most of the cobalt becomes water-soluble, leaving most of the copper and iron as insoluble oxides and basic sulfates.

Temperature control is a very important part of the roasting operation;
in practice, the difficulty is achieving maximum conversion of cobalt to
sulfate while leaving a minimum quantity of copper and iron in the water-
soluble state. It has been reported by Stephens, for instance, that cobaltiferous pyrite, when roasted at 650° C, yields 87 per cent of its cobalt and
1 per cent of its iron in the water-soluble form, whereas at a temperature
of 700° C the cobalt sulfate drops to 14 per cent.[61] At this temperature,
optimum solubilities for cobalt are attained when the fluidized-bed reactor
gas contains 8 per cent SO_2 and 4 per cent O_2. X-ray diffraction studies
have been published[41] which indicate that for certain roasting conditions
CoS at 240° C becomes Co_3S_4 and Co_3O_4. The latter change to $CoSO_4$ and
CoO at temperatures between 300 and 600° C; at 750° C, and above, CoO is
the stable product.

The calcines are leached with hot water and filtered, and the residue returned to the smelter. The filtrate is treated with air and milk-of-lime to precipitate iron and most of the copper at pH 5.2–5.5. The residues, containing a little cobalt, are redissolved in acid, reprecipitated and returned to the initial filtration stage. The cobalt solution is passed over metallic cobalt in cementation cells to remove the last traces of copper and then treated with milk-of-lime to precipitate cobalt as hydroxide. The latter is filtered, dissolved in sulfuric acid, and cobalt electrolyzed on mild steel cathodes with antimonial lead anodes. The spent electrolyte serves as a source of acid for dissolving the cobalt hydroxide in a continuous cycle. The excess acid generated during electrolysis is neutralized by cobalt hydroxide; this also serves to maintain the cobalt concentration of the electrolyte at about 25 g/l. The cell temperature is kept at 60° C to provide dense and adherent deposits, and a current density of about 15 amp/sq ft is maintained. The cathode deposits are either sold directly or melted in an electric furnace and granulated, and the granules burnished and sized for market.

Chibuluma Mines Ltd.

Chibuluma Mines Ltd., one of the Northern Rhodesian copper companies of the Rhodesian Selection Trust Group, began to produce cobalt concentrate in 1956, and cobalt matte in 1957. The output of Chibuluma is expected to be maintained at slightly above 1,500,000 pounds of cobalt annually.

Flotation of this ore has been described by Harper.[27] Lime is added to produce a pH in the pulp of approximately 11; sodium cyanide is added as a depressant for cobalt, and a 34 per cent copper concentrate is produced with the aid of methyl isobutyl carbinol as a frother and Aerofloat 208 as a collector. The tailing from the copper flotation is conditioned with copper sulfate and sulfuric acid to pH 9, and a cobalt concentrate containing about 3.6 per cent Co and 3.3 per cent Cu is floated with pine oil as a frother and sodium isopropyl xanthate as a collector. A total copper recovery between 97 and 98 per cent, and a cobalt recovery in cobalt concentrate of 80 per cent are achieved. The matte, averaging 9.2 per cent Co and 12.4 per cent Cu, is further treated in Belgium.

UGANDA

In western Uganda, Kilembe Mines Limited commenced operations in 1956 on a sulfide orebody containing 2.25 per cent Cu and 0.2 per cent Co. Pending construction of a cobalt leach plant, cobalt concentrates were still being stockpiled in 1958. It is anticipated that the annual cobalt output will be about 1,100,000 pounds.

ARSENIDE ORES OF MOROCCO, CANADA AND THE UNITED STATES

Cobalt arsenides are a vital source of production in several parts of the world. Their extractive metallurgy will be considered under two headings: (a) the combined pyrometallurgical and hydrometallurgical practices used for treating ores from Morocco and Canada; (b) the techniques of pressure leaching used for treating the Blackbird cobaltite concentrates at Garfield, Utah.

Moroccan and Canadian Ores

High grade Moroccan ores are hand sorted to give a direct charge to the blast furnace; lower grade material is concentrated by gravity on air shaking and Wilfley tables. The cobalt oxide minerals are magnetic; the arsenides are non-magnetic. Where only a very small percentage of arsenides are mixed with oxides, magnetic separation is simple, and a satisfactory concentration of cobalt in oxides can be made. For mixed oxide-arsenide ores, an oxidizing roast is employed to remove a good part of the arsenic as As_2O_3 and to leave the rest as arsenates. The latter are magnetic and can be separated with the oxide cobalt. In beneficiation operations, a recovery is reported of 93 per cent of the cobalt and nickel, and 91 per cent of the gold.[45] Concentrates are sent either to French refineries or to Deloro, Canada.

Unlike the Moroccan deposit, Canadian cobalt arsenides are derived from a number of small producers, mostly in the Cobalt-Gowganda area of northern Ontario. The earlier metallurgical practices for treating these ores have been described many times.[5,20,31,36,40,72]

These ores are now concentrated by hand sorting, tabling or flotation (or by a combination of these), and are treated at Deloro Smelting and Refining Company, Ltd., Deloro, Ont.

The extractive processes of the Deloro plant are sufficiently versatile to treat successfully concentrates having the following typical compositions:

	Canadian Concentrates %	Moroccan Concentrates %
Co	5–12	9.6
Ni	1–9	0.3
Cu	0.1–1	0.1
Fe	6–21	1.8
As	11–31	43.0
S	3–10	1.7
SiO_2	10–20	27.5
CaO	3–10	4.5
Ag (oz/ton)	100–2,500	6.7

The crushed ore and concentrates are charged to a blast furnace with coke, iron scrap, and limestone or silica, as required. Arsenic fume and dust are collected in a bag house and purified by sublimation in a small furnace to yield 99 per cent As_2O_3. The unsublimed residue of silver, lead, cobalt and nickel is returned to the blast furnace.

Matte, speiss and bullion are tapped together into pots where they separate into layers—matte on top with speiss beneath it, bullion at the bottom. After cooling, the layers can be easily separated. Bullion is obtained when there is more than a sufficient quantity of silver in the charge to saturate the speiss and matte. For cobalt ores, the principal impurities in bullion are copper and lead; these, together with arsenic and sulfur, are removed with fluxes and an air stream in an oil-fired furnace before electrolytic refining.

A typical speiss might contain the following (in percentages): Co 20, Ni 12, As 23, Fe 18, Cu 2, Sb 1 and Ag 2.7. The charge must contain enough arsenic to combine with the cobalt and nickel for the latter not to pass into the slag. The ratio of iron to arsenic maintained in the speiss is usually 18 per cent Fe:23 per cent As; this facilitates the removal of arsenic by iron in a later stage of the process. Nickel has the greatest affinity for arsenic; then cobalt, and then iron. Their affinity for oxygen is in the reverse order; iron is oxidized before cobalt and the latter before nickel. To prevent undue oxidation of cobalt, it is necessary to prevent excessive oxidation of iron in the blast furnace.

A typical matte in a cobalt blast furnace might contain the following in percentages: Co 9, Ni 4, As 5, Fe 27, Cu 12, S 23 and Ag 6–24. When matte and speiss are formed at the same time it is impossible to prevent Co, Ni and other metals from dividing between them. Matte formed in the cobalt blast furnace always contains some arsenic, occasionally as much as sulfur. It is preferable to form as little matte as possible to avoid a different roasting treatment. The use of large quantities of limestone in a charge is also avoided, if possible, since this encourages matte formation at the expense of speiss.

The iron not required for speiss and matte formation is oxidized and available for slag. The latter may contain (in percentages): SiO_2 27, Fe 13, Al_2O_3 12, CaO 20 and MgO 7, Co + Ni under 1.

The speiss, with an accompanying small quantity of matte, is crushed and ground to −80 mesh, and roasted in an Edwards roaster to eliminate a good part of the arsenic and sulfur, and to oxidize the iron. The roasted speiss may contain (in percentages): 10–12 As in the form of arsenate, 2.5 Cu, 23 Co, 9 Ni, 21.5 Fe, 8.6 S and 700–1,000 ounces per ton of Ag. It is mixed with dilute sulfuric acid to convert Co, Ni, Cu and Fe to water-soluble sulfates in mechanical agitators which discharge to Dorr thickeners. The solids are returned to the smelter while the solution passes to the iron-arsenic removal tanks.

Sodium chlorate is used to oxidize the iron, and lime additions bring the pH to 3.5 to precipitate ferric arsenate, ferric hydroxide, calcium sulfate and calcium arsenate. Most of the copper remains in solution if this pH is not exceeded. The iron precipitate is washed in Dorr thickeners, the underflow discarded and the overflow carried to cells for removal of copper either on scrap iron or by electrolysis. Final traces of iron and copper in the solution are removed with lime; the pulp is filtered under pressure, and the filter cake is re-treated for cobalt recovery. The solution containing cobalt and nickel is carried to the final stage of cobalt precipitation.

Cobalt separation depends on the fact that in neutral solutions, cobalt is more readily oxidized than nickel. The oxidized cobalt compound hydrolyzes and precipitates, leaving nickel in solution. The oxidant employed is sodium hypochlorite, made by passing chlorine into a solution of caustic soda and soda ash. The reactions involved in the hypochlorite separation of cobalt are not wholly understood, but the first step is probably the precipitation of a basic cobalt carbonate ($CoCO_3 \cdot Co(OH)_2 \cdot H_2O$). The sodium hypochlorite then reacts with cobaltous hydroxide to give hydrated cobaltic oxide ($2Co(OH)_2 + NaOCl + H_2O \rightarrow NaCl + Co_2O_3 \cdot 3H_2O$).

Cobaltic oxide undergoes rapid oxidation and reduction in the presence of hypochlorite, and a continuous evolution of oxygen occurs from the bleach solution. A certain amount of free hydrochloric acid is liberated from the hypochlorite solution; this reacts with $CoCO_3$ of the basic carbonate precipitate to form $CoCl_2$ from which cobalt is again precipitated by a fresh bleach solution.

In practice, sodium hypochlorite is usually added in stages to give, initially, a pure $Co(OH)_3$ precipitate, and then a mixed hydroxide of cobalt and nickel which is re-circulated. The cobalt precipitate is filtered on a press, and the solution is carried to the nickel recovery section. The cobalt hydrate is calcined, and soda ash is added to transpose $CaSO_4$ to $CaCO_3$ and Na_2SO_4. The latter is removed by washing, and the cobalt oxide is mixed with charcoal and reduced to metal in a rotary kiln at 1000°C. The metal fines are then melted in an electric furnace and granulated in water. Cobalt metal from arsenide ores such as that, for example, produced at the Deloro plant, usually contains (in percentages): Co 98.5, Ni 0.7, Fe 0.4, Cu 0.04, Mn 0.1, Si 0.1 and C 0.09.

Dettmer and Lichty have outlined a method for producing matte in an electric furnace from arsenical sulfide cobalt ores.[17] By maintaining an As:S ratio ≤ 1 in the furnace feed, a slag and a matte containing a small quantity of arsenic can be obtained, but no speiss. Results are best when electrodes are just out of contact with the surface of the molten bath.

The history of sodium hypochlorite separation is of interest since it has played such an important role in cobalt metallurgy. The firm of Evans and Askin was founded in Birmingham in 1835 for the purpose of refining nickel and manufacturing German silver. To separate nickel from cobalt in the mixed arsenide ores available at that period was a serious problem. A friend of Charles Askin, Mr. White Benson, suggested that bleaching powder might precipitate the cobalt, and the two men each agreed to try the experiment.

Benson, having an ample stock of bleaching powder, used enough to precipitate all the metals in solution. Obtaining a mixture of cobalt and nickel, he concluded that his suggestion was worthless. Askin, by chance having only about half the required amount of bleaching powder, emptied the entire bottle into the cobalt-nickel solution. As he expected, there was only a small precipitate; but on examination, he found, to his astonishment, that it was pure hydrated cobalt oxide. This discovery provided a pure cobalt for pottery work. Previously, the blue from cobalt ores had been a dirty blue, such as that found, for instance, in the famous "willow-pattern" pottery. Now, however, pure cobalt compounds make possible all shades of blue.

Pressure Treatment of Cobaltite Concentrates

From its Blackbird Mine in Idaho, Calera Mining Co., a subsidiary of the Howe Sound Company, produces a copper concentrate which is sent to custom smelters, and a cobalt concentrate which is treated at the company's refinery near Garfield, Utah. The characteristics of this cobaltite ore, and many important features of its beneficiation and electrowinning, have been studied and reported by the U. S. Bureau of Mines.[47,57,58,59,68,70]

Calera Mining Co. decided to adopt pressure acid leaching and reduction. This process proved disappointing for some time because of mechanical and corrosion problems, most of which appear to have been satisfactorily solved.[42,52]

The concentrating process consists of floating chalcopyrite, and depressing cobaltite and pyrite at pH 10.4, and 100° F. The cobalt mineral, then activated with sodium sulfide at pH 3.2, floats readily to give a low tailing of about 0.06 per cent Co.[19] Fresh water must be used for the differential floats. The concentrate contains (in percentages): Co 17.5, Fe 20.0, As 24.0, S 29.0, Ni 1.0, Cu 0.5 and insoluble 5.0. As in the conventional extractive process previously described, it is important to keep an arsenic:iron ratio of approximately 1.2:1.

The concentrate, in the form of a slurry, is fed continuously to a pressure autoclave operating at more than 500 psig and over 375° F, and a means for agitation and introduction of compressed air is provided. Exit gas from the autoclave, consisting of oxygen-deficient air and steam, is vented through scrubbers to the atmosphere. The exothermic chemical reaction converts over 95 per cent of the cobalt to sulfate, and the final slurry, which is discharged continuously, contains free acid, cobalt, nickel, iron and copper as sulfates, with small quantities of arsenic in solution. The insoluble portion of the discharge slurry consists largely of ferric arsenate and calcium sulfate.

Lime is added to neutralize the discharge slurry, and filtration is carried out in drum filters with repulping and refiltering. Iron and arsenic in the solution are removed by addition of lime, ammonia and air, and copper is then cemented out on cobalt powder. The purified solution is then ready for batch pressure reduction with hydrogen.

Ammonia is added to the cobalt solution to form a complex cobalt ammine. This is pumped to an autoclave and heated to 375° F; compressed hydrogen is admitted, and at a pressure of about 800 psig in the presence of a catalyst, the cobalt is reduced to a fine metal powder. An operating cycle consists of a seed run and several densifications. In the seed run, a very fine metal powder is obtained which acts as the nucleus in succeeding densifications to form powder of increasing particle size and density. Some cobalt is also formed as a plating on the interior surfaces of the reduction autoclaves.

The powdered metal contains about 0.15 per cent sulfur, which is eliminated by melting in an electric furnace with a high lime slag and a small quantity of coke. After degassing the metal with aluminum, it is granulated in water, dried and polished. An analysis (in percentages) has been reported: Co 95.6, Ni 3.9, Fe 0.2, As 0.03, Cu 0.02, S 0.03 and C 0.15.

In 1959, on the fulfillment of a government contract, Calera mine and refinery operations were suspended. Since this accounted for about three-quarters of American cobalt output, the United States may not, in the immediate future, maintain its post-war position among major producers.

BY-PRODUCT OF NICKEL REFINING

Electrolytic Refining of Sudbury Nickel

In concentrating and smelting copper-nickel ores at Sudbury, Canada—operations which have been described on many occasions—[1,3,30,46] cobalt accompanies nickel. Recovery of the cobalt commences at the nickel refineries.

International Nickel Company of Canada Ltd. initiated recovery of cobalt oxide at the Port Colborne electrolytic nickel refinery in 1947. In the normal refining process, nickel and cobalt, together with the major impurities (iron and copper), dissolve from the anode to yield an impure anolyte containing about 50 g/l Ni and 0.1 g/l Co. Most of the iron is precipitated from this solution by aeration and hydrolysis, and removed by filtration. Cobalt is precipitated from the resulting solution, together with the remainder of the iron and some copper, by treatment of the electrolyte with

elemental chlorine and basic nickel carbonate at pH 4. The impure cobaltic-
nickelic slime is separated from the partially purified electrolyte and treated
for cobalt recovery in the following manner:[48]

A water suspension of this slime is treated with sulfur dioxide to reduce
the cobalt and nickel to the bivalent state at about pH 4.5, together with
copper and iron. Sulfuric acid is then added to dissolve the slime completely, and fresh slime is added to re-oxidize the iron and precipitate it as
ferric hydroxide. Copper is removed by cementation on reduced nickel
powder from the iron-free solution. Cobalt as a crude cobaltic hydroxide is
then separated from the nickel by sodium hypochlorite at about pH 2.3 and
100° F. This precipitate is redissolved in sulfuric acid and sulfur dioxide,
and a second treatment with sodium hypochlorite is carried out to obtain
a cobalt precipitate carrying much less nickel than the original. This second
cobaltic hydroxide precipitate is roasted to oxide and leached with water to
remove soluble sulfur salts. The final black oxide contains (in percentages)
approximately: Co 70, Ni 0.8, Fe 0.1 and Cu 0.01.

A large part of the cobalt oxide is reduced, melted and cast into anodes
for production of electrolytic cobalt. Electrolysis is carried out in diaphragm cells similar to those used in nickel refining.

In 1952, Falconbridge Nickel Mines Ltd., at its refinery at Kristiansand,
Norway, commenced to produce cobalt from Sudbury matte. In 1958, its
cobalt output was reported at 756,000 pounds. The recovery processes are
similar to those of International Nickel, described above.

Carbonyl Refining of Sudbury Nickel

Part of the output of nickel oxide from the Sudbury operations of International Nickel is refined at the plant of its associate, Mond Nickel Company Ltd., in Clydach, Wales. Cobalt recovery from this source commenced in 1940.

Unlike nickel, reduced cobalt does not form a gaseous carbonyl when
carbon monoxide is passed over it at atmospheric pressure. The residues
from the carbonyl plant, therefore, contain all the cobalt, together with
copper, precious metals, unreacted nickel and iron. These are roasted and
leached, and copper and iron are removed by conventional means. Cobalt
is precipitated as cobaltic hydroxide by the addition of a nickel peroxide
slurry prepared from nickel sulphate, caustic soda and sodium hypochlorite. The first cobalt precipitate is purified, calcined to oxide, and refined to high grade black and gray cobalt oxides. A wide range of cobalt
salts is also produced, including acetates, carbonates, chlorides, formates,
nitrates, oxalates, phosphates and sulfates. Typical analyses of the two
oxides are given below.

	Co	Ni	Cu	Fe	SiO$_2$	S	MgO	CaO	Na$_2$O
Black cobalt oxide	71–72	0.8	0.03	0.30	0.25	0.05	0.03	0.05	0.1
Gray cobalt oxide	76–77	1.3	0.06	0.34	0.30	0.02	0.13	0.07	1.0

Pressure Ammonia Treatment of Nickel Concentrates

Nickel concentrates produced at the Lynn Lake, Manitoba mine of Sherritt Gordon Mines Ltd. are sent to the company's refinery at Ft. Saskatchewan, Alberta. They contain (in percentages): Ni 12–16, Cu 1–2, Co 0.2–0.5, Fe 33–40, S 28–34, insoluble 8–20 and less than 0.02 oz/ton precious metals. The concentrate is treated in a continuous leaching operation in which ammonia and compressed air are used at 180° F and 100 psig.[23,37] Nickel, cobalt and copper are dissolved in the form of complex metal ammines. Iron remains with the undissolved solids, mainly as ferric oxide, and is separated from the solution by thickening and filtration. Copper, precipitated from solution as sulfide, and excess free ammonia are removed in a continuous distillation and filtration operation. A stripping step using hydrogen sulfide removes the residual copper.

To purify the copper-free solution, the unsaturated sulfur compounds are oxidized and the ammonium sulfate hydrolyzed. The purified solution, containing 45 g/l Ni and 0.8 g/l Co, is given batch reduction; hydrogen is the reducing agent and ferrous sulfate the catalyst. Nickel is reduced selectively and precipitated as metal powder. Reduction is continued until the nickel concentration in solution decreases to about 0.8 g/l, at which point only about 8 per cent of the cobalt present in solution is reduced.

After nickel reduction, the solution contains about 0.8 g/l of both nickel and cobalt. These metals are precipitated with hydrogen sulfide and filtered; the solution is then sent to the crystallizer for recovery of fertilizer grade ammonium sulfate. The mixed nickel-cobalt sulfides are leached, with air and agitation, in sulfuric acid solution at 250° F and 100 psig for 2 hr. The concentration of ammonium sulfate in the leach solution is maintained at 80–100 g/l. The autoclave discharge solution is aerated, the pH raised to 5 with ammonia to precipitate iron, and the latter removed by filtration.

Nickel is then preferentially precipitated by reacting the solution with hydrogen under closely controlled conditions of pH, temperature and pressure. A nucleation leach at 200° F and 100 psig is conducted, with air, in an ammoniacal ammonium sulfate solution. Nucleation reduction produces seed powder for use as a catalyst in the subsequent densification reductions, and is carried out, with hydrogen, at a temperature of 350° F and 500 psig; ferrous sulfate is used as a catalyst. A number of densification reductions, perhaps 12–15, are then carried out, with hydrogen, at 350° F and 500 psig. A stearic acid solution is used as an antiplastering agent to prevent agglomeration of the metal particles and formation of plaster on the walls of the autoclave. Finally, a plating leach is carried out to remove metal deposits from the autoclave walls. This is effected with ammonium sulfate and air at 200° F and 100 psig.

The solutions from the densification reductions form the feed solution for cobalt reduction. The procedure for the latter is similar to that described for nickel, with the following exceptions:

(1) A mixture of sodium sulfide and sodium cyanide is used as the catalyst for the nucleation.

(2) Ammoniacal polyacrylic acid solution is employed as the antiplastering agent during the densification reductions.

(3) An excess of ammonia is added to the autoclave to ensure complete reduction of cobalt.

(4) The number of densification operations performed per cycle is greater, perhaps 25–30.

(5) The plating leach is carried out with an ammonium sulfate solution containing enough ammonia to give a free ammonia:cobalt ratio in excess of 5:1.

The cobalt powder is washed, dried in nitrogen, and either briquetted or sold in its original form. It contains (in percentages): Co 99.3, Ni 0.39, Fe 0.03 and S 0.02.

The catalytic reduction of cobalt with hydrogen from ammoniacal cobalt sulfate solutions using both colloidal graphite and cobalt powder as catalysts has been studied,[15,32] and the latter was found to be superior.

A large number of patents have been issued to Schaufelberger and Roy, and their associates of the Chemical Construction Company, for the precipitation of cobalt and other metals from salt solution by reduction with hydrogen in acid or ammoniacal solutions at elevated temperatures and pressures. The general principles and procedures have been described in two papers.[52,53] There also are patents for separations of nickel from cobalt by oxidation of the latter to the soluble cobaltic pentammine state and precipitation of nickel as nickel ammonium sulfate under controlled conditions of pH and other factors.

Acid Leaching of Nickeliferous Laterites

At Moa Bay in Cuba, Freeport Sulphur Company has a deposit of lateritic ore containing about 50 million tons averaging Ni 1.36 per cent and Co 0.13 per cent. To extract nickel and cobalt, processing requires acid leaching and precipitation of metallic values as a sulfide concentrate.[60,71] Extraction of nickel and cobalt at a refinery in Louisiana will be carried out by selective hydrogen reduction of sulfate solutions under elevated temperatures and pressures.

Ammonia Leaching of Nickeliferous Laterites

The leaching of selectively reduced nickel-bearing laterites with ammonia-ammonium carbonate solutions not only dissolves the nickel but also a large part of the associated cobalt. The Nicaro operation in Cuba, which produced appreciable tonnages of nickel during World War II by this process, did not recover the cobalt separately. Electrolytic separation studies of Nicaro plant products by the U. S. Bureau of Mines have not succeeded in evolving a commercial process.[21]

A number of factors in the recovery of nickel and cobalt from laterite deposits have been discussed throughout the years by a pioneer in this field, the late M. H. Caron.[7,8,9,10,11,12]

Extraction of cobalt from various lateritic ores can range from 96 per cent for an asbolite mineral containing 3.8 Ni, 8.8 Co and 2.5 Fe, to 60 per cent or less for a laterite analyzing 1.42 Ni, 0.15 Co and 52.5 Fe. Strong leach liquors, containing 7 per cent NH_3 and 6 per cent CO_2, are essential for high cobalt recovery, probably because cobalt with a low ammonia content tends to be co-precipitated with ferrous and ferric hydroxides and is not easily re-dissolved.

In the leaching operation, Ni, Co and Fe dissolve in the bivalent state, but aeration converts Co and Fe to the trivalent form. Cobalt losses are increased at high pulp temperatures because of decreased oxygen absorption and increased velocity of co-precipitation of cobalt with ferrous hydroxide. Satisfactory cobalt extractions may be expected only from liquors which are lean in iron, are saturated with dissolved oxygen, and have a sufficient ammonia content.

After leaching the reduced ores with ammonium carbonate, nickel and cobalt are recovered from the solution by distilling the NH_3 and CO_2, and precipitating a basic nickel carbonate containing cobalt. The latter is present by virtue of precipitation as $Co(OH)_3$, and by physical sorption. When basic nickel carbonate is washed with water, the washings contain small amounts of nickel and cobalt. By adding a small amount of $Ca(OH)_2$, nickel is quantitatively precipitated as the hydroxide and is almost free from cobalt; the latter may be precipitated by adding Na_2S to the clear, colored filtrate.

Caron suggested several procedures for separating nickel from cobalt in the basic nickel carbonate precipitate:

(a) By using a solution containing about 2 per cent CO_2:7 per cent NH_3, the nickel is re-dissolved preferentially to cobalt. By repeating this selective dissolution, the cobalt content of the solution can be reduced to a low value.

(b) By interrupted distillation of the pregnant solution, it is possible to obtain about 94 per cent of the nickel in the first two precipitations of basic nickel carbonate, leaving more than 90 per cent of the cobalt in the last two precipitations.

(c) A low temperature precipitation process gives a good separation. Distillation of pregnant liquor is carried out to the point where nickel commences to precipitate. The solution is cooled and saturated with CO_2; most of the nickel then precipitates. Cobalt, together with the impurities Fe, Mn, SiO_2 and MgO, remains in solution.

(d) An electrolytic process may be employed to separate cobalt from nickel. The precipitate of basic nickel carbonate containing cobalt is dissolved in HCl to form a slightly acid chloride solution. Ammonia of 20 per cent NH_3 is added at the rate of 2.5 parts to one of the chloride solution, and the whole is diluted with water to seven times the original volume of the chloride solution. When the electrolyte contains 0.76 per cent Co, 0.61 per cent Ni and 7.4 per cent NH_3, pure cobalt is deposited in the upper end of a circuit at a current density of 3.9 amp/dm^2 and a potential of 2.3 volts. At the lower end, the electrolyte is discharged as a solution containing most of the nickel and almost no cobalt.

Unsaturated sulfur compounds, derived from the ore or the gases used to reduce nickel and cobalt in laterites, restrict conversion of cobaltous to cobaltic ammines and decrease cobalt extraction. The use of oxygen in aeration during leaching increases the rate of oxidation of sulfur compounds and helps overcome their deleterious effect. Caron recommended that solutions heavily contaminated with sulfur first be distilled in the presence of sponge nickel. Cobalt is thus reduced to the cobaltous state and completely precipitated, together with nickel, from sulfur compounds which remain in the liquid and can be discarded. The mixed nickel-cobalt precipitate may then be dissolved and treated by one of the separation techniques described above.

COBALT FROM PYRITE

The recovery of cobalt and other metals from roasted pyrite has been carried out extensively in Germany. Iron pyrite from Finland, Spain, Sweden, Cyprus and other countries is roasted to obtain sulfur for acid manufacture. The addition of about 12 per cent sodium chloride to the calcined material, and roasting converts all the metals, except iron, to a soluble state. Leaching with dilute H_2SO_4 and HCl gives a solution of Cu, Zn, Co, etc., while the iron residue is sent to the blast furnace.

Copper and precious metals are removed from the solution with scrap iron and recovered by electrolysis. Iron is removed from the solution with air and lime. Bleaching powder and lime are then added to the solution, containing primarily Zn, Co and Ni, to precipitate cobalt. Although the quantities of cobalt present are very small—often about 0.05 per cent—the large tonnages of iron pyrite roasted in Germany have made a major contribution to the cobalt production of that country.

In the United States, cobalt has been recovered for many years from the pyrite associated with the magnetite at Cornwall, Pa., mined for its iron content by Bethlehem Cornwall Corp. Although the orebody contains less than 0.05 per cent Co, magnetic separation of magnetite, and flotation of the pyrite yields a concentrate of the latter containing about 1.5 per cent Co and a smaller quantity of copper. This pyrite concentrate is roasted for acid production at Baltimore, and the calcine is sent to Wilmington for chemical treatment. There it is given a chloridizing roast and a leaching with water; the copper is removed with scrap iron, and cobalt is finally precipitated with sodium hypochlorite.

Good descriptions of the various steps taken to recover cobalt from pyrite[4] and from cupriferous pyrite[44] have been published.

COBALT FROM LEAD PRODUCTION

Missouri

The St. Louis Smelting and Refining Division of National Lead Company, near Fredericktown, Mo., refines a nickel-cobalt-iron concentrate obtained as a by-product of its operations. A description of this process has been abstracted from a paper by McCormick.[39]

After removal of a lead concentrate and a copper concentrate, a nickel-cobalt-iron concentrate is obtained by selective flotation. The latter is partially roasted in a Wedge roaster to reduce the sulfur content from 40 per cent to about 15 per cent. The roasting step increases the refining capacity; it is not a sulfatizing operation. The concentrate grade to the roaster is about 2–2.5 per cent Co, 3 per cent Ni and 3 per cent Cu. The calcine, in the form of a slurry, is pumped to autoclaves equipped with an agitator, and steam and air lines. These oxidation autoclaves operate at 650 psig and 450° F; metal parts in contact with the slurry are made of titanium. The cobalt and nickel, together with copper and a small quantity of iron, are converted to sulfates. The latter are separated from the bulk of the insoluble iron by filtration and washing.

The solutions pass to a copper reduction autoclave operating at 325° F and 625 psig hydrogen pressure. The copper, present as sulfate, is reduced to the metallic state and discharged from the autoclave with the solution. Sedimentation, followed by cementation on iron, removes the copper from the solution. The latter is oxidized with air and neutralized with limestone to precipitate the iron from solution. The volume of solution is then reduced by evaporation, and the remaining traces of copper are removed by cementation on cobalt powder.

Cobalt is separated from nickel by oxidation of the cobalt in an ammoniacal solution with air to form stable cobaltic pentammine sulfate, which has a high solubility over a wide pH and temperature range. When sulfuric acid is added to the ammoniacal solution of nickel and cobalt, the nickel is precipitated as nickel ammonium sulfate crystals, whereas most of the cobalt remains in solution as the pentammine. Oxidation of cobalt to the pentammine takes place in an autoclave at 160° F and 370 psig air pressure. After the cobalt is oxidized, nickel is precipitated by the addition of sulfuric acid, and by cooling. The nickel salt is separated from the cobalt solution by a centrifuge.

Nickel ammonium sulfate is dissolved in an ammoniacal solution and reduced with hydrogen in an autoclave at 425° F and 600 psig. By controlling ammonia in the nickel reduction feed, it is possible to stop the metal reduction before any appreciable quantity of cobalt in solution is reduced by hydrogen. Reductions are carried out in series: a very fine nickel powder or "seed batch" is first precipitated; further growth of these particles follows, with reduction of successive additions of feed solution—a process known as densification—until the nickel powder reaches the desired size. It is then discharged from the autoclave, filtered and dried.

Cobalt solution is treated in a similar way, except that additional ammonia is not required for reduction. A seed batch is made and successive densifications follow until the proper particle size is reached. The metal powder is discharged from the autoclave into a flash cooling tank, washed, filtered, dried and briquetted. A typical analysis of the cobalt powder would be (in percentages): Co 98.4, Ni 0.5, Cu 0.02, Fe 0.05, S 0.06, C 0.05 and Si 0.01; loss in H_2, 0.9.

Burma

For many years prior to World War II, the rich lead-zinc ores of Bawdwin mine in Burma contributed to world cobalt production, the element being recovered at European refineries in copper-lead matte and copper-nickel speiss. The matte contained about 0.5 and the speiss 3–7 per cent Co. Operations at this property have been suspended since 1942.

OTHER PROCESSES

The recovery of cobalt from domestic ores has been studied extensively by the U. S. Bureau of Mines during and since World War II. A number of detailed reports were issued on the occurrence, beneficiation and refining of cobalt ores from the Blackbird district of Idaho,[38,47,59,70] the Goodsprings area of Nevada,[56,57,58] various manganese deposits in the United States,[28,54] the complex mineralization of southeastern Missouri,[22,33] and from laterite and related orebodies.[21] The results of these investigations have been of great value to cobalt metallurgists.

Despite visits to Gebroders Borchers plant at Goslar, and Letmathe refinery at Letmathe, Germany, in 1945, the Combined Intelligence Objectives Sub-committee discovered little that was not already known about cobalt refining.[14]

When a finely-ground reverberatory matte is treated with enough hot 20 per cent H_2SO_4 to combine with FeS only, soluble ferrous sulfate is formed, and copper, nickel and cobalt remain in the residue. The latter two may dissolve initially, but they will be precipitated later as sulfides by the H_2S at these pH values.[66]

Cobalt is a deleterious impurity in electrolytic zinc refining and is commonly removed by zinc dust in the presence of a copper salt and other metal ions such as As, Sb, Hg, Tl, etc.[25,26,51] The very small but consistent output of cobalt from Australia is, in fact, obtained from a unique recovery operation as a by-product of zinc refining. The cobalt is removed from the impure zinc electrolyte with α-nitroso β-naphthol to give a crude precipitate of cobalti-nitroso β-naphthol containing, in addition, gypsum, basic zinc sulfate, unconsumed lime, entrained zinc sulfate, and small amounts of iron and copper. The filter cake is pulped, H_2SO_4 added, and the nitroso-β-naphtholates of Co, Cu and Fe are floated away from the tailing suspension of gypsum in zinc sulfate. The concentrate is washed, and calcined at $800°$ C to oxide.[29,50]

In the recovery of cobalt from metallurgical slags, the following observations should be borne in mind. Over 5 per cent Co may be present in a sample of magnetite without causing any difference from pure magnetite in lattice spacing.[74] Cobaltous oxide is miscible with cobalt in the liquid state up to 15 per cent.[2] Cobaltous sulfide reacts violently with Co_3O_4 at about $950°$ C, giving CoO, Co and SO_2. Sulfides of iron and cobalt are miscible in all proportions in the liquid state. Cobaltous oxide and FeS are miscible in the liquid condition.[2] Iron sulfide reacts with $CoO \cdot SiO_2$ to give $FeO \cdot SiO_2$ and CoS, but cuprous sulfide does not react with $CoO \cdot SiO_2$. Cuprous oxide and CoS react to give Cu_2S and CoO. From 58 to 91 per cent of the cobalt present as silicates in nickel converter slag can be converted to sulfides by heating to $700-900°$ C in sulfur vapor.[13] Cobalt silicate reacts with metallic iron to produce cobalt metal; with calcium sulfide to yield cobalt sulfide; with iron arsenide to give cobalt arsenide.[49] In Russia, cobalt oxide from nickel converter slags has been treated with aluminum sulfide to give CoS and Al_2O_3.[43] A good miscibility, decrease in specific gravity and lowering of surface tension of cobalt droplets are claimed.

The separation of cobalt from nickel by extraction in organic solvents has been reported,[24,35,55] but the process has not been commercially developed.

Bibliographies on the extractive metallurgy of nickel and cobalt for the periods 1900–1928 and 1929–1955 were issued by the U. S. Bureau of Mines in 1959[30] and 1957,[3] respectively.

PRODUCTION OF COBALT METAL FRON COBALT COMPOUNDS

In many of the processes for extracting cobalt, calcination of hydroxide or carbonate is required to yield oxide as the final product or as the penultimate material in the preparation of electrolytic cobalt. Depending on the temperature and atmosphere of the calcining furnace, two commercial types of cobalt oxide are obtainable. With a temperature of 720–750° C and a large excess of air, a black oxide is produced. At 880° C and a neutral or slightly reducing atmosphere, gray cobalt oxide is formed. Both oxides are used in pottery production. Some powder metallurgists employ the black oxide, but for most metallurgical and chemical applications the gray form is used.

Commercial gray cobalt oxide usually contains 75–77 per cent Co and is over 90 per cent CoO, with some higher oxides, mostly Co_3O_4, invariably present. Cobaltous oxide, the stable form above about 809° C, will take up oxygen to reform a higher oxide at lower temperatures. The rate of reabsorption of oxygen depends on the temperature of previous calcination and on the ambient temperature when exposure to oxygen first occurs. Reversion of cobaltous oxide to higher forms can be minimized by a high temperature of calcination and rapid cooling of the product under a neutral or slightly reducing atmosphere.[6]

The black cobalt oxide of commerce usually contains 70–72 per cent Co. In general, this is largely Co_3O_4, with some Co_2O_3 and traces of CoO present. The stable temperature range for Co_3O_4 is from 373° C to 705–809° C. Complete conversion of Co_2O_3 to Co_3O_4 occurs at temperatures above 265° C. Although Co_3O_4 will absorb oxygen in sufficient quantity to correspond to the oxide Co_2O_3, there is no change in the lattice structure.[69] Most black oxides correspond more closely to the formula Co_2O_3 than to Co_3O_4, but their method of preparation indicates that the latter is the predominant form.

Metallic cobalt may be produced from all oxides by several classic methods of reduction.

Carbon. This is a common industrial procedure employed, for example, in electric furnaces with coke and in the production of rondels with charcoal.

$$2Co_2O_3 + 3C \longrightarrow 4Co + 3CO_2$$

$$Co_3O_4 + 2C \longrightarrow 3Co + 2CO_2$$

$$2CoO + C \longrightarrow 2Co + CO_2$$

With an excess of carbon, complete reduction is possible at 900° C.

Hydrogen. This method is also used industrially where a very pure product is desired, such as cobalt powders for cemented carbides, powder metallurgy, catalysts, etc. Reduction commences below 500° C and is rapid at 700–1100° C. The reduced cobalt should be cooled in a hydrogen or inert atmosphere to avoid oxidation. Low temperature reductions are especially prone to yield a pyrophoric product, necessitating cooling under hydrogen and finally quenching in water beneath a blanket of inert gas.

Carbon Monoxide. Reduction occurs rapidly above 600° C and is complete below 900°. Cobalt does not form a carbonyl at atmospheric pressure, and this metal, unlike nickel, can be reduced with carbon monoxide without the safety precautions required where a toxic carbonyl can be evolved.

The reducing activities of carbon monoxide and of hydrogen for cobalt oxide have been compared by Kuznetsov and Kulish.[34] Reaction with CO commences immediately and then, because of accumulation of CO_2 in the reaction sites, falls rapidly to a steady low rate. In hydrogen reduction, the initial speed is less, but the second portion of the reaction is autocatalytic, and the over-all reduction is faster.

Aluminum. The thermit process for reducing metallic oxides with aluminum powder can be employed, if required, to yield metallic cobalt: $3Co_3O_4 + 8Al \longrightarrow 4Al_2O_3 + 9Co + 9.9\,Cal.$

METALLOGRAPHIC DIFFERENTIATION OF COBALT METAL, OXIDE AND SULFIDE

In both the extractive and fabricating fields of cobalt metallurgy, to supplement information derived from chemical analyses, an examination of powder compacts or polished sections is occasionally required to determine the presence of metallic, oxide and sulfide forms of the element. These forms can be distinguished microscopically by prior etching of the sample with 1 per cent mercuric chloride for 30 seconds, or 35 per cent sodium bisulfite for 2 minutes.[73] Both reagents impart a brown stain to the metallic phase but leave unchanged the dark gray oxide and the yellowish-white sulfide. Manganese sulfide, if present, remains unaltered as a bluish-gray constituent.

References

1. Anonymous, "Operations of the International Nickel Company of Canada, Ltd.," *Can. Mining J., 67,* No. 5, 311-554 (1946).
2. Asanti, P., "Thermal Properties of Cobalt Compounds and their Appearance in Slags," *Valtion Tek. Tutkimuslaitos, Julkaisu,* **8,** (1948). *Chem. Abst.,* **46,** 7951 (1952).
3. Bauder, R. B., "Bibliography on Extractive Metallurgy of Nickel and Cobalt, January 1929-July 1955," *U. S. Bur. Mines Inf. Circ.,* 7805 (1957).
4. Beall, J., "Cobalt," *Mining Eng.,* **190,** 17-24 (1951).
5. Bridges, R. W., "The Metallurgy of Canadian Cobalt Ores," *Can. Mining J.,* **37,** No. 2, 48-50 (1916).
6. Bryant, P. S., "Cobalt Refining at Rainham Works of Murex, Ltd." The Refining of Non-Ferrous Metals, Proceedings of a Symposium Held in London in July, 1949, pages 259-79, London, Institution of Mining and Metallurgy, 1950.
7. Caron, M. H., "Fundamental and Practical Factors in Ammonia Leaching of Nickel and Cobalt Ores," *Trans. Am. Inst. Min. Met. Eng.,* **188,** 67-90 (1950).
8. —, "Separation of Nickel and Cobalt," *Trans. Am. Inst. Min. Met. Eng.,* **188,** 91-103 (1950).
9. —, "Some Aspects in Connection with the Application of the Ammonia Leaching Process," *De Ingenieur,* No. 32, 25-29 (1954).
10. —, "The Mechanism and Refined Application of Selective Reduction for Nickel-Cobalt Ores," *De Ingenieur,* No. 17, 9-15 (1955).
11. —, "Cobalt Recovery by Ammonia-Leaching with the Final Object to Secure Pregnant Liquors Most Adapted for its Separation from Nickel," *De Ingenieur,* No. 18, 8-12 (1956).
12. —, "Separation of Nickel and Cobalt," *De Ingenieur,* No. 36, 19-32 (1957).
13. Chizhikov, D. M., and Serebryakova, R. M., "Reaction of Iron, Nickel, and Cobalt Silicates with Elementary Sulfur," *Tsvetnye Metal.,* **29,** No. 2, 45-8 (1956). *Chem. Abst.,* **51,** 12780 (1957).
14. Combined Intelligence Objectives Sub-Committee, G-2 Division, S.H.A.E.F. (Rear), APO 413, Item No. 21, File No. XXI-20. "Refining of Cobalt in Germany," London,H. M. Stationery Office, (1946).
15. Courtney, W. G., "The Catalytic Reduction of Cobalt with Hydrogen from Ammoniacal Sulfate Solutions," *J. Phys. Chem.,* **61,** 693-4 (1957).
16. De Merre, M., (to Société Générale Métallurgique de Hoboken), U. S. Pat. 2,757,080, July 31, 1956.
17. Dettmer, P. B., and Lichty, L. J. (to Quebec Metallurgical Industries Ltd.), U. S. Pat. 2,741,553, April 10, 1956.
18. Dismant, J. H., Hamilton, J. H., Fassell, W. M., and Lewis, J. R., "Decarburization of High Carbon Cobalt Metal," *J. Metals,* **4,** 884 (1952).

19. Douglas, E. B., "Mining and Milling Cobalt Ore," *Mining Eng., 8*, 280–3 (1956).
20. Drury, C. W., "Cobalt, its Occurrence, Metallurgy, Uses, and Alloys," *Rept. Ontario Bur. Mines., 27*, 31–69 (1918).
21. Ferrante, M. J., Good, P. C., and Gruzensky, P. M., "Electrolytic Separation Studies of Nickel and Cobalt from Nicaro-Plant Products," *U. S. Bur. Mines Rept. Invest., 5394* (1958).
22. Fine, M. M., Vahrenkamp, G. J., Lankenau, A. W., and Moreland, O. N., "Upgrading Cobalt-Nickel Stockpiles by the Roast Flotation Process," *U. S. Bur. Mines Rept. Invest., 5388* (1958).
23. Forward, F. A., and Mackiw, V. N., "Chemistry of the Ammonia Pressure Process for Leaching Ni, Cu, and Co from Sherritt Gordon Sulphide Concentrates," *J. Metals, 7*, 457–66 (1955).
24. Garwin, L., and Hixson, A. N., "Separation of Nickel and Cobalt by Extraction from Aqueous Solution," *Ind. Eng. Chem., 41*, 2298–2310 (1949).
25. Griffith, D. L., and Rankin, M. J., U. S. Pat. 2,471,952, May 31, 1949.
26. —, U. S. Pat. 2,509,916, May 30, 1950.
27. Harper, J. E., "Flotation of a Copper-Cobalt Ore," *Mining World, 20*, No. 11, 38–42 (1958).
28. Jacobs, J. H., Shelton, F. K., and Knickerbocker, R. G., "Separation and Electrodeposition of Manganese and Cobalt from Manganese Electrolytes," *U. S. Bur. Mines Rept. Invest., 3866*, 13–18 (1946).
29. Johnstone, D. H., "Production of Cobalt Oxide," Extractive Metallurgy in Australia. Non Ferrous Metallurgy. Fifth Empire Mining and Metallurgical Congress, Australia and New Zealand, 1953, Vol. IV B, 105–6 (1953).
30. Jones, C. A., "Bibliography on Extractive Metallurgy of Nickel and Cobalt, 1900–1928," *U. S. Bur. Mines Inform. Circ., 7883* (1959).
31. Jones, R. J., "Cobalt in Canada," *Can. Dept. Mines and Tech. Surveys, Mines Branch Bull., 847* (1954).
32. Kaneko, T. M., and Wadsworth, M. E., "The Catalytic Reduction of Cobalt from Ammoniacal Cobalt Sulfate Solutions," *J. Phys. Chem., 60*, 457–62 (1956).
33. Kenworthy, H., and Kershner, K. K., "Metallurgical Investigations of Southeastern Missouri Cobalt-Nickel Resources," *U. S. Bur. Mines Rept. Invest., 4999* (1953).
34. Kuznetsov, A. N., and Kulish, N. F., "Comparison of the Reducing Activity of Carbon Monoxide and Hydrogen for Cobalt Oxide," *Ukrain. Khim. Zhur., 24*, 674–80 (1958). *Chem. Abst., 53*, 8983 (1959).
35. Kylander, R. L., and Garwin, L., "Extraction of Cobaltous Chloride with Capryl Alcohol in a Spray Tower," *Chem. Eng. Progress, 47*, 186–90 (1951).
36. Liddell, D. M., "Handbook of Nonferrous Metallurgy," Vol. 2, New York, McGraw-Hill Book Co. Inc., 1945.
37. Mackiw, V. N., Lin, W. C., Benoit, R. L., and Benz, T. W., "Nickel-Cobalt Separation at Sherritt Gordon," *J. Metals, 10*, 800–3 (1958).
38. Marchant, J. D., Banning, L. H., and Hergert, W. F., "Melting, Refining, and Granulation of Cobalt Powder," *U. S. Bur. Mines Rept. Invest., 5133* (1955).

39. McCormick, W. R., "Production of Cobalt, Nickel and Copper at the Fredericktown Metals Refinery," Mid-America Mineral Conference of A.I.M.E., (1958).
40. Mellor, J. W., "A Comprehensive Treatise on Inorganic and Theoretical Chemistry," Vol. XIV, London, Longmans, Green and Co., Ltd., 1935.
41. Meunier, F., Meunier, L., and Vanderpoorten, H., "The Mechansim of Roasting of Cobalt Sulfide." Compt. Rend. 27e. Congr. Intern. Chim. Ind. Brussels, 1954, 2; *Industrie Chim. Belge,* **20,** Special No. 494–9 (1955). *Chem. Abst.,* **50,** 16599 (1956).
42. Mitchell, J. S., "Cobalt Pressure Leaching and Reduction at Garfield," *J. Metals,* **9,** 343–5 (1957).
43. Murach, N. N., and Kisileva, E. V., "Precipitation of Cobalt from Convertor Slag by Aluminum Sulfide," *Isvest. Vysshikh. Ucheb. Zavedenii, Tsvetnaya Met.,* **1958,** No. 3, 63–5. *Chem. Abst.,* **53,** 8984 (1959).
44. Nakabe, S., "Metallurgy of Cobalt Production from Cupriferous Pyrite," *J. Metals,* **3,** 445–51 (1951).
45. Perrault, R., "Le Cobalt," Paris, Dunod, 1946.
46. Queneau, P., Bracken, E. H., and Kelly, D., "High-Grade Iron Ore at Copper Cliff, Ontario," *J. Metals,* **10,** 527–32 (1958).
47. Reed, G. C., and Herdlick, J. A., "Blackbird Cobalt Deposits, Lemhi County, Idaho," *U. S. Bur. Mines Rept. Invest.,* **4012** (1947).
48. Renzoni, L. S., Canadian Pat. 446,289, Jan. 20, 1948.
49. Reznik, I. D., "Laboratory Investigation of the Reaction of Cobalt Silicate with Molten Metallic Iron, and Sulfide and Arsenide of Iron," *Sbornik Nauch. Trudov Gosudarst. Nauch.-Issledovatel. Inst. Tsvetnoi Met.,* **1955,** No. 10, 230–42. *Chem. Abst.,* **52,** 14477 (1958).
50. Ross, S. W., "Electrolytic Zinc at Risdon, Tasmania. Major Changes Since 1936," *J. Metals,* **1,** 211–17 (1949).
51. Sato, S., "Purification of Zinc Sulfate Solution. The Removal of Cobalt and its Mechanism," *Nippon Kogyo Kaishi,* **72,** 413–19 (1956). *Chem. Abst.,* **51,** 9391 (1957).
52. Schaufelberger, F. A., "Precipitation of Metals from Salt Solution by Reduction with Hydrogen," *J. Metals,* **8,** 695–704 (1956).
53. Schaufelberger, F. A., and Roy, T. K., "Separation of Copper, Nickel and Cobalt by Selective Reduction from Aqueous Solution," *Bull. Instit. Mining Met.,* **64,** 375–93, 500–14 (1955).
54. Schlain, D., Cobalt Content of Manganese Ores," *U. S. Bur. Mines Rept. Invest.,* **3866,** 2–12 (1946).
55. Schlea, C. S., and Geankoplis, C. J., "Extraction of Iron, Cobalt, and Nickel Sulfates by Organic Liquids," *Ind. Eng. Chem.,* **49,** 1056–7 (1957).
56. Shelton, F. K., "Metallurgical Treatment of Ores from the Goodsprings Mining District, Nevada," *U. S. Bur. Mines Rept. Invest.,* **3836** (1946).
57. Shelton, F. K., Churchward, R. E., Stahl, J. C., and Davis, C. W., "Electrolytic Cobalt—A Commercially Feasible Process," *Electrochem. Soc. Preprint.,* **91–4,** 55–71 (1947).

58. Shelton, F. K., Churchward, R. E., Stahl, J. C., and Livingston, G. F., "A Study of Certain Factors in the Hydrometallurgy and Electrodeposition of Cobalt," *U. S. Bur. Mines Rept. Invest.,* **3832** (1945).

59. Shelton, F. K., Stahl, J. C., and Churchward, R. E., "Electrowinning of Cobalt from Cobaltite Concentrates," *U. S. Bur. Mines Rept. Invest.,* **4172** (1948).

60. Simons, C. S., "Materials Selection and Design Problems in a Nickel-Cobalt Extraction Plant," *Corrosion,* **15,** Tech. Topics 95–8 (1959).

61. Stephens, F. M., "The Fluidized Bed Sulfate Roasting of Nonferrous Materials," *Chem. Eng. Progress,* **49,** 455–8 (1953).

62. Talbot, H. L., and Chapman, F. H., "How Northern Rhodesia Meets Rising Base Metal Demands," *Eng. Mining J.,* **154,** No. 8, 82–7 (1953).

63. Talbot, H. L., and Hepker, H. N., "Investigations on the Production of Electrolytic Cobalt from a Copper-Cobalt Flotation Concentrate," *Trans. Inst. Mining Met.,* **59,** 147–79 (1949–50).

64. Tichenor, R. L., "Role of Oxide Composition in Oxidation of Nickel and Cobalt," *J. Chemical Physics,* **19,** 796–7 (1951).

65. Tougarinoff, B., "Removal of Nickel from Cobalt by Sulfur Cementation," Compt. Rend. 27e. Congr. Intern. Chim. ind., Brussels *1954,* 2. *Chem. Abst.,* **50,** 11191 (1956).

66. Udy, M. J., Brit. Pat. 656,142, Aug. 15, 1951.

67. Union Minière du Haut Katanga, "Union Minière's Golden Jubilee," *Mining World,* **19,** No. 2, 38–64 (1956).

68. U. S. Bur. Mines "Materials Survey, Cobalt," Washington, D. C., 1952..

69. Webb, H. W., "Cobalt, Nickel and Selenium in Pottery," London, Mond Nickel Company Ltd., undated.

70. Wells, H. R., Sandell, W. G., Snedden, H. D., and Mitchell, T. F., "Concentration of Copper-Cobalt Ores from the Blackbird District, Lemhi County, Idaho," *U. S. Bur. Mines Rept. Invest.,* **4279** (1948).

71. Wilson, F., "The Moa Bay—Port Nickel Project," *Mining Eng.,* **10,** 563–5 (1958).

72. Wright, S. B., "The Smelting and Refining of Silver Ore from the Cobalt Area, and the Production and Uses of Stellite," *Trans. Can. Mining Institute,* **21,** 269–78 (1918).

73. Young, R. S., "Metallographic Differentiation of Cobalt Metal, Oxide and Sulphide," *Metallurgia,* **59,** 210 (1959).

74. —, Golledge, A., and Grenville-Wells, H. J., "Magnetite Crystals from Copper Converter," *Am. Mineralogist,* **34,** 761–3 (1949).

Chapter 4

CHEMICAL AND PHYSICAL PROPERTIES OF COBALT

Cobalt is a member of the iron triad in the eighth group of Mendeleeff's Table, with atomic number 27 and atomic weight 58.94. When giving the electronic structure of the cobalt atom it is usually assumed that the electrons present are 2 for the K-shell; 2, 2, 4 for the L-shell; 2, 2, 4, 3, 4 for the M-shell; 2 for the N-shell. The orbital arrangement could be written $1s^2$, $2s^2$, $2p^6$, $3s^2$, $3p^6$, $3d^7$, $4s^2$.[26,32]

Cobalt exhibits a valency of 2 or 3, the bivalent being the stable state for the simple ion when not co-ordinated to anything but water. The simple trivalent cobaltic ion is unstable, cobalt occupying an intermediate position between iron (where the trivalent is the stable state) and nickel (where trivalent ions probably do not exist). Complexes of bivalent cobalt are few and unstable, but a large number of stable trivalent cobalt complexes may be found, particularly in the form of ammines.

Like other elements of Group VIII, cobalt is a grayish-white metal, but when polished it exhibits a faint bluish tinge. Its melting point is 1493°C, its boiling point about 3100°C. Its atomic volume is 6.7 cm³/g–atom; the effective atomic radius for bivalent cobalt has been reported as 0.72–0.82 A, and for neutral cobalt atoms, 1.25–1.39 A. Cobalt has a density of 8.9 g/ml or 0.32 lb/cu in. for most solid forms, and about 8.0 g/ml when molten.

In its compact state, the metal is virtually unattacked by oxygen or water at ordinary temperatures. When cobaltous oxide is reduced by hydrogen at low temperatures, it gives a pyrophoric powder which catches fire in air but is not attacked by water. Cobalt is readily dissolved by sulfuric, hydrochloric and nitric acids, but only very slowly by hydrofluoric acid, to form cobaltous salts. Cobalt dissolves with difficulty in ammonium hydroxide, forming a nitrite, and is slowly attacked by sodium hydroxide and dilute acetic acid.[17,33,34] The halogens combine with cobalt to form the respective halides. Cobalt in the finely-divided form occludes considerable quantities (50–150 volumes) of hydrogen, and adsorption of the latter by electrolytic cobalt can occur up to 35 times its volume.

Although it has been known, since 1921, that cobalt can exist in two forms, there is still some controversy about the temperature of transition between hexagonal close-packed and face-centered cubic cobalt.[25,31] The transformation is dependent on the purity of the cobalt and the grain size. Allotropic transformations of cobalt are discussed fully in Chapter 7.

The phases of cobalt were designated in the order of their discovery, hence the room-temperature, hexagonal close-packed cobalt was originally called α, and the medium temperature, face-centered cubic was named β. The adoption of such a method of distinguishing phases has led to a chaotic system in which isomorphous phases have been given different designations. In recent years, there has been general agreement that the face-centered cubic solid solutions should be called α—with the exception of systems based on iron, where the designation γ is too strongly entrenched to be changed. Conforming to this modern viewpoint, in the present edition of this book α is used for the face-centered cubic cobalt, and ϵ for hexagonal close-packed cobalt. The fact that in the literature α may refer either to hexagonal or cubic cobalt must always be borne in mind.

The heat of transformation is 60 cal/mol,[5] and the volume expansion on transforming from hexagonal close-packed cobalt to face-centered cubic is about 0.3 per cent. Lattice constants reported for hexagonal cobalt have varied from 2.5013 to 2.514 Å for a, and from 4.052 to 4.0821 Å for c,[1,17] giving c/a = 1.623–1.66. For cubic cobalt a = 3.537 at 18°C, 3.613 near 417°C and 3.631 at 1220°C. The lattice parameters reported by Taylor and Floyd[29] have been adopted in this book. According to their measurements, for hexagonal cobalt a = 2.5074 Å, and c = 4.0699 Å; for cubic cobalt a = 3.561 A. Interatomic distances for hexagonal cobalt are d_1 2.4995–2.4925, d_2 2.507; for the face-centered cubic form, 2.507.[5,9,21] The coefficient of thermal expansion of cobalt varies between 12.3×10^{-6} and 18.1×10^{-6}, depending on the temperature and impurities present.[17] The thermal expansion of the metal changes in the range 400–450°C, corresponding to the allotropic change which occurs in this interval. The linear coefficient of expansion has been quoted for hexagonal cobalt as $12.6 \times 10^{-6}/°C$, and for the cubic form at 430°C as $14.2 \times 10^{-6}/°C$.[5]

The specific heat of cobalt has been given as 0.0207–0.265 cal/g for temperatures from –253 to 1570°C.[2,17,22] The value of 0.103 given by Perrault[22] is probably a fair average for room temperatures. Thermal conductivity values have ranged from 0.1299 to 0.172 cal/sec/cm²/°C/cm, and the value of 0.165 given by Honda is probably a good average.

The vapor pressure of solid cobalt has been reported by Edwards, Johnston and Ditmars[6] to vary, in atmospheres $\times 10^{-8}$, from 0.216 at 1363°K to 9.55 at 1522°K. Kornev and Golubkin[12] found higher values for substantially the same temperature range, from 7.066×10^{-9} at 1050°C to 8.908×10^{-7} at 1250°C.

The latent heat of fusion has been reported as 58–68 cal/g,[5] and the latent heat of vaporization as 1540 cal/g.[17] The thermal neutron absorption is given as 34.8 barns/atom.[5]

The magnetic properties of cobalt and its alloys are important characteristics. Hysteresis loss for cobalt has been given as 6900 ergs/cm³/cycle for Bm = 5000 gauss, and magnetization (saturation) as 18700 gauss (4η Is). Residual induction is 4900 gauss for H_{max} = 1000 gauss, and coercive force is given as 8.9 oersteds for H_{max} = 1000 gauss.[5]

Permeability has been recorded as initial 68, maximum 245. Under weak magnetic forces the permeability of cobalt is increased by compressed stress, but when the magnetic force is large the reverse is the case. The magnetization of cobalt in a weak magnetic field rises at first with temperature, reaching a maximum at about 400° C, and then decreases slowly to vanish at the critical temperature. The coercive force of cobalt decreases with increase of temperature, for example from 12 oersteds at 0° C to 5 at 400° C. Curie point, or the temperature at which cobalt passes from the ferromagnetic to the paramagnetic state, is quoted as 1050–1150° C; in recent years, however, the figure 1121° C has been adopted.

Kalmus and Blake[10] found the influence of the magnetic field H on the intensity of magnetization I to be:

H	2.5	20.7	43.2	75.9	129.0	151.8
I	8.5	136.7	238.4	350.2	451.5	493.2

With single crystals of cobalt, the direction of the (0001)-axes is that of easy magnetization, while directions of (1010)- and (1120)-axes are difficult.

Myers and Suchsmith[19] found that face-centered cubic cobalt possesses greater magnetization that hexagonal cobalt, and that in the temperature range of 431–950° C it is dependent on the heat treatment which the specimen receives. The significant factor in this heat treatment is the speed with which the specimen is allowed to cool through the lower transformation temperature. Suchsmith and Thompson[28] found that face-centered cubic cobalt becomes magnetically isotropic at 1000° C. Scheidler[24] studied the stray magnetic field in the coarse crystalline surface of a compact cobalt sample by means of an electron beam. The magnetostriction of a low-density cobalt rondel was investigated by Stauss.[27]

Values reported for the electrical resistivity of cobalt vary considerably— from 5.5×10^{-6} to 15.9×10^{-6} ohm/cm cube—since this property is affected by impurities and the preheating or annealing treatment. For highly purified cobalt heated several hours *in vacuo*, electrical resistivity at 20° C may be taken as 6.3 microhm-cm.[5] The temperature coefficient of electrical resistance (0–100° C) has been reported as 0.0032–0.0066[17] and may be taken as 0.006/° C.[5] The electrochemical equivalent of bivalent cobalt is 0.3054 mg/coulomb. Volume conductivity of cobalt at 20° C, referred to standard copper, is 27.6 per cent.

The velocity of sound at room temperature has been given as 4724 metres/sec.[17] Surface tension of cobalt at 1550°C is reported as 1936 dynes/cm.[13]

The reflecting power of a cobalt surface has been found to vary with wave length as follows:[17]

Å	% of Incident Light
3,950	58
5,000	66
10,600	67.5
67,500	92.7
120,000	96.6

Total emissivity for an unoxidized surface alters with temperature in the following manner:

22°C	0.03
500°C	0.13
1000°C	0.23

Photoelectric emission was studied by Cardwell[4] and Marick.[14]

Solubility of oxygen in cobalt has been listed as follows:[5]

	Temp °C	Wt %
Hexagonal c.p. cobalt	600	0.6×10^{-2}
	700	0.9×10^{-2}
	810	1.6×10^{-2}
	875	2.05×10^{-2}
Face-centered cubic cobalt	875	0.58×10^{-2}
	945	0.7×10^{-2}
	1000	0.8×10^{-2}
	1200	1.3×10^{-2}

Mechanical properties of 99.9 per cent cobalt, and variation of these properties with temperature, for 99.6 per cent metal, are shown in Tables 4.1 and 4.2.

The hot hardness of wrought 99.65 per cent cobalt, held for one hour at room temperature to the following temperatures, is given below:[5]

Temp °C	Vickers Hardness Number
300	310
400	265
600	250
700	208
800	205

TABLE 4.1. MECHANICAL PROPERTIES OF 99.9% COBALT

	Cast	Annealed	Sintered	Cold-worked	Electrolytic
Tensile Strength, 1000 psi	34.4	37	98.5	100	
Yield Strength, 1000 psi	20–43	28–41	43.8		
Compressive Strength, 1000 psi	122.0	117.2			
Compressive Yield, 1000 psi	42.2	56.1			
Elongation in 2 in., %	0–4	0–8	13.5	2–8	
Hardness, Brinell	124–130	121–131	165		270–310

TABLE 4.2. VARIATION WITH TEMPERATURE OF MECHANICAL
PROPERTIES OF 99.6% COBALT

Temp °C	Ultimate Tensile Strength, psi	Elonga-tion	Reduction of Area, %	Elastic Modulus Kg/mm^2	Shear Modulus 10^6 psi
– 200					12.9
– 100				21,800	
room	100,000	14	16		
200				20,000	11.1
300	60,000	27	25		
400					10.2
500	36,000	63	43	18,600	
700	15,700	9	9		
800					6.7
900				14,700	

Other properties of cobalt at elevated temperatures have been recorded.

100 hr at Temp °C	Rupture Strength, psi
649	12,500
816	3,000

Variation with temperature, of strength of arc-melted electrolytic cobalt
is given below:

	Strength, psi		
Temp	Ultimate	Yield	Reduction of Area %
Room	57,500	43,000	3
927°C	12,400	8,100	12

Limited data on creep characteristics are of interest. A sample exposed to 500° C for 100 hours at 12,000 psi gave 2.7 per cent elongation, while creep at 1000° C for 1 per cent strain in 24 hours showed the following:

Sintered and swaged cobalt	13,900 psi
Vacuum melted cobalt	6,700 psi

The modulus of elasticity in tension has been given as 30×10^6 psi, that in shear as 11.1×10^6 psi. For single crystals of cobalt, Young's moduli perpendicular and parallel to the hexagonal axis are 1.60×10^{12} and 1.96×10^{12} dynes/sq cm, respectively, and the rigidity moduli perpendicular and parallel to the axis 0.537×10^{12} and 0.520×10^{12} dynes/sq cm, respectively.[8]

The hardness of 99.98 per cent cobalt single crystals, obtained by zone refining, varied from 70 to 249 Knoop hardness numbers, depending on orientation.

Cobalt is slightly harder than iron or nickel, and in a highly purified condition can be readily machined in a lathe, although it is somewhat brittle. Cobalt containing a small amount of carbon is machined like mild steel. Pure cobalt cannot be swaged down to fine wire without special heat treatment, but the metal containing carbon can be readily swaged or rolled from the hot condition.

In its electrochemical behavior, cobalt usually occupies a position between iron and nickel. Under certain conditions, cobalt becomes passive in acid or alkaline solution. Hedges[7] observed that cobalt dissolves vigorously in concentrated nitric acid at room temperature, but becomes passive immediately at -11° C. When the temperature is raised slowly, the first bubbles of gas appear at +9° C, and at 25° C a sudden dissolution commences. These phenomena are exactly similar to those regarding iron at higher temperatures. A brown film readily forms over a cobalt anode in 80 and 100 per cent sulfuric acid, and oxygen is evolved.

Periodicity was observed in solutions containing 1–50 per cent acid. The effect was much more striking than in the corresponding experiments with iron. At the end of each passive period, during which the cobalt was lustrous, evolution of oxygen stopped, and the surface of the metal became dull; immediately before the next passive period, a dark gray film traveled up the anode and peeled off as the evolution of oxygen was resumed. Cobalt does not become passive at the low current densities which nickel and iron require.

The electrode potential of cobalt has been variously reported as 0.237–0.278 volt for $Co \rightarrow Co^{++}$, and 1.8 volts for $Co^{++} \rightarrow Co^{+++}$.[17] The standard electrode potential at 25° C can be taken as +0.278 volts. The

hydrogen overvoltage, or minimum voltage for the first visible appearance
of hydrogen, with a cobalt electrode in N H_2SO_4 at 20° was found by
Harkins to be 0.22 volt.[17]

For many years, there have been scattered references to corrosion studies
in which cobalt was included. Cobalt is attacked by sea water, 10–15 per
cent sodium sulfide, citric and tartaric acids, chlorine water, sulfurous acid,
potassium and ammonium persulfates, phosphoric acid, magnesium chloride, hot stearic acid and 1 per cent formic acid + methanol. No attack was
observed with sulfur monochloride in the absence of air, selenium oxydi-
bromide, hot oleic acid, methanol, 2 per cent formaldehyde + methanol,
1 per cent formic acid. The corrosion rate of cobalt in various solutions is
given in the following table.[33,34]

TABLE 4.3. CORROSION OF COBALT AT 25°C IN
QUIET IMMERSION

Reagent	Corrosion rate, mg/dm²/day
5% acetic acid	12.5
5% ammonium hydroxide	5.3
5% sulfuric acid	56.8
10% sodium hydroxide	5.6
1 : 1 hydrofluoric acid	176.6
Conc. hydrofluoric acid	101.5
1 : 1 phosphoric acid	65.1
Conc. phosphoric acid	7.4
5% hydrazine	7.8
Distilled water	1.1

Contrary to a statement in Mellor, it will be observed that cobalt is appreciably attacked by hydrofluoric acid.

The ductility of cobalt is greatly reduced when the sulfur content exceeds
0.005 per cent, and bars containing more than 0.015 per cent S cannot be
swaged owing to the formation of intercrystalline cracks.[15] The significant
figure is not the total sulfur, but rather the sulfur which is free to form cobalt sulfide, and the magnesium or manganese which is effective in reducing
sulfur embrittlement of cobalt.

The solubility of graphite in cobalt has been determined;[30] the results are
summarized below.

Temp °C	Carbon, wt %
1319 (eutectic)	2.68
1350	2.73
1400	2.90
1450	3.02
1500	3.23
1550	3.28

The entropy of cobalt has been given as 7.2 cal per degree at 25° C.[17]

The diffusion of Co^{60} into cobalt and other metals has been studied by a few investigators.[3,16,20,23] The diffusion coefficient (in sq cm/sec) at temperatures of 1050–1250° C for 99.0–99.7 per cent cobalt was found by Nix and Jaumot, for example, to be $0.367e \dfrac{-67000}{RT}$.

The study of cobalt—its fundamental properties and its compounds—has been facilitated, in recent years, by the preparation of high purity cobalt. Some of the pioneer work of Honda regarding magnetic properties was done with 93 per cent cobalt; many other investigations were conducted with material of 98 per cent purity. A detailed procedure for purification of cobalt solutions and for electrolytic deposition of the metal has been described by the U. S. Bureau of Mines.[11] Cobalt metal having a purity of 99.99 per cent, with reference to metallic contaminations, was deposited electrolytically. In another investigation, zone refining gave a cobalt purity of 99.98 per cent.[18]

Cobalt does not impart a distinctive coloration to a colorless flame. References to flame, arc, spark, absorption, ultraviolet and infrared spectra, Stark and Zeeman effect, and X-ray investigations are given in Mellor.[17]

References

1. Anantharam, T. R., "Lattice Parameters and Crystallographic Angles of Hexagonal Cobalt," *Current Sci.,* (India) **27**, 51–3 (1958).
2. Armstrong, L. D., and Grayson-Smith, H., "High Temperature Calorimetry. 11. Atomic Heats of Chromium, Manganese, and Cobalt Between 0° and 800°," *Can. J. Res.,* **28 A**, 51–9 (1950).
3. Byron, E. S., and Lambert, V. E., "Diffusion of Cobalt in Molybdenum," *J. Electrochem. Soc.,* **102**, 38–41 (1955).
4. Cardwell, A. B., "Effects of a Crystallographic Transformation on the Photo-electric and Thermionic Emission from Cobalt," *Proc. Nat. Acad. Sci.,* **15**, 544–55 (1929).
5. Cobalt Information Center, "Data on Cobalt," Columbus, O., 1958.
6. Edwards, J. W., Johnston, H. L., and Ditmars, W. E., "The Vapor Pressures of Inorganic Substances. VII. Iron Between 1356° K and 1519° K and Cobalt Between 1363° K and 1522° K," *J. Am. Chem. Soc.,* **73**, 4729–32 (1951).
7. Hedges, E. S., "Protective Films on Metals," New York, D. Van Nostrand Co., 1937.
8. Honda, K., and Shirakawa, Y., "Young's Modulus of Elasticity of Single Crystals of Nickel and Cobalt," *Science Repts. Research Insts. Tohoku Univ. Ser. A,* **1**, No. 1, 9–15 (1949). *Chem. Abst.,* **44**, 9758 (1950).
9. Hume-Rothery, W., "The Structure of Metals and Alloys," London, Institute of Metals, 1945.

10. Kalmus, H. T., and Blake, K. B., "The Magnetic Properties of Cobalt and Ferro Cobalt," Ottawa, Can. Dept. Mines, 1917.

11. Kershner, K. K., Hoertel, F. W., and Stahl, J. C., "Experimental Production of High-Purity Cobalt," *U. S. Bur. Mines Rept. Invest.,* **5175,** 1956.

12. Kornev, Y. V., and Golubkin, V. N., "Determination of Vapor Pressure of Solid Cobalt and Iron," *Fiz. Metal. i Metalloved.,* **1,** 286–97 (1955). *Chem. Abst.,* **50,** 9811 (1956).

13. Kozakevitch, P., and Urbain, G., "Surface Tension of Pure Liquid Iron, Cobalt and Nickel at 1550° C," *J. Iron Steel Institute,* **186,** Part 2, 167–73 (1957).

14. Marick, L., "Variation of Resistance and Structure of Cobalt with Temperature and a Discussion of its Photoelectric Emission," *Phys. Rev.,* **49,** 831–7 (1936).

15. Martin, D. L., "Sulfur Embrittlement of Cobalt," *J. Metals,* **8,** 578–9 (1956).

16. Mead, H. W., and Birchenall, C. E., "Diffusion of Co^{60} and Fe^{55} in Cobalt," *J. Metals,* **7,** Section 2, 994–5 (1955).

17. Mellor, J. W., "A Comprehensive Treatise on Inorganic and Theoretical Chemistry," Vol. XIV, London, Longmans, Green and Co., Ltd., 1935.

18. Morral, F. R., "High-Purity Cobalt—Its Properties," *J. Metals,* **10,** 662–4 (1958).

19. Myers, H. P., and Sucksmith, W., "The Spontaneous Magnetization of Cobalt," *Proc. Roy. Soc.,* **207,** Ser. A, 427–46 (1951).

20. Nix, F. C., and Jaumot, F. E., "Self-Diffusion in Cobalt," *Physical Rev.,* **80,** 119 (1950).

21. Pauling, L., "Atomic Radii and Interatomic Distances in Metals," *J. Am. Chem. Soc.,* **69,** 542–53 (1947).

22. Perrault, R., "Le Cobalt," Paris, Dunod, 1946.

23. Ruder, R. C., and Birchenall, C. E., "Cobalt Self-Diffusion: A Study of the Method of Decrease in Surface Activity," *J. Metals Trans.,* **191,** 142–6 (1951).

24. Scheidler, G., "Study of the Stray Magnetic Field in the Coarse Crystalline Surface of a Compact Cobalt Sample by Means of an Electron Beam," *Arbeitstag. Festkorperphysik.* **11,** 181–5 (1954). *Chem. Abst.,* **52,** 8653 (1958).

25. Seybolt, A. U., and Mathewson, C. H., "Solubility of Oxygen in Solid Cobalt and the Upper Transformation Point of the Metal," *Trans. Am. Inst. Min. Met. Eng.,* **117,** 156–72 (1935).

26. Sidgwick, N. V., "The Chemical Elements and Their Compounds," Vol. **II,** Oxford, Clarendon Press, 1950.

27. Stauss, H. E., "Magnetostriction of Low-Density Cobalt Rondel," *J. Appl. Phys.,* **29,** 1690–1 (1958).

28. Sucksmith, W., and Thompson, J. E., "The Magnetic Anisotropy of Cobalt," *Proc. Roy. Soc.,* **A 225,** 362–75 (1954).

29. Taylor, A., and Floyd, R. W., "Precision Measurements of Lattice Parameters of Noncubic Crystals," *Acta Cryst.,* **3,** 285–9 (1950).

30. Turkdogan, E. T., Hancock, R. A., and Herlitz, S. I., "The Solubility of Graphite in Manganese, Cobalt, and Nickel," *J. Iron Steel Institute,* **182,** 274–7 (1956).

31. Van Arkel, A. E., "Reine Metalle," Berlin, J. Springer, 1939.

32. Wells, A. F., "Structural Inorganic Chemistry," London, Oxford University Press, 1945.
33. Young, R. S., "Corrosion Resistance of Cobalt," *Corrosion Technology,* **4,** 396–7, 403 (1957).
34. —, "Resistance of Cobalt Towards Certain Solutions," *Corrosion Technology,* **6,** 89 (1959).

Chapter 5

SIMPLE COMPOUNDS OF COBALT

Nearly all the simple compounds of cobalt are bivalent, since simple cobaltic salts are practically confined to oxides, sulfides, sulfates, fluorides and acetates; in fact, the latter three are considered by some investigators to be complex.[54] This is in marked contrast to the cobalt complexes, where the trivalent state is the stable and predominating form. The simple cobaltic salts are produced from the cobaltous only by the action of the strongest oxidizing agents, and are readily decomposed by water even at low temperatures with formation of the cobaltous salt.

Acetates

Cobaltous acetate $[Co(O \cdot CO \cdot CH_3)_2]$ is a red salt in both the anhydrous and tetrahydrate condition, easily soluble in water. Cobaltic acetate can be prepared by the oxidation of a cobaltous salt in acetic acid, or by the electrolytic oxidation of cobaltous acetate in glacial acetic acid containing 2 per cent water.

Carbides

Carbon dissolves in cobalt above 1300° C in a manner similar to its dissolution in iron. The carbides Co_3C, Co_2C and CoC_2 have been described. At atmospheric pressure and 226–230° C, carbon monoxide and finely divided cobalt react slowly to form a product with a composition corresponding to Co_2C. Hofer and Peebles[28] found that carbon hydrogenated with difficulty was in the form of finely divided carbon crystallites, and that in a partly carburized sample there was no evidence of a solid solution of carbon in α-cobalt. The structure and properties of cobalt carbide have also been discussed by Juza and Puff,[33] and Drain and Michel.[13]

Carbonates

Cobaltous carbonate $(CoCO_3)$ is found in nature as sphaerocobaltite. The precipitate formed when an alkaline carbonate is added to a cobaltous solution is usually a basic carbonate,[11,54] but in the presence of a slight pressure of carbon dioxide, the neutral carbonate is precipitated as a violet-red hexahydrate $(CoCO_3 \cdot 6H_2O)$. If this is heated in a sealed tube at 140° C, it is converted into an anhydrous carbonate, a pale red powder. The solubility of cobaltous carbonate in water is small.

74

Cobaltic carbonate can be obtained in a green solution by oxidizing a cobaltous salt in the presence of sodium bicarbonate.

Carbonyls

When carbon monoxide is passed over reduced nickel powder at atmospheric pressure and a temperature of 40–50°C, gaseous nickel carbonyl is formed which, at a higher temperature (around 200°C), is decomposed into pure nickel and carbon monoxide. Cobalt does not form a carbonyl at ordinary pressures, and this elegant separation has been employed in the Mond process of nickel refining to produce cobalt-free nickel on a large scale for over fifty years.

The usual conditions for the formation of the volatile carbonyl by the action of carbon monoxide on reduced cobalt have been given in technical and patent literature as pressures of 30–250 atmospheres and temperatures of 90–200°C. Cobalt tetracarbonyl ($Co_2(CO)_8$) is obtained as orange crystals, or a dark brown microcrystalline solid which decomposes when heated above its melting point of 51°C. Decomposition between 52 and 60°C leads to the formation of black crystals of cobalt tricarbonyl ($Co_4(CO)_{12}$), and higher temperatures give complete decomposition into cobalt metal and carbon monoxide.[36] Both cobalt carbonyls are readily oxidized by air, insoluble in water, soluble in benzene, and possess a very low vapor pressure which makes them much less hazardous than their nickel and iron analogues. The cobalt carbonyls have been discussed, in recent years, with relation to their spectra and structures;[17] analysis;[58] and reactions with organic compounds,[65] bases,[27] and metals.[26] The catalytic effect of cobalt carbonyls is described in Chapter 14.

Ferrites

In recent years, cobaltous ferrite ($CoO \cdot Fe_2O_3$) has been the subject of many investigations. Papers have appeared on its formation,[8,19,29] X-ray examination,[30,31] decomposition by roasting,[61] neutron-diffraction,[44] heat treatment[44,61,66] and various magnetic properties.[40,42,53,63,66] The latter are discussed in Chapter 8.

Formates

Cobaltous formate ($Co(O \cdot CHO)_2$) is a pink salt existing in the anhydrous and dihydrate states.

Halides

Bromide. Cobaltous bromide ($CoBr_2$) can be produced by the action of hydrobromic acid on cobaltous hydroxide or carbonate, or of bromine on cobalt.[39] The anhydrous salt is green, the hexahydrate red. The bromide is readily soluble in water and many organic solvents.

Chlorides. An aqueous solution of cobaltous chloride can be readily made by dissolving the metal, oxide, hydroxide or carbonate in HCl. Evaporation of this solution gives the pink hexahydrate, and dehydration yields the blue anhydrous salt. It has been suggested that the crystal structure of $CoCl_2 \cdot 6H_2O$ can be regarded as that of an octahedral complex $(Co^{++} \cdot 4H_2O \cdot 2Cl^-)$, with two molecules of water placed close to the Cl^-.[59]

Cobaltous chloride is readily soluble in water and a number of organic solvents. It furnishes the best illustration of the remarkable color changes of cobalt salts.[39] The aqueous solution is pink, but turns blue when warmed, or when hydrochloric or sulfuric acid is added. The pink of cobaltous chloride is favored by dilution, by the use of water as the solvent, by the absence of other salts such as alkalies, and by a low temperature. Blue is favored by the opposite conditions, and is nearly 90 times more intense than the pink.

Cobaltous chloride has been used as an invisible or sympathetic ink. On pink paper the writing is invisible when cold, blue when warmed. Papers impregnated with $CoCl_2 \cdot 6H_2O$ make cobalt chloride useful as an indicator of humidity and moisture.[45,56] Cobalt thiocyanate has also been recommended for this purpose.[57] Cobalt chloride is frequently added to silica gel to serve as a hygrometric indicator. Jaubert points out that at ordinary temperatures the desiccant turns from blue to rose, even though the silica gel has absorbed only 25-30 per cent of the water it is able to pick up, since cobaltous chloride reduces the efficiency of the gel by clogging its pores.[32] Because it causes the color in the carrier abrasive paste to change, cobalt chloride has been used to indicate when the temperature of grinding has exceeded a safe limit.[14] The cobalt chloride hygrometer, used for comparing permeability of films to moisture vapor, is still another application.[4]

Fluorides. Cobaltous fluoride may be obtained by the action of hydrogen fluoride on cobaltous chloride, or by dehydrating the tetrahydrate which is produced by dissolving the hydroxide in hydrofluoric acid. It is only moderately soluble in water.

Cobaltic fluoride exists in the hydrated and anhydrous states, and can be made by electrolyzing a saturated solution of cobaltous fluoride in hydrofluoric acid, or by treating anhydrous cobaltous chloride with fluorine.

The use of CoF_3 as a fluorinating agent depends on the fact that the lower fluoride (CoF_2) is changed to CoF_3 when fluorine is passed over it at $200-250°C$, and the compound CoF_3 reacts with hydrocarbons to replace hydrogen with fluorine: $2CoF_2 + F_2 \longrightarrow 2CoF_3$. $C_7H_{16} + 32CoF_3 \longrightarrow C_7F_{16} + 32CoF_2 + 16HF$.

Iodides. Cobaltous iodide is made by heating powdered cobalt in a stream of hydrogen iodide at 400–450° C to give a black crystalline α-form which yields the usual pink solution in water. This compound sublimes *in vacuo* mainly as the black form, but partly as an isomeric anhydrous yellow modification (β-cobalt iodide) which gives a practically colorless aqueous solution. By its change in color, cobaltous iodide has been reported as the most sensitive halide for determining water in organic solvents.[2]

Hydroxides

When an alkali hydroxide is added to a solution of a cobaltous salt, co-baltous hydroxide ($Co(OH)_2$) is formed. This compound may appear as blue, green or red, depending on the grain size, presence of adsorbed ions, temperature and alkalinity. The solubility of cobaltous hydroxide in water at 25° C has been reported to be 1×10^{-5} to 3×10^{-5} g/l.[18] The solubility of cobaltous ion is slightly greater in NaOH than in KOH up to 9 molar solutions, after which the solubility in KOH becomes greater.[20] For instance, solubility at room temperature ranges from 11.8 mg/l for NaOH and 10.2 mg/l for KOH in 3 M solution, to 374 mg/l for NaOH and 511 mg/l for KOH in 12 M solution.

Cobaltous hydroxide is oxidized slowly by air and rapidly by strong oxi-dizing agents to a hydrated form of cobaltic oxide ($Co_2O_3 \cdot H_2O$). Numerous suggestions have been made for the formation mechanism and structure of hydrated cobaltic oxide, or cobaltic hydroxide. For example, Krause and Wojciechowska[37] found that the freshly precipitated material corresponded to $2CoO \cdot OH \cdot 9Co_2O_3 \cdot 29H_2O$, and after standing for 10 months at 20° C, or several hours in boiling water or N NaOH, the product was $(Co_2O_3 \cdot H_2O)_n$. One of the most important industrial separations of cobalt from nickel is based on the fact that in neutral solutions cobalt oxidizes more readily than nickel—following the addition of sodium hypochlorite, for instance—and that the oxidized compound hydrolyses and precipitates, leaving nickel in solution.

Nitrates

When dilute nitric acid is added to cobalt metal, oxide, hydroxide or carbonate, an aqueous solution of cobaltous nitrate is formed which, on evaporation, yields red crystals of the hexahydrate $Co(NO_3)_2 \cdot 6H_2O$. This compound is exceedingly hygroscopic and is readily soluble in many or-ganic solvents.

Cobaltic nitrate is unstable and is known only in solution.

Oxalates

Cobaltous oxalate $[Co(C_2O_4)_2]$ is usually found as the pink dihydrate, but the tetrahydrate and anhydrous states exist. It is almost insoluble in water

but soluble in concentrated ammonia. Unstable cobaltic oxalate is found only in solution.

Oxides

Cobalt has less affinity for oxygen than has iron but more than nickel.[46] Like iron, cobalt has three well-known oxides: the monoxide or cobaltous oxide (CoO), cobaltic oxide (Co_2O_3) and cobaltosic oxide (Co_3O_4).

Cobaltous oxide is the final product formed when the carbonate or the other oxides are calcined to a sufficiently high temperature, preferably in a neutral or slightly reducing atmosphere. Pure cobaltous oxide is a difficult substance to prepare, since it readily takes up oxygen even at room temperature to re-form a higher oxide. The higher the temperature of calcining the less oxygen is absorbed. The rate of re-absorption of oxygen increases with a rise in temperature and is rapid at 400° C. To produce a reasonably pure cobaltous oxide, the calcination temperature should be above 1050° C, and the material should then be cooled to room temperature in an inert or slightly reducing atmosphere. Above about 850° C, the cobaltous form is the stable oxide. The color varies from olive green to red, depending on the grain size, but is usually dark gray. The theoretical cobalt content is 78.65 per cent, and the gray oxide of commerce, which is used for most metallurgical and chemical applications, generally contains 76 per cent Co and is essentially CoO with a little Co_3O_4 present. Many properties of cobaltous oxide have been investigated, such as heat capacity,[1,34,35] adsorption of oxygen,[50] self-diffusion,[9] magnetic structures,[15,49] and entropy.[34]

Cobaltic oxide (Co_2O_3) is formed when cobalt compounds are heated at a low temperature in the presence of an excess of air. Some authorities hold that cobaltic oxide exists only in the hydrated form.[54] The lower hydrate may be made as a black powder by oxidizing neutral cobalt solutions with substances like sodium hypochlorite. Co_2O_3 or $Co_2O_3 \cdot H_2O$ is completely converted to Co_3O_4 at temperatures above 265° C. Co_3O_4 will absorb oxygen in a sufficient quantity to correspond to the higher oxide Co_2O_3, but there is reported to be no change in the lattice structure. The magnetic properties of $Co_2O_3 \cdot H_2O$ have been described.[47]

Cobaltosic oxide (Co_3O_4) is formed when cobalt compounds, such as the carbonate or the hydrated sesquioxide, are heated in air at temperatures above approximately 265° C and not exceeding 800° C. This stable black oxide, with a cobalt content of 73.42 per cent, is the product weighed in the gravimetric determination of this element. Most commercial black cobalt oxides contain about 71 per cent Co, and since their calcination temperatures are usually around 700° C, they are largely Co_3O_4. Black oxide is used by some pottery manufacturers and powder metallurgists. Like the other oxides, it is readily reduced to metal by carbon, carbon monoxide or hydrogen. The heat capacity,[34,35] entropy,[34] reduction,[38] and magnetic properties[47] of Co_3O_4 have been reported.

Since the cobalt oxides readily form solid solutions with each other, there is no agreement on an exact temperature range of stability. When heating $Co_2O_3 \cdot H_2O$, Ovchinnikova, Ioffe and Rotinyan[41] found that Co_3O_4 formed at 240° C and CoO commenced to appear at 770° C. Smirnov and Abdeev[55] reported that $Co_2O_3 \cdot nH_2O$ was entirely decomposed at 250–280° C to Co_3O_4, and that the latter converted completely to CoO at 910° C. Webb[62] stated that Co_2O_3 is wholly converted to Co_3O_4 at 265° C and that above 809° C only the monoxide is stable.

The solubility of the oxides of cobalt in 10 per cent hydrazine, though very low, is higher than that of ferric oxide, cobaltic oxide being the most soluble and cobaltosic the least.[67]

Conflicting results concerning the action of ammonia on cobaltous and cobaltic oxides are cited by Mellor.[39] The solubility of cobalt oxides in 10 per cent by volume ammonium hydroxide at 25° C is (in mg/100 ml): CoO 0.55, $Co_2O_3 \cdot H_2O$ 0.61 and Co_3O_4 0.03.

Other oxides, such as CoO_2, have been reported, but evidence for their existence is rather contradictory. Confusion is caused by the tendency of cobalt oxides to absorb oxygen under certain conditions. For instance, during oxidation of finely ground cobalt, a substance is formed which has the structure of CoO but which has a higher oxygen content than that corresponding to the stoichiometric formula. At 900° C, this excess of oxygen is lost.[51] Several investigators have discussed an anode deposit which forms when cobalt is electrolyzed under certain conditions and which appears to be either Co_2O_3 or CoO_2.[52,60]

Oxide Films on Cobalt

The importance of cobalt base alloys in high temperature applications has led to many studies regarding the oxide films formed on cobalt and its alloys. Contributions from the Westinghouse laboratories[21,22,23,24,25,43] have indicated that at low temperatures and for short oxidation periods, CoO is formed, whereas Co_3O_4 appears as oxidation proceeds. CoO is the oxide that is stable in contact with the metal at temperatures up to 500° C. As the film thickens, Co_3O_4 begins to form on the surface, and when the film becomes very thick, as at 500° C for 1 hour, only CoO is found. In alloys, CoO, if observed, appears only at low temperatures. Films of CoO and Co_3O_4 on cobalt were found to consist of small crystals varying from 450Å at 200° C to 1000Å at 500° C.

Annealed at temperatures up to 550° C, cold rolled cobalt has a higher oxidation rate in the hexagonal crystal form than in the cubic form.[21] Reaction rates increase markedly at about 700° C. Below 700° C, the rate is controlled by the diffusion rate of cobalt cations through the Co_3O_4 layer; above 700° C, the rate is determined by diffusion through the CoO layer, both oxides being capable of coexistence.

Bridges, Bauer and Fassell studied the effect of oxygen pressure of 0.013–27.2 atm and 800–1200° C on the oxidation rate of cobalt.[5] The metal oxidized in accordance with the parabolic rate law above 950° C, and formed the single oxide CoO above 900° C. Pressure increase accelerated the rate of oxidation, but the latter eventually ceased to increase with increase of oxygen pressure at temperatures below 1150° C.

Carter and Richardson[10] found that the oxidation of cobalt metal occurs almost entirely, if not completely, by cation diffusion across the growing oxide film. At 1148° C, the oxidation rate of cobalt metal was proportional to the 0.29 power of the oxygen pressure. Frederick and Cornet[16] reported that the oxidation rate of nickel-cobalt alloys increases with increasing cobalt content, but that the effect is small until over 11 per cent cobalt has been added. The activation energy for oxidation decreases with increasing cobalt content from a value of 51 kcal/mole for pure nickel to about 28.8 kcal/mole for pure cobalt.

Phosphates

A number of cobaltous phosphates can be produced by heating cobaltous carbonate or hydroxide with phosphoric acid or alkaline phosphates. The commercial form, employed in pottery production, has the approximate formula $Co_3(PO_4)_2 \cdot 8H_2O$. It is almost insoluble in water.

Silicates

The orthosilicate of cobalt ($2CoO \cdot SiO_2$) seems to be the only one which can be obtained by direct heating of cobalt oxide and silica. An intense blue is obtained from the compound $CoO \cdot SiO_2$, which is made by the solution of cobalt oxide in melts containing alumino-silicates and borates such as those present in pottery fluxes and glazes. The silicate color is known in the pottery industry as mazarine blue or royal blue, and unlike the aluminate blue, it has a strong violet tint.

Sulfates

When cobalt oxide, hydroxide or carbonate is dissolved in dilute sulfuric acid, an aqueous solution of cobaltous sulfate is obtained which crystallizes out as a pink heptahydrate ($CoSO_4 \cdot 7H_2O$). This is the usual commercial form of cobalt sulfate, a compound which shows less tendency to alter in composition by deliquescence or dehydration than the chloride or nitrate, and is, therefore, preferred for many applications. A hexa- and mono-hydrate may be obtained from cobalt sulfate heptahydrate.

Oxidation of a solution of cobaltous sulfate in dilute sulfuric acid, either electrolytically or with ozone or fluorine, yields hydrated cobaltic sulfate ($Co_2(SO_4)_3 \cdot 18H_2O$). The solution is stable in dilute sulfuric acid, but on addition of water it quickly changes to cobaltous sulfate.

When NaOH is added to a solution of cobaltous sulfate, a basic blue sulfate is precipitated; stable in its mother liquor or in pure water, its composition is $CoSO_4 \cdot 5Co(OH)_2 \cdot xH_2O$.[3] In the presence of NaOH, the precipitated basic salt changes to pink cobaltous hydroxide.

Sulfides

The affinity of cobalt for sulfur is greater than that of iron but less than nickel.[46] Cobalt combines with sulfur to form ordinary cobaltous sulfide (CoS), two others which are probably cobaltous (CoS_2 and Co_3S_4) and a cobaltic compound (Co_2S_3). CoS is the common black precipitate formed when H_2S is passed into an alkaline or ammoniacal cobalt solution. It crystallizes with the NiAs structure, the sulfur atom being surrounded by six cobalt atoms at the apices of a trigonal prism. The immediate neighbors of a cobalt atom are six non-metal atoms arranged octahedrally, but there are also two cobalt atoms sufficiently near to be considered bonded to the first cobalt atom.[64] The solubility of cobalt sulfides in ammonia does not appear to be recorded in the literature, but the solubility of CoS in 10 per cent by volume ammonium hydroxide at 25° C has been found to be 3.3 mg/100 ml.

The disulfide CoS_2, which has a pyrite structure, can be produced by heating cobaltous oxide or sulfide with an excess of sulfur for an extended period. Cobaltosic sulfide (Co_3S_4) can be prepared by heating cobalt sulfide in a current of hydrogen sulfide for some time. The X-ray diagram is similar to that of linnaeite, with each cobalt atom linked tetrahedrally to four sulfur atoms at 2.19 Å.[54] At about 680° C, cobaltosic sulfide breaks up into $2CoS$ and CoS_2.

Cobaltic sulfide (Co_2S_3) can be made by fusing a cobaltous compound with sulfur and potassium carbonate. It is a gray, crystalline solid which is less readily dissolved in ordinary reagents than are the other sulfides of cobalt. Buerger and Robinson[7] reported that powder diagrams of Co_2S_3 are virtually indistinguishable from those of Co_3S_4. Donges[12] stated that if platinum electrodes are introduced during precipitation of cobalt sulfide from solutions with H_2S, almost pure cubic Co_9S_8 is collected at the cathode, whereas a mixture of Co_9S_8 and CoS is found at the anode. Rosenqvist[48] observed the following phases in the cobalt-sulfur system: Co_4S_3

780–930°C, Co_9S_8 up to 835°C, CoS 460°C (m.p.), Co_3S_4 up to 625°C, and CoS_2.

Color Changes of Cobalt Compounds

Cobaltous salts, both in the solid state and in solution, exhibit remarkable color phenomena which have long been studied. For instance, aqueous solutions of cobalt chloride may be pink, red, violet or blue, depending on the temperature, concentration and presence of other ions. The red form is favored by a low temperature, dilution and the absence of alkali chlorides; the opposite conditions favor the blue form. Chlorides of zinc and mercury will, however, change the blue of cobaltous chloride in alcohol to red.

Concentrated solutions in some organic solvents, like ethyl alcohol, are blue, but dilution with water yields the red form. These color differences also occur in the solid state; commercial cobaltous chloride hexahydrate is pink, the anhydrous salt blue. It must be kept in mind that since the blue is much more intense than the red, a very small amount of the former can mask the red. For example, a solution of cobaltous chloride in pyridine at 50°C appears to be pure blue; spectroscopic examination, however, shows that only a tenth of the cobalt is actually present in the blue form.[54]

Although these color changes have aroused interest among chemists for a long time, and although many hypotheses have been advanced, no theory is entirely satisfactory, and the problem is not yet solved.[6,39,54,64] Some investigators believe that the color changes are due to hydration or solvation, the red color being dependent on the existence of hexahydrate, the blue on the formation of a lower hydrate. Others have suggested that color depends on the state of coordination of the cobalt atoms. If the atom is surrounded by six other groups the color is red; if four, the color is blue. For instance, in a red aqueous solution, each cobalt atom is surrounded by six water molecules. Anhydrous cobaltous chloride, however, is an anomaly. According to the accepted structure of this compound, each cobalt atom is surrounded by six chlorine atoms at the corners of a regular octahedron. Thus in theory, the compound should be red, whereas in fact it is blue.

Another theory attributes colors to the presence of complexes, the blue being the result of a halide complex anion such as $(CoCl_4)^{--}$, while the pink is the color of the simple ion in which the cobalt is attached only to water, an undoubtedly weaker link. The nonionized salt in solution is blue; the complex anion in solution is also blue; the color due to the cobalt atom, however, when outside the immediate sphere of the chlorine atoms, appears to be red. The color produced by free cobalt cations in aqueous solution is red, while the red of solid hexahydrate is due to the water molecules interposed between the cobalt and chlorine atoms.

The color of an ion appears to depend on its ionic state rather than on its coordination, and the color does not seem to be influenced appreciably by the number of charges carried by the ions. Color in compounds of metals like cobalt is determined by the possibility of electron transference between different quantum levels. In cobaltous compounds, there are three electrons which are fairly mobile; two are on the outermost sheath, and one is on the next inner shell. If one or both of the two outer electrons have been lost, the third electron can move freely between the inner and outer shells. However, since the two outer positions are similar, the color is little affected if one or both are empty. This is also true for the red, positive ions. The accumulation of electrons around the cobalt atoms, as in $[Co(H_2O)Cl_3]$ and $CoCl_4$, tends to make one of the outer electrons move into an inner position, possible since the third quantum group in the cobalt atom is not completely filled. The deep blue of the complex cobalt anions appears to originate in this way.

The behavior of nonionic cobaltous compounds is more difficult to predict. Since each valency electron of the metal is replaced by a pair of shared electrons, the effect might be similar to that caused by the piling up of electrons in ions such as $CoCl_4^{--}$; this seems to be the case with many cobaltous compounds. Anhydrous cobalt chloride, considered to be nonionic, is pale blue; the nonionic $[Co(H_2O)Cl_2]$ should also be pale blue. The two shared electrons of a coordination covalency, when the coordination is to a neutral atom or molecule, do not have this effect, however, probably because they are too firmly held by the atom to which they properly belong. They seem to have little effect on the color of cobaltous compounds. Some effect is to be expected since the electronic environment, in which any electron shifts occur in the outer levels of the ion, must depend to some extent on the number and nature of the atoms coordinated with the ion.

If the electron shift which gives rise to the color is that of an unshared electron—passing from the third to the fourth quantum level or vice versa —then the compound has a red color. If, however, the electron which moves between the two levels is shared between cobalt and another atom (i.e., a covalency electron), then the color will be blue.

References

1. Assayag, G., and Bizette, H., "An Anomaly in the Heat Capacities of CoO and of CoO–NiO and CoO–CuO Solid Solutions," *Compt. rend.,* **239,** 238–40 (1954). *Chem. Abst.,* **49,** 5915 (1955).
2. Babko, A. K., and Shevchenko, L. L., "Colorimetric Determination of Water in Certain Organic Solvents by Change in Color of Cobalt Halide Complexes," *Dopovidi Akad. Nauk Ukr. R.S.R.,* **1958,** 1212–15. *Chem. Abst.,* **53,** 9890 (1959).

3. Besson, J., and Reese, G., "Précipitation et Propriétés du Sulfate Basique de Cobalt," *Bull. Soc. Chim. France,* **1959,** No. 2, 336–41.

4. Brekke, J. E., and Watters, G. G., "Simple Cobaltous Chloride Hygrometer for Comparing Permeability of Films to Moisture Vapor," *Chemist-Analyst,* **47,** 16 (1958).

5. Bridges, D. W., Baur, J. P., and Fassell, W. M., "Effect of Oxygen Pressure on the Oxidation Rate of Cobalt," *J. Electrochem. Soc.,* **103,** 614–8 (1956).

6. Brode, W. R., "Chemical Spectroscopy," New York, John Wiley and Sons, Inc., 1945.

7. Buerger, M. J., and Robinson, D. W., "Crystal Structure and Twinning of Co_2S_3," *Proc. Natl. Acad. Sci. U. S.,* **41,** 199–209 (1955).

8. Bulgakova, T. I., Gerasimov, Y. I., Simanov, Y. P., and Klyachko-Gurvich, L. L., "The Formation of Cobalt and Nickel Ferrites," *Zhur. Obshchei Khim.,* **18,** 154–64 (1948). *Chem. Abst.,* **43,** 3304 (1949).

9. Carter, R. E., and Richardson, F. D., "An Examination of the Decrease of Surface-Activity Method of Measuring Self-Diffusion Coefficients in Wustite and Cobaltous Oxide," *J. Metals,* **6,** 1244–57 (1954).

10. —, "Oxidation of Cobalt Metal," *J. Metals* **7,** 336–43 (1955).

11. Chernobrov, S. M., and Kolonina, N. P., "The pH of Formation of Cobalt Hydroxide and Carbonate," *Zhur. Priklad. Khim.,* **29,** 704–8 (1956). *Chem. Abst.,* **50,** 15313 (1956).

12. Donges, F., "The Precipitation of Cubic Cobalt Sulphide, Co_9S_8, with Hydrogen Sulphide from Aqueous Solutions of Cobalt Salts," *Z. anorg. Chem.,* **254,** 267–70 (1947). *Chem. Abst.,* **43,** 253 (1949).

13. Drain, J., and Michell, A., "Structure and Thermomagnetic Properties of Cobalt Carbide, Co_2C," *Bull. Soc. Chim. France,* **1951,** 517–9. *Chem. Abst.,* **46,** 3815 (1952).

14. Engis Equipment Co., Brit. Pat. 17076, June 27, 1947.

15. Fine, M. E., "Evidence for Domain Structure in Antiferromagnetic CoO from Elasticity Measurements," *Physical Rev.,* **87,** 1143 (1952).

16. Frederick, S. F., and Cornet, I., "The Effect of Cobalt on the High Temperature Oxidation of Nickel," *J. Electrochem. Soc.,* **102,** 285–91 (1955).

17. Friedel, R. A., Wender, I., Shuffer, S. L., and Sternberg, H. W., "Spectra and Structures of Cobalt Carbonyls," *J. Am. Chem. Soc.,* **77,** 3951–8 (1955).

18. Gayer, K. H., and Garrett, A. B., "The Solubility of Cobalt Hydroxide, $Co(OH)_2$, in Solutions of Hydrochloric Acid and Sodium Hydroxide at 25° C.," *J. Am. Chem. Soc.,* **72,** 3921–3 (1950).

19. Gerasimov, Y. I., Bulgakova, T. I., and Simanov, Y. P., "The Formation of Ferrites of Nickel and Cobalt, II," *Zhur. Obshchei Khim.,* **19,** 219–23 (1949). *Chem. Abst.,* **43,** 5354 (1949).

20. Gordon, S., and Schreyer, J. M., "The Solubility of Cobalt(II) in Sodium and Potassium Hydroxide Solutions," *Chemist-Analyst,* **44,** 95–6 (1955).

21. Gulbransen, E. A., and Andrew, K. F., "The Kinetics of the Oxidation of Cobalt," *J. Electrochem. Soc.,* **98,** 241–51 (1951).

22. Gulbransen, E. A., and Hickman, J. W., "An Electron Diffraction Study of

Oxide Films Formed on Iron, Cobalt, Nickel, Chromium, and Copper at High Temperatures," *Am. Inst. Mining Met. Eng. Tech. Publ.,* **2068** (1946).

23. Gulbransen, E. A., Phelps, R. T., and Hickman, J. W., "Oxide Films Formed on Alloys at Moderate Temperatures," *Ind. Eng. Chem. Anal. Ed.,* **18,** 640–52 (1946).

24. Hickman, J. W., "Oxide Films Formed on Metals and Binary Alloys. An Electron Diffraction Study," *Am. Inst. Mining Met. Eng. Tech. Publ.,* **2483** (1948).

25. —, and Gulbransen, E. A., "An Electron Diffraction Study of Oxide Films Formed on Alloys of Iron, Cobalt, Nickel, and Chromium at High Temperatures," *Am. Inst. Mining Met. Eng. Tech. Publ.,* **2096** (1946).

26. Hieber, W., and Breu, R., "Reactions of Cobalt Carbonyls," *Angew. Chem.,* **68,** 679–80 (1956). *Chem. Abst.,* **51,** 12732 (1957).

27. Hieber, W., and Sedlmeier, J., "Metal Carbonyls. LXV. The Reaction of Cobalt Tetracarbonyl with Various Types of Bases," *Chem. Ber.,* **87,** 89–92 (1954). *Chem. Abst.,* **49,** 766 (1955).

28. Hofer, L. J. E., and Peebles, W. C., "Preparation and X-ray Diffraction Studies of a New Cobalt Carbide," *J. Am. Chem. Soc.,* **69,** 893–9 (1947).

29. Inoue, T., "Ferrites. 1. Formation of Cobaltous Ferrite $CoFe_2O_4$ by Sintering Process," *J. Electrochem. Soc. Japan,* **22,** 466–9 (1954). *Chem. Abst.,* **49,** 10782 (1955).

30. —, "Ferrites, 11. X-ray Analysis of Cobaltous Ferrite," *J. Electrochem. Soc. Japan,* **23,** 24–9 (1955). *Chem. Abst.,* **49,** 10783 (1955).

31. —, "Ferrites. V. X-ray Examination of Cobaltous Ferrite," *J. Electrochem. Soc. Japan,* **23,** 179–82 (1955). *Chem. Abst.,* **49,** 14416 (1955).

32. Jaubert, G. F., "The Protection of Airplane Engines Against Rust and the Deceptive Indications Given by Cobalt Chloride as a Hygrometric Indicator," *Compt. rend.,* **228,** 826–8 (1949). *Chem. Abst.,* **43,** 5516 (1949).

33. Juza, R., and Puff, H., "Crystal Structure of Cobalt Carbide," *Naturwissenschaften,* **38,** 331–2 (1951). *Chem. Abst.,* **46,** 2870 (1952).

34. King, E. G., "Heat Capacities at Low Temperatures and Entropies at 298.15°K. of Nickelous Oxide, Cobaltous Oxide, and Cobalt Spinel," *J. Am. Chem. Soc.,* **79,** 2399–2400 (1957).

35. —, and Christensen, A. U., "Heat Contents Above 298.15° K. of Oxides of Cobalt and Nickel," *J. Am. Chem. Soc..* **80.** 1800–1 (1958).

36. Kirk, R. E., and Othmer, D. F., "Encyclopedia of Chemical Technology. Vol. 4," New York, The Interscience Encyclopedia Inc., 1949.

37. Krause, A., and Wojciechowska, W., "Structure and Catalytic Properties of Cobaltic Hydroxides," *Roczniki Chem.,* **31,** 1137–45 (1957). *Chem. Abst.,* **52,** 7832 (1958).

38. Kuznetsov, A. N., Shestopavalova, A. A., and Kulish, N. F., "Mechanism and Kinetics of the Reduction of Cobalt Oxide," *Zhur. Fiz. Khim.,* **32,** 73–8 (1958). *Chem. Abst.,* **52,** 13499 (1958).

39. Mellor, J. W., "A Comprehensive Treatise on Inorganic and Theoretical Chemistry, Vol. XIV, London, Longmans, Green and Co., 1935.

40. Okamura, T., Torizuka, Y., and Kojima, Y., "Ferromagnetic Resonance in

Cobalt Ferrite at High Temperature," *Physical Rev.,* **84,** 372 (1951).

41. Ovchinnikova, T. M., Ioffe, E. S., and Rotinyan, A. L., "Transformation of Cobalt Oxide Hydrates During Heating," *Doklady Akad. Nauk S.S.S.R.,* **100,** 469–71 (1955). *Chem. Abst.,* **49,** 12170 (1955).

42. Pauthenet, R., "Thermal Variation of the Spontaneous Magnetization of the Ferrites of Nickel, Cobalt, Iron, and Manganese," *Compt. rend.,* **230,** 1842–3 (1950). *Chem. Abst.,* **44,** 7601 (1950).

43. Phelps, R. T., Gulbransen, E. A., and Hickman, J. W., "Electron Diffraction and Electron Microscope Study of Oxide Films Formed on Metals and Alloys at Moderate Temperatures," *Ind. Eng. Chem. Anal. Ed.,* **18,** 391–400 (1946).

44. Prince, E., "Neutron-diffraction Observation of Heat Treatment in Cobalt Ferrite," *Physical Rev.,* **102,** 674–6 (1956).

45. Reichard, H. F., "Rapid Method for Moisture Content Estimation in Plant Products," *Chem. Engineering,* **60,** No. 2, 172–3 (1953).

46. Remy, H., "Treatise on Inorganic Chemistry. Vol. II," Amsterdam, Elsevier Publ. Co., 1956.

47. Richardson, J. T., and Vernon, L. W., "The Magnetic Properties of the Cobalt Oxides and the System Cobalt Oxide-Alumina," *J. Phys. Chem.,* **62,** 1153–7 (1958).

48. Rosenqvist, T., "A Thermodynamic Study of the Iron, Cobalt, and Nickel Sulphides," *J. Iron Steel Institute,* **176,** Part I, 37–58 (1954).

49. Roth, W. L., "Magnetic Structures of MnO, FeO, CoO, and NiO," *Physical Rev.,* **110,** 1333–41 (1958).

50. Rudham, R., and Stone, F. S., "Chemisorption on Cuprous, Nickel, and Cobaltous Oxides," Chemisorption, Proc. Symposium, Keele *1956,* 205–17. *Chem. Abst.,* **52,** 8678 (1958).

51. Satava, V., and Kochanovska, A., "The Effect of Milling on the Course of the Oxidation of Cobalt," *Chem. Listy,* **49,** 648–51 (1955). *Chem. Abst.,* **49,** 11524 (1955).

52. Shelton, F. K., "Metallurgical Treatment of Cobalt Ores from the Goodsprings Mining District, Nevada," *U. S. Bur. Mines. Rept. Invest.* **3836** (1946).

53. Shenker, H., "Magnetic Anisotropy of Cobalt Ferrite ($Co_{1.01}Fe_{2.00}O_{3.02}$) and Nickel Cobalt Ferrite ($Ni_{0.76}Fe_{0.20}Co_{0.08}Fe_2O_4$)," *Physical Rev.* **107,** 1246–9 (1957).

54. Sidgwick, N. V., "The Chemical Elements and Their Compounds. Vol. II," Oxford, Clarendon Press, 1950.

55. Smirnov, V. I., and Abdeev, M. A., "Dissociation Pressure of Cobalt Oxides," *Izvest. Akad. Nauk Kazakh. S.S.R., Ser. Gornogo Dela, Met. Stroitel i Stroimaterial,* **1957,** No. 1, 97–101. *Chem. Abst.,* **51,** 15237 (1957).

56. Solomon, M. E., "Use of Cobalt Salts as Indicators of Humidity and Moisture," *Ann. Appl. Biol.,* **32,** 75–85 (1945).

57. —, "Estimation of Humidity with Cobalt Thiocyanate Papers and Permanent Color Standards," *Bull. Entomol. Res.,* **48,** 489–506 (1957).

58. Sternberg, H. W., Wender, I., and Orchin, M., "Analysis of Mixtures of Dicobalt Octacarbonyl and Cobalt Carbonyl Anion," *Anal. Chem.,* **24,** 174–6 (1952).

59. Stroganov, E. V., Kozhina, I. I., and Andreev, S. N., "Crystal Structure of

$CoCl_2 \cdot 6H_2O$," *Vestnik Leningrad Univ.,* **13**, No. 10, *Ser. Fiz. i Khim.,* No. 2, 109–16 (1958). *Chem. Abst.,* **52**, 17880 (1958).

60. Torrance, S., "Electrolytic Separation of Cobalt from Nickel by Deposition as Cobaltic Oxide," *Analyst,* **64**, 109–11 (1939).
61. Umetsu, Y., and Suzuki, S., "The Decomposition of Cobalt Ferrite by Roasting in SO_2-O_2-N_2 Atmosphere," *J. Mining Inst. Japan,* **70**, 559–62 (1954). *Chem. Abst.,* **49**, 6058 (1955).
62. Webb, H. W., "Cobalt, Nickel and Selenium in Pottery," London, Mond Nickel Co., Ltd., undated.
63. Weil, L., Gallay, M., and Poensin, P., "A New Method of Measuring Magnetostriction; Application to Cobalt Ferrite," *Compt. rend.,* **231**, 224–6 (1950). *Chem. Abst.,* **44**, 10403 (1950).
64. Wells, A. F., "Structural Inorganic Chemistry," London, Oxford University Press, 1945.
65. Wender, I., Sternberg, H. W., and Orchin, M., "The Chemistry of Metal Carbonyls. I. New Concepts Applied to Carbonyls of Cobalt," *J. Am. Chem. Soc.,* **74**, 1216–19 (1952).
66. Williams, H. J., Heidenreich, R. D., and Nesbitt, E. A., "Mechanism by Which Cobalt Ferrite Heat-Treats in a Magnetic Field," *J. Appl. Physics,* **27**, 85–9 (1956).
67. Young, R. S., "Solubility of Ferric Oxide and of Cobalt Oxides in Dilute Hydrazine Solution," *The Industrial Chemist,* **35**, 549 (1959).

Chapter 6

COORDINATION COMPOUNDS OF COBALT

Daryle H. Busch

Department of Chemistry
The Ohio State University
Columbus, Ohio

INTRODUCTION

The coordination compounds of cobalt(III) are great in number, and exhibit substantial variety in both nature and behavior. Diversity is found in their oxidation state, coordination number, geometric structure, lability, and stability, as well as in many other aspects of their chemistry. Numerous studies have been directed toward understanding and application of these important substances. The more common techniques include synthetic, spectral, solution-stoichiometry, magnetic, kinetic, equilibrium, stereochemical, acid-base, and X-ray investigations.

Historically, the ammines of cobalt(III) have dominated the chemistry of cobalt complexes, and their influence on the entire field of chemistry has been substantial. Although many other classes of cobalt complexes have attracted much attention in recent years, the ammines of cobalt(III) have been the subject of detailed studies in the chemistry of transition elements. The compounds of cobalt(III) will be discussed first, those of cobalt(II) second, and those of cobalt in lower oxidation states last. Three excellent books have been published in the field of metal coordination compounds during recent years.[19,45,253]

COMPLEXES OF COBALT(III)

Stereochemistry and the Nature of Compounds

Cobalt(III) is characterized by the formation of six-coordinate, octahedral complexes which exhibit the structural integrity usually attributed to the formation of covalent bonds. The ammonia complexes and their analogs with similar donor molecules have been known for many years and have played a principal role in the evolution of the modern concepts of chemistry. The historical significance of these substances has been reviewed by Bailar,[20] and the reasoning invoked may be found in Werner's classic book[394] or the introductory text by Grinberg.[178] The number of known compounds of this general class is overwhelming, and relatively complete listings of the substances known in early years may be found in the standard reference works of Friend[158] and Gmelin.[167] Attention will be directed toward the more common examples, those of recent interest, and those illustrative of particular points in this discussion.

The parent of the many cobaltammines is hexamminecobalt(III) ion, $[Co(NH_3)_6]^{3+}$, in which six ammonia molecules are bonded, through their nitrogen atoms, to the central cobalt atom. This species may be isolated in the form of many salts having the formula $[Co(NH_3)_6]X_3$, where X^- is Cl^-, Br^-, I^-, NO_3^-, ClO_4^-, etc., 1/2 of a bivalent anion, or 1/3 of a trivalent anion. Series of pentammines may be obtained in which one of the ammonia molecules is replaced by an anion directly attached to the cobalt, e.g., $[Co(NH_3)_5X]Y_2$. (X^- and Y^- have the same significance as in the case of the hexammine.) Continued replacement of the ammonia molecules produces, successively, tetrammines, $[Co(NH_3)_4X_2]Y$; triammines, $[Co(NH_3)_3X_3]$; diammines, $M^I[Co(NH_3)_2X_4]$ (M^I is a unipositive cation); monammines, $M^I_2[Co(NH_3)X_5]$; and finally, materials containing only coordinated anion, $M^I_3[CoX_6]$. There appears to be no complete series of this kind in the chemistry of cobalt(III); however, only the monammine is unknown among the series of possible nitroammines.[22] The literature contains numerous references to the compounds of this class where the coordinated anion is I^-, Br^-, Cl^-, NO_2^-, NO_3^-, CO_3^{2-}, RCO_2^-, SO_4^{2-}, SO_3^{2-}, $C_2O_4^{2-}$, $C_4H_4O_6^{2-}$, SCN^-, OH^-, N_3^-, CrO_4^{2-}.[408] More recently, such compounds have been prepared containing ClO_2^-,[110,229] IO_3^-,[239] $C_6H_5CO_2^-$,[187] NH_2-$CH_2CO_2^-$,[347] PO_4^{3-},[112,349] HPO_4^{2+},[112,349] $CH_2FCO_2^-$,[328] $CH_2ClCO_2^-$,[328] $CCl_3CO_2^-$,[328] $CF_3CO_2^-$,[328] NO^-,[269,352] F^-.[260] The greatest variety of anions, X^-, is found in the case of the pentammines.

The number of compounds of this general class is greatly magnified by the replacement of ammonia by other neutral ligands. The most common monodentate, neutral replacements for ammonia are water, pyridine, and primary aliphatic amines, although a variety of other neutral monofunctional materials have been found to enter the coordination sphere of cobalt(III). Examples are hydrazine,[168,169] and hydroxylamine.[415] The hexaquocobalt(III) ion is much less stable than the corresponding hexammine. This may be illustrated by the electrode potentials for the Co(II)-Co(III) couple in the cases of the hydrates and ammines.[25]

$$[Co(NH_3)_6]^{2+} \longrightarrow [Co(NH_3)_6]^{3+} + e^- \qquad E^\circ = -0.1 \text{ V.}$$

$$[Co(H_2O)_6]^{2+} \longrightarrow [Co(H_2O)_6]^{3+} + e^- \qquad E^\circ = -1.82 \text{ V.}$$

The aquated cobalt(III) ion reacts with water to liberate oxygen, and is reduced by hydrogen peroxide.[57] In contrast, these reagents oxidize the hexammine of cobalt(II) to that of cobalt(III) under proper conditions. The relative stabilities are paralleled by similar differences in relative labilities (ease or rate of substitution reactions). It has been observed that $[Co(H_2O)_6]^{3+}$ exchanges its coordinated water molecules very rapidly with isotopically labeled solvent molecules,[157] while $[Co(NH_3)_6]^{3+}$ is inert toward exchange.[186,230] The very great lability of $[Co(H_2O)_6]^{3+}$ may result from the fact that such solutions cannot be kept free from the hydrated cobalt(II) ion and the relatively great velocities of the following reactions:[157]

$$[Co^*(H_2O)_6]^{3+} + [Co(H_2O)_6]^{2+} \rightleftarrows [Co^*(H_2O)_6]^{2+} + [Co(H_2O)_6]^{3+}$$

$$[Co(H_2O)_6]^{2+} + 6H_2O^* \rightleftarrows [Co(H_2O^*)_6]^{2+} + 6H_2O$$

From these considerations, it is not surprising to find that ammonia and its derivatives are frequently found to be the more abundant ligands in cobalt complexes.

An extremely large number of compounds exist in which two or more of the donor atoms attached to a single cobalt atom are a part of the same ligand molecule. Such ligands are called "chelating" agents. The simplest example is found in the very common substance, ethylenediamine, which coordinates to the cobalt through both nitrogen atoms, thus forming a five-membered ring. A chelating agent that coordinates in a bifunctional manner is termed "bidentate," while the higher members are: trifunctional, tridentate; tetrafunctional, tetradentate; pentafunctional, pentadentate; sexafunctional, sexadentate. The series of acidoammines containing bidentate groups is $[Co(AA)_3]^{3+}$, $[Co(AA)_2aX]^{2+}$, $[Co(AA)_2X_2]^+$, $[Co(AA)X_4]^-$; AA is the bidentate molecule, a a neutral monodentate ligand, and X^- the anion.

The stereochemistry of the ammines of cobalt(III) has received a great deal of attention and is of prime importance. Compounds of the pentammine class containing only monodentate groups exhibit simple stereochemistries; however, the existence of stereoisomers complicates the chemistries of many of the more highly substituted members of this family of compounds. Tetrammines of the series $[Co\ a_4\ X_2]$ exist in two forms as shown below:

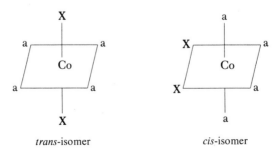

trans-isomer   cis-isomer

In the case of the corresponding compounds containing bidentate groups, the *cis-trans* isomerism occurs; however, the *cis* isomer in this case is further distinguished by its existence in antipodal forms as shown below:

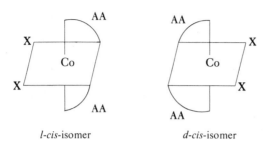

l-cis-isomer   *d-cis*-isomer

Table 6.1 lists examples of *cis-trans* isomers which have been substantiated. Since examples are also known for geometric isomers of the com-

TABLE 6.1. GEOMETRIC ISOMERS OF COBALT(III) COMPLEXES*

$[Co(en)_2(NH_3)_2]^{3+}$	$[Co(en)_2(NH_3)H_2O]^{3+}$
$[Co(en)_2(H_2O)_2]^{3+}$	$[Co(en)_2(NH_3)Cl]^{2+}$
$[Co(en)_2(NH_3)Br]^{2+}$	$[Co(en)_2(NH_3)NCS]^{2+}$
$[Co(en)_2(NH_3)F]^{2+}$	$[Co(en)_2(NH_3)NO_2]^{2+}$
$[Co(en)_2(NH_3)NO_2]^{2+}$	$[Co(en)_2(C_6H_5CH_2NH_2)Cl]^{2+}$
$[Co(en)_2(CH_2=CHCH_2NH_2)Cl]^{2+}$	$[Co(en)_2(H_2O)Cl]^{2+}$
$[Co(en)_2(H_2O)OH]^{2+}$	$[Co(en)_2(H_2O)NCS]^{2+}$
$[Co(en)_2(H_2O)NO_2]^{2+}$	$[Co(en)_2Cl_2]^+$
$[Co(en)_2F_2]^+$	$[Co(en)_2(ONO)_2]^+$
$[Co(en)_2Br_2]^+$	$[Co(en)_2(NCS)_2]^+$
$[Co(en)_2(NO_2)_2]^+$	$[Co(en)_2(NO_2)Cl]^+$
$[Co(en)_2(OH)Cl]^+$	$[Co(en)_2(NCS)Cl]^+$
$[Co(en)_2(NCS)Br]^+$	$[Co(en)_2(NCS)OH]^+$
$[Co(en)_2ClBr]^+$	$[Co(en)(pn)(NO_2)_2]^+$
$[Co(en)(NH_3)_2Cl_2]^+$	$[Co(pn)_2(NO_2)_2]^+$
$[Co(en)_2(NCS)NO_2]^+$	$[Co(Cptdin)_2Cl_2]^+$
$[Co(pn)_2Cl_2]^+$ (258)	$[Co(Stien)_2Cl_2]^+$
$[Co(bn)_2Cl_2]^+$	$[Co(NH_3)_4(NO_2)_2]^+$
$[Co(NH_3)_4Cl_2]^+$	$[Co(NH_3)_4(SO_3)_2]^-$
$[Co(NH_3)_2(C_2O_4)(NO_2)_2]^-$	$[Co(en)_2(NO_2)F]^+$ (261)
$[Co(NH_3)_4(H_2O)NO_2]^{2+}$ (212)	$[Co(NH_3)_3(H_2O)_3]^{3+}$
$[Co(NO_2)_3(OH)_3]^{3-}$ (96,97)	$[Co(CH_3CH(NH_2)CO_2)_3]$
$[Co(NH_2CH_2CO_2)_3]$	

*Unless separately annotated the examples are quoted from reference 41. For abbreviations see Table 6.2.

pounds of the class [Co a₃ X₃], these too, are included. Among the latter is [Co(AB)₃], where AB is an unsymmetric bidentate group. These are perhaps better called "facial" and "peripheral" forms rather than *cis* and *trans*.

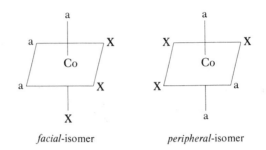

facial-isomer   *peripheral*-isomer

In some cases, only a single isomer was found when two or more were predicted. The structures of some of these were determined by the X-ray method. In the potassium, silver, and ammonium salts of [Co(NH₃)₂-(NO₂)₄]⁻, the complex anion contains *trans* ammonia groups.[68,218,219,391] The compounds [Co(NH₃)₃(NO₂)₃],[367] [Co(NH₃)₃(NO₂)₂Cl],[369] [Co(NH₃)₃-(NO₂)₂Br],[220] and [Co(NH₃)₃(H₂O)Cl₂]Cl[368] all exhibit *peripheral* structures; however, it is surprising to note that the two NO_2^- groups are mutually *trans* in the second compound, while the Br^- is *trans* to an NO_2^- group in the third case.

When both expected isomers may be prepared, it is sometimes possible to distinguish between them by simpler methods than the technique of X-ray structure determination.[23] In some cases, extreme chemical differences will be indicative, and, as pointed out above, the *cis* isomer sometimes exists as a racemate. The resolution of one isomer into optical antipodes provides unequivocal evidence for its structure. The visible and ultraviolet spectra provided one of the earliest techniques permitting this distinction to be made on a comparative basis.[16,19] This approach was given foundation in terms of the crystal field theory and was applied to show that the *alpha*-tris(glycino)cobalt(III) probably has the *peripheral* structure.[43] In some cases, the color difference is so extreme and distinct that visual distinction is possible. This is true of the dichlorotetrammines; the *cis* is violet, the *trans* is green. This simple criterion is adequate for identifying the single known isomer of dichloro(triethylenetetramine)cobalt(III) ion as *cis*, since it is violet,[39] although later work confirmed this by resolution into optical isomers.[115]

The symmetry of *cis* isomers is generally lower than that of the corresponding *trans* forms. Consequently, the number of bands occurring in the infrared spectra of *cis* isomers is usually greater than that occurring in the corresponding *trans* isomers.[85,144,163,266,278] Since *cis* isomers are more polar than *trans*, distinctions may be made on the basis of polarographic behavior (diffusion current),[184,185] diffusion,[95] conductivity,[95] ion exchange,[210,272,273] chromatography,[226] and electrophoresis.[94] Of course, these isomers differ in solubility; however, there is no formula for predicting the nature of the isomer from its solubility.

The compounds of the class $[Co(AA)_3]^{3+}$ are probably most typical of the substances which have been resolved into optical isomers. $[Co(en)_3]^{3+}$ and $[Co(C_2O_4)_3]^{3-}$ are common examples. The absolute configuration of the former has been determined and is given below.[292,293,318,335,336]

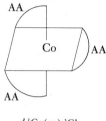

d-[Co(en)$_3$]Cl$_3$
$[\alpha]_{5461} = +440°$

In addition to this and the previously mentioned series of *cis*-$[Co(AA)_2X_2]^+$ compounds, a substantial variety of substances involving chelating agents has been studied from the standpoint of isomerism. Cobalt(III) complexes known to have been resolved into optical isomers are listed in Table 6.2.

Besides the classic methods of resolution, a few other techniques of interest have been employed. Bailar and his co-workers[115,171,201,202] showed that the diastereoisomeric complexes formed by an optically active ligand and a racemic complex such as D,L-[Co(en)$_2$(d-tartrate)]$^+$, react quite differently with an incoming group, permitting the resulting product to be at least partially resolved; e.g., D,L-[Co(en)$_2$(d-tartrate)]$^+$ + en → D-[Co(en)$_3$]$^{3+}$ + L-[Co(en)$_2$(d-tartrate)]$^+$. This process also represents a first example of the subtle asymmetric relationships found among cobalt(III) complexes. The use of adsorption on optically active quartz powder has been successful in the resolution of some cobalt(III) complexes.[28] Chromatographic resolutions have been attained using starch, cellulose, and lactose.[222-224,270] The effect of an asymmetric medium on the properties of enantiomorphs has been utilized to separate optical isomers. Dwyer and co-workers,[123,125] and Carassiti[99,100] applied this principle. In some cases, racemization may occur at a measurable rate between the two isomers in solution. Under these conditions, an optically active reagent which tends to crystallize only one of the diastereoisomeric salts will ultimately

TABLE 6.2. OPTICAL ISOMERS OF COBALT(III) COMPLEXES*

$[Co(en)_3]^{3+}$

$[Co(cptdin)_3]^{3+}$

$[Co(en)_2(cptdin)]^{3+}$

$[Co(en)_2(pn)]^{3+}$

$[Co(pn)_2(NH_3)_2]^{3+}$

$[Co(en)_2(dabp)]^{3+}$ (263)

$[Co(en)_2(H_2O)Cl]^{2+}$

$[Co(en)_2(H_2O)NO_2]^{2+}$

$[Co(en)_2(NH_3)Br]^{2+}$

$[Co(en)_2(NH_3)NCS]^{2+}$

$[Co(en)_2(gly)]^{2+}$

$[Co(en)_2(prac)]^{2+}$

$[Co(pn)_2(NH_3)Cl]^{2+}$

$[Co(en)_2(NH_3)F]^{2+}$ (261)

$[Co(en)_2Cl_2]^{+}$

$[Co(en)_2(NCS)Cl]^{+}$

$[Co(en)_2(NO_2)Cl]^{+}$

$[Co(en)_2(NO_2)Br]^{+}$

$[Co(en)_2(CO_3)]^{+}$

$[Co(en)(NH_3)_2Cl_2]^{+}$

$[Co(pn)_2Cl_2]^{+}$

$[Co(pn)_2(NCS)_2]^{+}$

$[Co(pn)_2(CO_3)]^{+}$

$[Co(cptdin)_2Cl_2]^{+}$

$[Co(bn)_2Cl_2]^{+}$

$[Co(en)_2(ONO)NO_2]^{+}$ (283)

$[Co(DMG)_2(NH_3)Cl]$

$[Co(EDTA)]^{-}$ (84,130)

$[Co(EDTA)NO_2]^{2-}$ (133)

$[Co(EDTA)Cl]^{2-}$ (133)

$[Co(acac)_3]$ (125,270)

$[Co(gly)_3]$ (222,223)

$[Co(pn)_3]^{3+}$

$[Co\{NH_2CH(CH_2NH_2)_2\}_2]^{3+}$

$[Co(en)_2(phen)]^{3+}$

$[Co(en)_2(NH_3)_2]^{3+}$

$[Co(en)_2(NH_3)H_2O]^{3+}$

$[Co(NH_3)_2(C_2O_4)(NO_2)_2]^{-}$

$[Co(BigH^{+})_3]^{3+}$

$[Co(en)_2(H_2O)NCS]^{2+}$

$[Co(en)_2(NH_3)Cl]^{2+}$

$[Co(en)_2(NH_3)NO_2]^{2+}$

$[Co(en)_2(alan)]^{2+}$

$[Co(en)_2(acac)]^{2+}$

$[Co(en)_2(hmac)]^{2+}$

$[Co(PDTA)]^{-}$ (136)

$[Co(en)_2(NO_2)NCS]^{+}$

$[Co(en)_2(OH)Cl]^{+}$

$[Co(en)_2ClBr]^{+}$

$[Co(en)_2(NO_2)_2]^{+}$

$[Co(en)_2(C_2O_4)]^{+}$

$[Co(en)(pn)(NO_2)_2]^{+}$

$[Co(en)_2(sal)]^{+}$

$[Co(pn)_2(NO_2)_2]^{+}$

$[Co(pn)_2(SO_3)]^{+}$

$[Co(pn)_2(tart)]^{+}$

$[Co(stien)_2Cl_2]^{+}$

$[Co(C_2O_2S_2)_3]^{3-}$ (135)

$[Co(en)_2(NO_2)F]^{+}$ (261)

$[Co(en)_2F_2]^{+}$ (259)

$[Co(EDTA)Br]^{2-}$ (133)

$[Co(C_2O_4)_3]^{3-}$ (131)

$[Co(S_2COC_2H_4SO_3)_3]^{3-}$ (222,223)

$[Co(S_2CN(CH_3)C_6H_4OH)_3]$ (222,223)

$$\left[(en)_2Co\underset{O_2}{\overset{NH_2}{<}}Co(en)_2 \right]^{3+}$$

$$\left[(en)_2Co\underset{NO_2}{\overset{NH_2}{<}}Co(en)_2 \right]^{4+}$$

$$\left[(en)_2Co\underset{O_2}{\overset{NH_2}{<}}Co(en)_2 \right]^{4+}$$

$$\left[(en)_2Co\underset{SO_4}{\overset{NH_2}{<}}Co(en)_2 \right]^{3+}$$

$$\left[(en)_2Co\underset{OH}{\overset{NH_2}{<}}Co(en)_2 \right]^{4+}$$

$$\left[Co\underset{OH}{\overset{OH}{<}}Co(NH_3)_4 \right\}_3 \right]^{6+}$$

TABLE 6.2 (*continued*)

$$\left[Co\left\{\begin{matrix}OH\\OH\end{matrix}Co(en)_2\right\}_3\right]^{6+} \quad (170)$$

$$[Co(NH_3)_2(CH_3\overset{O}{\overset{\|}{C}}=CH\overset{CH_3}{\overset{\|}{C}}=NCH_2-)_2]^+$$

$$[Co(O-C_6H_4CH=N(CH_2)_2SCH_2-)_2]^+$$

$$[Co(O-C_6H_4CH=N(CH_2)_3SCH_2-)_2]^+$$

$$[Co(O-C_6H_4CH=N(CH_2)_2S(CH_2)_3S(CH_2)_2N=CHC_6H_4-O)]^+$$

$$[Co(O-C_6H_4CH=N(CH_2)_3S(CH_2)_3S(CH_2)_3N=CHC_6H_4-O)]^+$$

$$[Co(O-C_6H_4CH=N(CH_2)_2S(CH_2)_2S(CH_2)_3N=CHC_6H_4-O)]^+$$

$$[Co(O-C_6H_4CH=N(CH_2)_2S(CH_2)_3S(CH_2)_3N=CHC_6H_4-O)]^+$$

$$[Co(O-C_{10}H_6CH=N(CH_2)_2S(CH_2)_2S(CH_2)_2N=CHC_{10}H_6-O)]^+ \quad (122)$$

$$[Co(O-C_{10}H_6CH=N(CH_2)_3S(CH_2)_2S(CH_2)_3N=CHC_{10}H_6-O)]^+ \quad (126)$$

$$[Co(O-C_6H_4CH=N(CH_2)_2O(CH_2)_2S(CH_2)_2N=CHC_6H_4-O)]^+ \quad (127)$$

$$[Co(O-C_6H_4CH=N(CH_2)_2NH(CH_2)_2NH(CH_2)_2N=CHC_6H_4-O)]^+ \quad (114)$$

*Unless otherwise annotated examples are quoted from reference 41. Abbreviations used: en, ethylenediamine; cptdin, cyclopentanediamine; pn, propylenediamine; bn, butylenediamine; DMG, dimethylglyoxime; EDTA, ethylenediaminetetraacetate; phen, 1,10-phenanthroline; Big·H, biguanidinium ion; acac, acetylacetone; stien, styrenediamine; dabp, 2,2'-diaminobiphenyl; PDTA, propylenediaminetetraacetate; prac, propionylacetone; hmac, 2-hydroxo-4-methoxo-acetophenone; sal, salicylic acid; gly, glycine; alan, alanine.

yield a very high percentage of the least soluble form. This technique was applied to obtain 75–80 per cent of the total amount of [Co(en)$_3$]$^{3+}$ present from solution as one isomer, although the solution originally contained only 50 per cent of that antipode.[86] Doron and Kirschner applied the zone melting technique to resolutions.[117]

Although the ammines constitute a useful starting point for discussion of the structures of complexes, it is more desirable to continue the discussion in terms of the nature of the ligand, particularly with regard to the number of donor atoms it possesses.

The number of bidentate groups known to form complexes with cobalt is very large. It includes inorganic materials such as CO_3^{2-}, SO_4^{2-} and $C_2O_4^{2-}$ and many more organic substances such as diamines, amino acids, aminomercaptans, hydroxyacids, thioacids, xanthates, dithiocarbamates, biguanides, and dioximes. The higher functional ligands involve the same donor groups in various combinations.

In cases involving asymmetric bidentate groups, the stereochemical relationships become quite complex. As mentioned previously, tris(glycine)-cobalt(III) should exist in two geometric forms. Further, each of these forms should be optically active, increasing the total number of isomers to four. This material is a nonelectrolyte, however, which has only recently been partially resolved into its antipodal forms.[223] The analogous *d*-alanine complex was reported to have yielded three of the four predicted forms.[232] Theoretically, tris(propylenediamine)cobalt(III) should exist in twenty isomeric forms. This multiplicity of isomers arises because the propylene-diamine, $NH_2CH(CH_3)CH_2NH_2$, is unsymmetrical, and both the complex and the propylenediamine are optically active.

If the configuration of the ligand is denoted by *d* or *l*, and that of the complex by D or L, the isomers based on configurations are D(*ddd*), D(*ddl*), D(*dll*), D(*lll*), L(*lll*), L(*lld*), L(*ldd*), L(*ddd*). In addition, the four isomers containing ligands of a single configuration should exist in *facial* and *peripheral* forms, depending on the orientation of their methyl groups (subtotal eight isomers). The isomers containing ligands of both configurations (e.g., D(*ddl*), etc.) would then each exist as *facial* and *peripheral* forms. The *facial* forms would thus provide four isomers. However, in the *peripheral* isomers of this class, the ligands of identical configuration may have their methyl groups *cis* or *trans* to each other, thus multiplying these isomers by two and providing eight forms (subtotal twelve isomers), making the total number of isomers twenty.

Early studies[355,381] revealed only two of these isomers, D-$[Co(d\text{-}pn)_3]^{3+}$ and L-$[Co(l\text{-}pn)_3]^{3+}$. It appeared that a strong asymmetric effect discriminated in favor of these particular isomers. Although the possibility remained that each of the isomers separated was actually a mixture of *facial* and *peripheral* forms whose properties were so similar that they were not separable, the investigations clearly showed that only a single configuration of the ligand was present in a given complex ion—a remarkable stereo-specificity.

Recently,[134] a detailed investigation revealed the four isomers D(*lll*), D(*ddd*), L(*ddd*), L(*lll*). The isomers D(*ddd*) and L(*lll*) are the more stable, the free energy difference between diastereoisomers being –1.02 kcal/mole [e.g., D(*lll*) $\longrightarrow$ L(*lll*)]. The possible existence of an additional isomer has been reported.[134] From the rotation of the recovered propylenediamine it is tentatively suggested to be L(*lld*). This would provide the first example of its kind among cobalt(III) complexes.

In an earlier study, Bailar and co-workers[27,247] showed that isomers D-$[Co(l\text{-}pn)_2CO_3]^+$ and L-$[Co(l\text{-}pn)_2CO_3]^+$ exist. In solution, the second appears to be converted into the first. Again, only a single antipode of the ligand is found in the complex.

Further aspects of the stereospecific relationship existing between the configuration of the complex and that of the ligand were revealed in studies on the reaction of D (or L)-$[Co(AA)_2X_2]^+$ with optically active bidentate and monodentate ligands which replace the acido- groups, X^-. Jaeger and

Blumenthal[195] reported the reaction of *l*-cyclopentanediamine with racemic [Co(en)$_2$Cl$_2$]$^+$ to yield the diastereoisomers D-[Co(en)$_2$(*l*-cptn)]$^+$ and L-[Co(en)$_2$(*l*-cptn)]$^+$. Dwyer and Sargeson[137] showed that the reactions of *cis* and *trans*-[Co(en)$_2$Cl$_2$]$^+$ with *l*-propylenediamine yield only mixtures of [Co(en)$_3$]$^{3+}$ and [Co(*l*-pn)$_3$]$^{3+}$, in contradiction to the earlier report by Pfeiffer, Grossman, and Pietsch.[320] The extensive rearrangements occurring in this system almost certainly result from the presence (apparently unavoidable) of some cobalt(II) which causes an electron transfer labilization. This phenomenon will be discussed later.

The existence of diastereoisomeric complexes[200] appears to be established in the case of D-[Co(en)$_2$(*d*-tartrate)]$^+$ and L-[Co(en)$_2$(*d*-tartrate)]$^+$. These diastereoisomers differ greatly in reactivity,[200] and this effect has been utilized in the partial resolution of organic substances.[171,201] The reaction of *d,l*-tartratobis(*l*-propylenediamine)cobalt(III) chloride with *l*-propylenediamine leads to partial resolution of the tartrate. Other systems have also been studied.[116,171,215]

The stereochemical relationships existing among molecules containing asymmetric optically active ligands, as reviewed to this point, may be summarized as follows. (a) Two or more such ligands in the same complex usually have the same configuration. (b) A single configuration of the octahedral complex is relatively stable. (c) *Alpha-beta* isomerism, in which corresponding extremities of the asymmetric ligand are *cis* and *trans*, or *facial* and *peripheral*, is rare. [This does occur for tris(*d*-alaninato)cobalt(III);[232] however, the presence of different functional groups renders the alternate extremities of the ligand quite different.]

The earliest report on the observation of *alpha-beta* isomerism depending on the permutation of the extremities of propylenediamine is found in the work of Smirnoff and Werner[400] on *cis*-dinitro(ethylenediamine)(propylenediamine)cobalt(III) ion. The possible optical isomers are D*d*, D*l*, L*d* and L*l*. The *alpha-beta* isomers are shown below.

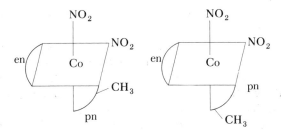

The total number of isomers found was equal to the theoretical number eight.[400] The relative stabilities of the isomers were not evaluated, and this very tedious work has not been repeated. The stereochemical work of Cooley, Liu, and Bailar[107] both substantiates and extends this early study. In their investigation, two complexes were designed with stereochemical restraints so that one of them would exhibit optical isomerism in the complex and in the ligand but no *alpha-beta* isomerism, while the other would exhibit optical isomerism in the complex and *alpha-beta* isomerism but no optical isomerism in the ligand. The first situation was found in *cis*-dinitro-(ethylenediamine)(*active*-2,3-butylenediamine)cobalt(III) ion, the second in *cis*-dinitro(ethylenediamine)(*iso*-butylenediamine)cobalt(III) ion. All the predicted isomers were found in each case. The isomerism is summarized below.

Isomers of *cis*-[Co(en)(bn)(NO$_2$)$_2$]$^+$

Compound containing 2,3-butylenediamine

Compound containing *iso*-butylenediamine

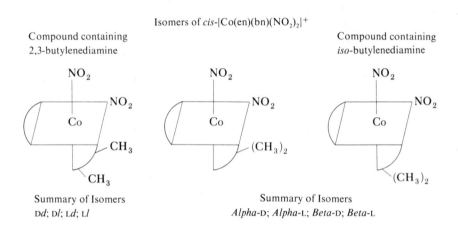

Summary of Isomers
Dd; Dl; Ld; Ll

Summary of Isomers
Alpha-D; Alpha-L; Beta-D; Beta-L

In both compounds, the distribution of isomers appeared to be statistical; however, the diastereoisomers containing ligand of different configurations (2,3-bn) racemized at different rates. No such difference was observed for *alpha*-D and *beta*-D complexes (*i*-bn).

The understanding of configurational and other stereochemical relationships among complexes may ultimately provide a basis for the understanding of the key role played by metal ions in biochemical systems. A total review of these subtle and greatly varied phenomena is not feasible here because of space limitations. A number of these systems will, however, be mentioned in the general discussion of complexes containing polydentate chelating agents. Before temporarily abandoning the discussion of bidentate reagents, a few additional cases require mention. The relatively hindered diamine, stilbenediamine[405] greatly favors the *trans* isomer of the compound of the type [Co(AA)$_2$Cl$_2$]$^+$. Furthermore, the *racemic* amine appears to form a complex of greater stability than the *meso* amine.

The importance of the size of the chelate ring is indicated by the nature of the compounds formed by cobalt(III). Relatively few compounds are known containing four-membered rings, while none are known to contain rings of only three members.(These may occur as intermediates in reactions.) Five-membered rings are associated with the largest group of stable complexes, while six-membered rings follow; the seven-membered chelate ring is quite rare.

Carbonate ion provides several good examples of four-membered rings. $[Co(NH_3)_4CO_3]^+$ is very well known. McCutcheon and Schuele[264] prepared $[Co(CO_3)_3]^{3-}$ in which three CO_3^{2-} groups presumably coordinate in a bidentate manner. This substance has been used as a starting material for the preparation of $K[Co(en)(CO_3)_2]\cdot H_2O$, which exhibits two isomeric forms.[274] If one of the carbonate groups is monodentate, these may be geometric isomers. Sulfate may also coordinate in a bidentate manner[119] to cobalt(III), although this has been questioned.[142] Although cobalt(III) complexes with sulfur donors do not appear to be as abundant as those of cobalt(II), the derivatives of the dithiocarboxyl group[207] (xanthates, dithiosemicarbamates, etc.) are expected to form four-membered rings. It is likely that a four-membered ring is present in the cobalt(III) derivatives of p-(mercaptoacetamido)benzoic acid[268] and those of thiohydroxamic acid.[89] Although in the latter case a five-membered ring might be formed, the nitrogen atom is probably a stronger donor than the oxygen atom. A similar mode of coordination is possible in the case of thiopicolinanilide;[18] however in this case, the most probable mode of coordination is:

The formation of doubly-bridged dinuclear complexes provides a number of examples of four-membered rings. The ions

and

have been known for many years. In the first example, a simple ring is formed; in the second, the structure involves face-shared octahedra, effectively incorporating three fused four-membered rings. The absorption spectra of these and similar complexes have recently been studied.[189] In the compound

$$[(NH_3)_3Co\overset{OH}{\underset{NO_2}{\diagdown\diagup}}OH{=}Co(NH_3)_3]^{3+}$$

one of the rings is four-membered; however, the rings containing the NO_2^- group are five-membered since nitrite ion is attached to one cobalt through the nitrogen atom and to the other through an oxygen atom.[291] Durant's salt

$$K_4[(C_2O_4)_2Co\overset{OH}{\underset{OH}{\diagdown\diagup}}Co(C_2O_4)_2]$$

and the hexol,[397]

$$\left[Co\left\{\overset{OH}{\underset{OH}{\diagdown\diagup}}Co(NH_3)_4\right\}_3\right]^{6+}$$

which was resolved into optical isomers by Werner, provide additional examples. Quite recently, Goodwin, Gyarfas, and Mellor[170] obtained four of the eight possible isomers of

$$\left[Co\left\{\overset{OH}{\underset{OH}{\diagdown\diagup}}Co(en)_2\right\}_3\right]^{6+}$$

It was shown that the conversion of

$$[(en)_2Co\overset{OH}{\underset{OH}{\diagdown\diagup}}Co(en)_2]^{4+}$$

into $[Co(en)_2(H_2O)(OH)]^{2+}$ proceeds by two paths, the more rapid involving protonation of one of the bridging OH groups.[327]

It should be pointed out that dinuclear complexes of cobalt(III) exist having single bridging groups as well as the double and triple bridges mentioned above. Simple examples are found in $[(NH_3)_4Co-NH_2-Co-(NH_3)_4]^{5+}$, $[(NH_3)_4Co-O_2-Co(NH_3)_4]^{4+}$, and $[(NH_3)_4Co-O_2-Co(NH_3)_4]^{5+}$. The latter compound has attracted considerable attention since it apparently contains one atom of cobalt(III) and one atom of cobalt(IV).[393] The magnetic moment (1.60–1.69 Bohr Magnetons)[166,243] is slightly lower than the value expected for one unpaired electron (see below), a result in agreement with the formulation involving both cobalt(III) and (IV). Malatesta proposed that the two cobalt atoms may be considered to be equivalent in terms of modern resonance concepts.[243] It has also been pointed out that the assumption of a bridged O_2^- group and two cobalt(III) atoms is also consistent with the chemical and magnetic properties of this and similar compounds.[78] This view has been held by others.[197]

Orgel and Dunitz[120] discussed this substance from the molecular orbital standpoint. They indicated that in proceeding from the reduced compound to that in question, the electron is removed from the peroxo bridge and not the cobalt(III) ion. Jahn-Teller distortion predicted a nonlinear structure for the Co—O—O—Co array, which has, in fact, been observed.[138] Recent paramagnetic resonance absorption studies[64,138] permitted resolution of this problem. The observed hyperfine splitting can be explained only by the assumption that the electron has equal probability of being associated with either cobalt atom.

The electron mobility expected of a system such as this led to electrical resistance studies. The material, however, is not an intrinsic semiconductor.[146] Although

$$[(en)_2Co \underset{O_2}{\overset{NH_2}{<\!\!\!\!\!\!-\!\!\!\!\!\!>}} Co(en)_2]^{4+}$$

should exist in three isomeric forms (*dextro, levo, meso*), Werner was able to isolate only the d and l antipodes.[398,399] He did succeed, however,[396] in isolating all three isomers of

$$[(en)_2Co \underset{NO_2}{\overset{NH_2}{<\!\!\!\!\!\!-\!\!\!\!\!\!>}} Co(en)_2]^{4+}.$$

Bridged complexes containing both cobalt(II) and cobalt(III) have recently been reported.[90,91]

Five-membered chelate rings appear to be more common and more stable than either the smaller four-membered rings or the larger six-membered rings. This may be seen in such common ligands as ethylenediamine, propylenediamine, α-dioximes, 2,2′-bipyridine, and oxalate. Trimethylenediamine does form a compound of the class $[Co(AA)_3]^{3+}$; however, it is not so readily formed nor so stable as the corresponding ethylenediamine compound.[29]

Complexes of cobalt(III) with dimethylglyoxime (H-DMG) were prepared by Tschugaeff.[379,380] The general formulas are $[Co(DMG)_2(NH_3)_2]X$, $[Co(DMG)_2(NH_3)X]$, and $[Co(DMG)_2X_2]^-$. This work was extended by Ablov, who replaced NH_3 by other neutral groups and permuted the anions X^-.[1-8] The compound containing three molecules of coordinated DMG, tris(dimethylglyoximo)cobalt(III), was recently synthesized.[287] Tsuchida, Koboyaski, and Nakamura[382] reported the resolution of $[Co(DMG)_2-(NH_3)Cl]$ into optical isomers. Such a result led naturally to the conclusion that the monodentate groups are mutually *cis* in this complex molecule; however, similar compounds were reported to have *trans* structures.[294,376] Consequently, Tsuchida and Koboyaski[383] suggested that the dimethylglyoximes may be in the same plane, but that the asymmetric nature of the ligands may give rise to the isomerism.

$$CH_3 \diagdown \qquad \diagup CH_3$$
$$C-C$$
$$HO-N \diagup \qquad \diagdown N-O^-$$

Later investigation of the infrared spectra of this and many similar compounds[159,288,289] indicated that the oxime oxygens of the two coordinated dimethylglyoxime groups are associated through hydrogen bonds. In consequence, tautomerism should render the resolution impossible. It appears that the original investigation merits repetition.

The complexes of cobalt(III) with 2,2′-bipyridine, 1,10-phenanthroline, and similar ligands have been reviewed by Brandt, Dwyer, and Gyarfas.[76] Although the *cis* and *trans* isomers of dichlorobis (1,10-phenanthroline)-cobalt(III) ion have been reported, attempts to isolate the optical isomers of the complexes of the form $[Co(AA)_3]^{3+}$ have failed, presumably because of the presence of catalytic amounts of cobalt(II).[44] The resolution of $[Co(en)_2(phen)]^{3+}$ has been reported.[194] The value of the standard potential for the couple $[Co(phen)_3]^{3+}—[Co(phen)_3]^{2+}$ is –0.37 volts.[309] Paglia[310] recently reported complexes containing both dimethylglyoxime and 2,2′-bipyridine, $[Co(DMG)(bipy)Br_2]$. Complexes containing both 2,2′-bipyridine or 1,10-phenanthroline, and cyanide ion have also been reported.[93] Perhaps the simplest are exemplified by $K[Co(bipy)(CN)_4]·8H_2O$.

As pointed out earlier, cobalt(III) forms neutral uncharged complexes with α-amino acids, such as glycine and alanine. Ogleva[305] recently showed that these complexes may coordinate glycine in a monodentate fashion. By treating $[Co(NH_2CH_2CO_2)_3]$ with HCl, he obtained $[Co(NH_2CH_2CO_2)_2-$

(NH$_2$CH$_2$CO$_2$H)Cl], [Co(NH$_2$CH$_2$CO$_2$)(NH$_2$CH$_2$CO$_2$H)$_2$Cl$_2$], and [Co-(NH$_2$CH$_2$CO$_2$H)$_3$Cl$_3$], in which the glycine was presumably coordinated through the amino group, as for example:

$$
\begin{array}{c}
NH_2CH_2CO_2H \\
| \\
Cl\overline{\quad\quad\quad}NH_2CH_2CO_2H \\
Co \\
Cl\overline{\quad\quad\quad}NH_2CH_2CO_2H \\
| \\
Cl
\end{array}
$$

This represents a first example of what has been termed *flexidentate*[363] chelation, the essential feature being a variability in the manner in which the ligand coordinates. A simpler example is found in the monodentate and bidentate chelation of CO$_3^{2-}$ in [Co(NH$_3$)$_5$CO$_3$]$^+$ and [Co(NH$_3$)$_4$CO$_3$]$^+$. The most thoroughly studied example is that of the nitrite ion, which may coordinate through the nitrogen atom (forming nitro complexes) or through one of the oxygen atoms (forming *nitrito* complexes). This will be discussed later.

The complexes of cysteine[297-300] constitute an interesting example of flexidentate behavior. The green tris(cysteinato)-cobalt(III) is reported to involve coordination through the sulfur and nitrogen atoms, while it has been concluded that the red modification involves coordination through the carboxyl group and the sulfur atom. A comparison with the complexes of 2-aminoethanethiol, thioglycolic acid, and glycine supported the conclusions. It is surprising to find a six-membered ring in a system which might form five-membered rings by alternate arrangements. Recent studies[61,252,402] revealed that cobalt(III) forms complexes with simple peptides such as glycylglycine and glycylglycylglycine. Under the proper conditions, the corresponding cobalt(II) systems combine reversibly with molecular oxygen.

A number of polydentate ligands merit mention at this point. A series of polyethylenepolyamines are known to form stable cobalt(III) complexes. Diethylenetriamine (dien) forms [Co(dien)$_2$]X$_3$ and [Co(dien)(NO$_2$)$_3$] analogs of [Co(NH$_3$)$_6$]X$_3$ and [Co(NH$_3$)$_3$(NO$_2$)$_3$], respectively.[36,250,251] The first compound should exist in three geometric forms, with one optically active. Triethylenetetramine (trien) coordinates in a tetradentate fashion with cobalt(III), forming only a *cis* isomer, as mentioned above. Since models indicate that the *trans* isomer is attainable, detailed structural information on this compound would be of much interest. In addition to

[Co(trien)X$_2$]$^+$, Basolo[39] also prepared [Co$_2$(trien)$_3$]$^{6+}$ salts. The most likely structure of the latter involves the bridging of three molecules of the tetrafunctional ligand between the two metal atoms in such a way that each ligand is bidentate toward each metal atom. This is proposed by analogy to some complexes of pyridinaldazine with iron(II), cobalt(II), and nickel(II).[363]

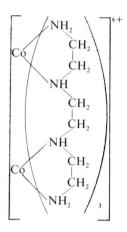

Tetraethylenepentamine is also reported to form complexes with cobalt(III).[203] The tetrafunctional amine, 2,2′,2″-tris(aminoethyl)amine (tren), N(CH$_2$CH$_2$NH$_2$)$_3$, forms [Co(tren)X$_2$]$^+$ in a single *cis* modification in accord with its structure.[36,249]

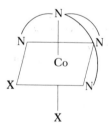

2,2′,2″-Terpyridine[76] and a series of tridentate analogs prepared by Lions and Martin[236,237] form hexammine analogs of the form [Co(AAA)$_2$]$^{3+}$. The resonance restriction, which should force these donor molecules to remain planar, limits the geometric forms to one—the peripheral array.

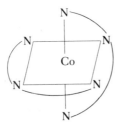

The corresponding 2,2′,2″,2‴-tetrapyridine (tetrpy) forms a complex which has been formulated as [Co(tetrpy)Cl$_2$]Cl·3H$_2$O, implying tetradentate coordination of the ligand.[271] The color is characteristic of a *trans*-dichlorotetrammine complex; however, it has been pointed out, on steric grounds, that this molecule cannot coordinate more than three nitrogen atoms with one metal atom.[76] A bridged structure is more likely.

Two polyfunctional amino acids are of interest. Nitrilotriacetic acid (NTA), N(CH$_2$CO$_2$H)$_3$, forms a series of cobalt(III) complexes:[275]

$$\alpha\text{-K[Co(NTA)(H}_2\text{O)(OH)]}\cdot 2\text{H}_2\text{O,}$$

$$\beta\text{-K[Co(NTA)(H}_2\text{O)(OH)]}\cdot 3\text{H}_2\text{O,}$$

$$\text{K}_2[(\text{NTA})\text{Co} \overset{\text{OH}}{\underset{\text{OH}}{<}} \text{Co(NTA)]}\cdot 6\text{H}_2\text{O,}$$

$$\text{K}_2[\text{Co(NTA)(CO}_3)]\cdot\text{H}_2\text{O,}$$

and

$$\text{K}_2[\text{Co(NTA)(C}_2\text{O}_4)].$$

The complexes of ethylenediaminetetraacetic acid (H$_4$EDTA) with cobalt(III) exhibit a number of interesting stereochemical features. Brintzinger, Thiele and Muller[79] prepared anhydrous Na[Co(EDTA)], which involves coordination through all six donor groups of the EDTA.

$$\begin{array}{c} \text{HO}_2\text{CCH}_2 \diagdown \qquad\qquad \diagup \text{CH}_2\text{CO}_2\text{H} \\ \qquad\qquad \text{NCH}_2\text{CH}_2\text{N} \\ \text{HO}_2\text{CCH}_2 \diagup \qquad\qquad \diagdown \text{CH}_2\text{CO}_2\text{H} \end{array}$$

In later studies,[133,276,337,342] complexes containing other groups, as well as EDTA, were prepared: M^I[Co(HEDTA)X] and M$^I_2$[Co(EDTA)X], where

X^- is NO_2^-, Cl^-, Br^-, and OH^-. The structures of these substances were established by infrared spectral correlations,[84,276] and it was shown that one of the carboxyl groups is free while the remainder are coordinated to the cobalt.

Most of these complexes have been resolved into optical isomers (see Table 6.2); however, the only evidence to date for the existence of the expected geometric isomers of the pentadentate complexes comes from studies on the kinetics of conversion of the complex $[Co(H{-}EDTA)X]^-$ into the sexadentate complex $[Co(EDTA)]^-$.[277] This conversion proceeds with complete retention of enantiomeric configuration.[84,133] The structure of the sexadentate salts $NH_4[Co(EDTA)]\cdot2H_2O$ and $Rb[Co(EDTA)]\cdot2H_2O$ was determined by Weakliem and Hoard.[389] As a consequence of their work, the geometric isomer for $[Co(H{-}EDTA)X]^-$ shown below may reasonably be considered more stable than the other two forms derived by permuting the position of the monodentate group X.

A remarkably stereospecific reaction occurs when optically active complexes of cobalt(III) with EDTA are treated with ethylenediamine.[130,133] Three molecules of ethylenediamine replace EDTA, forming $[Co(en)_3]^{3+}$, and although all of the bonds to cobalt are substituted, the reaction proceeds with some retention of antipodal configuration. The stereospecificity of this reaction was utilized by Kirschner, Wei, and Bailar[215] to partially resolve propylenediamine. Recently, Cooke and Busch[108] studied the kinetics of the reaction between $[Co(EDTA)]^-$ and ethylenediamine, showing that a partition of rates between paths retaining configuration and paths leading to a racemic product accounts quantitatively for the per cent of the original configuration retained in the products. It has also been shown that the absolute configuration of $[Co(EDTA)]^-$ and $[Co(EDTA)X]^{2-}$ may be deduced from this process, since the absolute configuration of the product is known ($[Co(en)_3]^{3+}$, see above).

ABSOLUTE CONFIGURATIONS

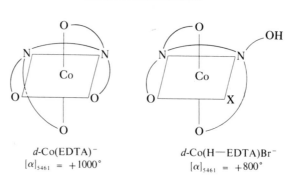

d-Co(EDTA)$^-$
$[\alpha]_{5461} = +1000°$

d-Co(H$-$EDTA)Br$^-$
$[\alpha]_{5461} = +800°$

Also quite recently,[136] the sexadentate cobalt(III) complexes of propylenediaminetetraacetic acid (H_4PDTA) have been prepared. The complexes found upon resolution, D-[Co(*l*-PDTA)]⁻ and L-[Co(*d*-PDTA)]⁻, indicated a substantial stereospecificity, since the configuration of the ligand and complex are interdependent. From the absolute configuration of propylenediamine and that of [Co(EDTA)]⁻, it is deduced that the CH_3 group in the propylenediamine chelate ring in [Co(PDTA)]⁻ has an equatorial orientation.[130]

Perhaps the first complexes recognized to contain sexadentate ligands were those prepared by Dwyer, Lions, and their co-workers.[122,124,127–129] The class of ligand is indicated below.

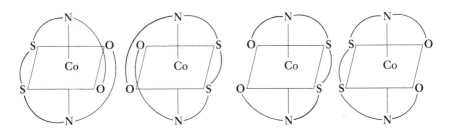

These investigators varied the lengths of the polymethylene chains, replaced them stepwise by o-phenylene groups, used different alpha-hydroxyaldehydes, and substituted oxygen atoms for the sulfur atoms. In most cases, optical isomers could be isolated, and in a number of cases, geometric isomers were also found. The structures proposed for the isomers are:

ISOMERS OF LINEAR SEXADENTATE COMPLEXES

The corresponding sexadentate complexes derived from the Schiff base of salicylaldehyde with triethylenetetramine have been applied.[113,114,279] Triply branched sexadentate chelating agents have also been reported:[132]

$$HC(CH_2N=CHC_6H_4OH)_3$$

$$HC(CH_2N=CHC_5H_4N)_3$$

A single report of tetrahedrally coordinated cobalt(III) is found in studies by Baker *et al.*[30,351,412] on heteropoly 12-tungstocobaltiate. The cobalt(III) is coordinated to four nearest neighbors at the center of the array of fused WO_6 octahedra.

Electronic Structure and the Nature of Bonding

Most coordination compounds of cobalt(III) are diamagnetic, indicating that the six $3d$ electrons are entirely paired. This is readily explained in terms of the valence bond theory of Pauling,[87,312] or in terms of the ligand field[46,303,307,308] or molecular orbital theories.[46,307,308]

According to the former set of concepts, two of the five $3d$ orbitals must be reserved for hybridization to form the six d^2sp^3 orbitals which are utilized to form bonds with the six donor atoms. In consequence, the six $3d$ electrons of the cobalt(III) ion must be assigned to the three remaining $3d$ orbitals in accord with the Pauli Exclusion principle. The configuration is shown below.

VALENCE BOND THEORY OF BONDING IN COBALT(III)

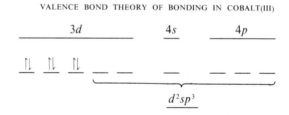

According to the ligand field theory, a strong interaction between the octahedrally arranged negative electric field of the ligands and the d-levels of the cobalt causes the originally five-fold degenerate $3d$ set to be split into an upper doublet of energy levels and a lower triplet. In most cases, separation between the upper doublet and the lower triplet is so great that energetically it is most feasible to pair the electrons in the lower set of levels.

LIGAND FIELD THEORY OF ENERGY LEVELS IN COBALT(III)

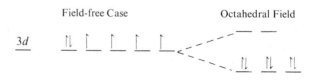

To the chemist, the ligand field theory leaves uncomfortably vague the question of the nature of the bonds uniting the metal atom to the ligands; however, the physical aspects of the problem are more appropriately treated. A molecular orbital theory appears to handle the several aspects of the problem more satisfactorily;[46,307,308] molecular orbital arguments and correlation diagrams will be omitted from this discussion, however, because of space limitations.

A few cobalt(III) compounds are reported to be paramagnetic. $K_3[CoF_6]$ has a magnetic moment of 4.26 Bohr Magnetons, in reasonable agreement with the presence of four unpaired electrons.[302] This may be accounted for in terms of the valence bond theory if it is assumed that $3d$ orbitals are not used for bonding so that the six $3d$ electrons are distributed among all five $3d$ levels, giving rise to four unpaired electrons. It has been assumed that $4d$ orbitals are utilized in bonding. Such complexes are usually denoted as outer orbital in bond type.

VALENCE BOND TREATMENT OF "OUTER ORBITAL" COBALT(III)

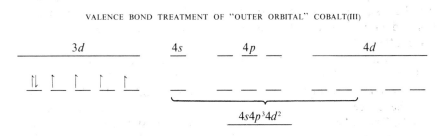

According to the ligand field theory, the splitting between the upper doublet and the lower triplet is sufficiently small to permit the spin-free to be lower in energy than the spin-paired state.

LIGAND FIELD TREATMENT OF "OUTER ORBITAL" COBALT(III)

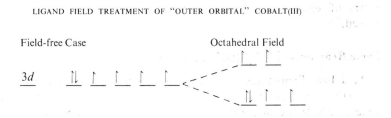

The magnetic moment of $[Co(H_2O)_3F_3]\cdot0.5H_2O$ is 4.47 Bohr Magnetons[106] from 189–326° K. This is explained in the same way as the above. Although originally reported to be paramagnetic, tris(acetylacetone)cobalt(III) is diamagnetic.[401] $K_3[Co(C_2O_4)_3]\cdot3H_2O$ is reported to exhibit a variable paramagnetism of 1.4 B. Mag.[319] It is also reported that the cobalt(III) complex of bis(salicylal) diglycylethylenediamine has a moment of 2.7 Bohr Magnetons.

Recent studies have been directed toward the diamagnetism of cobalt(III) complexes.[62,63,209] Although the compounds are diamagnetic, the application of Pascal's Law sometimes reveals an underlying residual paramagnetism on the part of cobalt(III). This effect has been discussed in theoretical terms by Ballhausen and Asmussen.[33]

Tsuchida and his co-workers[216,290,343 – 346,410,414] have carried out extensive experimentation and correlation on the spectra of cobalt(III) compounds. Some of this work was cited earlier; unfortunately, a detailed review of the deductions is not practical here. The most general result is the so-called Fajans-Tsuchida series, which correlates the strength of the interaction between ligand and central metal with spectral shifts.[345] The advent of the ligand field theory has permitted more detailed discussion of the spectra.[32,98,233,365,411] Crudely, the transitions occurring in such compounds are of two types: those confined to the d-levels of the central atom (ligand field bands), and those which amount to incipient charge transfer (oxidation-reduction) between the central atom and its ligands, ion partner, or solvent.[66,221,234,241,307,406]

The infrared spectra have been recorded for many cobalt(III) complexes and, as mentioned before, may prove to be helpful in distinguishing geometric isomers and in solving other structural problems. Most investigations have been concerned with vibrations localized principally on the ligands. The coordinated NH_3 group has been most thoroughly characterized.[38,58,85,88,160,182,217,285,286,324,364] The principal modes of vibration are a doublet stretching frequency at about $3200 \ cm^{-1}$, antisymmetric deformation at about $1600 \ cm^{-1}$, symmetric deformation at about $1400 \ cm^{-1}$, and a rocking mode in the vicinity of $800 \ cm^{-1}$. The spectra of many coordinated anions have also been reported.[85,162,350] The expected loss of symmetry of some anions upon coordination to cobalt(III) has been observed.[350]

Some Reactions of Cobalt(III) Complexes

Acid-base Properties. The acid base properties of complexes are generally those of the ligand as modified by coordination to the metal ion. An exception is found in the hydroxides of coordinately saturated complexes, of which the following are examples: $[Co(NH_3)_6](OH)_3$,[77,198,311] $[Co(en)_3]$-$(OH)_3$,[79,198] $[Co(NH_2OH)_6](OH)_3$,[77] $[Co(pn)_3](OH)_3$,[77] $[Co(dien)_2](OH)_3$,[77] $[Co(NH_3)_5OH](OH)_2$.[311] These bases are all strong; presumably, the free acids of similar complex anions would also be strong. Jaselkis and Diehl[198] titrated $H_3Co(CN)_6$ with $[Co(NH_3)_6](OH)_3$ and reported the neutralization reaction to be typical of strong acids and strong bases.

Coordinated molecules containing hydrogen atoms are at least potential Bronsted acids. The reaction

$$[Co(A)_5H_2O]^{3+} \longrightarrow [Co(A)_5OH]^{2+} + H^+$$

is a typical ionization process. Basolo and Pearson have summarized a number of the pK_a values for such reactions.[56] These are given in Table 6.3.

TABLE 6.3. ACID IONIZATION CONSTANTS OF COBALT(III) COMPLEXES

Ion	pKa	Conditions
$[Co(NH_3)_5H_2O]^{3+}$	5.7	$15\,^\circ C$, $\mu = 0$
$[Co(NH_3)_4H_2O)_2]^{3+}$	5.2	$15\,^\circ C$, $\mu = 0$
$[Co(NH_3)_3(H_2O)_3]^{3+}$	4.7	$15\,^\circ C$, $\mu = 0$
$[Co(NH_3)_2(H_2O)_4]^{3+}$	3.4	$15\,^\circ C$, $\mu = 0$
cis-$[Co(en)_2(H_2O)_2]^{3+}$	6.1	$pK_2 = 8.2$, $25\,^\circ C$
trans-$[Co(en)_2(H_2O)_2]^{3+}$	4.5	$pK_2 = 7.9$, $25\,^\circ C$
cis-$[Co(en)_2(NO_2)(H_2O)]^{2+}$	6.3	$25\,^\circ C$
trans-$[Co(en)_2(NO_2)(H_2O)]^{2+}$	6.4	$25\,^\circ C$
$[Co(NH_3)_6]^{3+}$	>14	$25\,^\circ C$
$[Co(en)_3]^{3+}$	>14	$25\,^\circ C$
$[Co(EDTA)(H_2O)]^-$ (342)	8.1	$25\,^\circ C$
$[Co(H\,-EDTA)(H_2O)]$ (342)	3.1	$25\,^\circ C$
$[Co(H\,-EDTA)Br]^-$ (337)	3.0	$25\,^\circ C$

Factors affecting acidity in such systems are discussed by Basolo and Pearson.[56]

Ion Pair Formation. This type of interaction is one of the least specific modes of combination which may involve a complex ion. The subject has been reviewed by Basolo and Pearson.[55] It is sufficient to point out that some of the previously reported values for association constants have been questioned in the case of cobalt(III) complexes.[70,211] Ion pair formation is viewed as the close association of ions of opposite charge as a consequence of coulombic attraction. Larsson[225] reported that the dipolar ammonia molecule is also capable of association with coordinately saturated cobalt(III) ammines. A contrasting phenomenon which bears formal resemblance to ion pair formation involves the complexing of groups coordinated to cobalt(III) with other metal ions. Werner[395] reported that silver ion coordinates to the sulfur atom of the thiocyanate group in $[Co(NH_3)_5NCS]^{2+}$. This phenomenon has been reinvestigated[262] and it has been revealed that Ag^+ and Hg^{2+} may either form isolable addition prod-

ucts with complexes involving NCS$^-$, or catalyze the replacement of NCS$^-$
by water. The latter behavior is encountered in other substitution and
oxidation-reduction reactions, discussed below.

Oxidation-reduction Reactions. The complexes of cobalt(III) and cobalt(II) have yielded significant information on the nature of oxidation-reduction reactions. These developments were reviewed by Taube,[374,375] Basolo and Pearson,[47] and Dainton.[111] Two primary types of mechanisms are apparent in reactions where the oxidation state of cobalt is altered. They are (a) direct electron transfer and (b) electron transfer via a bridged intermediate. These processes are not always readily distinguished; however, certain criteria permit some fairly distinct examples of each to be identified.

The true electron transfer process is expected in systems where a bridged intermediate is rendered unlikely (a) because at least one of the reactants is substitution inert and contains no ligands in its coordination sphere capable of forming a second coordinate bond (i.e., none with unshared electron pairs), or (b) because both reactants are substitution inert. Systems involving electron transfer between cobalt(II) and cobalt(III) satisfy the first condition more readily. Examples are listed in Table 6.4. The systems $[Co(en)_3]^{3+}$—

TABLE 6.4. ELECTRON-TRANSFER REACTIONS INVOLVING COMPLEXES OF COBALT(II) AND COBALT(III)

	k, M^{-1} sec^{-1}	E_a, Kcal	ΔS, eu	Ref.
$[Co^{III}(C_5H_5)_2]$ — $[Co^{II}(C_5H_5)_2]$	fast (py)	. . .	. . .	102
$[Co(tripy)_2]^{3+}$ — $[Co(tripy)_3]^{2+}$	12.3, 0°C	. . .	. . .	31
$[Co(phen)_3]^{3+}$ — $[Co(phen)_3]^{2+}$	1.1, 0°C	17.0	4.0	31
$[Co(bipy)_3]^{3+}$ — $[Co(bipy)_3]^{2+}$	2.1, 0°C	. . .	. . .	31
$[Co(en)_3]^{3+}$ — $[Co(en)_3]^{2+}$	4.5×10^{-5}	14.3	-33	230
$[Co(EDTA)]^-$ — $[Co(EDTA)]^{2-}$	4.0×10^{-7}	22.0	-17	10,188
$[Co(NH_3)_6]^{3+}$ — $[Co(NH_3)_6]^{2+}$	very slow	. . .	. . .	230
$[Co(acac)_3]$ — $[Co(acac)_3]^-$ (?)	very slow	. . .	. . .	102
$[Co(C_2O_4)_3]^{3-}$ — $[Co(C_2O_4)_3]^{4-}$	very slow	. . .	. . .	10
$[Co(H_2O)_6]^{3+}$ — $[Co(H_2O)_6]^{2+}$	0.75, 0°C	. . .	. . .	71

$[Co(en)_3]^{2+}$, $[Co(NH_3)_6]^{3+}$—$[Co(NH_3)_6]^{2+}$, $[Co(phen)_3]^{3+}$—$[Co(phen)_3]^{2+}$ all conform; however, the remaining systems in Table 6.4 could undergo electron transfer via bridged intermediates. On the basis of available information, the classification made is probable. In any case, the reaction is:

$$[Co^{*III}(A)_6] + [Co^{II}(A)_6] \rightleftarrows [Co^{*II}(A)_6] + [Co^{III}(A)_6]$$

A number of factors may be responsible for slow electron transfer processes. The frequency of electron transfer between identical nuclei (ignoring the extra electron) will depend on the extent to which orbitals centered on the individual nuclei overlap. The Franck-Condon principle requires that the coordinated groups be rearranged prior to electron transfer in such a manner that the state of the system after transfer will be identical to that before transfer. There can be no change in the number of unpaired electrons during the course of the reaction. The environments of the exchanging ions must be readjusted in accord with the Franck-Condon principle prior to electron transfer. Although these systems have been discussed from a number of points of view, only a single feature will be considered here; the reviews may be consulted for more complete discussion.

With regard to the first three considerations mentioned above, systems involving cobalt are not unique; however, these cobalt systems provide examples, rapidly becoming classic, of exchange between ions having substantially different spin-multiplicities in the ground state. The six $3d$ electrons of cobalt(III) in its complexes are usually completely paired, while the corresponding complexes of cobalt(II) usually exhibit magnetic moments (see below) consistent with the presence of three unpaired electrons. In order for electron transfer to occur, either cobalt(III) must undergo a transition to a spin-free state (such as exists in $[CoF_6]^{3-}$, discussed earlier), or cobalt(II) must undergo a transition to a spin-paired state. According to the Franck-Condon principle, the spin-paired state of cobalt(II) would probably involve a regular octahedral structure, rather than the expected tetragonal arrangement, or, alternatively, both the cobalt(II) and the cobalt(III) would undergo tetragonal distortions in the transition state. The latter concept is consistent with the notion that the reaction coordinate will act as a linear perturbing field.

The order in which the rates of electron transfer change with ligand is particularly illuminating. The rate is slowest for ligands of intermediate bond strength (ligand field strength), increasing both with field strength and with a decrease in field strength. In those cases where the ligand field strength is very high, cobalt(II) should be quite readily converted to the spin-paired state, while in the case of very weak ligand fields, the spin-free state of cobalt(III) should lie very close to the ground state. As is discussed in the section on cobalt(II), the first situation is well justified by recent magnetic studies, while the presence of spin-free cobalt(III) in fluoride complexes lends credence to the second possibility. Although most studies have involved the use of radioactive tracers, the system $[Co(EDTA)]^-$ —$[Co(EDTA)]^{2-}$ has recently been studied using optical activity, giving results in complete accord with tracer experiments.[188]

The particular advantage[374] of the bridged intermediate in facilitating electron transfer is probably related to the ability of the electron to influence the environment just prior to electron transfer. Taube and Myers[371,372] have shown that $[Co(NH_3)_5Cl]^{2+}$ reacts with chromium(II) ion, forming cobalt(II) and $[Cr(H_2O)_5Cl]^{3+}$ in which the chlorine atom is transferred quantitatively to the chromium during the reaction. Such a process leads to the postulation of an intermediate of the form $[(NH_3)_5CoCl\cdots Cr(H_2O)_5]^{4+}$. A useful analogy is found in the bridged ion $[(NH_3)_5Co-O_2-Co(NH_3)_5]^{5+}$, discussed earlier. As in that stable species, the bridged intermediate would be expected to involve the transferring electron in an orbital associated with both metal atoms. It has been shown that efficient transfer occurs with F^-, Br^-, I^-, SO_4^{2-},[372] N_3^-, NCS^-, carboxylic acids, $P_2O_7^{4-}$,[373] PO_4^{3-}, and OH^-.[284]

From these observations, it may be concluded that group transfer occurs when a substitution inert oxidant reacts with a substitution labile reductant, forming products in which the order of labilities is reversed.[374] Since no NO_3^- transfer is observed when $[(NH_3)_5Co(NO_3)]^{2+}$ reacts with chromium(II) ion, it is suggested that $[Cr(H_2O)_5(NO_3)]^{2+}$ is labile. Complication is reported in the case of $[(NH_3)_5Co(NCS)]^{2+}$, which is stated to undergo considerable exchange of ligand with free ligand in solution during the oxidation-reduction reaction.[101] Adamson[11,13] has pointed out that the oxidations of some other cobalt(II) complexes probably proceed by group transfer reactions, e.g.,

$$[Co(CN)_5]^{3-} + 1/2Br_2 \longrightarrow [Co(CN)_5Br]^{3-}$$

$$[Co(C_2O_4)_2]^{2-} + H_2O_2 \longrightarrow [(C_2O_4)_2Co(OH)_2Co(C_2O_4)_2]^{4-}$$

while others apparently involve direct electron transfer, e.g.,

$$[Co(C_2O_4)_3]^{4-} + Ce^{IV} \longrightarrow [Co(C_2O_4)_3]^{3-} + Ce^{III}$$

$$[Co(EDTA)]^{2-} + [Fe(CN)_6]^{3-} \longrightarrow [Co(EDTA)]^- + [Fe(CN)_6]^{4-}$$

The following reactions also probably belong to the first case:

$$[Co(EDTA)]^{2-} + 1/2X_2 \longrightarrow [Co(EDTA)X]^{2-}$$
$$(X_2 = Cl_2, Br_2, N_2O_4, H_2O_2)$$

The interaction of complexes containing cobalt with molecular oxygen and hydrogen peroxide is of considerable importance.[21] Independently,

Calvin, Diehl, and their co-workers studied a series of cobalt compounds capable of reversibly absorbing oxygen both in the solid state and in solution.

Histidine solutions of cobalt(II) salts absorb oxygen reversibly, producing diamagnetic solutions; and it has been reported that cobalt glycylglycine forms a complex with oxygen.[366] The catalytic action of cobalt compounds upon the decomposition of hydrogen peroxide has been studied.[57,326,384,407,409] The catalytic effect of cobalt(II) in autoxidation reactions is closely related.[53,143]

A number of other oxidation-reduction processes deserve at least passing mention. Shimura[348] reported the synthesis of $[Co(en)(NH_3)_4]_2(SO_4)_3$ by reaction of $[Co(en)(NH_3)_2(NCS)_2]^+$ with H_2O_2 in sulfuric acid solution. Spacu and Brezeanu[356-358] have observed a novel reaction involving hexammines of cobalt and hexachloroplumbate(IV). Oxygen is introduced into the complex in some unexplained manner. Perhaps there is some oxidation of ammonia groups to hydroxylamine derivatives. The reduction of water to hydrogen in solutions containing cobalt, cyanide, and precipitates of $Co(CN)_2$ has been reported.[213]

Substitution Reactions. Most kinetic and stereochemical data related to the mechanism of substitution in transition metal complexes have been obtained on derivatives of cobalt(III). Further, the cobalt ammines have dominated these investigations. A number of reviews are available,[41,49,190] the one by Basolo and Pearson[49] being most current and complete.

The replacement by water of anions from the complexes $[Co(A)_5X]$ and $[Co(A)_4X_2]$ has been termed "aquation" or "acid" hydrolysis. These reactions have received the greatest amount of attention. Two types of information have been utilized, rate measurements and stereochemical changes. These reactions uniformly follow a first order rate law in water. From the aquation reaction

$$[Co(NH_3)_5X]^{2+} + H_2O \longrightarrow [Co(NH_3)_5H_2O]^{3+} + X^-,$$

where X^- is a series of substituted acetates, RCO_2^-, it is observed[40] that the reaction rate increases as the steric requirements of the departing group increase. Such a result militates against a bimolecular displacement involving approach of the incoming water molecule in a position adjacent to that of the departing anion. This leaves the possibility of approach from the opposite side of the complex, or that of dissociation of X^- prior to entry of the water molecule.

In a similar study[313] in which the steric requirements of N- and C-substituted ethylenediamines in complexes of the type $[Co(AA)_2Cl_2]^+$ were increased regularly, it was observed that the rate of aquation increases as the steric requirements of AA increase. This is, of course, consistent with a dissociation mechanism, such as given below, rather than with a bimolecular process.

$$[Co(AA)_2X_2]^+ \xrightarrow{\text{slow}} [Co(AA)_2X]^{2+} + X^-$$

$$[Co(AA)_2X]^{2+} + H_2O \xrightarrow{\text{fast}} [Co(AA)_2(H_2O)X]^{2+}$$

Similarly, it is shown that the rate of aquation decreases as the extent of chelation[315] is increased in analogous complexes of the class $[Co(A)_5Cl]^{2+}$, and *cis*- and *trans*-$[Co(A)_4Cl_2]^+$. Additional studies have supported this view of the mechanism of aquation of cobalt(III) acidoammines. These will not be reviewed here. The reader is referred to reference 49.

It should be pointed out that substitution reactions such as

$$[Co(en)_2Cl(NO_2)]^+ + X^- \longrightarrow [Co(en)_2(NO_2)X]^+ + Cl^-$$

are preceded by aquation[42] and presumably involve S_N1 processes.

Base hydrolysis occupies a unique position in the rates of substitution reactions of cobalt(III) ammines, since only in this case is there a definite order, other than zero, for the incoming group. This unusual state of affairs impelled Garrick[161] to propose an S_N1cb mechanism for the acceleration due to hydroxide ion.

$$[Co(NH_3)_5Cl]^{2+} + OH^- \xrightarrow{\text{fast}} [Co(NH_3)_4(NH_2)Cl]^+ + H_2O$$

$$[Co(NH_3)_4(NH_2)Cl]^+ \xrightarrow{\text{slow}} [Co(NH_3)_4(NH_2)]^{2+} + Cl^-$$

$$[Co(NH_3)_4(NH_2)]^{2+} + H_2O \xrightarrow{\text{fast}} [Co(NH_3)_5OH]^{2+}$$

The detailed investigations of Basolo, Pearson and their co-workers[49] support this view. In addition to deductions related to experiments in connection with aquation of the class described above, complexes containing ligands with no replaceable hydrogen atoms were shown to react at the same rate in basic and acidic media.[314] Pearson and Basolo[316] explained the S_N1cb mechanism for base hydrolysis on the grounds that the five-coordinate transition state is stabilized by *pi*-bonding between the NH_2^- group and the cobalt atom.

Although brevity dictates that the total argument and some of the papers concerned not be mentioned, it should be recognized that the isomer distributions observed by Ingold, Nyholm, and Tobe,[191,304] in reactions involving optically active and other cobalt ammines, agree satisfactorily with an

S_N1 mechanism proceeding through a five-coordinate, trigonal bipyramidal intermediate.

In the case of *trans*-$[Co(en)_2F_2]^+$, acid catalysis of the aquation reaction is observed.[316] This is attributed to the electrophilic attack of the proton on the coordinated fluoride, and is analogous to metal ion-catalyzed aquation.[323]

The release of CO_2 from carbonato complexes is very rapid in the presence of hydrogen ion, indicating a very strong catalysis. Detailed studies[50] have been made on the complexes $[Co(NH_3)_5CO_3]^+$, $[Co(NH_3)_4$-$CO_3]^+$, and $[Co(en)_2CO_3]^+$. The reactions proceed with retention of the Co—O bond in the case of the monodentate CO_3^{2-} group. In the case of bidentate CO_3^{2-}, the chelate ring is broken at the Co—O bond, but the second step involves breaking the C—O, not the Co—O bond. It is indicated that the carbonate is largely monodentate in all cases, i.e., $[Co(NH_3)_4$-$(H_2O)CO_3]^+$.

The formation of nitritoammines of cobalt(III) and their isomerization to nitroammines provides another interesting example of a process in which the Co—O bond is not broken during substitution.[51] The formation reaction follows a rate law similar to that associated with the nitrosation of amines. The mechanism for formation of nitritopentamminecobalt(III) may be written as follows:

$$[(NH_3)_5Co(OH_2)]^{3+} + H_2O \underset{\rightleftharpoons}{\overset{fast}{}} [(NH_3)_5Co(OH)]^{2+} + H_3O^+$$

$$[(NH_3)_5Co—ONO]^{2+} + HNO_2$$

The rate of conversion of the nitrito complexes into nitro complexes is a first order, intramolecular process, proceeding without exchange of oxygen. The probable mechanism is shown below.

It has recently been reported that this isomerization is actually an equilibrium process.[59] In this connection, it is interesting to find that the exposure of the nitro complex to sunlight for long periods of time leads to a red product which reconverts to the original color at the same rate as $[Co(NH_3)_5(ONO)]^{2+}$.[14] Murmann[283] resolved *cis*-nitritonitrobis(ethylenediamine)cobalt(III) into optical isomers and showed that the complex mutarotates, without racemization, at a rate equivalent to that of the formation of *cis*-$[Co(en)_2(NO_2)_2]^+$. Penland, Lane, and Quagliano studied the infrared spectra of nitrito and nitro complexes.[317]

A number of other types of isomerization reactions produce additional diversity in the reaction mechanisms of cobalt(III) complexes. The interconversion of certain pairs of *cis-trans* isomers of the type $[Co(en)_2XY]^+$ has been studied, and, in some cases, the isomerization appears to be related to substitution processes. The following mechanism has been suggested[52,80] for the isomerization of *cis*- and *trans*-$[Co(en)_2Cl_2]^+$ in methanol:

$$l\text{-}cis\text{-}[Co(en)_2Cl_2]^+ \xrightarrow{\text{slow}} [Co(en)_2Cl]^{2+} \begin{array}{l} \nearrow trans\text{-}[Co(en)_2Cl_2]^+ \\ \searrow d,l\text{-}cis\text{-}[Co(en)_2Cl_2]^+ \end{array}$$

In aqueous solution, racemization does not occur, but optical rotation vanishes because of the formation of the *trans* isomer. It has also been shown that *cis*-$[Co(en)_2Cl_2]^+$ rearranges entirely to the *trans* isomer in 2-methoxyethanol as a solvent.[378]

The cobalt(III) complexes of ethylenediaminetetraacetic acid (H_4EDTA) have been the subject of a number of recent studies paralleling those described above for cobalt ammines (though far less extensive). An interesting aspect of these reactions is the fact that either the incoming group or the departing group will be one of the functional groups of the coordinated EDTA ion, depending on whether the transformation involves a change on the part of the EDTA from pentadentate to hexadentate, or vice versa.

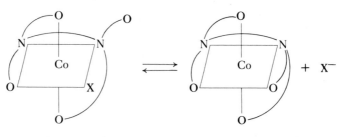

pentadentate complex   hexadentate complex

Shimi and Higginson[342] studied the following rate processes:

$$[Co(H-EDTA)H_2O] \xrightarrow{k_1} [Co(EDTA)]^- + H_3O^+$$

$$[Co(EDTA)H_2O]^- \xrightarrow{k_2} [Co(EDTA)]^- + H_2O$$

$$[Co(EDTA)OH]^{2-} \xrightarrow{k_3} [Co(EDTA)]^- + OH^-$$

The reactants were related to each other by equilibria. It was concluded that the first and third processes proceed via an S_N1 mechanism, while the second proceeds via an intramolecular displacement reaction (INS or Sni) in which the free carboxyl group attacks the cobalt atom, forming a seven-coordinate intermediate. Morris and Busch[277] proposed that $[Co(H-EDTA)Br]^-$ and $[Co(H-EDTA)Cl]^-$ also react by S_N1 processes. It was shown that these reactions are accelerated by metal ions, presumably by the electrophilic attack of the metal ion on the coordinated halide.[181,277] Cooke, Im, and Busch[108,188] showed that the racemization of $[Co(EDTA)]^-$ is independent of pH in acidic media, but that it is base catalyzed. Further, the rate of base catalyzed racemization is first order in hydroxide ion concentration and more rapid than base hydrolysis. Since a dissociative mechanism would require extensive rearrangement in order to produce racemization, it is assumed that the reaction proceeds by means of a seven-coordinate symmetrical intermediate, as shown below. The rate of racemization in acid is very slow and is assumed to involve an intramolecular rearrangement.

$$d\text{-}[Co(EDTA)]^- + OH^- \xrightarrow{\text{slow}} \begin{bmatrix} 7\text{-coordinate} \\ \text{intermediate} \end{bmatrix} \xrightarrow{\text{fast}} [Co(EDTA)OH]^{2-}$$

$$\text{slow} \Updownarrow \text{fast}$$
$$d,l\text{-}[Co(EDTA)]^-$$

A more complete demonstration of intramolecular racemization is found in the case of $[Co(C_2O_4)_3]^{3-}$.[196] The substance racemizes in the solid state and in solution. The rate is not retarded by $C_2O_4^{2-}$, and no exchange is observed with tagged oxalate under conditions which lead to complete racemization.[172,240]

Douglas[118] showed that $d\text{-}[Co(en)_3]^{3+}$ racemizes rapidly in the presence of decolorizing charcoal, although its solutions are usually optically stable. It has also been shown that this complex may be labilized by the presence of small amounts of the corresponding cobalt(II) complex.[86]

The conversion of optically active dichlorobis(ethylenediamine)cobalt-(III) into carbonatobis(ethylenediamine)cobalt(III) provides an intriguing example of the interdependence of configuration of substitution products and the mechanism of substitution.[24] The rapid reaction of Ag_2CO_3 with *l*-$[Co(en)_2Cl_2]^+$ yields the *levo* product, while the reaction of K_2CO_3 with solutions of *l*-$[Co(en)_2Cl_2]^+$ leads to the formation of *d*-$[Co(en)_2CO_3]^+$. The sign and magnitude of the rotation of the product are quite sensitive to the nature of the reagents and other environmental conditions, clearly indicating at least two competing paths for the formation of the product.

COMPLEXES OF COBALT(II)

Although hundreds of papers give reference to cobalt(II), it is inappropriate to attempt to review these thoroughly. In most cases, particularly in synthetic studies and in investigations relating to equilibria in solutions, the behaviors of the systems often fall clearly into one of the few well known classes of stereochemical types of cobalt(II), while in many others, information is insufficient to determine such basic features as coordination number or geometric configuration. In these and similar situations, the information provided is most useful in characterizing the particular system. In consequence, convenient examples will be chosen, without prejudice, to illustrate the various points to be made.

The chemistry of cobalt(II) is associated with three distinct stereochemical configurations and, possibly, a fourth. These are tetrahedral, octahedral, square planar, and trigonal bipyramidal (or tetragonal pyramidal). Whereas the majority of the compounds of cobalt(III) are clearly covalent, being nonlabile in the sense that substitution reactions are commonly slow, those of cobalt(II) tend to react rapidly, reaching equilibrium in the time of measurement. Consequently, the study of reactions commonly centers on equilibrium rather than rate determinations. Also, the stereochemical varieties of cobalt(II) compounds are more often discussed in terms of magnetic data than on the basis of isomerism. It appears to be true that no well established examples of geometrical isomers or optical isomers are known, although recent investigations indicate the types of systems which should yield such stereoisomers.[147]

The halogen complexes of cobalt, $[CoX_4]^{2-}$, are tetrahedral in structure,[165,322] as is the compound Cs_2CoCl_5, despite the misleading stoichiometry of this substance.[325] Solution studies[17,60,208,377] reveal the stepwise formation of these compounds (i.e., $[CoCl]^+$, $[CoCl_2]$, $[CoCl_3]^-$, $[CoCl_4]^{2-}$); the relative stabilities[17] are $F^- > Cl^- > Br^- > I^-$. These compounds are in rapid equilibrium, as is readily demonstrated by dilution of a solution of cobalt(II) chloride in concentrated hydrochloric acid, the color changing from the characteristic blue of tetrachlorocobaltate(II) to the pink of the hexaquocobalt(II) ion. The tetrahedral structure for cobalt(II) is readily understood in terms of both the valence bond theory and the ligand field theory.

According to the valence bond theory, tetrahedral coordination is associated with the utilization of the sp^3 hybridized orbitals of the cobalt atom in the formation of *sigma* bonds. As a result, the $3d$ level is undisturbed and the seven $3d$ electrons of cobalt(II) are distributed among all five of these orbitals.

VALENCE BOND TREATMENT OF TETRAHEDRAL COBALT(II)

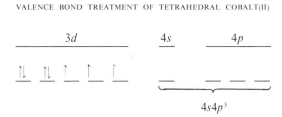

It follows that there are three unpaired electrons in the tetrahedral compounds.

From the standpoint of the ligand field theory, the electrostatic field exerted by four ligands arranged about a transition ion at the apices of a regular tetrahedron splits the d-levels into a doublet and triplet; however in this case, the triplet lies at the higher energy. The extent of splitting is much less pronounced in the tetrahedral case than in the octahedral one, so that the pairing of electrons is not ordinarily favored.[46,206] It can be seen from the diagram below, that the electronic structure of the d^7 cobalt(II) ion is symmetrical (nondegenerate), involving a filled lower doublet and a half-filled triplet. In this case, the pairing of electrons cannot be accounted for on the basis of the tetrahedral field. It appears to be true that ligands favoring the pairing of electrons often produce other structures (planar or octahedral).

LIGAND FIELD TREATMENT OF TETRAHEDRAL COBALT(II)

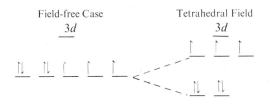

The nature of the ground state for tetrahedral cobalt(II) suggests[144,148] that the orbital contribution to the magnetic moment is quite small. The spin-only moment $[\sqrt{4S(S + 1)}]$ should be 3.88 Bohr Magnetons, while the maximum moment expected for a d^7 ion with orbital contribution is 5.2 Bohr Magnetons $[\sqrt{4S(S + 1) + L(L + 1)}; L = 3; S = 3/2]$. The idealized ground state would exhibit no orbital contribution, since it is represented as a singlet orbital state; however, the moments are usually in excess of this value, as indicated in Table 6.5. Referring to the tetrahalocobaltates,

TABLE 6.5. MAGNETIC MOMENTS OF FOUR-COORDINATE COBALT(II) COMPLEXES[a]

Probable Tetrahedral Structures

Compound	μ_{eff}	Ref.
$[Co(C_6H_5NH_2)_2Cl_2]$ (blue)	4.19	149
$[Co(C_6H_5NH_2)_2Br_2]$ (blue)	4.46	303
$[Co(C_6H_5NH_2)_2I_2]$	4.61	303
$[Co(py)_2Cl_2]$ (blue)	4.51	303
$[(C_6H_5)_3CH_3As][CoCl_4]$	4.69	165
$[CoBr_4]^=$	4.62	303
$[CoI_4]^=$	4.50	303
$Hg[Co(CNS)_4]$	4.33	149
$[Co(salicylaldehyde)_2]$	4.5	253
$[Co(acac)_2]$	4.2	253
$[Co(quinaldinate)_2]$	4.21	253
$[Co(anthranilate)_2]$	5.05	238
$[Co(o-aminophenolate)_2]$	4.03	238

Probable Planar Structures

Compound	μ_{eff}	Ref.
$[Co(phthalocyanine)]$	2.72	149
$[Co(bis(salicylal)ethylenediimine)]$		
O_2 carrying	2.52	253
inactive	2.28	253
$[Co(bis(3-fluorosalicylal)ethylenediimine)]$		
O_2 carrying	2.57	253
inactive	2.57	253
brown hydrate	3.50	253
red hydrate	2.17	253
$[Co(bis(4-hydroxosalicylal)ethylenediimine)]$	2.25	282
$[Co(bis(salicylal)-cis-1,2-cyclohexanediimine)]$	2.40	253
$[Co(bis(salicylal)-trans-1,2-cyclohexanediimine)]$	2.40	253
$[Co(sulfosalicylalanil)_2] \cdot 2H_2O$	3.72	280

TABLE 6.5 (*continued*)

Compound	μeff	Ref.
[Co(o-aminobenzenethiolo)$_2$]	2.6	238
[Co(C$_2$H$_5$S(CH$_2$)$_3$S)$_2$]	2.54	238
[Co(phen)(NO$_2$)$_2$]	1.71	92
[Co(bipy)(CN)$_2$]	1.81	93
[Co(diarsine)$_2$]Cl$_2$	2.1	301
[Co(diarsine)$_2$]Br$_2$	2.0	301
[Co(diarsine)$_2$]I$_2$	2.4	301
[Co(diarsine)$_2$](NCS)$_2$	2.3	301
[Co(diarsine)$_2$](ClO$_4$)$_2$	2.1	149
K$_2$[Co(oxamide)$_2$]	2.91	148
[Co(salicylaldoxime)$_2$]	2.6	148
[Co(dimethylglyoxime)$_2$]	2.6	148
[Co(C$_2$S$_2$(NH)$_2$)$_2$]	2.8–2.9	148
[Co(thiosemicarbazide)$_2$]	2.3	148
[Co(biguanidinium)$_2$]SO$_4$	2.0	148
[Co(protoporphyrindimethyl ester)]	2.8	148

[a]Abbreviations used in Tables 6.5, 6.6, and 6.7. py, pyridine; en, ethylene-diamine; PAT, 2-pyridinal-p-tolylimine; BdH, biacetyldihydrazone; PAA, 2-pyridinaldazine; bipy, 2,2′-bipyridine; phen, 1,10-phenanthroline; PAH, 2-pyridinal hydrazone; PPMI, 2-pyridinal-2-pyridylmethyleneimine; PMI, 2-pyridinal methylimine; PdBI, 2,6-pyridindial bis(benzylimine); BMI, biacetyl bis-(methylimine); PdAdH, 2,6-pyridindial dihydrazone; PdMI, 2,6-pyridindial bis-(methylimine); triarsine, bis(dimethylarsinopropyl)-methylarsine; diarsine, o-phenylene bis(dimethylarsine); acac, acetylacetone; terpy, 2,2′,2″-terpyridine; EDTA, ethylenediaminetetraacetate.

which are clearly tetrahedral, the magnetic moment is substantially lower than the maximum value of 5.2 Bohr Magnetons. Nyholm[303] suggested that a moment lying between 4.3 and 4.74 Bohr Magnetons is associated with a tetrahedral structure. Although these limits appear to be rather arbitrary and somewhat too narrow, the well established examples of tetrahedral structures in Table 6.5 (the first eight entries) fall close to these limits. Ballhausen and Liehr report that the ligand field theory is not adequate for predicting the intensities of absorption bands in tetrahedral cobalt(II) complexes, such as [CoCl$_4$]$^{2-}$, but that the molecular orbital theory is appropriate.[34]

Compounds of [Co(NCS)$_4$]$^{2-}$ are also reported to involve tetrahedral coordination.[149,322] As was true in the case of the halogen complexes, solution studies reveal stepwise formation of the complexes,[81,227,228,334,341,353,413] and it has been reported that [Co(NCS)$_6$]$^{4-}$ may exist,[81] although the well characterized compounds contain four moles of thiocyanate. It can be seen from Table 6.5, that μ = 4.33 for Hg[Co(NCS)$_4$].

A number of dihalodiamines of cobalt(II) exist in two forms, at one time thought to represent the *cis* and *trans* isomers of square planar cobalt compounds. Mellor and Coryell[265] suggested that the blue form of [Co-(py)$_2$Cl$_2$] was tetrahedral, the violet form condensed octahedra, resulting from the bridging of chlorides between adjacent octahedra. This has been confirmed by recent crystallographic[121,145,321] and chemical studies.[303] The corresponding isomers of [CoCl$_2$·2toluidine] have also been shown to be structural isomers of this class.[69] These isomers stand in contrast to the stereoisomers first expected, in that only the monomeric tetrahedral form exhibits structural integrity upon dissolution in a solvent.

It has been pointed out that tetrahedral cobalt(II) is more common and, theoretically, should be more stable than tetrahedral nickel(II).[164] The other examples cited in Table 6.5 appear to be less certain; however, only one of them exhibits an alarmingly high value for the magnetic moment, bis-(anthranilato)cobalt(II). In view of the similar donor groups, it would be surprising to find this compound to be octahedral if the others are tetrahedral.

The valence bond theory associates a square planar structure with relatively strong covalent bonds involving $3d4s4p^2$ hybridized orbitals on the central atom. The reorganization of the $3d$-level of cobalt(II) would lead to a single unpaired electron in such a structure, as shown below.

VALENCE BOND TREATMENT OF SQUARE PLANAR COBALT(II)

$3d$	$4s$	$4p$

$3d4s4p^2$

As indicated in Table 6.6, the notion of strong covalent bonds in square planar cobalt(II) would appear to be justified by the fact that a large number of the compounds of this class undergo isotopic exchange rather slowly. This is particularly in evidence in the case of polydentate ligands forming three or four chelate rings. The square planar structure is most clearly present in such species as cobalt phthalocyanines, since these molecules contain four donor nitrogen atoms so arranged that only planar structures are possible, as long as the coordination number is four. The other typical planar cobalt(II) chelates may be illustrated by bis(salicylal)ethylenediiminecobalt(II).

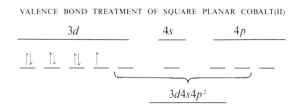

TABLE 6.6. ISOTOPIC EXCHANGE REACTIONS OF COBALT(II) COMPLEXES*

Reactants	Concentration(M)	Medium	Rate
Probable Planar Structures			
$[Co(salicylal\ anil)_2]$—Co^*SO_4	0.008, 0.008	py	C, 50 sec
$[Co(salicylal\ tolilimine)_2]$—$Co^*Ac_2$	0.008, 0.008	py	C, 45 sec
$[Co(salicylaldoxime)_2]$—Co^*SO_4	0.008, 0.008	py	C, 18 min
$[Co\ bis(salicylal)ethylenediimine]$—$Co^*Ac_2$	0.0001, 0.0001	py	20 min, 15°
$[Co\ bis(salicylal)$-o-phenylenediimine$]$—Co^*Ac_2	0.0017, 0.0017	py	7.5 hr, 15°
$[Co(4,4'$-dicarbethoxy-3,3',5,5'-tetramethyldipyrromethene$)]$— Co^*Ac_2	0.008, 0.008	py	2 days
$[Co(phthalocyanine)]$—Co^*Ac_2	0.004, 0.008	py	N, 5 days
$[Co(phthalocyanine\ tetrasulfonate)]$—$Co^*Ac_2$	0.001, 0.017	pH = 1	N, 13 days
$[Co(meso$-porphyrin$)]$—Co^*Ac_2		py	slow
Vitamin B 12—$[Co^*(H_2O)_6]^{2+}$		pH2 – 12	N, 14 days, 55°
Probable 'Octahedral' Structures			
$[Co(H_2O)_6]^{2+}$—H_2O^*	1.55, excess	3.0, HClO₄	C, 2 min, 1°
$[Co(CN)_5H_2O]^{3-}$—C^*N^-	0.02, 0.03	H_2O	C, 2 min, 0°
$[Co(acac)_2(H_2O)_2]$—Co^*Ac_2 (82)	0.008, 0.008	py	C, 50 sec
$[Co(salicylaldehyde)_2]$—Co^*Ac_2	0.008, 0.008	50% py	C, 40 sec
$[Co(EDTA)]^{2-}$—$[Co^*(H_2O)_6]^{2+}$	0.005, 0.005	pH 2.4–5	fast
$[Co(phen)_3]^{2+}$—$[Co^*(H_2O)_6]^{2+}$	0.005, 0.005	...	< 28 sec, 15°
$[Co(5$-CH₃—phen$)_3]^{2+}$—$[Co^*(H_2O)_6]^{2+}$	0.005, 0.005	...	< 36 sec, 15°
$[Co(5$-NO₂—phen$)_3]^{2+}$—$[Co^*(H_2O)_6]^{2+}$	0.005, 0.005	...	< 25 sec, 15°
$[Co(terpy)_2]^{2+}$—$[Co^*(H_2O)_6]^{2+}$	0.005, 0.005	...	2.8 hr, 15°

*Data taken from reference (362). For abbreviations see footnote, Table 6.5.

The structures of these two classes of planar chelates are discussed by Martell and Calvin.[254]

Taube[370] called attention to the phenomenological relationship between lability as measured by isotopic exchange experiments and magnetic moment. He pointed out that compounds in which the magnetic moment corresponds to the pairing of electrons are accountable by the formation of bonds utilizing hybridized penultimate $3d$ orbitals on cobalt (in terms of the valence bond theory). Accordingly, it appears more appropriate to classify spin-paired nonlabile complexes as "inner orbital" and spin-free complexes as "outer orbital," rather than to discuss these classes strictly in terms of relative covalent character. From Table 6.5, it can be seen that nonlabile (toward exchange) planar complexes of cobalt(II) with tetradentate ligands exhibit moments substantially lower than those corresponding to the labile, tetrahedral species. It is apparent, however, that the moments are only rarely in the vicinity of the spin-only value of 1.73 Bohr Magnetons required for one unpaired electron. This relationship will be considered further after presentation of the ligand field interpretation of the planar structure.

The ligand field interpretation of the square planar structure is most simply viewed in terms of a linear perturbation on an octahedral field, resulting from the removal of groups along one axis (z). Intermediate tetragonal structures are known and will be discussed below.

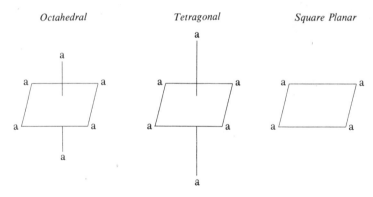

Ligand Field Treatment of Square Planar and Tetragonal Structures

In the square planar case, separation between the two upper levels should be comparable to separation between the upper doublet and the lower triplet in the octahedral case.[46,149,183] This conclusion is derived from considerations of symmetry in the two structures; the remaining three levels are still lower in energy in the square planar case. Separations between the low doublet and the closest singlet levels is relatively small. The spin-paired and spin-free states are given below for the d^7 cobalt(II) ion. Since separation between the two highest energy levels is great, the electrons should be paired. Further, the proximity of the two lower singlet electronic levels may produce the apparent degeneracy required to give rise to significant orbital contributions to the magnetic moment. This latter hypothesis has been discussed by Figgis and Nyholm[149] in connection with the temperature dependence of the magnetic moments.

SPIN-PAIRED AND SPIN-FREE PLANAR COBALT(II) ACCORDING TO THE
LIGAND FIELD THEORY

Spin-free Case   Spin-paired Case

Close correspondence to the Curie-Weiss law in two cases (e.g., bis-(salicylal)ethylenediiminecobalt(II) and bis(ethylthiopropanethiolo)cobalt-(II)) has led to the conclusion that the high moments are essentially temperature independent and result from substantial orbital contribution. Barkelew and Calvin[37] observed an anomalous temperature dependence for some of the planar tetradentates of cobalt(II) and ascribed this to the presence of two electronic states, the populations of which varied with temperature. Although reasonable and deserving of additional investigation, the model was not explicitly tested, and it has recently been challenged.[149] It should be pointed out that Figgis and Nyholm[149] encountered a distinct temperature dependence in the case of cobalt phthalocyanine which might be explained in terms of the model suggested by Barkelew and Calvin. This accidental proximity of states has been predicted by Orgel[307] in the case of iron(II) compounds.

Of the examples included in Table 6.5 as representative of the planar structure, a number are poorly characterized; however, they do represent a judicious selection. The cases of [Co(bipy)(CN)$_2$] and [Co(phen)(NO$_2$)$_2$] are especially questionable in view of the known ability of cyanide and nitrite

ions to form bridge structures. Also, it is interesting to find that the bidentate salicylalimines and related ligands usually have distinctly high values
for their magnetic moments. This relationship is paralleled by their relatively great labilities, as indicated in Table 6.6.

A particular difficulty is associated with establishing the coordination
number of complexes which appear to be square planar in nature. The possibility of coordination of additional ligands in solution must always be
admitted; in the solid state, however, the forced planar distribution of
bonds in a ligand does not always obviate the possibility of bridged octahedral or tetragonal structures.

The valence bond treatment of octahedral cobalt(II) arises naturally, but
with special difficulty,[83,87] from that of cobalt(III). The treatment of the
outer orbital complex (spin-free) is straightforward, and, as shown below,
is assumed to involve $4s4p^34d^2$ hybridized orbitals and to have three unpaired electrons.

VALENCE BOND TREATMENT OF OUTER ORBITAL OCTAHEDRAL COBALT(II)

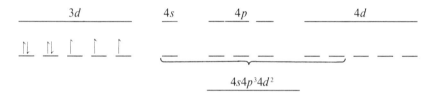

The original Pauling description is given below for the spin-paired case.

EARLY VALENCE BOND TREATMENT OF SPIN-PAIRED OCTAHEDRAL COBALT(II)

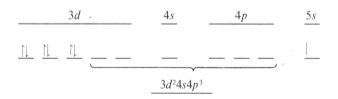

The ready oxidizability of spin-paired octahedral cobalt(II) complexes
was rationalized in terms of the promoted $5s$ electron. This view is generally
conceded to be untenable at the present time, and a modified view has been
presented which effectively predicts a tetragonal distortion of the octahedral structure.[83] According to this later view, four of the bonds (xy plane)
are formed by inner-orbital $3d4s4p^2$ hybrid orbitals, while the remaining

MODERN VALENCE BOND TREATMENT OF SPIN-PAIRED OCTAHEDRAL COBALT(II)

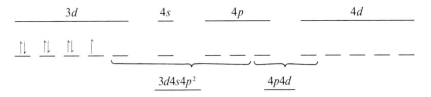

bonds are formed on the third (z) axis by the additional outer orbital *4p4d* hybrid. This revised theory does not require the promotion of an electron from *3d* to *5s* and therefore is more acceptable, since the energy for this promotion would be quite large.[87] Further, the predicted tetragonal distortion is in accord with the Jahn-Teller principle, and the modern ligand field and molecular orbital concepts. Only quite recently have a significant number of examples of spin-paired, six-coordinate complexes of cobalt(II) come to light. This is seen clearly in the very small numbers of such examples in the excellent papers of Figgis and Nyholm.[148,149]

The simple ligand field energy level diagram for the regular octahedral structure for spin-free and spin-paired cobalt(II) is given below.

LIGAND FIELD TREATMENT OF REGULAR OCTAHEDRAL COBALT(II)

Spin-free Case   Spin-paired Case

In these diagrams, a true orbital degeneracy is depicted—a result which conflicts with the Jahn-Teller principle (see Ref. 46, 307). In consequence, this orbital degeneracy will be removed by a distortion of the structure, giving rise to a less symmetric array of ligands about the central atom. In these cases, the elongation of a single bond axis (2 bonds) presents the necessary distortion. The resultant energy level diagrams are given below.

LIGAND FIELD TREATMENT OF TETRAGONAL COBALT(II)

Spin-free Case   Spin-paired Case

The extent of the tetragonal distortion, as well as the extent of the splitting due to the octahedral field, are dependent on the individual ligand. In general, the *tetragonal* splitting in the spin-free case is much less than that in the spin-paired case. The splitting in the spin-paired case is expected to be great enough to produce an elongation of the unique axis of sufficient magnitude to be detectable in definitive X-ray structural determinations.[307] In general, spin-free six-coordinate complexes are essentially octahedral, the corresponding spin-paired compounds tetragonal in structure (tetragonal bipyramidal).

Figgis and Nyholm[149] presented the view that spin-free octahedral structures should be associated with magnetic moments having large orbital contributions. Such a result is in keeping with the retention of much of the original degeneracy in the *3d* electronic energy levels. The expected moments are approximately 5.2 Bohr Magnetons. The first nine or so examples in Table 6.7 are in accord with this view. It should be recalled, at this point, that spin-free tetrahedral structures were associated with lesser orbital contributions. Quite recently, a number of new six-coordinate cobalt(II) compounds have been found to exhibit relatively small magnetic moments (i.e., μ eff. <3.1 Bohr Magnetons). These constitute the last fifteen entries in Table 6.7. Casual inspection of Table 6.7 also reveals that six-coordinate complexes are known for moments spanning the entire range from 5.24–1.72 Bohr Magnetons, i.e., extending continuously from the spin-free case with the maximum orbital contribution to the spin-paired case with the spin-only value. The significance of the high values was discussed above.

The orbital contribution to the magnetic moment in spin-paired six-

TABLE 6.7. MAGNETIC MOMENTS OF SIX-COORDINATE COBALT(II) COMPLEXES*

Compound	μ eff	Ref.
$[CoCl_2(py)_2]$ (violet form)	5.24	303
$[Co(SCN)_2(C_6H_5NH_2)_2]$ (pink)	5.11	303
$[Co(H_2O)_6]^{2+}$	5.1	83
$[Co(PAT)_3]I_2 \cdot 3H_2O$	5.06	360
$[Co(en)_3]^{2+}$	5.0 (sol'n)	253
$[CoCl_2(C_6H_5NH_2)_2(C_2H_5OH)_2]$ (pink)	5.0	303
$[CoBr_2(C_6H_5NH_2)_2(C_2H_5OH)_2]$ (pink)	5.0	303
$[Co(BdH)_2Cl_2]$	4.91	360
$[Co_2(PAA)_3]I_4 \cdot 2H_2O$	4.9 (per Co)	363
$[Co(bipy)_3]I_2 \cdot 3H_2O$	4.76	309
$[Co(phen)_3]I_2$	4.78	309

TABLE 6.7 (*continued*)

Compound	μ_{eff}	Ref.
[Co(1a,3a,5a-tris(α-pyridylmethyleneamino)-cyclohexane)] (ClO$_4$)$_2$	4.7	235
K[Co(acac)$_3$]	4.7	149
[Co(PAH)$_3$]I$_2$	4.63	360
[Co(phen)$_3$](ClO$_4$)$_2 \cdot$2H$_2$O	4.61–4.70	149,309
$\left[\text{Co} \left\{ 2,4\text{-(HO} -)_2 \text{C}_6\text{H}_3\text{CH} = \text{NCH}_2\text{C} \begin{smallmatrix} O \\ O \end{smallmatrix} \right\}_2 \right]$	4.49	281,282
[Co(PMI)$_3$](BF$_4$)$_2$	4.39	147
[Co(bipy)$_3$](ClO$_4$)$_2 \cdot$2H$_2$O	4.34	309
[Co(PPMI)$_2$](ClO$_4$)$_2$	4.3	236
[Co(O $-$C$_6$H$_4$CH $=$NNHC$\overset{O}{-}$CH$_2$SCH$_2$ $-$)$_2$]	4.3	237
[Co(BdH)$_3$]I$_2$	4.17	360
[Co(PdBI)$_2$]I$_2$	3.8	236
[Co(bipy)$_2$(CN)$_2$]	3.65	93
$\left[\text{Co} \left\{ 2\text{-(HO)C}_{10}\text{H}_6\text{CH} = \text{NCH}_2\text{C} \begin{smallmatrix} O \\ O \end{smallmatrix} \right\}_2 \right]$	3.06	282
[Co(BMI)$_3$]I$_2 \cdot$H$_2$O	2.98	147
[Co(PdAdH)$_2$]I$_2$	2.96	360
$\left[\text{Co} \left\{ 2\text{-(HO} -)\text{C}_{10}\text{H}_6\text{CH} = \text{NCH(CH}_3)\text{C} \begin{smallmatrix} O \\ O \end{smallmatrix} \right\}_2 \right]$	2.77	282
[Co(2-NC$_5$H$_4$NHN $=$CHCH$_2$S $-$CH$_2$ $-$)$_2$]	2.5	237
[Co(PdMI)$_2$]I$_2 \cdot$H$_2$O	2.31	147
†[Co(triarsine)I$_2$]	2.3	303
$\left[\text{Co} \left\{ 2,4\text{-(HO} -)_2 - \text{C}_6\text{H}_3\text{CH} = \text{NCH(CH}_3)\text{C} \begin{smallmatrix} O \\ O \end{smallmatrix} \right\}_2 \right]$	2.17	282
[Co(triarsine)$_2$](ClO$_4$)$_2$	2.02	148
[Co(diarsine)$_3$]I$_2$	1.92	83
[Co(2-NC$_5$H$_4$CH $=$NCCH$_2$)$_2$S $-$)$_2$](ClO$_4$)$_2$	1.85	132
[Co(phen)$_2$(CN)$_2$] $\cdot$ 2H$_2$O	1.75	92,93
†[Co(CN)$_5$]$^{3-}$	1.72 (sol'n)	9
K$_2$Ba[Co(NO$_2$)$_6$]	1.88	149
K$_2$Pb[Co(NO$_2$)$_6$]	1.81	149
[Co(C$_5$H$_5$)$_2$]	1.76	154
Na$_4$[Co(C$\equiv$CCH$_3$)$_6$]	1.8	295

*For abbreviations see footnote, Table 6.5.
†Compound reported to be five-coordinate.

coordinate structures is small, as indicated by the last five examples of Table 6.7. The source of the intermediate range of values, 1.9–4.8 Bohr Magnetons (24 examples), remains to be considered. In some cases, notably those of fairly high moment,[149] this variation appears to be associated with differences in the orbital parts of the moment; however in other cases, it is much more probable that the values come about because of the coexistence of the spin-paired and spin-free states. This has been demonstrated[361] by the study of the temperature dependence of the magnetic moment of bis(2,6-pyridindialdihydrazone)cobalt(II) iodide. The moment varies from 1.9 Bohr Magnetons at 80° K to 3.7 Bohr Magnetons at 373° K, and is accountable over the entire range in terms of the assumed presence of a spin-free state and a spin-paired state in equilibrium. The enthalpy difference in the two isomers is –2.14 Kcal/mole in favor of the spin-paired form.

It is suggested that the following compounds follow this pattern of behavior, although this has not yet been confirmed experimentally: Bis(2,6-pyridindial bis(benzylimine)) cobalt(II) iodide, dicyanobis-(bipyridine)-cobalt(II), bis(salicylalglycine)cobalt(II), tris(biacetylbis(methylimine))cobalt(II) iodide one-hydrate, bis(salicylalalanine)cobalt(II), bis(2,6-pyridindial bis(methylimine))cobalt(II) iodide one-hydrate, and 3,6-dithiaoctan-1,8-dial-bis-α-pyridylhydrazonecobalt(II). It would not be surprising to find that the moments of some of the other extreme spin-paired compounds increase at elevated temperatures. In this same regard, it may be significant that some of the compounds with maximum values for their magnetic moments deviate slightly from the Curie-Weiss law. The nature of the ligands giving rise to spin-pairing in six-coordinate cobalt(II) complexes is revealing. The most characteristic donor atom is unsaturated, conjugated nitrogen. This is particularly well illustrated in the tridentate imines and hydrazones of 2,6-pyridindialdehyde.

Essentially all the donor atoms in the ligands forming complexes of this class are capable of entering into pi-bonding with the metal atom. This factor has been considered in the general theoretical references cited above.

It is particularly significant to find that the only example of a six-coordinate cobalt(II) compound which undergoes isotopic exchange with the hydrated cobalt(II) ion at a distinctly slow rate (Table 6.6) is bis(2,2',2''-terpyridine)cobalt(II) ion, a close structural analog of the 2,6-pyridindial bis(imines). Although the moment does not appear to have been measured, the value is expected to be low. The molecular orbital theory has been applied to the problem of magnetism of octahedral ions.[177]

A number of examples of compounds which may contain five-coordinate cobalt(II) have been reported. These include nitrosyl-(N-N-dimethyldithio-carbamate)cobalt(II),[15] diiodobis(dimethylarsinopropyl)methylarsineco-balt(II),[35] penta(arylisonitrile)cobalt(II) perchlorates.[330] Although [Co-(CN)$_5$]$^{3-}$ is reported[9] to be five-coordinate, this does not seem to be the case.[176] The structures of such species remain an open question; however, they are probably tetragonal pyramidal, or trigonal bipyramidal.[87,303]

To attempt to review stability constant measurements or all the types of ligands incorporated in compounds of cobalt(II) would be inappropriate here. The examples given in Table 6.5, 6.6, and 6.7 are representative, though the relative abundance of some classes of compounds is poorly designated. For example, the large numbers of amine and amino acid complexes are not clearly indicated. The amino acid complexes provide particularly good examples of the influence of chelate ring size on the stabilities of complexes. All of the chelate rings formed by ethylenediamine tetra-acetate, N,N'-ethylenediaminediacetate, nitrilotriacetate, and iminodiace-tate are five-membered, while those of the corresponding β-propionic acids form rings containing six members. The compounds which involve only five-membered rings are 2–9 pK units more stable.[103–105,109,338,339] Excellent compilations and discussions of stability constants are to be found in reviews.[48,65,67,192,193,255] Recent studies have been made on the polyamines; e.g., dien,[36] tren,[36,204] trien,[204] tetraethylenepentamine,[202] and tetrakis-(2-aminoethyl)ethylenediamine.[340]

The cyclopentadienyl compounds of metals have come into prominence in the last few years.[154] Cobalt forms three types of compounds: the very stable cobalticinium salts, [Co(C$_5$H$_5$)$_2$]X,[151,403] the neutral cobalt(II) compounds, [Co(C$_5$H$_5$)$_2$],[150,152,404] and the novel substance [Co$_2$(C$_5$H$_5$)$_5$].[154] Analogs of the first two are also known with indene.[153] The neutral compounds are spin-paired showing moments of 1.76 Bohr Magnetons; the indene derivative may be sublimed. Numerous physical measurements have been made on the compounds.[154] The structures of [Co(C$_5$H$_5$)$_2$]$^+$ and [Co-(C$_5$H$_5$)$_2$] may be described as pentagonal antiprismatic, with the cobalt atom located between the parallel planes of two cyclopentadiene rings. The bonding has been discussed in terms of all current theories of valence and perhaps is most simply viewed as derived from the octahedron (d^2sp^3 bonds), with each C$_5$H$_5$$^-$ group donating three electron pairs to the metal and the rings occupying opposite trigonal faces of the octahedron.[154] The problem of the structure of [Co$_2$(C$_5$H$_5$)$_5$] is relatively complex.[154,390] Mesit-ylene forms a compound of the cobalticinium class [Co(sym-(CH$_3$)$_3$-C$_6$H$_3$)$_2$]$^{3+}$.[156]

Although not of the "sandwich" type, the complexes of cobalt with other unsaturated organic materials merit consideration, particularly because of their probable significance as intermediates in such reactions as the oxo process.[54,214] Nast and Lewinsky[295] prepared $Na_4[Co(C\equiv CCH_3)_6]$ and $Na_3[Co(C\equiv CCH_3)_6]$. Other compounds reported to contain unsaturated molecules are $K_6[(CN)_5Co(CH=CH)Co(CN)_5]$,[174] $[(CO)_6Co_2-(C_6H_5C\equiv CC_6H_5)]$,[354] $[(CO)_9Co_2(HC\equiv CR)]$,[359] and the butadiene derivative $[(CO)_3Co(C_4H_7)]$.[205]

OTHER OXIDATION STATES OF COBALT

A number of compounds are known in which cobalt exhibits oxidation states of plus one, zero, and minus one. These will be discussed simultaneously in order to emphasize properly certain derivative relationships. The zero valence state is best characterized in the carbonyls, of which there are two: dicobalt octacarbonyl, $[Co_2(CO)_8]$, an orange crystalline material melting at $51°C$; and the polymeric material, $[Co(CO)_3]_n$, a black crystalline substance decomposing at $60°C$.[26,392] Cobalt hydrocarbonyl may be derived from this substance by reduction.

$$[Co(CO)_4]_2 + H_2 \longrightarrow 2H[Co(CO)_4]$$

or by solvolytic disproportionation. Perhaps the simplest examples of the latter are

$$CO + [Co(CO)_4]_2 \longrightarrow [Co(CO)_5]^+ + [Co(CO)_4]^- \tag{267}$$

and

$$[Co(CO)_4]_2 + X \longrightarrow [Co^I(CO)_3X]^+ + [Co(CO)_4]^- \tag{386}$$

where X is Cl^-, NH_3, en, CN^-. In the case where X is $P(C_6H_5)_3$, it is possible to prepare a large number of salts derived from a similar cation, i.e., $[Co(CO)_3\{P(C_6H_5)_3\}_2]Y$.[331-333] From this, it can be seen that the zero valent carbonyl disproportionates to form derivatives of cobalt(I) and cobalt(−I). Analogs of the tetracarbonylcobaltate(−I) group may be obtained by replacement of carbon monoxide with $P(C_6H_5)_3$ in the case of the nonpolar metal and organometallic derivatives;[180] e.g.,

$$Hg[Co(CO)_4]_2 + 2P(C_6H_5)_3 \longrightarrow Hg[Co(CO)_3\{P(C_6H_5)_3\}]_2$$

The carbonyl hydride has a tetrahedral array of carbon monoxide molecules; the hydrogen atom is probably located at the center of a tetrahedral face, and bound to three carbon atoms and a metal orbital.[139-141,231]

The mixed cyclopentadienyl-carbonyl derivative of cobalt(II), $[Co(C_5H_5)(CO)_2]$,[155] is diamagnetic and has an eighteen-electron, inert gas structure.[306]

The monomeric diamagnetic nitrosyl carbonyl, $[Co(CO)_3NO]$, is tetrahedral. The assumption must be that NO donates three electrons to cobalt in order to assign an inert gas structure to the central atom, the resulting structure being isoelectronic and essentially isostructural with $[Ni(CO)_4]$. This amounts to assigning a negative one oxidation state to the cobalt.[26] Bor and Mohai reported a variety of syntheses of the substance. They preferred to assign an oxidation state of zero to the cobalt.[72-75] Analogous isonitrile derivatives are known, $[Co(RNC)_3NO]$.[244,247] In a similar derivative in which one CO has been replaced by CN^-,[296] $K[Co(CN)(CO)_2NO]$, the cobalt has been assigned an oxidation state of $-I$ on the basis of infrared data.[175] Malatesta and Araneo[248] have prepared $[Co(CO)NO(MR_3)]$ in which MR_3 is $P(OC_6H_5)_3$, $P(C_6H_4CH_3)_3$, $Sb(C_6H_4CH_3)_3$, $Sb(C_6H_5)_3$, $Sb(C_6H_4Cl)_3$. From the infrared spectrum, $K_3[Co(NO)(CN)_5] \cdot 2H_2O$ has been shown to contain cobalt(III) and NO^-, not Co(I) and NO^+.[173]

The reduction of cyanide derivatives of cobalt provides some novel observations. The hexacyanocobaltate(III) is sufficiently resistant to reduction to be useful as a supporting electrolyte in polarography;[199] however, Adamson's salts, $K_3[Co(CN)_5X]$,[12] and their analogs all reduce polarographically.[242] The complex ions in which X is Cl^-, Br^-, I^-, or SCN^- all undergo two-step reduction to cobalt(I), while those containing $S_2O_3^{2-}$, NO^-, N_3^-, SO_3^{2-} reduce in a single step to cobalt(I). Under strong reducing conditions, $K_8[Co(CN)_4]_2$[179] and $K_3[Co(CN)_4]$[388] are reported to form. Griffith and Wilkinson[176] concluded that the reduction of Adamson's salt $K_3[Co(CN)_5]$ produces a cobalt(I) hydride $[HCo^I(CN)_5]^{3-}$, or $[HCo^I(CN)_4]^{2-}$ They also pointed out the planarity of the anion $[Co^I(CN)_3CO]^{2-}$. The unipositive oxidation state of cobalt is well demonstrated in the pentaisonitriles, $[Co^I(RNC)_5]X$,[245,246,329] and in the tris(bipyridine)- and bis-(bipyridine)cobalt(I) salts.[256,385,387]

References

1. Ablov, A. V., "Spatial Configuration of Cobalt Dimethylglyoxime Complexes," *Doklady Akad. Nauk S.S.S.R.*, **97**, 1019 (1954).

2. —, "Isomers of Cobalt Dioximes," *Zhur. Obshchei Khim.*, **25**, 2053 (1955).

3. —, "The Complex Compounds of Trivalent Cobalt with Dimethylglyoxime. I. Nitro Derivatives,"*Izvest. Sektora Platiny i Drug. Blagorod. Metal*, **30**, 67, 76, 86 (1955).

4. —, and Syrtsova, G. P., "Di(thiocyanato)bis(dimethylglyoximo)cobaltic Acid," *Zhur. Obshchei Khim.*, **25**, 1304 (1955).

5. Ablov, A. V., Samus, N. M., and Popov, M. S., "Isothiocyanatonitro and Isothiocyanatobis(dimethylglyoximo)Cobaltic Acids," *Doklady Akad. Nauk S.S.S.R.*, **106**, 665 (1956).

6. Ablov, A. V., and Syrtsova, G. P., "Complex Compounds of Trivalent Cobalt with Dimethylglyoxime. IV. Iodo Derivatives," *Zhur. Neorg. Khim.*, **1**, 687 (1956).

7. Ablov, A. V., "Bases of Cobalt Dioximes," *Zhur. Neorg. Khim.*, **3**, 1118 (1958).

8. —, and Samus, N. M., "Complex Compounds of Trivalent Cobalt Containing Thiourea," *Doklady Akad. Nauk S.S.S.R.*, **123**, 457 (1958).

9. Adamson, A. W., "Exchange Studies with Complex Ions. III. The Nature of the Complex Formed between Cobalt(II) and Potassium Cyanide, Its Exchange with Radiocyanide Ion in Aqueous Solution," *J. Am. Chem. Soc.*, **73**, 5710 (1951).

10. —, and Vorres, K. S., "Charge Transfer Rates between the Ethylenediaminetetraacetate Complexes of Cobalt(II) and Cobalt(III) and of Iron(II) and Iron(III)," *J. Inorg. Nuclear Chem.*, **3**, 206 (1956).

11. Adamson, A. W., "Atom Transfer and Electron Exchange Processes with Cobalt Complexes," *Rec. trav. chem.*, **75**, 809 (1956).

12. —, "Halopentacyano Compounds of Cobalt(III)," *J. Am. Chem. Soc.*, **78**, 4260 (1956).

13. —, Ogata, H., Grossman, J., and Newberry, R., "Oxalato Complexes of Cobalt(II) and Cobalt(III), *J. Inorg. Nuclear Chem.*, **6**, 319 (1958).

14. Adell, B., "The Velocity of the Reconversion of Irradiated Solid Nitropentamminecobalt(III) Chloride," *Z. anorg. u allgem. Chem.*, **279**, 219 (1955).

15. Alderman, P. R. H., and Owston, P. G., "The Square Pyramidal Configuration in Five-coordinate Nitrosyl Complex," *Nature*, **178**, 1071 (1956).

16. Babaeva, A. V., and Rudyi, R. I., "Electronic Absorption Spectra of Complex Compounds in the Crystalline State," *Zhur. Neorg. Khim.*, **1**, 921 (1956).

17. Babko, A. K., and Shevchenko, L. L., "Stabilities of Halogen Complexes of Cobalt," *Ukrain Khim. Zhur.*, **25**, 120 (1959).

18. Bahr, G., and Scholz, E., "Heavy Metal Complexes with Thiopicolinanilide," *Z. anorg. u allgem. Chem.*, **299**, 281 (1959).

19. Bailar, J. C., Jr., "The Chemistry of the Coordination Compounds," ACS Monograph No. 131, New York, Reinhold Publishing Corp., 1956.

20. *Ibid.*, Chapter 2.

21. *Ibid.*, p. 46.

22. *Ibid.*, p. 115.

23. *Ibid.*, p. 294.

24. *Ibid.*, p. 344.

25. *Ibid.*, p. 400.

26. *Ibid.*, Chapter 16.

27. —, and McReynolds, J. P., "The Stereochemistry of Complex Inorganic Compounds. V. The Reaction of Carbonates with Dichloro-dipropylenediamine Cobaltic Chloride. A New Method for Determining Relative Configurations," *J. Am. Chem. Soc.*, **61**, 3199 (1939).

28. Bailar, Jr., J. C., and Peppard, D. F., "The Stereochemistry of Complex Inorganic Compounds. II. A Study of the Stereoisomers of the Dichloro-Diamminoethylenediamine Cobaltic Ion," *J. Am. Chem. Soc.*, **62**, 105 (1940).

29. Bailar, J. C., Jr., and Work, J. B., "Some Coordination Compounds of Cobalt Containing Trimethylenediamine and Neopentanediamine," *J. Am. Chem. Soc.*, **68**, 232 (1946).

30. Baker, L. C. W., and McCutcheon, T. P., "Heteropoly Salts Containing Cobalt and Hexavalent Tungsten in the Anion," *J. Am. Chem. Soc.*, **78**, 4503 (1956).
31. Baker, B. R., Basolo, F., and Newmann, H. M., "Electron Transfer in the System, Tris(1,10-phenanthroline)cobalt(II) — Tris(1,10-phenanthroline)cobalt(III)," *J. Phys. Chem.*, **63**, 371 (1959).
32. Ballhausen, C. J., and Jorgenson, C. K., "Studies of Absorption Spectra. X. *d*-Electrons in Crystal Fields of Different Symmetries," *Kgl. Danske Videnskab mat. fis. medd.*, **29**, No. 11, 29 pp. (1955).
33. Ballhausen, C. J., and Asmussen, R. W., "Diamagnetic Susceptibility and the High-frequency term in Cobalt(III) and Rhodium(III) Complexes," *Acta Chem. Scand.*, **11**, 479 (1957).
34. Ballhausen, C. J., and Liehr, A. D., "Intensities in Inorganic Complexes. II. Tetrahedral Complexes," *J. Mol. Spectroscopy*, **2**, 342 (1950).
35. Barclay, G. A., and Nyholm, R. S., "A Tri-tertiary Arsine and Its Metal Complexes," *Chem. and Ind.*, **1953**, 378.
36. Barclay, G. A., and Barnard, A. K., "Complexes of Bivalent and Trivalent Cobalt with a Tridentate and a Quadridentate Amine," *J. Chem. Soc.*, **1958**, 2540.
37. Barkelew, C. H., and Calvin, M., "Oxygen-carrying Synthetic Chelate Compounds. IV. Magnetic Properties," *J. Am. Chem. Soc.*, **68**, 2267 (1946).
38. Barrow, G. M., Krueger, R. H., and Basolo, F., "Vibrational Assignments for Metal Ammines," *J. Inorg. Nuclear Chem.*, **2**, 340 (1956).
39. Basolo, F., "Quadridentate Ammines. I. Some Coordination Compounds of Cobalt(III) and Triethylenetetramine," *J. Am. Chem. Soc.*, **70**, 2634 (1948).
40. —, Bergmann, J. G., and Pearson, R. G., "Mechanism of Substitution Reactions in Complex Ions. I. Kinetics of Aquation and Hydrolysis of Some C-Substituted Acetatopentamminecobalt(III) Ions," *J. Phys. Chem.*, **56**, 22 (1952).
41. Basolo, F., "Stereochemistry and Reaction Mechanisms of Sexacovalent Inorganic Complexes," *Chem. Rev.*, **52**, 459 (1953).
42. —, Stone, B., Bergmann, J. G., and Pearson, R. G., "Mechanism of Substitution Reactions of *cis* and *trans*-|Co(en)$_2$NO$_2$Cl|$^+$ and |Co(en)$_2$NO$_2$H$_2$O|$^{2+}$ with various Reagents in Aqueous Solution," *J. Am. Chem. Soc.*, **76**, 3079 (1954).
43. Basolo, F., Ballhausen, C. J., and Bjerrum, J., "Absorption of Geometrical Isomers of Hexacoordinated Complexes," *Acta Chem. Scand.* **9**, 810 (1955).
44. Basolo, F., private communication.
45. —, and Pearson, R. G., "Mechanisms of Inorganic Reactions," New York, John Wiley and Sons, Inc., 1958.
46. *Ibid.*, Chapter 2.
47. *Ibid.*, Chapter 7.
48. *Ibid.*, pp. 14 ff.
49. *Ibid.*, p. 115.
50. *Ibid.*, p. 158.
51. *Ibid.*, pp. 159 and 254.
52. *Ibid.*, p. 244.
53. *Ibid.*, p. 339.

54. *Ibid.*, p. 345.
55. *Ibid.*, p. 376.
56. *Ibid.*, p. 387.
57. Baxendale, J. H., and Wells, C. F., "Reactions of Cobalt(III) with Water and Hydrogen Peroxide," *Trans. Faraday Soc.,* **53**, 800 (1957).
58. Beattie, I. R., and Tyrrell, H. J. V., "The Spectra of Some Cobaltic Nitro-ammines and Certain Other Cobaltic Complexes in the 2–15 Micron Region," *J. Chem. Soc.,* **1956**, 2849.
59. Beattie, I. R., and Satchell, D. P. N., "Isomerization of $[Co(NH_3)_5NO_2]Cl_2$," *Trans. Faraday Soc.,* **52**, 1590 (1956).
60. Beaver, W. D., and Trevorrow, L. E., "Aquo and Chloro Complexes of Co-balt(II) and Nickel(II) in 2-octanol," *J. Am. Chem. Soc.,* **75**, 4556 (1953).
61. Beck, M. T., "The Irreversible Oxidation of Oxygen-carrying Cobaltous Com-plexes," *Naturwissenschaften,* **45**, 162 (1958).
62. Belova, V. I., "The Magnetic Susceptibility of Some Complex Compounds of Trivalent Iridium," *Izvest. Sektora Platiny i Drug. Blagorod. Metal.,* **30**, 120 (1955).
63. —, and Syrkin, Y. K., "Magnetic Susceptibility of Trivalent Cobalt Complex Compounds," *Izvest. Sektora Platiny i Drug. Blagorod. Metal.,* **30**, 109 (1956).
64. Bernal, I., Ebsworth, E. A. V., and Weil, J. A., "Paramagnetic Resonance Absorption in Peroxydicobalt Complexes," *Proc. Chem. Soc.,* **1959**, 57.
65. Bjerrum, J., "On the Tendency of Metal Ions toward Complex Formation," *Chem. Rev.,* **46**, 381 (1950).
66. —, Adamson, A. W., and Bostrup, O., "Solvent Dependence of the Spectra of Complex Ions," *Acta Chem. Scand.,* **10**, 329 (1956).
67. Bjerrum, J., Schwarzenbach, G., and Sillen, L. G., "Stability Constants," Chemical Society, London, 1957.
68. Bokii, G. B., and Gilinskaya, E. A., "The Determination of the Structural Type of $K[Co(NO_2)_4(NH_3)_2]$," *Doklady Akad. Nauk S.S.S.R.,* **88**, 461 (1953).
69. Bokii, G. B., Malinovski, T. I., and Ablov, A. V., "Structure of Cobalt-di-amines," *Kristallografiya,* **1**, 49 (1956).
70. Bole, W. D., Davies, E. W., and Monk, C. B., "Spectrophotometric Studies of Electrolytic Dissociation. III. Lead Nitrate, Cupric Sulfate, and Cobalt-hexammine in Water," *Trans. Faraday Soc.,* **52**, 816 (1956).
71. Bonner, N. A., Hunt, J. P., and Taube, H., "The Exchange Reactions between Cobaltous and Cobaltic Ions in Perchloric Acid Solutions," *J. Am. Chem. Soc.,* **74**, 1866 (1952).
72. Bor, G., and Mohai, B., "Preparation of Cobalt Nitrosyl-Carbonyl by the Dithionite Method," *Acta Chem. Acad. Sci. Hung.,* **8**, 335 (1956).
73. —, "Formation of Cobalt Nitrosyl-Carbonyl from Aqueous Solutions," *Research Correspondence,* **9**, S22 (1956).
74. —, "Chemistry of Carbonyl Complexes of Cobalt. IV. The Problem of the Bonding and Oxidation State in Cobalt Nitrosyl-Carbonyl," *Z. anorg. u. allgem. Chem.,* **293**, 84 (1957).
75. —, "Chemistry of Carbonyl Complexes of Cobalt. II. The Reaction of Car-bonylcobaltate(–I) Anion and Nitric Oxide," *Acta Chim. Acad. Sci. Hung.,* **12**, 57 (1957).

76. Brandt, W. W., Dwyer, F. P., and Gyarfas, E. C., "Chelate Complexes of 1,10-phenanthroline and Related Compounds," *Chem. Rev.,* **54,** 959 (1954).
77. Brigando, J., "Metallic Complexes. I. Some Hydroxides of Cobalt(III) Hexammines," *Bull. Soc. Chim.,* France, **1957,** 211.
78. Brimm, E., private communication to Kleinberg, "Unfamiliar Oxidation States," p. 100, U. Kansas Press, 1950.
79. Brintzinger, H., Thiele, H., and Muller, J., "Komplexverbindungen and Salze of Athylendiamintetraessigsaure," *Z. anorg. allgem. Chem.,* **251,** 285 (1943).
80. Brown, D. D., Ingold, C. K., and Nyholm, R. S., "Mechanism, Kinetics, and Stereochemistry of Octahedral Substitutions. I. Edge Displacement as a Hypothesis Linking Mechanism with Stereochemistry of Substitution," *J. Chem. Soc.,* **1953,** 2674.
81. Brubaker, C. H., Jr., and Johnson, C. E., "The Spectra of Solutions of Cobalt(II) Thiocyanate Complexes in 4-Methyl-2-pentanone," *J. Am. Chem. Soc.,* **80,** 5037 (1958).
82. Bruno, M., and Belluco, U., "Isotopic Exchange Reactions between Ionic Cobalt and a Cobalt Complex," *Ricerca Sci.,* **26,** 2711 (1956).
83. Burstall, F. H., and Nyholm, R. S., "Magnetic Moments and Bond Types of Transition Metal Complexes," *J. Chem. Soc.,* **1952,** 3570.
84. Busch, D. H., and Bailar, J. C., Jr., "The Stereochemistry of Complex Inorganic Compounds. XVII. The Stereochemistry of Hexadentate Ethylenediaminetetraacetic Acid Complexes," *J. Am. Chem. Soc.,* **75,** 4574 (1953).
85. Busch, D. H., thesis, University of Illinois, Urbana, Illinois, 1954.
86. —, "High Yield Resolution of Tris(ethylenediamine)cobalt(III) by a Second Order Asymmetric Process," *J. Am. Chem. Soc.,* **77,** 2747 (1955).
87. —, "The Coordinate Bond and the Nature of Complex Inorganic Compounds," *J. Chem. Ed.,* **33,** 376, 498 (1956).
88. Caglioti, V., Silvestroni, P., Sartori, G., and Scrocco, M., "Infrared Investigations of Ammine Complexes of Transition Metals," *Ricerca Sci.,* **26,** 1743 (1956).
89. Cambi, L., Bacchetti, T., and Paglia, E., "Complex Salts of the First Series of Transition Elements with the Thiohydroxamic Acids," *Rend. inst. lombardo. sci.,* Pt. I, **90,** 577 (1950).
90. Cambi, L., "Magnetic Susceptibility of Cobalt(II)—Cobalt(III) Complexes," *Atti accad. Nazl. Lincei,* **18,** 581 (1955).
91. —, and Canonica, L., "Benzimidazole and Benzopyrazole—Cobalt(II) and —Cobalt(III) Complexes," *Atti accad. Nazl. Lincei,* **20,** 17 (1956).
92. Cambi, L., and Paglia, E., "Phenanthroline and Bipyridine Cobalt Cyanides," *Atti accad. Nazl. Lincei,* **21,** 372 (1956).
93. —, "Cobalt Dipyridyl and Phenanthroline Cyanides," *J. Inorg. Nuclear Chem.,* **8,** 249 (1958).
94. Carassiti, V., "Electrophoresis of Inorganic Complexes in Solution. I. Ion Mobility Measurements on Some Complexes of Trivalent Cobalt by the Moving Boundary Method," *Gazz. chim. ital.,* **84,** 405 (1954).
95. —, and Vittori, M. G., "The Diffusion of Complex Electrolytes in Aqueous Solutions," *Ann. chim.* (Rome), **45,** 644 (1955).

96. Carassiti, V., "Electrophoresis of Inorganic Complexes in Solution. The Isomeric Trinitro-trihydroxy-cobalt Ions," *Ann. chim.* (Rome), **45**, 653 (1955).

97. —, and Martelli, R., "Absorption Spectra of Solutions of Complex Salts: The Isomeric Trinitrotrihydroxy Ions," *Ann. chim.* (Rome), **46**, 1229 (1956).

98. —, "Absorption Spectra of Solutions of Complex Salts. II. Cobalt Tetra- and Pentammines," *Ann. chim.* (Rome), **47**, 402 (1957).

99. Carassiti, V., "Optical Isomers and Asymmetric Agents: Continuing with the Scission of a Complex Racemic Salt by Diffusion in Molecularly Asymmetric Solvents," *J. Inorg. Nuclear Chem.*, **8**, 227 (1958).

100. —, "Optical Isomerism and Asymmetric Agents. IV. Diffusion of Optical Antipodes in Liquid Media of Opposite Symmetry," *Ann. chim.* (Rome), **48**, 873 (1958).

101. Carlin, R. L., and Edwards, J. O., "Reaction of Thiocyanatopentammine-cobalt(III) Ion With Chromous Ion," *J. Inorg. Nuclear Chem.*, **6**, 217 (1957).

102. Cattrall, R. W., McKellar, J. R., and West, B. O., "Electron Transfer Reactions," *Proc. Australian At. Energy Symposium*, **1958**, 628.

103. Chaberek, S., Jr., and Martell, A. E., "Stability of Metal Chelates. I. Iminodiacetic and Iminodipropionic Acid," *J. Am. Chem. Soc.*, **74**, 5052 (1952).

104. —, "Stability of Metal Chelates. II. N,N'-Ethylenediaminediacetic Acid and N,N'-Ethylenediaminediacetic-N,N'-dipropionic Acid," *J. Am. Chem. Soc.*, **74**, 6128 (1952).

105. —, "Stability of Metal Chelates. VI. Nitrilotricarboxylic Acids," *J. Am. Chem. Soc.*, **75**, 2888 (1953).

106. Clark, H. C., Cox, B., and Sharpe, A. G., "Complex Fluorides. X. The Magnetic Moment of Hydrated Cobalt(III) Fluoride," *J. Chem. Soc.*, **1957**, 4132.

107. Cooley, W. E., Liu, C. F., and Bailar, J. C., Jr., "The Stereochemistry of Complex Inorganic Compounds. XXIII. Double Optical Isomerism and Optical-geometric Isomerism in Cobalt(III) Complexes," *J. Am. Chem. Soc.*, **81**, 4189 (1959).

108. Cooke, D. W., thesis, The Ohio State University, Columbus, Ohio, 1959.

109. Courtney, R. C., Chaberek, S., Jr., and Martell, A. E., "Stability of Metal Chelates. VII. N,N'-Ethylenediaminetetrapropionic Acid and N,N'-Ethylenediaminedipropionic Acid," *J. Am. Chem. Soc.*, **75**, 4814 (1953).

110. Curti, R., "Cobaltopentammine Chlorite $[Co(NH_3)_5ClO_2]^{2+}$ and Cobalto-tetrammine Dichlorite $[Co(NH_3)_4(ClO_2)_2]$," *Gazz. chim. ital.*, **85**, 1093 (1955).

111. Dainton, F. S., "Principles and Mechanisms in Electron Transfer Reactions," Chemical Society, Special Publication No. 1, Burlington House, London, 1957.

112. Daniel, S. S., and Salmon, J. E., "Cobalt Phosphates. I. The Orthophosphate Group as Ligand in Some Cobalt(III) Ammine Complexes," *J. Chem. Soc.*, **1957**, 4207.

113. Das Sarma, B., and Bailar, J. C., Jr., "The Stereochemistry of Metal Chelates of a Polydentate Ligand," *J. Am. Chem. Soc.*, **76**, 4051 (1954).

114. —, "The Stereochemistry of Metal Chelates with Polydentate Ligands," *J. Am. Chem. Soc.,* **77,** 5476 (1955).

115. —, "The Stereochemistry of Complex Inorganic Compounds. XVIII. A New Method for Preparation of Inorganic Complexes in Their Optically Active Forms," *J. Am. Chem. Soc.,* **77,** 5480 (1955).

116. —, "Partial Resolution of Diamines, Amino Acids, and Dicarboxylic Acids through Coordination with Optically Active Complexes," *J. Am. Chem. Soc.,* **78,** 895 (1956).

117. Doron, V. F., and Kirschner, S., "Application of Zone Melting to the Resolution of Two-Component Inorganic Systems and Racemic Mixtures of Optically Active Compounds and their Diastereoisomers," paper presented at 136th National Meeting of the American Chemical Society, Atlantic City, N. J., Sept. 13–18, 1959.

118. Douglas, B. E., "Racemization of Tris(ethylenediamine)cobalt(III) Ion in the Presence of Decolorizing Carbon," *J. Am. Chem. Soc.,* **76,** 1020 (1954).

119. Duff, J. C., "Complex Metallic Ammines. Conductivities of Di(ethylenediamine)cobaltic Bromides," *J. Chem. Soc.,* **1922,** 450.

120. Dunitz, J. D., and Orgel, L. E., "The Application of Molecular Orbital Theory to Some Binuclear Coordination Compounds," *J. Chem. Soc.,* **1953,** 2594.

121. Dunitz, J. D., "The Crystal Structure of Copper Dipyridine Dichlorides and the Violet Form of Cobalt Dipyridine Dichloride," *Acta Cryst.,* **10,** 307 (1957).

122. Dwyer, F. P., and Lions, F., "Sexadentate Chelate Compounds. I," *J. Am. Chem. Soc.,* **72,** 1545 (1950).

123. Dwyer, F. P., Gyarfas, E. C., and O'Dwyer, M. F., "Configurational Activity," *Nature,* **167,** 1036 (1957).

124. Dwyer, F. P., Lions, F., and Mellor, D. P., "Sexadentate Chelate Compounds. II," *J. Am. Chem. Soc.,* **72,** 5037 (1950).

125. Dwyer, F. P., and Gyarfas, E. C., "Preparation of the Optical Forms of Tris-(Acetylacetono)cobalt(III)," *Nature,* **168,** 29 (1951).

126. Dwyer, F. P., Gill, N. S., Gyarfas, E. C., and Lions, F., "Sexadentate Chelate Compounds. III," *J. Am. Chem. Soc.,* **74,** 4188 (1952).

127. Dwyer, F. P., Gyarfas, E. C., and Lions, F., "Sexadentate Chelate Compounds, V," *J. Am. Chem. Soc.,* **75,** 1526 (1953).

128. Dwyer, F. P., Gill, N. S., Gyarfas, E. C., and Lions, F., "Sexadentate Chelate Compounds. VI," *J. Am. Chem. Soc.,* **75,** 2443 (1953).

129. —, et al., "Sexadentate Chelate Compounds. VII," *J. Am. Chem. Soc.,* **76,** 383 (1954).

130. Dwyer, F. P., Gyarfas, E. C., and Mellor, D. P., "The Resolution and Racemization of Potassium Ethylenediaminetetraacetatocobaltate(III)," *J. Phys. Chem.,* **59,** 296 (1955).

131. Dwyer, F. P., and Sargeson, A. M., "Resolution of Tris-oxalato Metal Complexes," *J. Phys. Chem.,* **60,** 1331 (1956).

132. Dwyer, F. P., Gill, N. S., Gyarfas, E. C., and Lions, F., "Sexadentate Chelate Compounds. VIII," *J. Am. Chem. Soc.,* **79,** 1269 (1957).

133. Dwyer, F. P., and Garvan, F. L., "The Resolution of Quinquedentate Co-

balt(III) Complexes with Ethylenediaminetetraacetic Acid," *J. Am. Chem. Soc.*, **80**, 4480 (1958).

134. Dwyer, F. P., Garvan, F. L., and Shulman, A., "Stereospecific Influences in Metal Complexes Containing Optically Active Ligands. I. Some of the Optical Isomers of Tris(propylenediamine)cobalt(III) Ion," *J. Am. Chem. Soc.*, **81**, 290 (1959).

135. Dwyer, F. P., and Sargeson, A. M., "Resolution of the Tris(thiooxalato)-complexes of Co(III), Cr(III), and Rh(III)," *J. Am. Chem. Soc.*, **81**, 2335 (1959).

136. Dwyer, F. P., and Garvan, F. L., "The Preparation of 1,2-Propylenediamine-tetraacetic Acid and its Resolution Through the Cobalt(III) Complex," *J. Am. Chem. Soc.*, **81**, 2955 (1959).

137. Dwyer, F. P., and Sargeson, A. M., "Stereospecific Influences in Metal Complexes Containing Optically Active Ligands. II. The Reaction of Dichlorobis-(ethylenediamine)cobalt(III) with *l*-Propylenediamine," *J. Am. Chem. Soc.*, **81**, 5269 (1959).

138. Ebsworth, E. A. V., and Weil, J. A., "Paramagnetic Resonance Absorption in Peroxo-dicobalt Complexes," *J. Phys. Chem.*, **63**, 1890 (1959).

139. Edgell, W. F., and Gallup, G., "The Bonding of the Hydrogen Atom in $Co(CO)_4H$," *J. Am. Chem. Soc.*, **77**, 5762 (1955).

140. Edgell, W. F., Magee, C., and Gallup, G., "The Infrared Spectrum of Cobalt Carbonyl Hydride," *J. Am. Chem. Soc.*, **78**, 4185 (1956).

141. Edgell, W. F., Asato, G., Wilson, W., and Angell, C., "Infrared Spectra of Metal Carbonyl Hydrides," *J. Am. Chem. Soc.*, **81**, 2022 (1959).

142. Ephriam, F., and Flugel, W., "Uber Kobaltiake des Schwefelstukstoffsauren und uber Sulfatokobaltiake," *Helv. chim. Acta*, **7**, 724 (1924).

143. Fallab, S., "Metal Ion Catalyzed Amine Oxidation," *J. Inorg. Nuclear Chem.*, **8**, 631 (1958).

144. Faust, J. P., and Quagliano, J. V., "The Trans Effect in Inorganic Coordination Compounds. I. Ultraviolet and Infrared Studies of *cis* and *trans*-Dinitro-tetramminecobalt(III) Chloride," *J. Am. Chem. Soc.*, **76**, 5346 (1954).

145. Ferroni, E., and Bondo, E., "Structural Analysis on the Violet Form of $CoCl_2 \cdot 2py$," *J. Inorg. Nuclear Chem.*, **8**, 458 (1958).

146. Fielding, P. E., "The Electrical Properties of Some Complex Compounds," *J. Chem. Phys.*, **22**, 1153 (1954).

147. Figgins, P. E., and Busch, D. H., "Complexes of Iron(II), Cobalt(II), and Nickel(II) with Biacetyl bis(methylimine), 2-Pyridinal methylimine, and 2,6-Pyridindial bis(methylimine)," *J. Am. Chem. Soc.*, **82**, 820 (1960).

148. Figgis, B. N., and Nyholm, R. S., "Magnetic Moments and Stereochemistry of Cobaltous Compounds," *J. Chem. Soc.*, **1954**, 12.

149. —, "Magnetochemistry. II. The Temperature Dependence of the Magnetic Susceptibilities of Bivalent Cobalt Compounds," *J. Chem. Soc.*, **1959**, 338.

150. Fischer, A. K., and Wilkinson, G., "Reduction of Biscyclopentadiene Compounds," *Naturwissenschaften*, **42**, 96 (1955).

151. Fischer, E. O., and Jira, R., "The Dicyclopentadienyl Complex of Cobalt," *Z. naturforsch.*, **8b**, 1 (1953).

152. —, "Di-cyclopentadienyl-Kobalt(II)," *Z. naturforsch.*, **8b**, 327 (1953).

153. Fischer, E. O., Seus, D., and Jira, R., "Metal Complexes of Indene with Cobalt," *Z. naturforsch.*, **8b**, 629 (1953).
154. Fischer, E. O., and Fritz, H. P., "Advances in Inorganic Chemistry and Radiochemistry," Vol. I, p. 55, Academic Press, New York, 1959.
155. Fischer, E. O., and Jira, R., "Cyclopentadienylcobalt Dicarbonyl," *Z. naturforsch.*, **10b**, 355 (1955).
156. Fischer, E. O., and Böttcher, R., "Ein Mesitylene Komplex des Zweivertigen Eisens. Uber Aromatenkomplexe von Metallen VIII," *Chem. Ber.*, **89**, 2397 (1956).
157. Friedman, H. L., Hunt, J. P., Plane, R. A., and Taube, H., "The Magnetic Susceptibility of Co^{3+}Aq.," *J. Am. Chem. Soc.*, **73**, 4028 (1951).
158. Friend, J. A. N., "Textbook of Inorganic Chemistry. Vol. X. The Metal Ammines," by Miss M. M. J. Sutherland, Charles Griffin and Co., Ltd., 1928.
159. Fujita, J., Nakahara, A., and Tsuchida, R., "Intramolecular O—H—O Bonds in Bis(dimethylglyoximato)cobalt(III) Complexes," *J. Chem. Phys.*, **23**, 1541 (1955).
160. Fujita, J., Nakamoto, K., and Kobayashi, M., "Infrared Spectra of Metallic Complexes. I. The Effect of Coordination on the Infrared Spectra of Ammine, Rhodanato, and Azido Complexes," *J. Am. Chem. Soc.*, **78**, 3295 (1957).
161. Garrick, F. J., "A Possible Acid-dissociation of Metal-ammonia Ions, and its Bearing on Certain Reactions," *Nature*, **139**, 507 (1937).
162. Gatehouse, B. M., Livingstone, S. E., and Nyholm, R. S., "Infrared Spectra of Some Nitrato and Other Oxyanion Coordination Compounds," *J. Inorg. Nuclear Chem.*, **8**, 75 (1958).
163. Gatehouse, B. M., "Survey of the Infrared Spectra of NO_2 in Metal Complexes," *J. Inorg. Nuclear Chem.*, **8**, 79 (1958).
164. George, P., McClure, D. S., Griffith, J. S., and Orgel, L. E., "Ligand Field Theory and the Stability of Transition Metal Compounds," *J. Chem. Phys.*, **24**, 1269 (1956).
165. Gill, N. S., Nyholm, R. S., and Pauling, P., "Stereochemistry of the Complex Halides of the Transition Metals," *Nature*, **182**, 168 (1958).
166. Gleu, K., and Rehm, K., "Zur Konstitution der Grunen Peroxokobaltamine," *Z. anorg. Chem.*, **237**, 79 (1938).
167. "Gmelin's Handbuch Der Anorganischen Chemie. No. 58. Cobalt. Part A. The Ammines of Cobalt," Berlin, 1932.
168. Gogorishvili, P. V., Tsitsishvili, L. D., and Karkaroshivili, M. V., "Compounds of Trivalent Cobalt with Hydrazine," *Zhur. Neorg. Khim.*, **2**, 1040 (1957).
169. —, et al., "Carbonates of Cobalt Complexes of Hydrazine," *Trudy Inst. Khim. im "P. G. Melikarashvili," Akad. Nauk Gruzin. SSSR*, **12**, 121 (1956).
170. Goodwin, H. A., Gyarfas, E. C., and Mellor, D. P., "The Resolution of tris-{cis-dihydroxy-bis(ethylenediamine)cobalt(III)} cobalt(III) Nitrate," *Australian J. Chem.*, **11**, 426 (1958).
171. Gott, A. D., and Bailar, J. C., Jr., "A Partial Resolution of Racemic Mixtures of Organic Acids by Means of Preferential Coordination," *J. Am. Chem. Soc.*, **74**, 4820 (1952).
172. Graziano, F. D., and Harris, G. M., "Substitution Reactions of Oxalato Com-

plex Ions. I. Oxalate Exchange Reactions of the Tris(oxalato)cobalt(III) and Chromium(III) Complex Anions," *J. Phys. Chem.,* **63,** 330 (1959).
173. Griffith, W. P., and Wilkinson, G., "Complex Cyanides Involving Metal-metal Bonds," *J. Inorg. Nuclear Chem.,* **7,** 295 (1958).
174. —, "An Acetylene Cyanide Complex of Cobalt(III)," *J. Chem. Soc.,* **1959,** 1629.
175. Griffith, W. P., Lewis, J., and Wilkinson, G., "Studies on Transition-metal—Nitric Oxide Complexes. V. Nitric Oxide Complexes of Tetrahedral Bivalent Nickel and Some Other Metals," *J. Chem. Soc.,* **1959,** 1775.
176. Griffith, W. P., and Wilkinson, G., "The Pentacyanohydride Complexes of Cobalt(I) and Rhodium(I)," *J. Chem. Soc.,* **1959,** 2757.
177. Griffith, J. S., "Octahedral Complexes. I. Magnetic Susceptibilities in the First Transition Series," *Trans. Faraday Soc.,* **54,** 1109 (1958).
178. Grinberg, A. A., "An Introduction to the Chemistry of Complex Compounds," trans. by J. R. Leach, ed. by R. F. Trimble and D. H. Busch, Addison-Wesley Publishing Co., in press.
179. Hieber, W., and Bartenstein, C., "Metal Carbonyls. LXIII. Carbonylcyano Complexes of Univalent Cobalt," *Z. anorg. u. allgem. Chem.,* **276,** 1 (1954).
180. Hieber, W., and Breu, R., "Reactions of Cobalt Carbonyls," *Angew. Chem.,* **68,** 679 (1956).
181. Higginson. W. C. E., and Hill, M. P., "Catalysis by Lead Ion of the Formation of Ethylenediaminetetraacetatocobalt(III) from the Corresponding Monobromocomplexes," *J. Chem. Soc.,* **1959,** 1620.
182. Hill, D. G., and Rosenberg, A. F., "Infrared Absorption Spectra of Complex Cobalt Compounds," *J. Chem. Phys.,* **24,** 1219 (1956).
183. Holmes, O. G., and McClure, D. L., "Optical Spectra of Hydrated Ions of the Transition Metals," *J. Chem. Phys.,* **26,** 1686 (1957).
184. Holtzclaw, H. F., Jr., "Polarographic Behavior of Isomeric Inorganic Co-ordination Compounds," *J. Phys. Chem.,* **59,** 300 (1955).
185. —, and Sheetz, D. P., "Polarographic Study of Several *cis* and *trans* Co-ordination Compounds of Cobalt," *J. Am. Chem. Soc.,* **75,** 3053 (1953).
186. Hoshowsky, S. A., Holmes, O. G., and McCollum, K. J., "Exchange Reactions of Cobalt(II)—Cobalt(III), and Their Hexammino Complexes," *Can. J. Research,* **27b,** 258 (1949).
187. Illuminati, G., "Complexes of Pentammine Cobalt(III) Benzoate," *Atti accad. Nazl. Lincei,* **24,** 258 (1958).
188. Im, Y. A., and Busch, D. H., "Thermal and Electron Transfer Racemization of Ethylenediaminetetraacetatocobaltate(III)," *Nature,* **182,** 1368 (1958).
189. Inamura, Y., and Kondo, Y., "Spectrochemical Studies on Polynuclear Complexes. Cobalt Polynuclear Complexes," *J. Chem. Soc.,* Japan, **74,** 627 (1953).
190. Ingold, C. K., "Mechanism and Stereochemistry of Octahedral Substitutions," Chemical Society Special Publication No. 1, Burlington House, London, 1954.
191. —, Nyholm, R. S., and Tobe, M. L., "Mechanism, Kinetics and Stereochemistry of Octahedral Substitutions. IV. Bimolecular Basic Hydrolysis and Aquation of Some Haloisothiocyanatobis(ethylenediamine)cobalt(III) Ions," *J. Chem. Soc.,* **1956,** 1691.

192. Irving, H., and Williams, R. J. P., "Stability of Transition Metal Complexes," *J. Chem. Soc.,* **1953,** 3192.
193. Irving, H., and Rossotti, H., "Some Relationships among the Stabilities of Metal Complexes," *Acta Chem. Scand.,* **10,** 72 (1956).
194. Jaeger, F. M., "Uber Razemische und Optisch-active α-Phenanthrolinediathylendiamin-kobalti Salze," *Z. anorg. Chem.,* **170,** 370 (1928).
195. —, and Blumenthal, H. B., "Rotations dispersion and Raumliche Konfigurations bei Komplexsalzen des Kobalts and des Rhodiums, welche Athylendiamin and *trans*-1,2-Diaminocyclopentan Enhalten," *Z. anorg. allgem. Chem.,* **175,** 161 (1928).
196. Johnson, C. H., "Studies in Optical Activity. IV. Racemization of the Optically Active Oxalates," *Trans. Faraday Soc.,* **31,** 1612 (1935).
197. Jakob, W., and Ogorzalek, M., "The Nature of the Peroxide Linkage in Dicobaltamines," *Roczniki Chem.,* **30,** 1055 (1956).
198. Jaselskis, B., and Diehl, H., "A Titration of a Strong Tribasic Acid with a Strong Triacidic Base," *Anal. Chim. Acta,* **16,** 274 (1957).
199. —, "Preparation and Properties of Tetraaklylammonium Hexacyanocobaltates(III) and Hexacyanoferrates(III)," *J. Am. Chem. Soc.,* **80,** 4197 (1958).
200. Jonassen, H. B., Bailar, J. C., Jr., and Huffman, E. H., "The Stereochemistry of Complex Inorganic Compounds. IX. The Diastereoisomers of dextro-Tartratobis(ethylenediamine)cobaltic Ion," *J. Am. Chem. Soc.,* **70,** 756 (1948).
201. —, —, and Gott, A. D., "The Stereochemistry of Complex Inorganic Compounds. XIII. A Partial Resolution of Racemic Tartaric Acid by Means of Different Stabilities of Isomers of Complex Ions," *J. Am. Chem. Soc.,* **74,** 3131 (1952).
202. Jonassen, H. B., and Frey, F. W., "Complexes of Cobalt(II) Perchlorate with Tetraethylenepentamine," *J. Am. Chem. Soc.,* **75,** 1524 (1953).
203. —, "Inorganic Complex Compounds Containing Polydentate Groups. XII. Cobalt(II) Complexes of Tetraethylenepentamine," *J. Am. Chem. Soc.,* **79,** 2454 (1957).
204. Jonassen, H. B., and Strickland, G. T., "Inorganic Complex Compounds Containing Polydentate Groups. XVII. Reactions of Complexes of Cobalt(II) and Quadridentate Amines with Hydroxide Ions," *J. Am. Chem. Soc.,* **80,** 312 (1958).
205. Jonassen, H. B., Stearns, R. I., Kenttamea, J., Moore, D. W., and Whittaker, G., "The Complex Formed from Cobalt Hydrocarbonyl and Butadiene," *J. Am. Chem. Soc.,* **80,** 2586 (1958).
206. Jorgenson, C. K., and Bjerrum, J., "Crystal Field Stabilization of First Transition Group Complexes," *Acta Chem. Scand.,* **9,** 180 (1955).
207. Kakovskii, I. A., "Theoretical Foundations of Xanthate Method of Precipitating Cobalt from Solutions," *Isvetnye Metal.,* **30,** No. 7, 42 (1957).
208. Kapustinskii, A. F., and Solokhin, V. A., "Complex Formation in the System Cobalt(II) Chloride—Acetone and the Solvation Theory of Solutions," *Izvest. Vysshylsh Ucheb. Zavedenii, Khim. i Khim. Technol.,* **1958,** No. 4, 3 (1958).
209. Kernahan, J. L., and Sienko, M. J., "Residual Paramagnetism and the Susceptibility of Some Isoelectronic Cobaltammines," *J. Am. Chem. Soc.,* **77,** 1978 (1955).

210. King, E. L., and Walters, R. R., "The Ion Exchange Separation of Isomeric Dinitrotetramminecobalt(III) Ions," *J. Am. Chem. Soc.*, **74**, 4471 (1952).
211. King, E. L., Esperson, J. H., and Visco, R. E., "A Spectrophotometric Investigation of Outer-Sphere Association of Hexamminecobalt(III) Ion and and Halide Ion," *J. Phys. Chem.*, **63**, 755 (1959).
212. King, H. J. S., and Mistry, S. N., "Ammines. XI. *cis*-Nitroaquotetramminecobaltic Salts," *J. Chem. Soc.*, **1957**, 2402.
213. King, N. K., and Winfield, M. E., "Reduction of Water to Hydrogen by a Complex Cyanide of Cobalt," *J. Am. Chem. Soc.*, **80**, 2000 (1958).
214. Kirsh, L., and Orchin, M., "Intermediate Cobalt Hydrocarbonylolefin Complex in the Oxo Reaction," *J. Am. Chem. Soc.*, **80**, 4428 (1958).
215. Kirschner, S., Wei, Y., and Bailar, J. C., Jr., "The Stereochemistry of Complex Inorganic Compounds. XXI. The Resolution of Racemic Substances through Optically Active Complex Inorganic Compounds," *J. Am. Chem. Soc.*, **79**, 5877 (1957).
216. Kobayashi, M., "The Absorption Spectra of Cobalt(III) Ammine Complexes Containing Dibasic Acid Radicals as Ligands," *J. Chem. Soc.*, Japan, **75**, 1192 (1954).
217. —, and Fujita, J., "Infrared Absorption Spectra of Hexammine Metal Complexes," *J. Phys. Chem.*, **23**, 1354 (1955).
218. Komiyama, Y., "The Crystal Structure of Potassium Tetranitrodiamminecobaltate(III)," *Bull. Chem. Soc.*, Japan, **29**, 300 (1956).
219. —, "Structures of Erdmann's Salt, $NH_4[Co(NH_3)_2(NO_2)_4]$, and Some Other Related Nitroammine Cobalt(III) Complexes," *Bull. Chem. Soc.*, Japan, **30**, 13 (1957).
220. —, "The Crystal Structure of Bromodinitrotriamminecobalt(III)," *Bull. Chem. Soc.*, Japan, **31**, 26 (1958).
221. Kondo, Y., "Electron Transfer Spectra in the Crystals of Hexamminecobalt(III) Salts," *Bull. Chem. Soc.*, Japan, **28**, 497 (1955).
222. Krebs, H., and Rasche, R., "Chromatographic Process for Optical Activation of Racemates," *Naturwissenschaften*, **41**, 63 (1954).
223. —, Chromatographic Resolution of Racemates. Optically Active Cobalt Complexes with Dithio Acids," *Z. anorg. u. allgem. Chem.*, **276**, 236 (1954).
224. Krebs, H., Diewald, J., Arlitt, H., and Wagner, J. A., "Chromatographic Resolution of Racemates. II. Attempts to Resolve Octahedral Complexes," *Z. anorg. u. allgem. Chem.*, **287**, 98 (1956).
225. Larsson, R., "Cobaltammines. II. Association of Ammonia with the Hexammine of Cobalt(III) Ion in Aqueous Solution," *Acta Chem. Scand.*, **12**, 708 (1958).
226. Lederer, M., "Paper Chromatography of Inorganic Ions. XI. Behavior of Cobalt(III) Complexes," *Anal. chim. Acta*, **13**, 350 (1955).
227. Levoshova, L. B., Darienko, E. P., and Degtyarev, V. F., "Investigation of the Distribution of Cobalt Thiocyanates in Two Nonmiscible Solvents by the Method of Radioactive Indicators," *Zhur. Obshchei Khim.*, **25**, 1066 (1955).
228. —, "Investigation of the Distribution of Cobalt Thiocyanates in Two Nonmiscible Solvents by the Method of Radioactive Indicators," *J. Gen. Chem.*, USSR, **25**, 1025 (1955).

229. Levi, G., Curti, R., and Brignani, G., "Metal Complexes Containing Chlorite Groups Coordinated With the Metal. Complexes of the Type $[Co(NH_3)_5-ClO_2]^{2+}$," *Gazz. chim. ital.*, **84**, 753 (1954).

230. Lewis, W. B., Coryell, C. D., and Irvine, J. W., "The Electron Transfer (Exchange) between Cobaltous and Cobaltic Amine Complexes," *J. Chem. Soc.*, Suppl. Issue, No. 2, **1949**, S386.

231. Liehr, A. D., "Structure of $Co(CO)_4H$ and $Fe(CO)_4H_2$," *Z. naturforsch*, **12b**, 95 (1957).

232. Lifschitz, J., "Untersuchung uber Rotationsdispertion," *Z. Physik. Chem.*, **114**, 493 (1925).

233. Linhard, M., Siebert, H., and Weigel, M., "Light Absorption of Nitrito, Nitro, Thiocyanato, Isothiocyanato, and Azidopentammines of Cobalt(III) and Chromium(III)," *Z. anorg. u. allgem. Chem.*, **278**, 287 (1955).

234. Linhard, M., and Weigel, M., "Complex Compounds. XXII. Light Absorption of Halopentamminecobalt(III) Complexes in Red and Near Infrared," *Z. physik Chem.* (Frankfurt), **11**, 308 (1957).

235. Lions, F., and Martin, K. V., "Sexadentate Chelate Compounds. IX," *J. Am. Chem. Soc.*, **79**, 1572 (1957).

236. —, "Tridentate Chelates. I," *J. Am. Chem. Soc.*, **79**, 2733 (1957).

237. —, "Sexadentate Chelate Compounds. X," *J. Am. Chem. Soc.*, **80**, 3858 (1958).

238. Livingston, S. E., "Complexes of Nickel and Cobalt with Certain Chelate Compounds," *J. Chem. Soc.*, **1956**, 1042.

239. Lobanov, N. I., "Cobaltammine Iodates," *Akad. Nauk S.S.S.R.*, **28**, 277 (1954).

240. Long, F. A., "A Study of the Interchange Between Chromioxalate Ion and Oxalate Ion Using Radiocarbon," *J. Am. Chem. Soc.*, **61**, 570 (1939).

241. Ludwig, H., "Electron Affinity Spectra of Inorganic Complex Compounds. II. Aquo and Amino Complex Compounds," *Z. physik. Chem.*, **3**, 263 (1955).

242. Maki, N., Fujita, J., and Tsuchida, R., "Polarography of Pentacyanocobaltate(III) Complexes," *Nature*, **183**, 458 (1959).

243. Malatesta, L., "Contributs alla Conoscenza della Structura della μ-perosso—cobalt(III)–Cobalt(IV)—Ammine," *Gazz. chim. ital.*, **72**, 287 (1942).

244. Malatesta, L., and Sacco, A., "Nitrosocarbamylamine Compounds of Iron and Cobalt," *Atti accad. Nazl. Lincei*, **13**, 264 (1952).

245. —, "Isonitrile Complexes of Univalent Cobalt," *Atti accad. Nazl. Lincei*, **15**, 93 (1953).

246. —, "Isonitrile Complexes of Univalent Cobalt," *Z. anorg. u. allgem. Chem.*, **273**, 247 (1953).

247. —, "Nitrosyl-isonitrile Compounds of Iron and Cobalt," *Z. anorg. u. allgem. Chem.*, **274**, 341 (1953).

248. Malatesta, L., and Araneo, A., "The Interaction of Cobalt Nitrosyl Carbonyls with Triaryl Phosphites and Triaryl Phosphines, Arsines, and Stibines," *J. Chem. Soc.*, **1957**, 3803.

249. Mann, F. G., "The Cobaltic Derivatives of β,β',β''-Triaminotriethylamine," *J. Chem. Soc.*, **1929**, 409.

250. —, "The Constitution of Complex Metallic Salts. I. The Platinum Derivatives of β,β'-Diaminodiethylamine," *J. Chem. Soc.,* **1930,** 1745.

251. —, "The Constitution of Complex Metallic Salts. II," *J. Chem. Soc.,* **1934,** 466.

252. Manyak, A. R., Murphy, C. B., and Martell, A. E., "Metal Chelate Compounds of Glycylglycine and Glycylglycylglycine," *Arch. Biochem. and Biophys.,* **59,** 373 (1955).

253. Martell, A. E., and Calvin, M., "Chemistry of the Metal Chelate Compounds," New York, Prentice-Hall, Inc., 1952.

254. *Ibid,* p. 320.

255. *Ibid,* p. 514.

256. Martin, B., and Waind, G. M., "Low Valency Stabilization. 2,2'-Bipyridine Complexes of Cobalt, Rhodium, and Iridium," *Proc. Chem. Soc.,* **1958,** 169.

257. Martinette, M. M., and Bailar, J. C., Jr., "The Stereochemistry of Complex Inorganic Compounds. XII. The Diastereoisomers of Carbonatobis (*levo*-propylenediamine)Cobalt(III) Ion," *J. Am. Chem. Soc.,* **74,** 1054 (1952).

258. Martinette, M. M., Busch, J., and Gulbinskas, M., "Preparation of *cis*- and *trans*-dichloro-bis(*l*-propylenediamine)cobalt(III) Chloride," *J. Am. Chem. Soc.,* **77,** 6507 (1955).

259. Matoush, W. R., and Basolo, F., "Resolution and Synthesis of an Optically Active Fluoro-Complex," *J. Am. Chem. Soc.,* **77,** 1072 (1955).

260. —, "Synthesis and Properties of Some Fluorobis(ethylenediamine)Cobalt(III) Complexes," *J. Am. Chem. Soc.,* **78,** 3972 (1956).

261. —, "Resolution and Synthesis of an Optically Active Fluorocomplex," *Rec. trav. chim.,* **75,** 580 (1956).

262. Mattern, J. A., and Cartledge, G. H., "Coordinated Properties of the Thiocyanate Radical I. The Bonding of Silver and Mercury Ions by Thiocyanate Complexes of Cobalt(III) and Chromium(III)," *J. Am. Chem. Soc.,* **81,** 2958 (1959).

263. McCollough, F., Jr., and Bailar, J. C., Jr., "The Stereochemistry of Complex Inorganic Compounds. XIX. The Resolution of Bis(ethylenediamine) (2,2'-diaminobiphenyl)cobalt(III) Chloride," *J. Am. Chem. Soc.,* **78,** 714 (1956).

264. McCutcheon, T. P., and Schuele, W. J., "Complex Acids of Cobalt and Chromium. The Green Carbonatocobalt(III) Anion," *J. Am. Chem. Soc.,* **75,** 1845 (1953).

265. Mellor, D. P., and Coryell, C. D., "The Magnetic Properties and Structures of Manganous and Cobaltous Dipyridine Chlorides," *J. Am. Chem. Soc.,* **60,** 1786 (1938).

266. Merritt, P. E., and Wiberly, S., "Infrared Absorption Spectra of *cis-trans* Isomers of Coordination Compounds of Cobalt(III)," *J. Phys. Chem.,* **59,** 55 (1955).

267. Metlin, S., Wender, I., and Sternberg, H. W., "Behavior of Dicobalt Octacarbonyl at Elevated Temperatures and Carbon Monoxide Pressure," *Nature,* **183,** 457 (1959).

268. Misra, R. N., and Pani, S., "Complex of Trivalent Cobalt with p-(Mercaptoacetamido)-benzoic Acid," *Current Sci.* (India), **24,** 371 (1955).

269. Moeller, T., and King, G. L., "Nitrosylpentamminecobalt(II) Chloride, Black, and Nitrosylpentamminecobalt(III), Pink," *Inorganic Syntheses*, **IV**, 168 (1953).

270. Moeller, T., and Gulyas, E., "The Partial Resolution of Certain Inner Complexes by Means of a Chromatographic Technique," *J. Inorg. Nuclear Chem.*, **5**, 245 (1958).

271. Morgan, G. T., and Burstall, F. H., "Researches on Residual Affinity and Coordination. II. Complex Metallic Salts containing 6:6-Di-2"-pyridyl-2:2'-dipyridyl (2,2',2",2'''-Tetrapyridyl)," *J. Chem. Soc.*, **1938**, 1672.

272. Mori, M., Shibata, M., and Azami, J., "Use of Ion Exchangers for the Separation of Geometrical Isomers. I. Separation of Flavo and Croceo Salts," *Nippon Kagaku Zasshi*, **76**, 1003 (1955).

273. Mori, M., Shibata, M., and Nanasawa, M., "Use of Ion Exchangers for the Separation of *cis* and *trans* Isomers of $[Co(en)_2Cl_2]^+$ and $[Co(en)_2(NCS)_2]^+$," *Bull. Chem. Soc., Japan*, **29**, 947 (1956).

274. Mori, M., Shibata, M., Kyuno, E., and Hoshiyama, K., "The Synthesis of Metal Complexes. III. Synthesis of Ethylenediaminecarbonato, Ammineoxalato, and Ethylenediamineoxalato Series of Cobalt(III) Complexes," *Bull. Chem. Soc., Japan*, **31**, 291 (1958).

275. Mori, M., Shibata, M., Kyuno, E., and Okubo, Y., "Synthesis of Metal Complexes. IV. Cobalt(III) Complexes of Nitrilotriacetic Acid," *Bull.. Chem. Soc., Japan*, **31**, 940 (1958).

276. Morris, M. L., and Busch, D. H., "Properties and Infrared Absorption Spectra of Complexes of Cobalt(III) with Pentadentate Ethylenediaminetetraacetic Acid and Hydroxyethylethylenediaminetriacetic Acid," *J. Am. Chem. Soc.*, **78**, 5178 (1956).

277. —, "The Rates of Acid 'Hydrolysis' of the Pentadentate Cobalt(III) Complexes of Ethylenediaminetetraacetic Acid and Hydroxyethylenediaminetriacetic Acid," *J. Phys. Chem.*, **63**, 340 (1959).

278. —, "Infrared Spectral Studies on the *cis* and *trans* Isomers of Diacidobis-(ethylenediamine)cobalt(III) Complexes," *J. Am. Chem. Soc.*, **82**, 1521 (1960).

279. Mukherjee, A. K., "Sexadentate Cobaltic Complexes," *Science and Culture* (India), **19**, 107 (1953).

280. Mukherjee, A. K., and Ray, P., "Metal Chelate Complexes of Sulfosalicylaldehyde with Polycyclic Rings," *J. Indian Chem. Soc.*, **32**, 633 (1955).

281. —, "Inner-metallic Complex Salts of Hydroxyaldimino Hydroxamic Acids with Polycyclic Rings. I.," *J. Indian Chem. Soc.*, **32**, 567 (1955).

282. —, "Inner-metallic Complex Salts of Hydroxyaldimino Acids with Polycyclic Rings. I.," *J. Indian Chem., Soc.*, **32**, 581 (1955).

283. Murmann, R. K., "Resolution and Mutarotation of *cis*-Nitritonitrobis(ethylenediamine)-cobalt(III)," *J. Am. Chem. Soc.*, **77**, 5190 (1955).

284. —, Taube, H., and Posey, F. A., "Mechanisms of Electron Transfer in Aquo Cations. Reaction of RH_2O^{3+} with Cr^{2+}," *J. Am. Chem. Soc.*, **79**, 262 (1957).

285. Mizushima, S., Nakagawa, I., and Quagliano, J. V., "Infrared Absorption Spectra of Inorganic Coordination Complexes. Deformation Frequencies of the NH Ligand," *J. Chem. Phys.*, **23**, 1367 (1955).

286. Nakagawa, I., and Mizushima, S., "Hydrogen Deformation Vibration," *Bull. Chem. Soc.,* Japan, **28**, 589 (1955).

287. Nakahara, A., and Tsuchida, R., "Synthesis of Tris(dimethylglyoximo)cobaltate(III)," *J. Am. Chem. Soc.,* **76**, 3103 (1954).

288. Nakahara, A., "Dimethylglyoximatocobalt(III) Complexes. III. Direct Evidence for the Planar Coordination of two Dimethylglyoximate Ions in Bis(dimethylglyoximato)-cobalt(III) Complexes," *Bull. Chem. Soc.,* Japan, **28**, 473 (1955).

289. Nakahara, A., Fujita, J., and Tsuchida, R., "Dimethylglyoximato Cobalt(III) Complexes. IV. Intramolecular Hydrogen Bonds in Bis(dimethylglyoximato) cobalt(III) Complexes," *Bull. Chem. Soc.,* Japan, **29**, 296 (1956).

290. Nakamoto, K., Kobayashi, M., and Tsuchida, R., "Polar Solvent Effects on the Absorption Spectra of Metallic Complexes," *J. Chem. Phys.,* **22**, 957 (1954).

291. Nakamoto, K., Fujita, J., and Murata, H., "Infrared Spectra of Metallic Complexes. V. Nitro and Nitrito Complexes," *J. Am. Chem. Soc.,* **80**, 4817 (1958).

292. Nakatsu, K., Saito, Y., and Kuroya, H., "Crystals of Metallic Tris(ethylenediamine) Complexes. I. The Crystal Structure of D,L-Tris(ethylenediamine) cobalt(III) Chloride Trihydrate, $[Co(en)_3]Cl_3 \cdot 3H_2O$," *Bull. Chem..Soc.,* Japan, **29**, 428 (1956).

293. Nakatsu, K., Shiro, M., Saito, Y., and Kuroya, H., "Crystals of Metallic Tris(ethylenediamine) Complexes. II. The Crystal Structure of Sodium *D*-tris-(ethylenediamine)cobalt(III) Chloride Hexahydrate," *Bull. Chem. Soc.,* Japan, **30**, 158 (1957).

294. Nakatsuka, Y., and Iiuma, H., "Uber Di(dimethylglyoxim-diammin-kobalt. III. Salze und Ihre Konfiguration," *Bull. Chem. Soc.,* Japan, **11**, 48 (1936).

295. Nast, R., and Lewinsky, H., "Alkynyl Compounds of Transition Metals. IV. Alkynyl Complexes of Cobalt(II) and Cobalt(III)," *Z. anorg. u. allgem. Chem.,* **282**, 210 (1955).

296. Nast, R., and Rohmer, M., "Nitrosylcyano Complexes of Cobalt," *Z. anorg. u. allgem. Chem.,* **285**, 271 (1956).

297. Neville, R. G., and Gorin, G., "Cysteine Complexes with the Cobalt(III) Ion. I. The Mononucleate Structure of Cobalt(III) bis-cysteinate," *J. Am. Chem. Soc.,* **78**, 4891 (1956).

298. —, "Cysteine Complexes with the Cobalt(III) Ion. II. Spectrophotometric Study of the Nature of Coordination in the Complexes of Cysteine with Cobalt(III) Ion," *J. Am. Chem. Soc.,* **78**, 4893 (1956).

299. —, "Cysteine Complexes with the Cobalt(III) Ion. III. The Role of Gaseous Oxygen in the Formation of Cysteine Complexes of Cobalt(III) from Cobalt-(II) and Cysteine," *J. Am. Chem. Soc.,* **78**, 5511 (1956).

300. —, "Cysteine Complexes with the Cobalt(III) Ion. IV. Structure and Inter-relationships of the Bis- and Tris(Cysteinates) of Cobalt(II) and Cobalt(III)," *J. Am. Chem. Soc.,* **79**, 518 (1957).

301. Nyholm, R. S., "Studies in Coordination Chemistry. VI. Complexes of Bi-

valent and Tervalent Cobalt with a Di(tertiary) Arsine," *J. Chem. Soc.,* **1950,** 2071.

302. —, and Sharpe, A. G., "Studies in Coordination Chemistry. XIV. The Magneto-Chemistry of Simple and Complex Fluorides of Transition Metals," *J. Chem. Soc.,* **1952,** 3579.

303. Nyholm, R. S., "Complex Compounds of the Transition Elements," Report to the X*th* Solvay Council, Brussels, May, 1956.

304. —, and Tobe, M. L., "Mechanism, Kinetics, and Stereochemistry of Octahedral Substitutions. V. Bimolecular Basic Hydrolysis and Aquation of Halo and Nitroammine-ethylenediamine Cobalt(III) Ions," *J. Chem. Soc.,* **1956,** 1707.

305. Ogolera, V. D., "Action of Acids on Modifications of Cobalt Triglycine," *Trudy Degeston. Sel'skokhoz. Inst.,* **7,** 130 (1955).

306. Orgel, L. E., "Electronic Structures of Some Mixed Compounds of Cyclopentadienyl and Carbon Monoxide or Nitric Oxide with the Transition Metals," *J. Inorg. Nuclear Chem.,* **2,** 315 (1956).

307. —, "Some Applications of Crystal-field Theory to Some Problems in Transition-metal Chemistry," Report to the X*th* Solvay Council, Brussels, May, 1956.

308. —, and Griffith, J. S., "Ligand Field Theory," *Quart. Revs.,* **11,** 381 (1957).

309. Paglia, E., and Sironi, C., "Relative Oxidation-reduction of Bipyridine and Phenanthroline Cobalt Complexes," *Gazz. chim. ital.,* **87,** 1125 (1957).

310. —, "Dimethylglyoxime Cobalt Complexes with 2,2'-Bipyridine and 1,10-phenanthroline," *Gazz. chim. ital.,* **87,** 1133 (1957).

311. Paris, R., "Hydroxides of Metalammines," *Ann. chim.* (Paris), **10,** 353 (1955).

312. Pauling, L., "Nature of the Chemical Bond," Ithaca, New York, Cornell University Press, 1948.

313. Pearson, R. G., Boston, C., and Basolo, F., "Mechanism of Substitution Reactions in Complex Ions. Kinetics of Aquation of Some Cobalt(III) Ions," *J. Am. Chem. Soc.,* **75,** 3089 (1953).

314. Pearson, R. G., Meeker, R. E., and Basolo, F., "Mechanism of Basic Hydrolysis of Cobalt(III) Complexes," *J. Inorg. Nuclear Chem.,* **1,** 341 (1955).

315. Pearson, R. G., Boston, C., and Basolo, F., "Effect of Chelation on the Rates of Acid Hydrolysis of Some Cobalt(III) Complex Ions," *J. Phys. Chem.,* **59,** 304 (1955).

316. Pearson, R. G., and Basolo, F., "Mechanism of Reactions of Complex Ions. X. Pi-bonding in Dissociation Reactions of Octahedral Complexes," *J. Am. Chem. Soc.,* **78,** 4878 (1956).

317. Penland, R. B., Lane, T. J., and Quagliano, J. V., "Infrared Absorption Spectra of Inorganic Coordination Complexes. VII. Structural Isomerism of Nitro and Nitritopentamminecobalt(III) Chlorides," *J. Am. Chem. Soc.,* **78,** 887 (1956).

318. Pepinsky, R., and Okaya, Y., "Determination of Crystal Structures by Means of Anomalously Scattered X-rays," *Proc. Natl. Acad. Sci.,* U. S., **42,** 286 (1956).

319. Perakis, N., Wucher, J., and Karantossis, T., "The Magnetic Behavior of the Coordinated Cobaltic, Ferric, and Chromic Ions," *Compt. rend.*, **238**, 475 (1954).

320. Pfeiffer, P., Grossman, I., and Pietsch, H., "Zur Stereochemie des Chroms. VII. Uber Gemischte Luteosalze," *Z. anorg. Chem.*, **58**, 301 (1908).

321. Porai-Koshits, M. A., and Antsishkina, A. S., "Structure of Crystals of Dichlorotetrapyridinenickel and Dichlorotetrapyridinecobalt," *Doklady Akad. Nauk S.S.S.R.*, **92**, 333 (1953).

322. Porai-Koshits, M. A., "X-ray Structure of Complex Compounds of Bivalent Cobalt and Nickel," *Trudy Inst. Krist., Akad. Nauk, S.S.S.R.*, **10**, 117 (1954).

323. Posey, F. A., and Taube, H., "The Mechanism of Substitution Reactions of Octahedral Complexes. The Induced Aquation of the Halogenopentamminecobaltic Ions by Metal Cations," *J. Am. Chem. Soc.*, **79**, 255 (1957).

324. Powell, D. B., and Sheppard, N., "Infrared Spectra of Some Metal Ammines and Deuteroammines," *J. Chem. Soc.*, **1956**, 3108.

325. Powell, H. M., and Wells, A. F., "The Structure of Caesium Cobalt Chloride, Cs_3CoCl_5," *J. Chem. Soc.*, **1935**, 359.

326. Preschanski, D., and Wormser, Y., "The Action of Hydrogen Peroxide on Cobaltous Salts in Various Aqueous Media," *Compt. rend.*, **246**, 1212 (1958).

327. Rasmussen, S. E., and Bjerrum, J., "Polynuclear Complexes. I. Formation of Polynuclear Hydroxo Complexes in Aged Solutions of Diaquobis(ethylenediamine)cobalt(III) Ions and Kinetics of Decomposition of μ-dihydroxotetrakis(ethylenediamine)dicobalt(III)," *Acta Chem. Scand.*, **9**, 735 (1955).

328. Riolo, C. B., and Soldi, T., "New Complex Salts of Cobalt Containing Haloacetic Groups as Ligands," *Gazz. chim. ital.*, **86**, 282 (1956).

329. Sacco, A., "Complex Cobaltcarbonyl Isocyanide Salts," *Gazz. chim. ital.*, **83**, 632 (1953).

330. —, "Isonitrile Complexes of Cobalt. II. Penta(arylisonitrile)cobalt(II) Perchlorate," *Gazz. chim. ital*, **84**, 370 (1954).

331. —, "Salts of Bis(triphenylphosphine)tris(carbonyl)Cobalt(I)," *Atti accad. Nazl. Lincei*, **21**, 442 (1956).

332. Sacco, A., and Freni, M., "Tricarbonylbis(triphenylphosphine)cobalt(I) Salts," *J. Inorg. Nuclear Chem.* **8**, 566 (1958).

333. —, "Salts of Bis(triphenylphosphine)tricarbonylcobalt(I)," *Ann. chim.* (Rome), **48**, 218 (1948).

334. Saini, G., and Sapetti, C., "The Complex Ions $Fe(SCN)^{++}$ and $Co(SCN)^+$ in Aqueous Solution," *Atti accad. sci. Torino*, **86**, 247 (1952).

335. Saito, Y., Nakatsu, K., Shiro, M., and Kuroya, H., "Determination of the Absolute Configuration of the Optically Active Ion $[Co(en)_3]^{3+}$ by means of X-rays," *Acta Cryst.*, **8**, 729 (1955).

336. —, "Crystals of Metallic Tris(ethylenediamine) Complexes. III. The Determination of the Absolute Configuration of Optically Active Complex Ion $[Co(en)_3]^{3+}$ by Means of X-rays," *Bull. Chem. Soc.*, Japan, **30**, 795 (1957).

337. Schwarzenbach, G., "Komplexone. XIII. Chelatkomplexe des Kobalts mit und Ohne Fremdliganden," *Helv. chim. Acta*, **32**, 839 (1949).

338. Schwarzenbach, G., and Freitag, E., "Komplexone. XX. Stabilitatskonstan-

ten von Schwermetallkomplexen der Athylendiamin-tetraessigsaure," *Helv. Chim. Acta,* **34**, 1503 (1951).

339. —, "Komplexone. XIX. Die Bildungskonstanten von Schwermetallkomplexen der nitrilotriessigsaure," *Helv. chim. Acta,* **34**, 1492 (1951).

340. Schwarzenbach, G., and Moser, P., "Metal Complexes with Polyamines. X. With Tetrakis(2-aminoethyl)ethylenediamine," *Helv. Chim. Acta,* **36**, 581 (1953).

341. Sharp, R. A., and Wilkinson, G., "Solvent-extraction Separation of Cobalt and Nickel with Thiocyanate and the Preparation of Nickel-free Cobalt Salts," *J. Am. Chem. Soc.,* **77**, 6519 (1955).

342. Shimi, I. A., and Higginson, W. C. E., "Kinetics of Formation of Ethylenediaminetetraacetatocobalt(III) from the Corresponding Monoaquo- and Monohydroxo-Complexes in Aqueous Solutions," *J. Chem. Soc.,* **1958**, 260.

343. Shimura, Y., and Tsuchida, R., "Absorption Spectra of Cobalt(III) Complexes. I. Curve Analyses of the First and Second Bands," *Bull. Chem. Soc., Japan,* **28**, 572 (1955).

344. —, "Splitting of the First Band of $[Co^{III}(EDTAH)X]^=$-type Complexes," *Bull. Chem. Soc., Japan,* **29**, 643 (1956).

345. —, "Absorption Spectra of the Cobalt(III) Complexes. II. Redetermination of the Spectrochemical Series," *Bull. Chem. Soc., Japan,* **29**, 311 (1956).

346. —, "Absorption Spectra of Nitratoamminocobalt(III) Complexes," Nippon *Kagaku Zasshi,* **77**, 734 (1956).

347. Shimura, Y., "Cobalt(III) Complexes Containing Only One Chelate Ring. I. Syntheses of $[Co(NH_3)_4gly]X_2$ and $[Co(NH_3)_4alan]X_2$," *Bull Chem. Soc., Japan,* **31**, 173 (1958).

348. —, "Cobalt(III) Complexes Containing Only One Chelate Ring. II. Synthesis and Properties of Ethylenediaminetetramminecobalt(III) Complexes, $[Co(en)(NH_3)_4]X_3$," *Bull. Chem. Soc., Japan,* **31**, 311 (1958).

349. Siebert, H., "The Phosphatotetramminecobalt(III) Complex," *Z. anorg. u. allgem. Chem.,* **296**, 280 (1958).

350. —, "Infrared Spectra of Cobalt(III) Complexes with Ammonia and Anions of Oxyacids as Ligands," *Z. anorg. u. allgem. Chem.,* **298**, 51 (1958).

351. Simmons, V. E., Yannoni, N. F., Eriks, K., and Baker, L. C. W., "Heteropoly 12-Tungstocobaltoate and 12-Tungstocobaltiate Anions," paper presented at 136th National Meeting of the American Chemical Society, Atlantic City, N. J., Sept. 13–18, 1959.

352. Sirotkin, G. P., "Absorption of Nitric Oxide by Aqueous Ammoniacal Solutions of Bivalent Cobalt Salts," *Zhur. Neorg. Khim.,* **1**, 1750 (1956).

353. Sitaramaiah, G., and Sanghi, C. L., "Composition of the Cobalt Thiocyanate Complex in Acetone," *Proc. Natl. Acad. Sci.,* India, Sect. A, **27**, 103 (1958).

354. Sly, W. G., "The Molecular Configuration of Dicobalt Hexacarbonyl(diphenylacetylene)," *J. Am. Chem. Soc.,* **81**, 18 (1959).

355. Smirnoff, A. P., "Zur Stereochemie des Platinatoms: uber Relativ Asymmetrische Synthese bei Anorganischen Komplexen," *Helv. Chim. Acta,* **3**, 177, 194 (1920).

356. Spacu, P., and Brezeanu, M., "Hexachlorolead(IV) Ammines, A New Class of Compounds," *Rev. chim., Acad, rep. populaire,* **3,** 227 (1958).
357. —, "Hexachloroplumbates," *Analeleuniv.* "C. I. Parhon," **14,** 55 (1957).
358. —, "Hexachloroplumbates. A New Class of Complex Compounds," *Rev. chim. Acad. rep. Populaire,* Roumaine, **2,** 27 (1957).
359. Sternberg, H. W., Shukys, J. G., Donne, C. D., Markby, R., Friedel, R. A., and Wender, I., "Addition of Carbon Monoxide to Acetylenedicobalthexacarbonyl. A New Type of Complex," *J. Am. Chem. Soc.,* **81,** 2339 (1959).
360. Stoufer, R. C., and Busch, D. H., "Complexes of Biacetyl Dihydrazone and Pyridinal Hydrazones with Iron(II), Cobalt(II), and Nickel(II)," *J. Am. Chem. Soc.,* **78,** 6016 (1956).
361. Stoufer, R. C., Hadley, W. B., and Busch, D. H., "Magnetic Isomers of Cobalt(II) Complexes," papers presented at the 136th National Meeting of the American Chemical Society, Atlantic City, N. J., Sept. 13–18, 1959.
362. Stranks, D. R., and Wilkins, R. G., "Isotopic Tracer Investigations of Mechanism and Structure in Inorganic Chemistry," *Chem. Rev.,* **57,** 743 (1957).
363. Stratton, W. J., and Busch, D. H., "The Complexes of Pyridinaldazine with Iron(II) and Nickel(II). II," *J. Am. Chem. Soc.,* **80,** 3191 (1958).
364. Svatos, G. F., Sweeny, D. M., Mizushima, S., Curran, C., and Quagliano, J. V., "Infrared Absorption Spectra of Inorganic Coordination Complexes. XII. The Characteristic NH_3 Deformation Vibrations of Solid Inorganic Complexes," *J. Am. Chem. Soc.,* **79,** 3313 (1957).
365. Tanabe, Y., and Sugano, S., "The Absorption Spectra of Complex Ions," *J. Phys. Soc.,* Japan, **9,** 753, 766 (1954).
366. Tanford, C., Kirk, D. C., Jr., and Chantooni, M. K., Jr., "A Kinetic Study of the Formation of the Cobalt—Glycylglycine Oxygen Complex," *J. Am. Chem. Soc.,* **76,** 5325 (1954).
367. Tanito, Y., Saito, Y., and Kuroya, H., "Crystal Structure of Trinitrotriamminecobalt(III)," *Bull. Chem. Soc.,* Japan, **25,** 188 (1952).
368. —, "The Crystal Structure of Dichloroaquotriamminecobalt(III) Chloride," *Bull. Chem. Soc.,* Japan, **25,** 328 (1952).
369. —, "Crystal Structure of Chlorodinitrotriamminecobalt(III)," *Bull. Chem. Soc.,* Japan, **26,** 420 (1953).
370. Taube, H., "Rates and Mechanisms of Substitution in Inorganic Complexes in Solution," *Chem. Rev.,* **50,** 69 (1952).
371. —, Myers, H., and Rich, R., "The Mechanism of Electron Transfer in Solution," *J. Am. Chem. Soc.,* **75,** 4118 (1953).
372. Taube, H., and Myers, H., "Evidence for a Bridge Activated Complex for Electron Transfer Reactions," *J. Am. Chem. Soc.,* **76,** 2103 (1954).
373. Taube, H., "Anions as Bridging and Nonbridging Ligands in Reactions of Cobalt(III) Compounds with Chromium(II) Ion," *J. Am. Chem. Soc.,* **77,** 4481 (1955).
374. —, "Advances in Inorganic Chemistry and Radiochemistry," ed. by H. J. Emeleus and A. G. Sharpe, Vol. I, Chap. 1, New York, Academic Press Inc., 1959.

375. —, "Bridging and Nonbridging Ligand Effects in Redox Reactions of Metal Ions," *Can. J. Chem.*, **37**, 129 (1959).

376. Thilo, E., and Heilborn, H., "Uber die Grunde fur den Unterschiedim Verhalten Analoger Diacetyldioxim-haltigen Verbindungen der Zweivertigen Metalle Kobalt, Nickel, und Kupfer," *Ber.*, **64**, 1441 (1931).

377. Tremillon, B., "Utilization of Frontal Analysis in Ion-exchange Chromatography for the Study of Formation Reactions of Complexes in Solution. Application to HCl Complexes of Nickel(II), Cobalt(II), and Copper(II)," *Bull. Soc. Chim.*, France, **1958**, 1483.

378. Trimble, R. F., Jr., "The *cis-trans* Isomerization of the Cobaltic Chloride Ethylenediamine Complex in 2-Methoxyethanol," *J. Am. Chem. Soc.*, **76**, 6321 (1954).

379. Tschugaeff, L., "Uber Kobaltidioxime," *Ber.*, **39**, 2692 (1906).

380. —, "Uber eine Neue Komplexsaure (Studien uber Kobaltdioxime. III)," *Ber.*, **41**, 2226 (1908).

381. —, and Sokoloff, W., "Uber das *d*-Propylendiamin and uber Einige Derivative der Optisch-aktiven Propylendiamin," *Ber.*, **42**, 55 (1909).

382. Tsuchida, R., Kobayashi, M., and Nakamura, A., "The Configuration of Chlorobis(dimethylglyoximo)aminecobalt," *Bull. Chem. Soc.*, Japan, **11**, 38 (1936).

383. Tsuchida, R., and Kobayashi, M., "The Third Absorption Bands of Coordination Compounds. III. The Configuration of [Co(DMG)₂(NH₃)Cl]. A New Type of Optically Active Complex Radical," *Bull. Chem. Soc.*, Japan, **12**, 83 (1937).

384. Uri, N., "Inorganic Free Radicals in Solution," *Chem. Rev.*, **50**, 375 (1952).

385. Vlcek, A. A., "New Compound of Univalent Cobalt," *Nature*, **180**, 753 (1957).

386. —, "Reaction Kinetics of the Decomposition of Cobalt Carbonyl in Ethanol Solutions," *Z. anorg. u. allgem. Chem.*, **298**, 270 (1959).

387. Waind, G. M., and Martin, B., "Low Valence Stabilization. Salts of Tris-(2,2'-bipyridine)-cobalt(I) Cation," *J. Inorg. Nuclear Chem.*, **8**, 551 (1958).

388. Watt, G. W., and Thompson, R. J., "Reduction of Iodopentamminecobalt-(III) Iodide and Potassium Hexacyanocobaltate(III) with Potassium in Liquid Ammonia," *J. Inorg. Nuclear Chem.*, **9**, 311 (1959).

389. Weakliem, H. A., and Hoard, J. L., "The Structures of Ammonium and Rubidium Ethylenediaminetetraacetatocobaltate(III)," *J. Am. Chem. Soc.*, **81**, 549 (1959).

390. Weiss, E., "Dipole Moments of Complexes of Aromatic Substances," *Z. anorg. u. allgem. Chem.*, **287**, 236 (1956).

391. Wells, A. F., "Structural Inorganic Chemistry," London, Oxford Press, p. 657, 1950.

392. Wender, I., Sternberg, H. W., and Orchin, M., "Dicobalt Octacarbonyl," *Inorganic Syntheses*, **V**, 190 (1957).

393. Werner, A., "Uber Mehrkernige Metallammoniake. II. Ableitung der Konstitution der Mehrkernigen Kobaltiake,' *Ann.*, **375**, 9 (1910).

394. —, "New Ideas on Inorganic Chemistry," Trans. by E. P. Hedley, London, Longmans, Green and Co., 1911.

395. —, "Uber die Raumisomeren Kobaltverbindungen. III. Uber Additionsverbindungen bei Kobaltiaksalzen," *Ann.*, **386**, 50 (1912).

396. —, "Zur Kenntnis des Asymmetrischen Kobaltatoms," *Ber.*, **46**, 3674 (1913).

397. —, "Zur Kenntnis des Asymmetrischen Kobaltatoms. XII. Uber Optische Aktivat bei Kohlenstoffreien Verbindungen," *Ber.*, **47**, 3087 (1914).

398. —, "Uber Mehrkernige Metallammoniake, I. Zur Kenntnis des Assymmetrischen Kobaltatoms. X.," *Ber.*, **47**, 1961 (1914).

399. —, Uber Mehrkernige Metallammoniake. II.," *Ann.*, **375**, pt. 9, 70 (1910).

400. —, "Uber eine Neue Isomerieart bei Kobatlverbindungen and Verbindungen mit Asymmetrischen Kobalt and Kohlenstoff," *Helv. Chim. Acta*, **1**, 5 (1918).

401. Whipple, R. O., West, R., and Emerson, K., "Bond Type in Tris(acetylacetone)cobalt," *J. Chem. Soc.*, **1953**, 3715.

402. White, J. M., Weismann, T. J., and Li, N. C., "Magnetic Studies of Some Cobalt Complexes of Amino Acids and Peptides," *J. Phys. Chem.*, **61**, 126 (1957).

403. Wilkinson, G., "The Preparation and Some Properties of the Cobalticinium Salts," *J. Am. Chem. Soc.*, **74**, 6148 (1952).

404. —, Pauson, P. L., and Cotton, F. A., "Biscyclopentadienyl Compounds of Nickel and Cobalt," *J. Am. Chem. Soc.*, **76**, 1970 (1954).

405. Williams, O. F., and Bailar, J. C., Jr., "The Stereochemistry of Complex Inorganic Compounds. Cobalt Stilbenediamine Complexes," *J. Am. Chem. Soc.*, **81**, 4464 (1959).

406. Williams, R. J. P., "Absorption Spectra and Stability of Complex Ions," *J. Chem. Soc.*, **1956**, 8.

407. Wormser, Y., "Transformation of a Cobaltous Salt to Cobaltammine," *Compt. rend.*, **241**, 1293 (1955).

408. Yalman, R. G., "Preparation of Iodopentamminecobalt(III) Salts from Cobalt(II)," *J. Am. Chem. Soc.*, **77**, 3219 (1955).

409. —, and Warga, M. B., "Peroxodicobalt(III) Complexes as intermediates in the Catalytic Decomposition of Hydrogen Peroxide," *J. Am. Chem. Soc.*, **80**, 1011 (1958).

410. Yamada, S., and Tsuchida, R., "Absorption Spectra of Coordination Compounds. The Hyperchromic Series of Ligands," *Bull. Chem. Soc.*, Japan, **26**, 15 (1953).

411. Yamatera, H., "The Absorption Spectra of Substituted Cobalt(III) Ammines," *Naturwissenschaften*, **44**, 357 (1957).

412. Yannoni, N. F., Simmons, V. E., Eriks, K., and Baker, L. C. W., "The Crystal Structure of Potassium 12-Tungstocobaltiate, $K_5[CoW_{12}O_{40}] \cdot 2OH_2O$," paper presented at the 136th national Meeting of the American Chemical Society, Atlantic City, N. J., Sept. 13–18, 1959.

413. Yatsimirskii, K. B., and Korableva, V. D., "The Thiocyanate Complexes of Manganese, Cobalt, and Nickel," *Zhur. Neorg. Khim.*, **3**, 339 (1958).

414. Yoneda, H., Kida, S., and Kobayashi, M., "Absorption Spectra of Cobaltic Salts in the Very Near Infrared Region," *J. Chem. Soc.*, Japan, **73**, 518 (1952).

415. Yoneda, H., "Stabilities of Metal-amine Complexes. II. Absorption Spectra and Chemical Behavior of the Hexahydroxylaminecobalt(III) Complex," *Bull. Chem. Soc.*, Japan, **30**, 924 (1957).

Chapter 7

THE PHASE DIAGRAMS FOR COBALT

A. G. Metcalfe

Assistant Director of Research, Solar Aircraft Company
San Diego, California

There is no other metal comparable to cobalt in importance for which phase diagrams are known so imperfectly. Köster,[25] in 1952, attempted to classify the phase diagrams for cobalt in the same way that the iron-base systems had been classified. He proposed three main types with several minor groupings; all showed some inconsistencies with the Phase Rule, e.g., a range of temperature over which the two allotropes exist in pure cobalt, and a corresponding three-phase field in the binary system. Thus, an understanding of the allotropy of cobalt is a prerequisite for an appreciation of the problems of cobalt phase diagrams.

THE ALLOTROPY OF COBALT

With the use of X-ray analysis, Hull[21] was the first to detect the transformation near 400°C from hexagonal to cubic cobalt. Later, Umino,[52] claiming that a second allotropic transformation occurred at 1150°C, raised a question which has not yet been settled. While evidence on either side with regard to high temperature allotropic transformation is inconclusive, papers on the character of low temperature transformation should be considered since available evidence indicates that if a high temperature allotropic transformation does exist, it must be a reversion to the low temperature hexagonal form.

Low Temperature Transformation

Edwards, Lipson, and Wilson[8,9] showed that the hysteresis of the low temperature transformation is related to the presence of stacking faults. These faults arise as a result of a breakdown in the order in which the close-packed planes of one form of cobalt are stacked, so that the structure becomes that of the other form. If the probability of a fault is N, then the entropy of disorder for a crystal containing M atoms per plane is given by

$$S = \frac{R}{M}[N \log N + (1 - N) \log (1 - N)], \text{ where } R \text{ is the gas constant. If the}$$

difference in free energy of the two fault-free allotropic forms is not large, then it is possible for some of the thermodynamically unstable allotrope to be stabilized by the faults introduced in the mixture.

Troiano and Tokich[51] made the next important contribution. They showed that the transformation from cubic to hexagonal cobalt occurs as the result of a martensite reaction, when the grain size is large, with $M_s =$ 388°C. A martensite reaction could not be detected, thermally, in fine-grained cobalt. The time required for the isothermal transformation from hexagonal cobalt to cubic cobalt decreased as the transformation temperature was raised. Later, Hess and Barrett[19] showed that the transformation had another characteristic of the martensite transformation. They determined that the M_d temperature for cobalt was 417 ±7°C, or, in other words, that cubic cobalt broke down to hexagonal when worked below 417°C, and hexagonal cobalt became cubic when worked above 417°C. The shear mechanism which operates during the martensite transformation has recently been investigated,[2,4] but consideration of the mechanism is outside the scope of this study.

Owen and Madoc-Jones[38] studied the effect of grain size and concluded that

"the stable structure of cobalt depends on the grain size: between room temperature and about 450°C when the grain size is very small, as in cobalt sponge, the stable structure is face-centered cubic; when the grain size is larger, as in a solid rod, the stable structure is close-packed hexagonal; and when there is a range of grain size, as in fine filings, a mixture of these two structures is observed."

The lattice parameter was found to be 3.5331Å at 18°C, but when the cobalt filings were annealed in the range 600–840°C, a progressive increase occurred which reached a maximum value of 3.5612Å. They attributed this increase to the formation of a metastable structure. Since the lattice parameter could be made to revert to the lower value by annealing at higher temperatures, contamination could not be responsible. This observation explains the scatter in published data, most of which lies between these limits.[29,36,46,50,55] On the other hand, no satisfactory mechanism was advanced to explain the change of lattice parameter.

The present position is that low temperature allotropic transformation occurs over a range of temperature because of stabilization by faults in the lattice. If the grain size is fine enough, cubic cobalt appears to be stable at room temperature. The theory of Edwards, Lipson, and Wilson[8,9] predicts this, assuming that some faults are present in the stabilized cubic cobalt and that very few faults are required when the grain size is small. Coarse-grained cubic cobalt transforms by an insuppressible martensite reaction both on cooling and on deformation in an appropriate temperature range.

It has been claimed that a metastable cubic phase exists at intermediate temperatures.

On the basis of this discussion, it is apparent that the diagrams presented by Köster[25] may represent neither the failure of earlier investigators to reach equilibrium nor a breakdown of the Phase Rule. It appears likely that cobalt presents a special case in which the free energies of the two allotropes diverge slowly on either side of the true temperature of equilibrium, so that minor energy contributions have to be considered. The entropy of faults and surface energy are two such minor effects which may be capable of upsetting the energy balance, thus stabilizing a two-phase structure in a one-component system.

High Temperature Transformation

High temperature transformation, first claimed by Umino,[52] has not been investigated nearly as thoroughly as low temperature transformation; even its existence is doubted. An additional complication, arising from the loss of ferromagnetism of cobalt at $1121 \pm 3°C$,[35] has resulted in many investigators attributing discontinuous changes in physical properties to the Curie point rather than to allotropic transformation.

The principal claimants for a second allotropic transformation have used a variety of methods. Umino[52] based his claim on measurements of physical properties, particularly on measurements indicating a sharp drop in specific heat at $1150°C$. This change was verified later by Jaeger, Rosenbohm, and Zuithoff,[22] although they were not concerned with its cause. They found the heat of transformation at $1120°C$ to be 1.6 cal/g, close to the value of 1.5 cal/g found at the transformation near $400°C$, and far exceeding values usually associated with a magnetic transformation. Hendricks, Jefferson, and Schultz[18] used a method similar to that employed in the determination of the Co–Fe system (see below), in which they reduced cobalt oxide at various temperatures and determined that the powder was cubic when reduced below $1050°C$, hexagonal when reduced above this temperature. In view of subsequent work, these results can be criticized on the grounds of grain-size effect; grain growth above $1050°C$ might permit the martensitic transformation to occur on cooling. Cardwell,[6] on the basis of photoelectric and thermionic emission, and Seybolt and Mathewson,[47] on the basis of oxygen solubility isotherms, claimed a transformation at somewhat lower temperatures. Sykes,[48] and Sykes and Graff[49] claimed a transformation at $1020°C$ on the basis of thermal analysis and microscopy, and traced the influence of molybdenum on this transformation. Because molybdenum, as well as certain other alloying elements, depresses the Curie temperature but raises the temperature of the structural transformations, it can be used to separate magnetic and structural effects. Metcalfe[31,32] utilized two high-temperature methods—dilatometry and thermal etching—as well as alloying with molybdenum and chromium to depress the Curie temperature so that unambiguous conclusions could be reached. On this basis, it was claimed that a cubic-to-hexagonal reversion with vacuum-cast, coarse-grained cobalt occurred over a 1119–1145° C temperature range. On cooling, hysteresis was observed; the hexagonal-to-cubic transformation was completed in 20 hours at 1050° C, and in about 1-1/2 hours at 1000° C. Finally, Buhl and Schüler,[5] after making direct observations by means of the field emission microscope, concluded that cubic cobalt could transform to the hexagonal close-packed structure at 1150° C.

The disclaimers of a transformation include Schulze,[45] who based his argument on a lack of hysteresis of electrical resistance effects. Wasserman[54] and Marick[29] found similar abrupt changes in electrical resistance, but because of the lack of hysteresis in both cases, attributed the change to the Curie point rather than to a structural change. The temperature coefficient of resistance changes from 16.6×10^{-3} per °C over the interval 700–1000° C to 6.7×10^{-3} at 1200–1300° C.[16] Similar results were obtained by Schulze[45] for a break in the thermoelectric power against platinum at 1120° C, which exhibited no hysteresis. Marick[29] studied a cobalt wire by X-ray diffraction and claimed that the cubic lattice persisted to 1187° C, although an analysis[33] of his results shows that an expansion of 0.7 per cent, in excess of the thermal expansion, occurred between 1100° and 1140° C, which he did not attempt to explain. Newkirk and Geisler,[37] also studying a cobalt wire by X-ray diffraction, took two photographs at elevated temperatures, neither of which show any hexagonal cobalt up to 1223° C.

Significant work disclaiming the existence of a high-temperature allotrope was performed with wires, indicating specimens of fine-grained size; thermal analysis, dilatometry, thermal etching, and other methods used by the investigators who favor a transformation, were performed on massive specimens of larger grain size. In view of the effect of grain size on the low temperature transformation, these facts may account for the differences between apparently reliable investigations. More work, particularly an investigation similar to that conducted by Owen and Madoc-Jones[38] on the low temperature transformation, is required to resolve this problem.

Phase diagrams showing a high temperature allotrope have been published for some systems: Co-Mo;[32,44] Co-Cr;[32] and Co-Cr-Mo.[32] In these systems, the high temperature allotrope is shown as a tentative phase field.

PRESENTATION OF DIAGRAMS

For uniformity, the following standards are used:

Temperature —1948 International Temperature Scale
               —melting point . . . . . . 1493° C
               —Curie point . . . . . . 1121° C (shown in phase dia-
                 grams as –·–)
Composition —atomic percentage where possible (at per cent)
Nomenclature—low temperature hexagonal cobalt—ϵ
                 —face-centered cubic cobalt—α

The choice of atomic percentages is based on the increasing acceptance of this scale among industrial metallurgists, in addition to the preference shown among scientists as noted by Hansen and Anderko, hereafter referred to as HA.[17] Their collection of binary phase diagrams as well as that of Morral,[34] hereafter referred to as M, has contributed valuable background to this chapter and is given this special acknowledgement. Nomenclature follows HA rather than M for consistency in the naming of the face-centered cubic phase as α. A full bibliography is available in both sources, but reference to made to critical papers especially relied on for the selection of a particular form of the phase diagram.

The order of presentation of diagrams follows HA and M; the alphabetical list of chemical symbols is used, rather than the name. Thus, cobalt-silver appears first since Ag is its symbol.

Although selection of diagrams is somewhat arbitrary, consideration has been given to multiple factors: extent of usage; reliability of the available diagram; scientific importance.

Cobalt-Silver

HA give the solubility of cobalt in molten silver as 0.0007 wt per cent at 1000° C, and 0.0004 wt per cent at 1200° C. The solubility of silver in cobalt is reported to be low. The two metals are immiscible in the liquid state.

Cobalt-Silver-Arsenic

Unpublished work has shown that liquid immiscibility in the cobalt-silver system is reduced and disappears at high arsenic contents. This is an important factor in the smelting of cobalt ores with high arsenic contents since the bullion and speiss may become completely miscible.

Cobalt-Aluminum

Figure 7.1 presents this diagram after HA. The eutectic is at 19.5 at (10.0 wt) per cent Al. The remarkable stability of the Co-Al phase (ordered

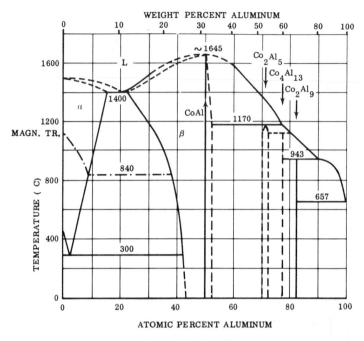

Figure 7.1. Co-Al.

bcc structure) forms the basis for the Alnico series of permanent magnet alloys. Aluminum is almost completely insoluble in ϵ cobalt.

Cobalt-Aluminum-Iron

This phase diagram has not been determined, but similarity of the nickel-aluminum and cobalt-aluminum diagrams has led to use of the nickel-aluminum-iron diagram in lieu of the cobalt-aluminum-iron diagram. Figure 7.2 presents this diagram after Kiuti.[24]

Cobalt-Aluminum-Nickel

The nickel-aluminum system resembles the cobalt-aluminum system (Figure 7.1) in many respects, but an additional phase, Ni_3Al, appears between the α solid solution and bcc β-phase. The Ni_3Al phase is an ordered fcc lattice (Cu_3Au type) and hence is designated α' by HA and Schramm,[44] who determined the Co-Ni-Al system up to the β-phase (NiAl to CoAl). This phase is the principal strengthening precipitate in many of the nickel-base high temperature alloys and is sometimes termed γ'.

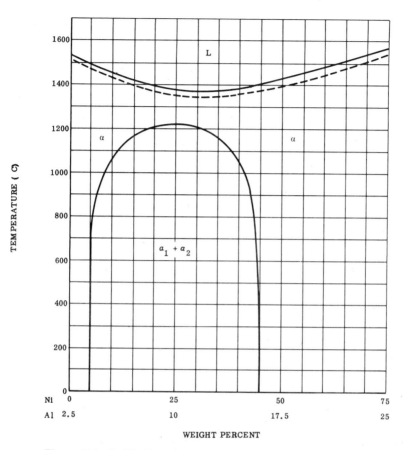

Figure 7.2. Fe-Ni-Al section from 97.5 Fe–2.5 Al to 75 Ni–25 Al.

Schramm[44] showed that the α' phase becomes progressively more unstable as nickel is replaced by cobalt. Figure 7.3 shows, in weight percentage, a "room temperature" isothermal section (alloys cooled from 800°C
for a period of five weeks). Table 7.1 shows how the α' corner of the
ternary field moves with temperature. The restricted extent of the composition of the α' phase explains the limited additions of cobalt made to the
nickel-base alloys.

Cobalt-Arsenic

A recent paper by Heyding and Calvert[20] has enabled the phase diagram
for the cobalt-arsenic system to be revised. Their high temperature X-ray

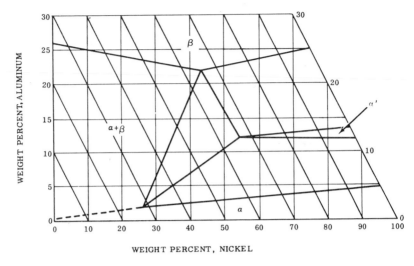

Figure 7.3. Co-Ni-Al.

diffraction results have resolved objections raised by HA to earlier interpretations. The new results (Figure 7.4) show that the reaction at 828° C must be the eutectoid decomposition of Co_5As_2 rather than an allotropic transformation in this phase. Similarly, the reaction at 930° C involving Co_3As_2 becomes a eutectoid decomposition. Allotropic transformations in Co_2As at 450° C and in $CoAs$ at 950° C are believed to occur. The low temperature allotropic transformation of cobalt is raised by arsenic. The reactions on heating and cooling differ less than is usual.

Although higher arsenides, Co_2As_3 and $CoAs_2$, are formed, the phase diagram is not known beyond the $CoAs$ phase.

TABLE 7.1. THE MAXIMUM EXTENT OF THE α′ PHASE IN THE Co-Al-Ni SYSTEM

| Temperature (°C) | Maximum Extent of α′ Phase (wt. %) | |
	Cobalt	Aluminum
Room	47	12
900	40	12
1000	37	12
1100	33	12
1200	30	12
1300	20	12

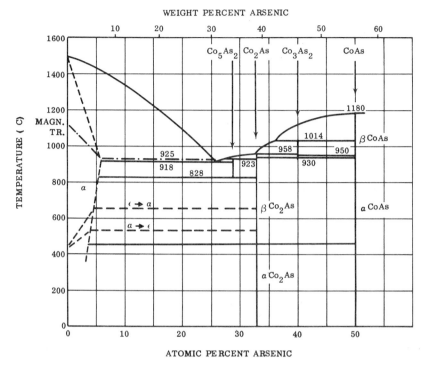

Figure 7.4. Co-As.

Cobalt-Gold

A recent determination by Grigorev, Sokolovskaia, and Maksimova[14] agrees well with the selected values of HA. The cobalt-gold system is a simple eutectic system with the eutectic composition 27 at (10 wt) per cent Co at temperature 996°C (HA) and 995°C.[14] Gold has little effect on the Curie temperature of cobalt. The solid solubilities are given in Table 7.2.

TABLE 7.2. MUTUAL SOLID SOLUBILITIES OF COBALT AND GOLD

Temperature °C	Solubility Co in Au wt %		Temperature °C	Solubility Au in Co wt %	
995–996	8.4 (HA)	8 (14)	995–996	6.1 (HA)	6 (14)
900		5 (14)	900	4.5 (HA)	5 (14)
800	2.6 (HA)		700	1.6 (HA)	
600	0.7 (HA)		500	1.0 (HA)	
400	0.1 (HA)				

Cobalt-Carbon-Tungsten

Several studies have been made of this system to determine the mechanism by which cemented carbides are sintered; the recent study of Rautala and Norton[40] is by far the most satisfactory. Figure 7.5 shows that three

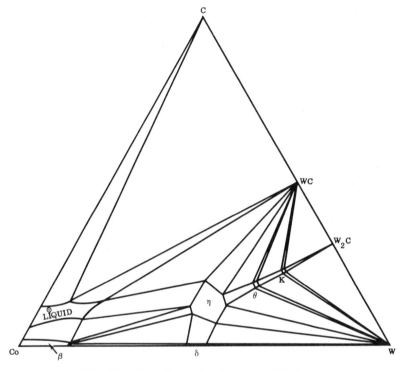

Figure 7.5. 1400° C isothermal section of equilibrium diagram.

ternary phases, η, θ, and K are formed. Both η and θ are cubic double carbides with lattice parameters near 11.0 and 11.25A. Small differences in the intensity of the lines suggest differences in the distribution of cobalt and tungsten atoms among the 96 metal atom sites in the lattice. It is likely that these phases have been referred to as η_1 and η_2 in Russian and Czechoslovakian work. The new ternary phase, K, was found to be hexagonal, with a = c = 7.848Å and an approximate composition represented by $Co_3W_{10}C_4$.

Figure 7.6 shows a partial section of the ternary diagram of Rautala and Norton[40] with a constant cobalt content of 16 wt per cent according to

Gurland.[15] There actually is no pseudo-binary, Co-WC, as was assumed by many previous authors, although, as indicated in Figure 7.7, the eutectic approaches a simple binary, and the greatest departure from the pseudo-binary system occurs above 2000° C as a result of the peritectic, L + C →

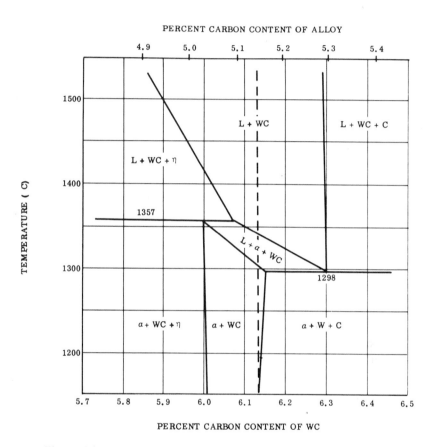

Figure 7.6. Vertical section through ternary diagram at 16 per cent Co.

WC, at 2600° C in the W-C binary. Figure 7.7 shows a special case, but the spread of temperatures between the eutectic valley (1357° C) and the ternary eutectic (1298° C) spans the temperature quoted for the eutectic reaction, the assumption being that the system behaves like a simple binary (e.g., Sandford and Trent[43] quote 1325° C).

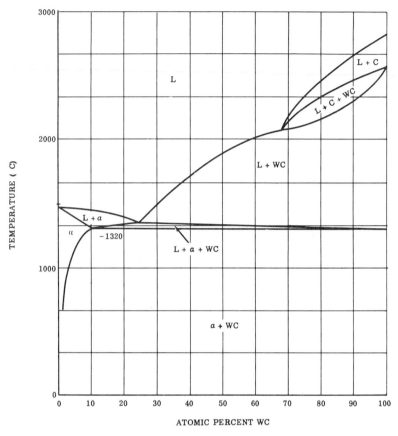

Figure 7.7. Section Co-WC for special case after Rautala and Norton.[40]

Cobalt-Chromium

Elsea, Westerman, and Manning[11] determined the diagram for cobalt-chromium in 1949 and removed many sources of doubt remaining from earlier work. Recognizing that the difficulties were a result of failure to reach equilibrium, these authors introduced a special method of extrapolation to predict the equilibrium positions of the boundaries between the α- and ϵ-phases. Figure 7.8 illustrates their findings for most of the solid-phase boundaries with the liquidus and solidus curves from earlier work (HA). The eutectic is at 45.5 at (42.5 wt) per cent Cr. The phase transformation in the sigma phase was confirmed by Metcalfe,[32] who placed the peritectoid reaction at 1285° C by high temperature dilatometry, probably a more accurate value than that of 1310° C obtained on quenched

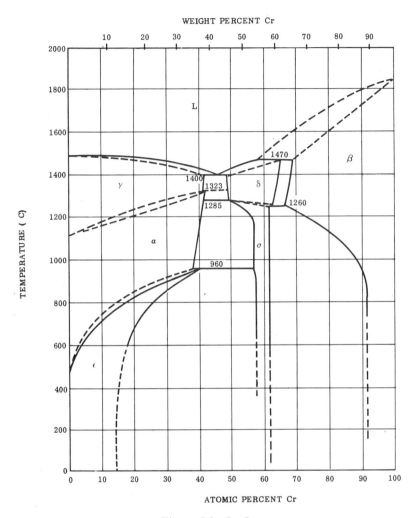

Figure 7.8. Co-Cr.

alloys.[11] Metcalfe[32] claimed to have detected a phase change by high temperature dilatometry in the solid solution, shown as a transformation to the high temperature allotrope, γ.

Cobalt-Chromium-Carbon

The fcc allotrope of cobalt (α) is in equilibrium with carbon at 800° C until about 5 per cent chromium is present, when a wide two-phase field is formed, $\alpha + Cr_7C_3$, with more than 20 per cent cobalt dissolved in the carbide.[27] A narrow two-phase field is formed between α containing approximately 30 per cent Cr and $Cr_{23}C_6$. The latter also contains about 20 per cent Co in solution. According to this source,[27] there is no equilibrium between Cr_3C_2 and the cobalt-rich solid solutions.

Cobalt-Chromium-Iron

Elsea and McBride[10] have shown that in the range of compositions of industrial importance, iron has a stabilizing influence on the α-phase so that the $\alpha/\alpha + \epsilon$ boundary is lowered in temperature. The small ϵ-field (Figure 7.8) is eliminated because the formation of the σ-phase is favored. Elsea and McBride term this phase γ, but the designation σ is preferred to establish this phase as an isomorph of the Fe-Cr σ. Beck and Manly[3] have shown that the Co-Cr and Fe-Cr-σ-phases form a continuous series of solid solutions at 800° C. Kamen and Beck[23] have shown how this continuous σ-field is restricted at 1200° C.

Cobalt-Chromium-Nickel

Elsea and McBride[10] have shown that nickel, like iron, has a stabilizing influence on the α-phase in the cobalt-chromium system so that the $\alpha/\alpha + \epsilon$ boundary is lowered in temperature. The small ϵ-field is eliminated by nickel (Cf. Figure 7.8) because the formation of σ is promoted. No σ-phase is formed in the Ni-Cr system, but more than half the cobalt atoms in the Co-Cr σ can be replaced by nickel according to the studies of Beck and co-workers.[3,23]

Cobalt-Chromium-Molybdenum

Fletcher and Elsea[12] studied the industrially useful alloys having chromium contents equal to 20 per cent and 32 per cent in the cobalt-chromium binary alloys, and having molybdenum additions up to 12 per cent. Figure 7.9 shows the 20 per cent chromium alloys in the lower portion and the 32 per cent chromium alloys in the upper portion. Also shown is the influence of molybdenum on the high temperature allotropic transformation $\alpha \rightleftharpoons \gamma$ for the higher chromium content.[32] The dilatometric work[32] indicates that the γ corner of the $\alpha + \gamma + \sigma$ field for this chromium content lies at 1250° C and 12 per cent molybdenum, while the diagram of Fletcher and Elsea indicates that this corner would be at 1260° C and 8 per cent molybdenum.

Beck and his co-workers,[7,41] after studying the ternary system at 1200° and 1300° C, concluded that two new ternary phases are formed; but more work is required before the high-temperature portion of the diagram can

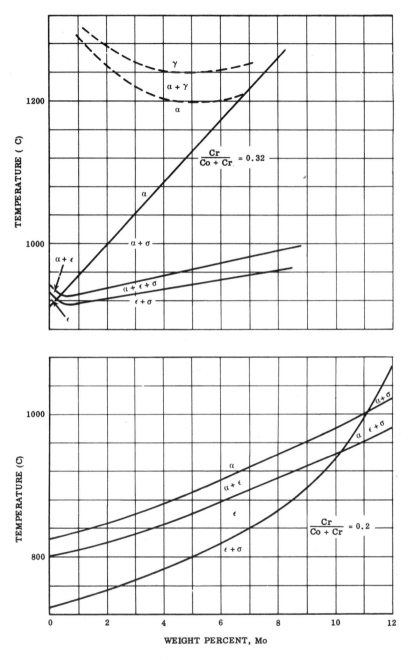

Figure 7.9. Co-Cr-Mo.

be established. The liquidus surface[32] shows a ternary eutectic at 11 wt per cent Cr: 34 wt per cent Mo at 1325°C.

Cobalt-Chromium-Tungsten

Fletcher and Elsea,[12] in a study of the effect of tungsten on the industrially important cobalt-chromium base alloys, concluded that tungsten has much less effect on the transformations than other elements, especially molybdenum.

Cobalt-Copper

The shape of the liquidus curve is similar to that of the iron-copper system, and in both cases the existence of a monotectic and miscibility gap has been disproven (Figure 7.10). The peritectic reaction has been placed at

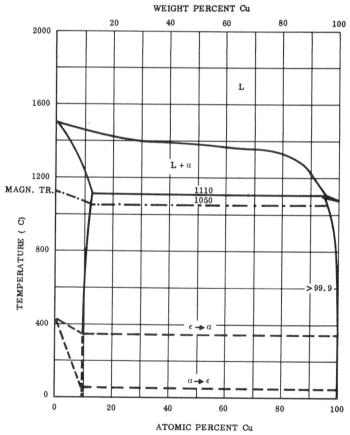

Figure 7.10. Co-Cu.

1100° C after consideration of prior work by HA. The magnetic transformation was placed at 1050° C by HA as a weighted mean between values
of 1040° and 1065° C. A recent determination placing this at 1045° C[13] is
preferred.

The allotropic transformation is depressed by the addition of copper, but
the eutectoid temperature is in considerable doubt, ranging from 340° C on
heating to 53° C on cooling.

Cobalt-Iron

Figure 7.11 shows the small temperature interval between liquidus and

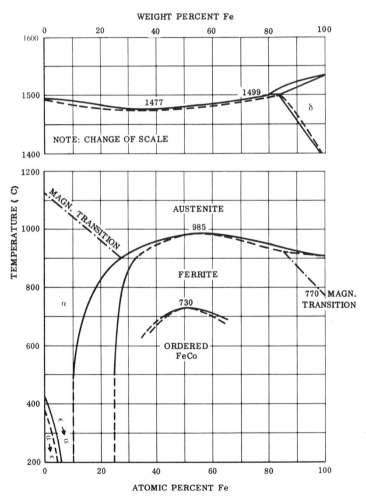

Figure 7.11. Co-Fe.

solidus in this system. The austenite and ferrite two-phase field has been established by classical methods for alloys with more than 30 per cent iron. The extent of this field for alloys richer in cobalt depends on the method of determination: deformation of the alloys at low temperatures indicates a range of 10–24 per cent iron, in contrast to the 18–22 per cent determined by classical methods.[39] Other techniques which avoid the metastable γ phase, e.g., decomposition of Co-Fe amalgams or reduction of Co-Fe formates, agree with the wider extent of the α and γ field (HA). The metastability of phases probably accounts for the hysteresis in the allotropic transformation of cobalt-rich alloys ($\alpha \rightleftharpoons \epsilon$), as discussed by Hess and Barrett[19] in their determination of this transformation in cobalt-nickel alloys.

Anomalies in the properties of the ferrite phase with composition suggest an ordered lattice based on FeCo (51.35 wt per cent Co), supported by X-ray and neutron diffraction studies. Japanese investigators have claimed the existence of ordered lattices based on Fe_3Co and $FeCo_3$ (HA).

Cobalt-Iron-Vanadium

Figure 7.12 shows a section of this ternary diagram at 52 wt per cent cobalt.[26]

Cobalt-Molybdenum

The problems introduced by the allotropic transformation of cobalt are well illustrated by this system. M presents a diagram in which the 417°C transformation is depressed to 250°C for the eutectoid decomposition of α, but HA indicate a preference for a peritectoid transformation at 980°C, similar to Co-Cr (Figure 7.8).

Three intermetallic phases—$MoCo_3$, Mo_6Co_7, and Mo_3Co_2—have been identified, with claims[49] that a fourth phase (θ) at 17 at per cent (25 wt per cent) Mo exists between 1020° and 1200°C. High-temperature dilatometry identified a phase change at 1205°C in an alloy with 26 at per cent Mo,[32] lending support to these views. This work confirmed the existence of an allotropic transformation, α to γ, first claimed by Sykes and Graff,[49] although the transformation temperature was found to rise to a peritectoid reaction at 1240°C[32] rather than 1310°C.[49]

Figure 7.13 shows the diagram according to Sykes and Graff, modified by Metcalfe.[32] The peritectoid decomposition of ϵ seems likely, and was placed at 980° ± 60°C by HA. In this event, three univariant reactions are required in the narrow temperature range from 980° to 1040°C. The present disagreement may result from the complexity of reactions in

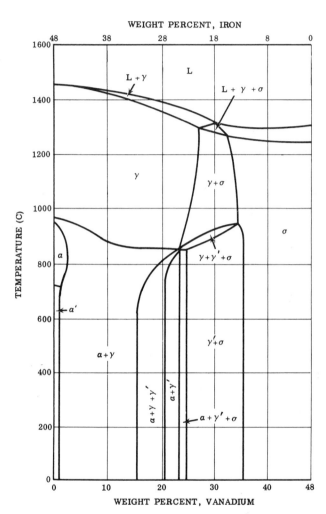

Figure 7.12. Co-Fe-V section at 52 per cent Co.

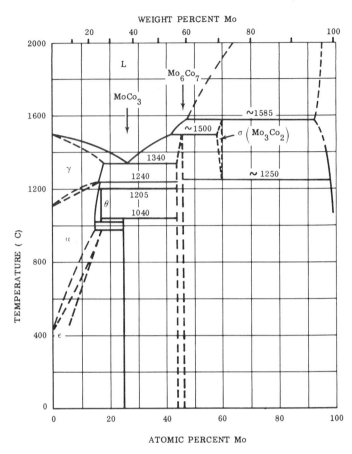

Figure 7.13. Co-Mo.

this narrow temperature range. More work is necessary to resolve these difficulties.

Cobalt-Nickel

Cobalt-nickel melts solidify over temperature intervals of a few degrees to form a continuous series of solid solutions (Figure 7.14).

The effect of nickel on the allotropic transformation of cobalt was studied by Hess and Barrett,[19] using deformation of massive specimens to promote transformation. Agreement was obtained between results starting with the hexagonal and the cubic phase. Lihl,[28] in establishing the boundaries by decomposition of cobalt-nickel amalgams, found values higher in temperature and richer in nickel for the $\alpha/\alpha + \epsilon$ boundary. Powdered al-

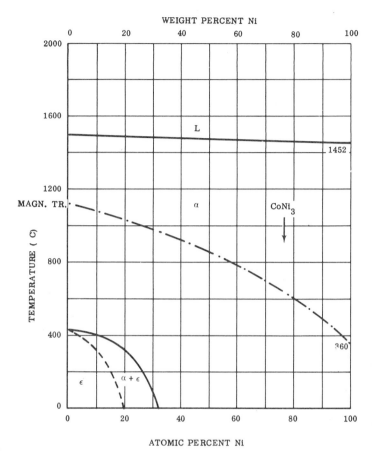

Figure 7.14. Co-Ni.

loys were produced by the decomposition of the amalgams, introducing problems such as those discussed by Owen and Madoc-Jones.[38] The values of Hess and Barrett[19] on massive specimens are preferred.

The lattice parameters of cobalt-nickel alloys show anomalies indicating the possibility of superlattice formation at Co_3Ni and $CoNi_3$.[50] Because of the similarity of scattering factors of cobalt and nickel atoms, X-ray diffraction does not permit an unambiguous determination; but other physical properties show anomalies. The diagram must be more complicated than shown, particularly in the region near 25 per cent nickel.

Cobalt-Oxygen

Oxygen depresses the melting point of cobalt from 1493° C to a eutectic point at 1450° C and 0.23 wt per cent oxygen. The eutectic reaction involves the formation of CoO (21.35 wt per cent O_2) which melts at 1810° C[1] or 1935° C.[53] Higher oxides Co_3O_4 (26.58 wt per cent O_2) and Co_2O_3 (28.94 wt per cent O_2) exist.

Seybolt and Mathewson[47] determined the solid solubility (in wt per cent) of oxygen in cobalt to be 0.013 at 1200° C; 0.008 at 1000° C; 0.007 at 945° C; 0.010 at 875° C; 0.016 at 810° C; 0.009 at 700° C; 0.006 at 600° C. From these results, it was claimed that an allotropic transformation occurred in pure cobalt at 850° C, rising to a peritectoid reaction at 875° C in cobalt-oxygen alloys.

Cobalt-Platinum

Figure 7.15 shows the phase diagram for the cobalt-platinum system. A continuous series of solid solutions are formed with liquidus temperatures as indicated.

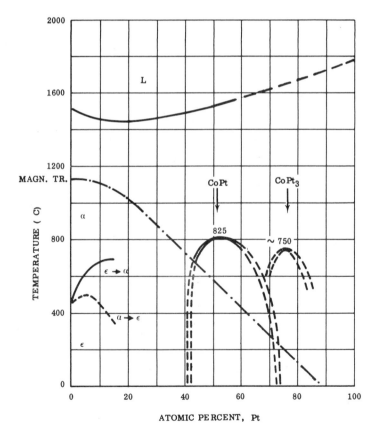

Figure 7.15. Co-Pt.

The only phase change involving complete lattice rearrangement is the $\epsilon \rightleftharpoons \alpha$ transformation. That this change is more uncertain than usual is shown by the transformation curves on heating and cooling. Two ordering reactions have been detected, based on the compositions CoPt and CoPt$_3$. The former resembles the CuAu ordering, with the movement to a face-centered tetragonal lattice, a = 3.793Å, c = 3.675Å from the face-centered cubic solid solution with a = 3.751Å (HA). The CoPt$_3$ ordering resembles the ordering of Cu$_3$Au.

Cobalt-Sulfur

Rosenqvist[42] made a thermodynamic study of the cobalt-sulfur system, from which he was able to obtain more accurate data on the phase diagram. Figure 7.16 is plotted largely from his results. The diagram differs from

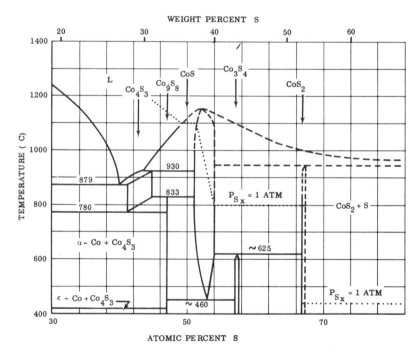

Figure 7.16. Co-S.

earlier diagrams (e.g., Figure 292 in HA) mainly in the placement of the CoS phase outside the stoichiometric composition. This phase decomposes at 460°C.

The solid solubility of sulfur in cobalt is very low. Martin[30] has observed the onset of brittleness in cast cobalt at 0.005 per cent sulfur, the result of a low melting eutectic grain-boundary network. Other evidence suggests that the solubility may be a little higher in homogeneous (e.g., wrought) alloys.

Cobalt-Tungsten

The tentative diagram selected by HA is illustrated in Figure 7.17. Other diagrams show a eutectoid resulting from an initial depression of the 417° C allotropic transformation in cobalt, whereas HA believe the data available support a diagram similar to that of cobalt-chromium. There is little agreement on the solid solubility below 1100° C.

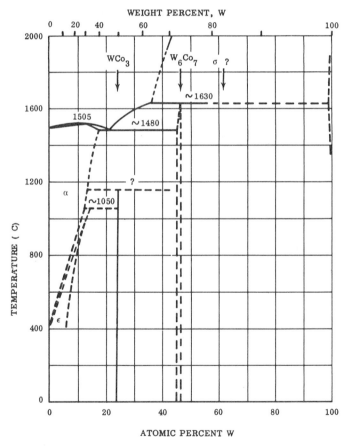

Figure 7.17. Co-W.

The phases Co_3W and Co_7W_6 have been identified, but claims that other phases exist have yet to be substantiated. The solubility of cobalt in tungsten is claimed to be 0.9 at (0.3 wt) per cent Co.

References

1. Asanti, P., and Kohlmeyer, E. J., "Thermal Properties of Compounds of Cobalt with Oxygen and Sulphur," *Z. anorg. Chem.,* **265,** 90–98 (1955).
2. Basinski, Z. S., and Christian, J. W., "The Martensitic Transformation in Cobalt," *Phil Mag.,* **44,** 791–792 (1953).
3. Beck, P. A., and Manly, W. D., "The Sigma Phase in Ternary Cr-Co-Fe and Cr-Co-Ni Alloys," *Trans. AIME,* **185,** 354 (1949).
4. Bibring, H., and Sebilleau, F., "Structure et Transformation Allotropique du Cobalt," *Rev. de Metallurgie,* **52,** 369–378 (1955).
5. Buhl, O., and Schüler, C., "Field Electron Microscope Observations of Allotropic Transformations in Cobalt," *Z. Metallkunde,* **48,** 116–118 (1957).
6. Cardwell, A. B., "Photoelectric and Thermionic Emission from Cobalt (Allotropic Forms of Cobalt)," *Phys. Rev.,* **38,** 2033–2040 (1931).
7. Darby, J. B., Jr., and Beck, P. A., "Intermediate Phases in the Cr-Mo-Co System at 1300° C," *Trans. AIME,* **203,** 765–766 (1955).
8. Edwards, O. S., and Lipson, H., "An X-ray Study of the Transformations in Cobalt," *J. Inst. Metals,* **69,** 177–187 (1943).
9. —, and Wilson, A. J. C., "Imperfection in the Structure of Cobalt," *Proc. Roy. Soc.* (London), **180A,** 268–285 (1942).
10. Elsea, A. R., and McBride, C. C., "The Effects of Nitrogen, Iron, and Nickel upon the Alpha/Beta and Gamma Precipitation in Cobalt-Chromium Alloys," *Trans. AIME,* **188,** 154–161 (1950).
11. Elsea, A. R., Westerman, A. B., and Manning, G. K., "The Cobalt-Chromium Binary System," *Trans. AIME,* **180,** 579–602 (1949).
12. Fletcher, E. E., and Elsea, A. R., "Effects of Tungsten and Molybdenum upon the Alpha/Beta Transformation and Gamma Precipitation in Cobalt-Chromium Alloys," *Trans. AIME,* **191,** 897–902 (1951).
13. Grigorev, A. T., Panteleimonov, L. A., Viting, L. M., and Kuprina, M. N., "A Study of the Copper-Cobalt System," *Zhur. Neorg. Khim.,* **1,** 1064–66 (1956); *Chem. Abstr.,* **50,** 16625 (1956).
14. Grigorev, A. T., Sokolovskaia, E. M., and Maksimova, M. V., "Investigation of the Alloys in the System Au-Co," *Zhur. Neorg. Khim.,* **1,** 1047–1051 (1956); *Chem. Abstr.,* **50,** 16626 (1956).
15. Gurland, J., "A Study of the Effect of Carbon Content on the Structure and Properties of Sintered WC-Co Alloys," *Trans. AIME,* **200,** 285–290 (1954).
16. Hampel, C. A., Editor, "Rare Metals Handbook," pp 114–119, New York, Reinhold Publishing Corp., 1954.
17. Hansen, M., and Anderko, K., "Constitution of Binary Alloys," New York, McGraw Hill Book Company, Inc., 1958.
18. Hendricks, S. R., Jefferson, M. E., and Schultz, J. F., "The Transition Temperatures of Cobalt and Nickel," *Z. Kristallogr.,* **73,** 376–380 (1930).

19. Hess, J. B., and Barrett, C. S., "Transformation in Cobalt-Nickel Alloys," *Jour. of Metals*, **4**, 645–647 (1952).
20. Heyding, R. D., and Calvert, L. D., "Arsenides of Transition Metals: the Arsenides of Iron and Cobalt," *Can. J. Chem.*, **35**, 449–457 (1957).
21. Hull, A. W., "Crystal Structure of Ferromagnetic Metals," *Phys. Rev.*, **14**, 540–541 (1919).
22. Jaeger, E. M., Rosenbohm, E., and Zuithoff, A. J., "The Exact Determination of Specific Heats at High Temperatures. XIII. Cobalt," *Rec. trav. Chim.*, **59**, 831–856 (1940); *Chem. Abstr.*, **35**, 4667 (1941).
23. Kamen, E. L., and Beck, P. A., "Survey of Portions of the Cobalt-Chromium-Iron-Nickel Quaternary System; NACA Tech. Note 2603, (February 1952).
24. Kiuti, S., "Mechanism of a New Transformation and Some Associated New Reactions in the Fe-Ni-Al System," *Rept. Aeronaut. Inst., Tokyo Imp. Univ.*, **15** (No. 17) 601–720 (1940); *Chem. Abstr.*, **35**, 5843 (1941).
25. Köster, W., "The Effects of the Elements on the Polymorphic Transformation of Cobalt," *Z. Metallkunde*, **43**, 297–303 (1952); *Chem. Abstr.* **47**, 85 (1953).
26. —, and Schmid, H., "Das Dreistoffsystem Eisen-Kobalt-Vanadin," *Arch. Eisenhüttenwesen*, Teil I, **26**, 345–353 (1955), Teil II, **26**, 421–425 (1955).
27. Köster, W., and Sperner, F., "Das Dreistoffsystem Kobalt-Chrom-Kohlenstoff," *Arch. Eisenhüttenwesen*, **26**, 555–559 (1955).
28. Lihl, F., "Die Amalgame als Hilfsmittel in der Metallkundlichen Forschung," *Z. Metallkunde*, **46**, 434–441 (1955).
29. Marick, L., "Variation of Resistance and Structure of Cobalt with Temperature and a Discussion of its Photoelectric Emission," *Phys. Rev.*, **49**, 831–837 (1936).
30. Martin, D. L., "Sulfur Embrittlement of Cobalt," *Trans. AIME.*, **206**, 578–579 (1956).
31. Metcalfe, A. G., "The Allotropy of Cobalt," Proc. First World Met. Congress (ASM), 1951, 717–731.
32. —, "Thermal and Dilatometric Investigation of the Alloys of Cobalt with Chromium and Molybdenum," *Trans. AIME.*, **194**, 357–364 (1953).
33. —, "The High Temperature Hexagonal Phase of Cobalt," *Acta Metallurgica*, **1**, 609–610 (1953).
34. Morral, F. R., "Cobalt and its Alloys," Columbus, Ohio, Cobalt Information Center (1958).
35. Myers, H. P., and Sucksmith, W., "The Spontaneous Magnetism of Cobalt," *Proc. Roy. Soc.*, **207A**, 427–446 (1951): also, private communication from Professor Sucksmith dated 26 April, 1952.
36. Neuberger, M. C., "Lattice Constants for the Year 1936," *Z. Kristallogr.*, **93**, 9 (1936).
37. Newkirk, J. B., and Geisler, A. H., "High Temperature Hexagonal Phase of Cobalt," *Acta Metallurgica*, **1**, 456–457 (1953).
38. Owen, E. A., and Madoc-Jones, D., "Effect of Grain Size on the Crystal Structure of Cobalt," *Proc. Phys. Soc.*, **67**, (6B), 456–466 (1954).
39. Papier, J., "Contribution à l'étude des alliages fer-cobalt," *Comptes Rendus*, **242**, 2455–2457 (1956).

40. Rautala, P., and Norton, J. T., "Tungsten-Cobalt-Carbon System," *Trans. AIME,* **194,** 1045–1050 (1952).

41. Rideout, S. P., Manly, W. D., Kamen, E. L., Lement, B. S., and Beck, P. A., "Intermediate Phases in Ternary Alloy Systems of Transition Elements," *Trans. AIME,* **191,** 872–876 (1951).

42. Rosenqvist, T., "A Thermodynamic Study of the Iron, Cobalt, and Nickel Sulphides," *Jour. Iron and Steel Inst.,* **176,** 37–57 (1954)

43. Sandford, E. J., and Trent, E. M., "The Physical Metallurgy of Sintered Carbides," Iron and Steel Inst., Symposium on Powder Metallurgy. Special Report No. 38, 84 (1947).

44. Schramm, J., "Das Dreistoffsystem Nickel-Kobalt Aluminum," *Z. Metallkunde,* **33,** 403–412 (1941).

45. Schulze, A., "Uber die Umwandlungspunkte von Metallen," *Z. Metallkunde,* **22,** 308–310 (1930).

46. Sekito, S., "On the Lattice Constants of Metallic Cobalt," *Sci. Rep. Tohôku Imp. Univ.,* **16,** 545–553 (1927); *Chem. Abstr.,* **21,** 3594 (1927).

47. Seybolt, A. U., and Mathewson, C. H., "Solubility of Oxygen in Solid Cobalt and the Upper Transformation Point of the Metal," *Trans. AIME,* **117,** 156–172 (1935).

48. Sykes, W. P., "The Cobalt-Tungsten System," Trans., *Amer. Soc. for Steel Treating,* **21,** 385–423 (1931).

49. —, and Graff, H. F., "The Cobalt-Molybdenum System," *Trans. ASM.,* **23,** 241–285 (1935).

50. Taylor, A., "Lattice Parameters of Binary Nickel-Cobalt Alloys," *J. Inst. Metals,* **77,** 585–594 (1950).

51. Troiano, A. R., and Tokich, J. L., "The Transformation of Cobalt," *Trans. AIME,* **175,** 728–741 (1948).

52. Umino, S., "The Heat of Transformation of Nickel and Cobalt," *Sci. Rep. Tohôku Imp. Univ.,* **16,** 593–611 (1927); *Chem. Abstr.,* **21,** 3534 (1927).

53. Wartenberg, H., von, and Gurr, W., "Melting Point Diagrams of Highly Inert Oxides," *Z. anorg. Chem.,* **196,** 374–383 (1931).

54. Wasserman, G., "Uber die Umwandlung des Kobalts," *Metallwirtschaft,* **11,** 61–65 (1932).

55. Wyckoff, R. W. G., "The Structure of Crystals," p. 204, New York, Chemical Catalog Co., Inc., 1931.

Chapter 8

MAGNETIC, ELECTRICAL, AND ELECTRONIC APPLICATIONS

E. A. NESBITT

Bell Telephone Laboratories
Murray Hill, New Jersey

INTRODUCTION

The role of cobalt in magnetic, electrical, and electronic applications is mainly that of an alloying element in magnetic materials. Cobalt is also used as an alloying element in electronic applications where alloys having a low coefficient of linear expansion are required. The metal itself has always been of major interest to those concerned with magnetism because it is one of three elements that are ferromagnetic at room temperature. Every alloy with a high magnetic saturation at room temperature contains either cobalt or iron. Since 1916, the best permanent magnet has always contained a substantial amount of cobalt. Today, the Alnico family of permanent magnet alloys accounts for 25 per cent of the cobalt consumed in this country. In addition, Supermendur, a soft magnetic material which contains 50 per cent cobalt, has the highest values of permeability at high flux densities of any magnetic material.

COBALT

The outstanding magnetic property of cobalt metal is its high Curie point—higher than that of any other metal or alloy. This is illustrated in Figure 8.1 by the data of Myers and Sucksmith,[46] which shows the saturation magnetization in gauss versus temperature in degrees centigrade. It can be observed from the curve that in the region of 900–1000°C, where practically all other metals are nonmagnetic, cobalt still has a high saturation value of 10,300–12,600 gauss. There is a small discontinuity in the magnetization versus temperature curve in the vicinity of 400°C because of the transformation from the room temperature hexagonal phase to the high temperature face-centered cubic phase. Data indicate that the latter phase has a slightly higher saturation value than the hexagonal phase. The Curie temperature was found to be 1121°C by extrapolation, and this value and

184

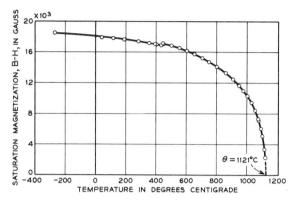

Figure 8.1. Saturation magnetization versus temperature for cobalt.

the saturation value at 0° K are in reasonable agreement with that obtained by various other investigators.[14,18,68]

Another unusual magnetic property of cobalt is its high crystal anisotropy.[1,26,65] This is illustrated by the large spread in the single crystal magnetization curves of Kaya, shown in Figure 8.2. The intrinsic magnetization in the axial direction [00·1] of the crystal rises sharply compared to the lateral direction, [10·0] which is a hard direction of magnetization. The area

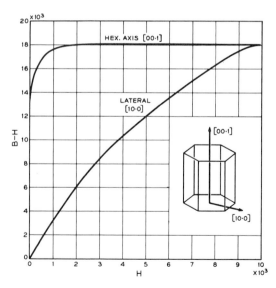

Figure 8.2. Magnetization curves for a single crystal of cobalt in [00·1] and [10·0] directions.

between these curves is a measure of the crystal anisotropy. Bozorth has measured the crystal anisotropy of hexagonal cobalt at room temperature and found it to be 5.5×10^6 ergs/cm^3. This is approximately ten times higher than that of iron (460,000), and one hundred times higher than that of nickel (51,000).

The most recent values obtained on the magnetostriction of cobalt are those of Bozorth,[1] shown in Figure 8.3. These indicate that along the hexa-

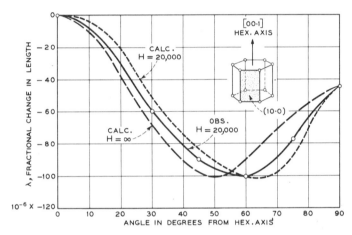

Figure 8.3. Magnetostriction in (10·0) plane of a single crystal of cobalt.

gonal axis in the (10·0) plane, the magnetostriction is zero; that it reaches a maximum of -100×10^{-6} in the neighborhood of 50–60° from the hexagonal axis; and that it then reduces to a value of -44×10^{-6} in a lateral direction. Bozorth has calculated the value of magnetostriction in polycrystalline cobalt to be -70×10^{-6} at saturation.

The available data on the variation of magnetization with magnetizing field in cobalt are meager. G. A. Kelsall, in unpublished work, tested a coil made of tape (.006″ × .125″) that was annealed at 1000° C and that yielded a maximum permeability of 245. It required a field of 1000 oersteds to raise the magnetization to a value of approximately 14,000 gauss. Since cobalt possesses substantial values of crystal anisotropy and magnetostriction, exceptionally high permeability is not expected in randomly-oriented polycrystalline samples of cobalt. In recent years, the magnetic domain structure of cobalt has been investigated; Figure 8.4 shows a pattern obtained by H. J. Williams. The picture on the right shows the magnetic domains which lie along the easy direction of magnetization (hexagonal axis). The domain patterns reveal the twofold symmetry of the hexagonal crystal lattice. The spike-like domains in this figure reduce the magnetostatic energy

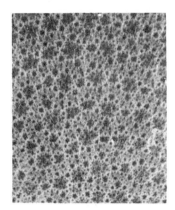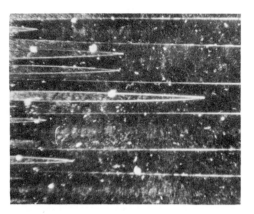

Figure 8.4. Left: end view of magnetic domains on cobalt single crystal (hexagonal face). Right: side view of magnetic domains on cobalt single crystal (along hexagonal axis).

of the crystal. The figure on the left is an end view of these same magnetic domains as seen for a hexagonal face.

The electrical resistivity of cobalt is 6.24 microhm-cm at 20° C. This is the lowest value of the three ferromagnetic elements, iron and nickel having values of 9.7 and 6.8 microhm-cm, respectively.

PERMANENT MAGNET THEORY

In order to discuss permanent magnets, one must have some knowledge of the fine particle theory of coercive force,[29,47,63] since this theory accounts for the permanent magnet properties of practically all the important permanent magnets. Fine particles are necessary for limiting the magnetization process to one of rotation, as shown by the arrows in the particles represented in the upper part of Figure 8.5. In general, it requires high energy to change the direction of magnetization in this manner.

If the particles are larger than the sizes indicated in the upper part of Figure 8.5, a change of magnetization will take place by a mechanism called "domain wall motion." As shown in the lower part of the illustration, this mechanism requires the existence of a domain wall—a transition region with about 4 millionths of an inch between domains—wherein the magnetization changes in direction from that of one domain to that of the adjacent domain. When the magnetization is changed in these larger particles, the wall moves across the particle in accordance with the change. This is the type of change that occurs in high permeability materials which will be discussed later. It is a low energy process since the magnetization does

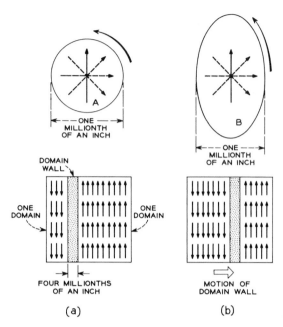

Figure 8.5. Above: in very small particles, reversing of magnetization is indicated by rotation of arrows. Below: in larger particles, magnetization is reversed by motion of domain wall.

not have to overcome directly the anisotropy of the material as it does in the rotational type of change. For this reason, in most important permanent magnet materials, the particles are smaller than the thickness of a domain wall.

The spherical particle A of Figure 8.5, in addition to being small in size, must have crystal properties permitting both an easy and a hard direction of magnetization. The degree of difference in difficulty of magnetization is a measure of what is termed magnetic crystal anisotropy, usually designated by the letter K. If the crystal anisotropy is determined, the coercive force of the particle can be calculated. According to Kittel and Galt,[31] this is

$$H_c = \frac{2K}{I_s}$$

where I_s is the saturation magnetization. This equation applies for a uniaxial crystal or for a cubic crystal in a [001] direction. For a compact of cubic particles of random orientation,[47]

$$H_c = 0.64K/I_s$$

Apparently, high coercive force occurs with high crystal anisotropy.

In the small elongated particle *B* of Figure 8.5, it is easy to magnetize along the long dimension, difficult along the narrow dimension; therefore, the magnetization vector will tend to lie along the length of the particle. The ratio of the length to the width of the particle is a measure of its shape anisotropy. Since high shape anisotropy results in high permanent magnet properties, needle-like shapes of fine particles are very desirable. The coercive force of an elongated particle (prolate spheroid) may be calculated according to Kittel and Galt,[31]

$$H_c = (N_e - N_o)I_s$$

where N_e is a demagnetizing factor in the narrow direction, N_o is a demagnetizing factor in the long direction. Stoner and Wohlfarth[64] have shown that for particles with axes distributed in random orientations, the coercive force is given by

$$H_c = 0.48 (N_e - N_o)I_s$$

Neel[47] derived the value of coercive force of the compact to be

$$H_c = (1 - P) 2\pi I_s$$

where *P* is the packing fraction of the magnetic particles, when an assembly of long cylindrical rods interact with each other. It is evident from the above equation that when shape anisotropy is employed the density of packing of the particles becomes a critical factor.

Experimental values obtained on compacts of elongated single domain particles have been much lower than those predicted by the above equation. In this connection, Jacobs and Bean[22] have considered a "chain of spheres" model. This consists of a linear chain of spheres barely in contact with each other in which the magnetization fans out in opposite directions in alternate spheres. Coercive forces calculated for this model closely match those values obtained experimentally.

PERMANENT MAGNET MATERIALS CONTAINING COBALT

Alnico 2

This alloy is a direct development of the discovery, by Mishima,[45] of the permanent magnet properties of the Fe-Ni-Al alloys. After this discovery, Mishima,[44] Ruder,[58] and Horsburgh and Tetley[20] added cobalt to these alloys. The latter two investigators added copper, in addition to cobalt, which resulted in an alloy known as Alnico 2 (17 per cent Ni; 10 per cent Al; 13 per cent Co; 6 per cent Cu; rest, Fe). This alloy has a maximum energy product of 1.6×10^6 gauss-oersteds, a coercive force of 560 oersteds, and a residual induction of 7400 gauss. It was used extensively before the advent of Alnico 5. One objective in adding cobalt and copper was to make the alloy easier to heat-treat, and to obtain more reproducible results on bars of various thicknesses than in the case of the straight Fe-Ni-Al alloys. A typical heat treatment for this alloy is air cooling from 1250° C and aging at 600° C.

The phase diagram for the Alnico system is not known, but Figure 8.6 shows one by Kiuti[32] for the closely related Fe-Ni-Al system. The addition

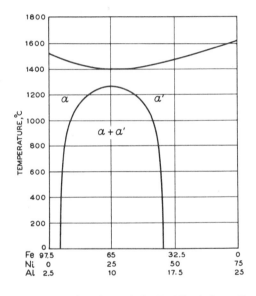

Figure 8.6. Section through the Fe-Ni-Al phase diagram.

of cobalt to this system is not thought to change substantially the nature of the phase diagram. In this connection, it is well to remember that some of the important structural changes in permanent magnet systems are transitional in nature[16,52] and are not revealed by equilibrium diagrams. Alnico is a fine particle magnet, the particles having, in general, both crystal and shape anisotropy. Nesbitt, Williams, and Bozorth,[54] in an investigation of Fe_2NiAl (near Alnico 3 composition), showed that approximately 75 per cent of the coercive force was due to shape, the remainder to crystal anisotropy in this alloy.

Alnico 5

This alloy was discovered by Jonas and van Emden[24] just prior to World War II; since then, it has become the most important permanent magnet alloy. Previously, the work of Oliver and Shedden,[57] in 1938, showed a definite increase of 20 per cent in residual induction of Alnico 2 when it was cooled in a field from a high temperature. Alnico 5 contains, by weight, 14 per cent Ni, 8 per cent Al, 24 per cent Co, 51 per cent Fe, and 3 per cent Cu; and it has a unique property—its figure of merit $(BH)_{max}$ is increased threefold by heat treatment in a magnetic field. A vast amount of research has been done on this alloy; for this reason, one can now understand why it is an excellent permanent magnet. In order to interpret this alloy, two major effects must be considered. First, what is the mechanism which causes the alloy to have high coercive force; secondly, what is the mechanism which causes the alloy to respond to heat treatment in a magnetic field?

According to the theory of Kittel, Nesbitt, and Shockley,[30] if a polycrystalline bar of Alnico 5 is heat-treated in a field H_t, theoretically, plates of precipitate parallel to the field direction but not at right angles to it will be obtained. The bar will be divided up into plates of precipitate and rods of matrix. Nuclei are formed parallel to the field since in this direction they have a low demagnetizing factor; nuclei formed at right angles to the field have a high demagnetizing factor and are therefore suppressed. These nuclei will retain their general shape as they grow into the final state.

Structures Obtained by Electron Metallography

The work of Heidenreich and Nesbitt,[16] illustrated in Figure 8.7, shows an experimental confirmation of the theory. These electron micrographs are thermal oxide replicas of single crystal surfaces of Alnico 5 for the (100) plane. In Figure 8.7b, the crystal was heat-treated with the field H_t applied in the vertical direction as indicated; the precipitate (black regions) is elongated in the field direction, as predicted by the theory. The experiment has added a refinement to the theory since it can now be seen that the precipitate is, in reality, composed of rods which aggregate to form plates. Figure 8.7b is a side view of the rods, Figure 8.7c an end view.

In Figure 8.7a, the magnetic field is not applied during heat treatment; as a result, additional information about the precipitate is obtained. In this state, the precipitate grows in all three $<100>$ directions. It can be deduced from this micrograph that the precipitate has a higher Curie point than the matrix because, if it did not, the matrix would become magnetic first on cooling; its spontaneous magnetization would orient the precipitate in each domain just as the applied field does in the entire crystal, and the micrograph would show regions similar to Figure 8.7b.

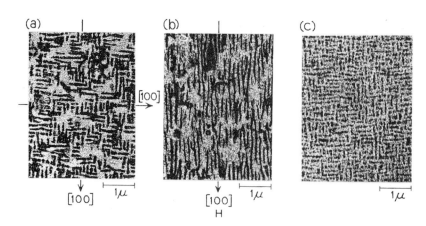

Figure 8.7. Electron micrographs illustrating effects of a magnetic field, applied during the 2° C per second cool from 1300° C on the permanent magnet precipitate in Alnico 5. Single crystal (100) face. Aged 2 hours at 800° C to grow the precipitate. (a) no field; (b) with field along [100]; (c) section normal to applied field showing the ends of the rods of precipitate.

The spacing between the rows of rods at optimum properties was found to be 200Å, and the size of the precipitate rod approximately 75–100Å by 400Å long. These sizes have since been confirmed by other investigators.[5,10,35]

When the rows of precipitate rods are 850Å apart, the coercive force is only of the order of 20 oersteds. To obtain such a low value of coercive force there must be domain boundaries. It seems unlikely that a mechanism which produces only 20 oersteds coercive force when the spacing is 850Å could produce 600 oersteds coercive force when the spacing is 200Å. The conclusion is that in the vicinity of 200Å, domain boundaries no longer exist, and that the magnetization process has to take place by rotation.

Torque Measurements on Single Crystals of Alnico 5

This type of measurement yields important information about Alnico 5. Briefly, it consists of rotating single crystal disk specimens in a strong magnetic field and measuring the torque necessary to turn the crystal away from a direction of easy magnetization. From these measurements, one of the factors obtained is the value of the crystal anisotropy K. The most significant torque curves on Alnico 5 are shown in Figure 8.8.[53]

This crystal was cut with a (100) face and was heat-treated in a field perpendicular to its face. The torque curves have fourfold symmetry because there are two sets of plates at right angles to each other (see Figure 8.7c).

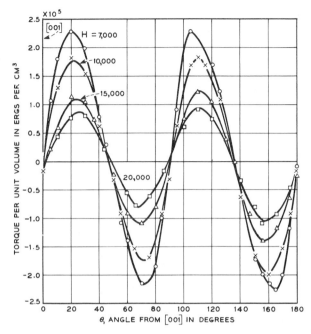

Figure 8.8. Torque curves for Alnico 5 single crystal disk (100) heat treated in a field perpendicular to its face.

The torque diminishes with increasing field strength. This has been shown[54] to be a characteristic of shape anisotropy in the precipitate. It is important because it shows that the precipitate acts magnetically, like a collection of plates, since all the rods of precipitate lie perpendicular to the measuring field. In this case, it is the ratio of the width to the thickness of the plates which determines the shape anisotropy of the precipitate. In order to obtain this effect the rods must be stacked close enough together so that they can act in a crosswise manner like a plate. Furthermore, if the peak value of the torque curve versus $1/H$ is plotted, the linear curve obtained intersects the point of zero torque at $H = \infty$, indicating practically zero crystalline anisotropy for optimum permanent magnet conditions. This is why it is possible to heat-treat Alnico 5 in a magnetic field in all crystallographic directions.

Heat Treatment of Alnico 5

A general treatment for this alloy is as follows: heat it to $1300°$ C (solid solution temperature); cool it in a magnetic field at approximately $2°$ C/sec between $890°$ and $760°$ C (nucleation temperatures); age it at approximately $600°$ C for 8 hours (growth temperature). If the alloy is held too long in the

COBALT

region of 1300–890° C, an unwanted phase will appear, and the alloy will not respond properly to the field heat treatment. In heat-treating, it is convenient to first cool the alloy rapidly from the cast state (this eliminates unwanted high temperature phase). Then, merely by raising the alloy to 880° C, cooling it in a field at 2° C/sec from this point, and aging it at 600° C, excellent properties can be obtained. The most effective part of the temperature range of nucleation is 840–790° C, as shown in Figure 8.9. If

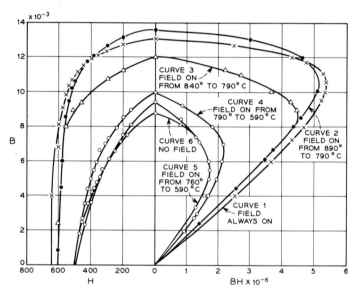

Figure 8.9. Nucleation experiments on Alnico 5 heat treatment as indicated, plus aging at 600° C.

the magnetic field is applied only during this range, and then air-quenched from 790° C and aged at 600° C, a maximum energy product of 4.5 × 10⁶ gauss-oersteds is obtained (curve 3 of Figure 8.9).

Heidenreich and Nesbitt[16] found a face-centered cubic transition structure associated with the permanent magnet heat treatment. Koch, van der Steeg, and de Vos[33] measured a coercive force of 260 oersteds at 800° C after 5 minutes, indicating that a substantial amount of a second phase had appeared after this short time. They also found a third phase after tempering the alloy at 600° C. Hansen[15] reported that heating the alloy to 650° C and then air-cooling it reduced the energy product from 5.80 to 3.64 × 10⁶ gauss-oersteds. However, if the alloy was furnace-cooled to 538° C, the energy product recovered to a value of 5.3 × 10⁶ gauss-oersteds. These facts are not inconsistent with the theory of nucleation of the permanent magnet precipitate in the vicinity of 800° C and the growth of the precipitate plates at 600° C.

Alnico 6 and Alnico 7

In general, the criterion for permanent magnet design is the maximum energy product $(BH)_m$; sometimes, however, a lower value is used in order to obtain a material with a higher coercive force. The higher coercive force means that a shorter magnet can be used; this is desirable in some designs, for example, in a permanent magnet rotor for a generator or motor. It has long been known that titanium increases the coercive force of the Alnico family, but at the same time it reduces its ability to respond to the magnetic field heat treatment and therefore lowers the energy product. Alnico 6 (15Ni, 8Al, 24Co, 3Cu, 1.25Ti, bal. Fe) and Alnico 7 (18Ni, 8.5Al, 24Co, 5Ti, bal. Fe) are two such magnet alloys. The former has a coercive force of 750 oersteds, the latter 1050 oersteds; their energy products are 3.8×10^6 and 2.5×10^6 gauss-oersteds, respectively.

Sintered Alnicos

Sintered magnets are sometimes used in very small sizes, 20 g or less when units of 10,000 or more are desired. Sintering permits greater mechanical strength and greater freedom of design in the use of complicated shapes. Alnico 5 sintered has a residual induction of 10,500 gauss, a coercive force of 600 oersteds, and a maximum energy product of 3.75×10^6 gauss-oersteds. Alnico 2 sintered has a residual induction of 7200 gauss, a coercive force of 550 oersteds, and a maximum energy product of 1.5×10^6 gauss-oersteds. Because of the small size of sintered Alnico magnets, they are used in miniature parts, such as ear phones and thermostatic switches.

Directional Grain Alnico 5 and Single Crystals

Single crystal work has shown that maximum torque is developed when a crystal is heat-treated in a [001] direction.[51] The plates of precipitate normally grow in [001] directions when not influenced by a field. Hoselitz[42] and others showed that magnets of the Alnico 5 type could be improved if columnar crystals were formed during the melt, and the heat-treating field was aligned parallel to them. Figure 8.10 shows demagnetizing curves comparing polycrystalline Alnico 5 with commercial directional grain Alnico 5. The energy product is increased from 4.5 to 6.0×10^6 gauss-oersteds. A still greater improvement may be obtained by using single crystals. The author cut single crystals in a [001] direction and obtained energy products over 8.0×10^6 gauss-oersteds, as shown in Figure 8.10. The results were re-

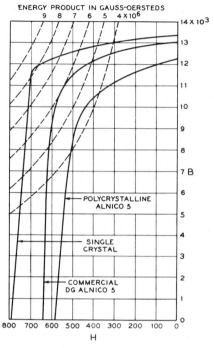

Figure 8.10. Comparison of demagnetization curves of single crystal of Alnico 5, commercial directional grain Alnico 5, and commercial polycrystalline Alnico 5.

producible, and the crystals were grown without difficulty. The specimens were usually 1 in. long by 1/4 in. square.

Ticonal X

Recognizing the advantage of oriented crystals in Alnico 5, Luteyn and de Voss[38] applied this technique to an alloy of 35 per cent Fe; 34 per cent Co; 15 per cent Ni; 7 per cent Al; 4 per cent Cu; 5 per cent Ti (Ticonal X). Rods of these alloys contained large crystals oriented in a [001] direction; after heat treatment they attained a $(BH)_m$ value of 11.0×10^6 gauss-oersteds, a residual induction of 11,800 gauss, and a coercive force of 1315 oersteds. Curve 1 of Figure 8.11 shows the magnetic properties of this remarkable material. Of further interest are its properties when the crystals are not oriented and it is heat-treated in a manner similar to that of Alnico 5. These are shown by curve 3 in Figure 8.11; the values obtained are a $(BH)_m$ of 3.5×10^6 gauss-oersteds and a coercive force of 1150 oersteds. However, unlike Alnico 5, this alloy shows an improvement when an isothermal heat treatment is used. These properties are illustrated

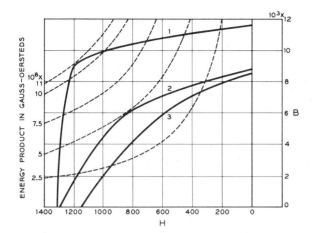

Figure 8.11. Demagnetization curves of Ticonal X: (1) directional grain specimen; (2) polycrystalline specimen having isothermal heat treatment; (3) polycrystalline specimen having controlled cooling rate heat treatment.

by curve 2 in Figure 8.11: a $(BH)_m$ of 5.0×10^6 gauss-oersteds and a coercive force of 1300 oersteds.

This alloy has the highest energy product of any permanent magnet material at the present time. The Alnico family, therefore, has energy products which range from 1.4 to 11.0×10^6 gauss-oersteds and coercive forces of 500–1300 oersteds. From an industrial viewpoint, Alnico 5 still remains the most important alloy of this family.

Iron-Cobalt Powders

In recent years,[43] a new type of micro-powder has been developed for permanent magnets which is superior to the older type obtained by hydrogen reduction of iron-cobalt compounds. It is called elongated single-domain powder and is obtained by plating particles into a pool of mercury from solutions of salts of iron and cobalt. The iron-cobalt alloy particles are then magnetically concentrated into a thick slurry which is compacted under the influence of a magnetic field to lower the mercury content and impart a parallel orientation of the resulting compact. The last traces of mercury are removed by vacuum distillation and the particles then compacted in the presence of a strong field in a matrix which is either organic or metallic. The matrix is frequently lead, and sometimes the particles are not oriented in a field in order to obtain isotropic magnetic properties.

Iron-cobalt alloy particles obtained in this way have a diameter of approximately 200Å and a length to diameter ratio of 5.4:1; they owe their permanent magnet properties to their shape anisotropy and small size. Their behavior is very similar to that of the precipitate particles in Alnico 5, and the two cases have been compared.[37] Iron particles obtained in the same manner have a diameter of 150Å and a length to diameter ratio of 2.7:1. As a result of a lower length to diameter ratio and a lower value of magnetic saturation, the iron particles have energy products that are only 70 per cent of that of the iron-cobalt particles. The matrix has two important functions: first, to prevent the particles from oxidation; secondly, to space the particles correctly. A maximum energy product is obtained when the matrix occupies approximately 50 per cent of the volume of the compact. The curves in Figure 8.12 illustrate how the energy product, co-

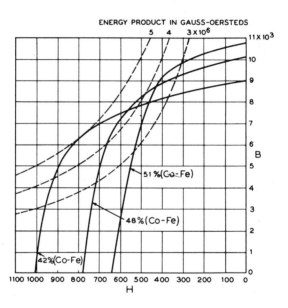

Figure 8.12. Demagnetization curves for oriented elongated single domain iron-cobalt powders for 42, 48, and 51 per cent packing fractions. Composition of iron-cobalt alloy is 40 per cent Co, 60 per cent Fe.

ercive force, and residual induction vary with the packing factor for an oriented iron-cobalt alloy particle of 40 per cent Co–60 per cent Fe. Similar curves in Figure 8.13 indicate nonoriented particles. Elongated single domain magnets have an advantage over other types in that the coercive force needed for a particular design may be selected. The dimensions of the magnet may also be accurately controlled.

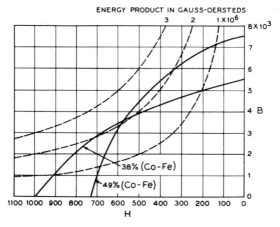

Figure 8.13. Demagnetization curves for nonoriented elongated single domain iron-cobalt powders for 38 and 49 per cent packing fractions. Composition of iron-cobalt alloy is 40 per cent Co, 60 per cent Fe.

Iron-Cobalt-Molybdenum

In 1932, Seljesater and Rogers,[62] and, independently, Koster[34] developed these precipitation-hardening alloys frequently called "Remalloy" or "Comol." Their permanent magnetic properties are obtained by an oil quench of 1200–1300° C; this puts the alloys into a super-saturated state with a coercive force of about 5 oersteds. Aging at 675° C for one hour then results in coercive forces of over 200 oersteds. There are two important compositions, 17 per cent Mo, 12 per cent Co, 71 per cent Fe; and 20 per cent Mo, 12 per cent Co, 68 per cent Fe. The first has a $(BH)_m$ of 1.1×10^6 gauss-oersteds, a coercive force of 250 oersteds, and a residual induction of 10,500 gauss; the second has a $(BH)_m$ of 1.3×10^6 gauss-oersteds, a coercive force of 320 oersteds, and a residual induction of 8800 gauss. The author found an alloy of 17 per cent Mo, 5 per cent Co, 5 per cent Cr, 73 per cent Fe to have properties comparable to the first alloy. These alloys can be hot-forged and are machinable. They have been used in the Bell System telephone receiver in the United States for many years.

Cobalt Steel

Prior to the advent of the Fe-Co-Mo and Ni-Fe-Al alloys in 1932, the cobalt steels were by far the best permanent magnets available. The 35 per cent cobalt alloy was invented by Takagi and Honda[19] and is frequently called "Honda," or KS steel. The permanent magnet properties of this alloy are developed by a quench from the austenitic region (approximately 940° C) which produces a martensitic structure at room temperature. This structure is somewhat unstable at that temperature; therefore, aging at 100° C is desirable. Figure 8.14 shows demagnetization curves for cobalt

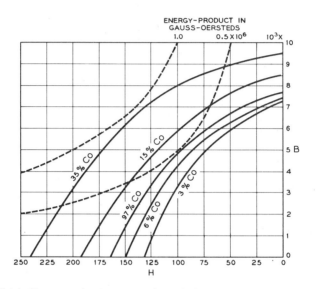

Figure 8.14. Demagnetization curves for cobalt steels containing 3, 6, 9, 15, and 36 per cent cobalt.

steels containing 3, 6, 9, 15, and 36 per cent cobalt. The steels are machinable after annealing. It is sometimes necessary, after this treatment, to heat the alloy first to 1200° C in order to dissolve all the carbides before heating it to 750° C and applying the permanent magnet heat treatment.

DUCTILE PERMANENT MAGNET ALLOYS

Iron-Cobalt-Vanadium

In 1936, Nesbitt and Kelsall[28,49,50] discovered the age-hardening magnetic properties of these alloys; they cover a composition range of 30–52 per cent iron, 36–62 per cent cobalt, and 4–16 per cent vanadium. Alloys in this region are called "Vicalloy," and their use has been limited largely to the production of tape and sheet material. In a recent commercial application 1000-foot lengths of Vicalloy sheet 4 in. wide by .001 in. thick were produced. The behavior of these alloys may be better understood by considering the constitutional diagram of the iron-cobalt-vanadium system shown

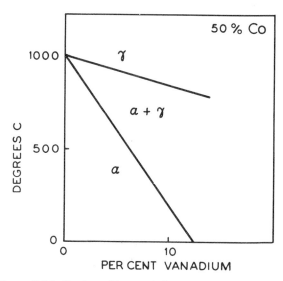

Figure 8.15. Section of iron-cobalt-vanadium phase diagram.

in Figure 8.15. In this system, when the alloy is at low temperatures, only one phase is present; this is advantageous for cold working operations, and is in contrast to the typical permanent magnet system in which at least two phases are present at low temperatures.

Vicalloy I has a composition of 38 per cent iron, 52 per cent cobalt, and 9.5 per cent vanadium; it also has isotropic properties. It may be annealed or drastically quenched from 850–1300° C for its first treatment, since either of these operations leaves the alloy in the low temperature alpha state. In this condition, it may be cold-rolled. The final heat treatment, which results in a high coercive force, is obtained by merely raising the temperature of the alloy to the two-phase region (600° C), thereby dispersing some of the high temperature gamma phase in the low temperature alpha phase. The demagnetization curve obtained by quenching Vicalloy I from 1000° C in oil and baking it at 600° C is illustrated by curve 1 in Figure 8.16. The energy product is 1.0×10^6 gauss-oersteds, the coercive force 300 oersteds, and the residual induction 8800 gauss. If sheet material of the alloy is lightly cold-rolled and aged at 600° C, the energy product will be 1.0×10^6 gauss-oersteds, the coercive force 200 oersteds, and the residual induction 10,000 gauss.

Vicalloy II treatment permits the use of high vanadium contents, and results in higher coercivities and anisotropic properties. A preferred composition for Vicalloy II is 13 per cent vanadium. Curve 2 in Figure 8.16 shows the properties obtained on a .006 in. diameter wire that was cold-drawn

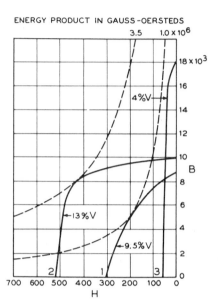

Figure 8.16. Demagnetization curves for several Vicalloy compositions. Curves show wide range of properties available with these alloys.

98 per cent and aged at 600° C. Curve 3 in Figure 8.16 illustrates the high residual induction of 18,000 gauss obtainable in this system.

Platinum-Cobalt

These alloys[11,23] are of great scientific interest because of their high co-ercivity and high energy product. Alloys near the composition PtCo have the highest maximum energy product of any isotropic magnet. Alloys in this region owe their unusual magnetic properties to an order-disorder re-action illustrated in Figure 8.17. At 900° C and above, the alloys are face-centered cubic and disordered; at 700° C and below, the alloys are face-centered tetragonal and ordered. At the condition of maximum coercive force, it has been determined that there are about equal amounts of ordered and disordered material.[39,56] It appears reasonable, although it has not been proved conclusively, that these alloys are fine particle magnets whose permanent magnet properties are due to a high crystal anisotropy (10^7 ergs/cm^3).

The magnetic properties of these alloys are shown in Figure 8.18. These curves indicate that at approximately 49 per cent cobalt, a $(BH)_m$ of 9×10^6 gauss-oersteds, a coercive force of 4100 oersteds, and a residual induc-tion of 6500 gauss can be obtained. These are highly desirable values in

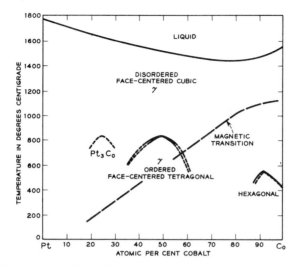

Figure 8.17. Phase diagram for the cobalt-platinum system.

many permanent magnet designs, but the expense of the metal platinum in this alloy prohibits its general use. The data shown in Figure 8.18 are quite variable for reasons which are not obvious. For the three alloys shown in the vicinity of 49 per cent cobalt, the maximum energy product varies from 7.5 to 9.0 $\times$ 10^6 gauss-oersteds. Similar variations can be noted

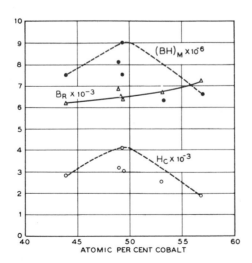

Figure 8.18. Variation of maximum energy product $(BH)_m$, residual induction B_r, and coercive force H_c, with cobalt content for the platinum-cobalt alloys.

in the coercive force data. A typical heat treatment for these alloys is as follows: disorder the alloy at 1000° C; cool it at the rate of 100° C per minute; age it at 600° C for 1 hour. The rate of cooling is the same as that used for Alnico 5.

These alloys may be hot- and cold-worked. The latter operation, however, is difficult since the alloy must be kept in the disordered state by quenching. Small wires of .020 in. diameter have been drawn.

Cu-Ni-Co

In 1938, Dannohl and Neuman,[4] and others[12,67] studied the magnetic properties and structure of these alloys. The constitutional diagram is similar to that shown for Fe-Ni-Al alloys in Figure 8.6. The solution temperature for the two important alloys in this system, however, is lower than that of the Ni-Fe-Al alloys. In general, they are homogenized for 15 hours at 1150° C, then quenched and aged at 700° C to develop their permanent magnet properties. The alloy containing 29 per cent Co, 21 per cent Ni, and 50 per cent Cu is called Cunico 1; it has an energy product of 0.8×10^6 gauss-oersteds, a residual induction of 3400 gauss, and a coercive force of 660 oersteds. The alloy containing 41 per cent Co, 24 per cent Ni, and 35 per cent Cu is called Cunico 2; it has an energy product of 1.0×10^6 gauss-oersteds, a residual induction of 5300 gauss, and a coercive force of 450 oersteds.

The virtue of these alloys is that relatively high coercive forces can be obtained in thin cold-worked sheets. Their drawbacks are limited small-size casting (about 1 in. dia max), long homogenization times, and the fact that they cannot be hot-worked.

SOFT MAGNETIC ALLOYS CONTAINING COBALT

At the present time, cobalt is not used to the same extent in soft magnetic materials as in permanent magnet alloys. Nevertheless, there are a number of important and interesting high permeability materials containing the element. In general, these alloys are single-phase solid solutions, and any inhomogeneities that may exist are of second order magnitude. The effect of magnetostriction is usually more important in these higher permeability materials than in permanent magnet alloys. In recent years, there has been great improvement in the properties of these materials due, in many instances, to the removal of interstitial impurities such as carbon, sulfur, nitrogen, and oxygen. These elements sometimes form compounds, or impurity faults which may impede the uniform movement of the domain walls.

Ni-Fe-Co

In 1921, Elmen[7] discovered that many of these alloys possessed a remarkable combination of low hysteresis and high permeability at low flux densities, and exhibited constricted hysteresis loops at higher flux densities. Such alloys are called "Perminvar" because of their constant permeability at low flux densities. A standard perminvar composition is 45 per cent nickel, 30 per cent iron, and 25 per cent cobalt.

When heat-treated in a magnetic field, the alloys yield the squarest hysteresis loops of all magnetic materials. Current interest in soft, square-loop materials has renewed interest in the problem of why these materials respond to heat treatment in a magnetic field. The nature of the mechanism causing this squareness has, for the most part, been attributed to the order-disorder phenomenon.[3,27,48,66] However, it has recently been shown, by means of single crystal torque curves, that these alloys have an inhomogeneous structure,[55] and that such inhomogeneity is due to an impurity fault.[17] Evidence suggests that small amounts of oxygen as an impurity in perminvar causes both the faulting and the heat treatment in a magnetic field. An extremely small amount of oxygen (.0014 per cent) is sufficient to produce such effects. On the basis of this work, oxygen is also believed to be responsible for the effect of field heat treatment in the closely related permalloys.

Iron-Cobalt

The magnetic properties of these alloys have been investigated by Weiss,[68] Ellis,[6] and Elmen.[8] In 1926, Elmen worked with alloys of approximately 50 per cent cobalt which he named "Permendur" because their permeability endures to high values of flux density. This is evident from the curves of Cioffi[9] shown in Figure 8.19, comparing "Permendur" with iron. The curves in Figure 8.20 show the saturation value of the iron-cobalt alloys for fields of 3, 10, 100, 1500, and 17,000 oersteds. The composition represented by Fe_2Co has the highest value of any alloy at room temperature—24,600 gauss.

In 1932, White and Wahl[70] added 2 per cent vanadium to the 50 per cent cobalt alloy, thereby greatly increasing its ductility without materially harming its magnetic properties. This alloy, known as "V Permendur," has had practical applications for magnet pole pieces and telephone diaphragms. The magnetic properties are a maximum permeability of 4500, a saturation induction of 24,000 gauss, a coercive force of 2.0 oersteds, and a residual induction of 14,000 gauss. The permeability and squareness of the hysteresis loop of this alloy may be improved by heat treatment in a magnetic field.

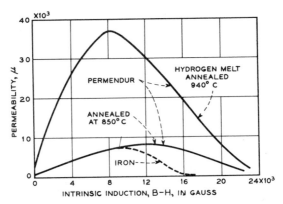

Figure 8.19. Comparison of permeability at high flux densities of "Permendur" (hydrogen melted and air melted) with that of iron.

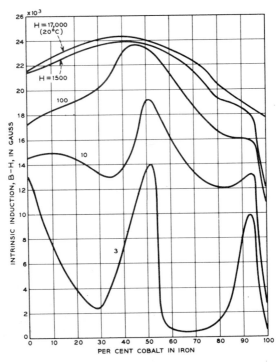

Figure 8.20. Intrinsic induction of annealed iron-cobalt alloys at various field strengths.

Libsch, Both, Beckman, Warren, and Franklin,[36] using this latter treatment and preparing specimens of the 50 per cent cobalt alloy by powder metallurgy, obtained a square hysteresis loop. They measured an induction of 22,400 gauss, a coercive force of 0.68 oersted, and a residual induction of 19,000 gauss.

Recently, Gould and Wenny[13] made substantial improvements in the magnetic and mechanical properties of the 50 per cent cobalt alloy containing 2 per cent vanadium; they name the alloy "Supermendur." The process was as follows: the purest available raw materials were selected; the alloy was melted and purified in wet and dry hydrogen atmospheres, then heated at 850° C and furnace-cooled in a magnetic field. The resulting magnetic properties were a maximum permeability of 60,000, a saturation induction of 24,000 gauss, a coercive force of 0.2 oersted, and a residual induction of 21,500 gauss. The remarkable magnetic properties of this alloy are shown in Figure 8.21, in comparison with other important magnetic alloys.

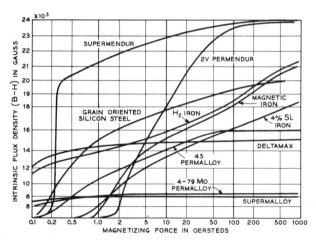

Figure 8.21. Comparison of magnetization curves for Supermendur and other important magnetic materials.

Hiperco has properties similar to those of the standard V Permendur. It is an alloy of 35 per cent cobalt and 63 per cent iron, with 1 or 2 per cent of an additional element. The magnetic properties are a maximum permeability of 10,000, a saturation induction of 24,200 gauss, a coercive force of 1.0 oersted, and a residual induction of 14,000 gauss.

Glass-to-Metal Seals

Some nickel-iron-cobalt alloys are also useful because they have thermal expansion characteristics similar to those of certain glasses. Invar (36 per cent Ni; bal., Fe) is well known for its low linear expansion, but the substitution of 5 per cent Co for 5 per cent Ni results in a coefficient even smaller than that of Invar and an alloy with less susceptibility to heat treatment. An extensive investigation of this class of alloys has been made by Masumoto.[40] Scott[60] investigated the effect of cobalt up to 40 per cent and concludes that such additions increase the coefficient of expansion at room temperature but produce an alloy with a moderately low coefficient of expansion over a wider temperature range. Scott's alloy[61] is called "Kovar," and its composition is approximately 28 per cent Ni, 54 per cent Fe, 18 per cent Co. Hull and Burger[21] developed a similar alloy called "Fernico." Masumoto[41] investigated an alloy—37 per cent Fe, 54 per cent Co, 9 per cent Cr—with a very low coefficient of expansion. Hull suggests an alloy called "Fernichrome" containing 30 per cent Ni, 37 per cent Fe, 25 per cent Co, 8 per cent Cr for use with special glasses. Important applications of these alloys are lead-in wires for vacuum tubes and other electronic equipment where it is necessary to seal out air or moisture.

Magnetically-Soft Ferrites Containing Cobalt

The ferrites are a class of magnetic materials which are formed by mixing certain metallic oxides and causing them to react at high temperatures. A typical ferrite has a composition which can be expressed by the formula MFe_2O_4, where M represents a divalent metal, for example, Co, Mn, Ni, Fe, or Zn. In general, many of these materials have high permeability, low coercive force, low magnetic saturation, and extremely high resistivity.

In some of these ferrites, cobalt is useful as a minor component.[59] An effective series of ferrites for transformer and inductor cores is the Fe-Ni-Zn-Co system. These ferrites work above 150 megacycles, and have comparatively high permeability and low loss. Another application of cobalt in ferrites is its addition to nickel-ferrite. The latter has a direct-current resistivity of approximately 10^6 ohm-centimeters. By adding a small amount of cobalt (e.g., $Ni_{1.0}Fe_{1.9}Co_{.02}O_4$), the resistivity can be increased to a value of 10^{11} ohm-centimeters.

Cobalt-ferrite is of considerable scientific interest and has been the subject of many investigations. Kato and Takei[25] first showed that sintered mixtures of Fe_3O_4 and $CoFe_2O_4$ responded to heat treatment in a magnetic field; they developed a permanent magnet utilizing this effect. Williams, Heidenreich, and Nesbitt,[71] found that single crystals of cobalt-ferrite rich in iron ($Co_{.78}Fe_{2.27}O_4$) responded to heat treatment in a magnetic field and contained particles of a second phase. Single crystals near the stoichiometric value ($Co\ Fe_2\ O_4$) did not respond to the field heat treatment and did not contain precipitated particles. Bozorth, Tilden, and Williams[2] measured the magnetic anisotropy of cobalt-ferrite at room temperature and found it to be as high as 4×10^6 ergs/cm^3. They also found the magnetostriction to be as high as 800×10^{-6}—the highest value of magnetostriction known to the author.

In conclusion, it may be stated that the most important permanent magnet (Alnico 5), the permanent magnet with the highest energy product (Ticonal X), the permanent magnet with the highest coercive force (PtCo), and the soft magnetic material with the highest permeability at high-flux densities (Supermendur) all depend on cobalt for their outstanding properties.

References

1. Bozorth, R. M., "Magnetostriction and Crystal Anisotropy of Single Crystals of Hexagonal Cobalt," *Phys. Rev.,* **96,** 311–5 (1954).
2. —, Tilden, E. F., and Williams, A. J., "Anisotropy and Magnetostriction of Some Ferrites," *Phys. Rev.,* **99,** 1988–98 (1955).
3. Chickazumi, S., and Oomura, V., "On the Origin of Magnetic Anisotropy Induced by Magnetic Annealing," *Phys. Soc. Japan,* **10,** 842–49 (1955).
4. Dannohl, W., and Neumann, H., "Uber Dauermagnetlegierungen ans Kobalt, Kupfer und Nickel," *Z. Metallkunde,* **30,** 217–31 (1938).
5. De Jong, J. J., Smeets, J. M. G., and Haanstra, H. B., "Small Particles and Permanent Magnets," *J. Appl. Phys.,* **29,** 297–8 (1958).
6. Ellis, W. C., "Study of Physical Properties of Electrolytic Co and Its Alloys with Fe," Rensselaer Polytechnic Institute, *Bull. Eng. Sci.,* Ser. 16, 1–57 (1927).
7. Elmen, G. W., "Magnetic Properties of Perminvar," *J. Franklin Inst.,* **206,** 317–8 (1928).
8. —, "Magnetic Alloys of Iron, Nickel and Cobalt," *J. Franklin Inst.,* **207,** 583–617 (1929).
9. —, "Magnetic Alloys of Iron, Nickel and Cobalt," *Elect. Eng.,* **54,** 1292–9 (1935).
10. Fahlenbrach, H., "Du Grundprozess der Magnetisurung bei Alni-v. Alnico Dauermagnetlegurungen," *Tech. Mitt. Krupp,* **12,** 177 (1954).
11. Gebhardt, E., and Koster, W., "Das System Platin-Kobalt mit besonderer Berucksechtigung der Phase CoPt," *Z. Metallkunde,* **32,** 253–61 (1940).
12. Geisler, A. H., and Newkirk, J. B., "Mechanism of Precipitation in a Permanent Magnet Alloy," *Metals Tech.,* **15,** No. 2444, 1–20 (1948).
13. Gould, H. L. B., and Wenny, D. H., "Supermendur, A New Rectangular Loop Magnetic Material with High Flux Density and Low Coercive Force," Conf. on Magnetism and Magnetic Materials, A.I.E.E., 1957.
14. Guillaud, C., and Roux, M., "Propriétés ferromagnétiques d'un monocristal de cobalt," *C. R. Acad. Sci. Paris,* **229,** 1062 (1949).
15. Hansen, J. R., Proc. on Conf. on Magnetism and Magnetic Materials, A.I.E.E., Pittsburg, 1955.
16. Heidenreich, R. D., and Nesbitt, E. A., "Physical Structure and Magnetic Anisotropy of Alnico 5," (Part I), *J. Appl. Phys.,* **23,** 352–66 (1952).

17. Heidenreich, R. D., Nesbitt, E. A., and Burbank, R. D., "Magnetic Annealing in Perminvar," (Part I), *J. Appl. Phys., 30,* 995–1000 (1959).
18. Honda, K., and Masumoto, H., "Magnetization of Single Crystals at High Temperatures," *Sci. Repts. Tohoku Imp. Univ., 20,* 323–41 (1931).
19. Honda, K., and Saito, S., "On KS Magnet Steel," *Sci. Repts. Tohoku Imp. Univ., 9,* 417–22 (1920).
20. Horsburgh, C., and Tetley, F., Bri. Pat. 431600. (Appl. 1934).
21. Hull, A. W., and Burger, E. E., "Glass to Metal Seals," *Physics, 5,* 384 (1934).
22. Jacobs, I. S., and Bean, C. P., "An Approach to Elongated Fine-Particle Magnets," *Phys. Rev., 100,* 1060 (1955).
23. Jellinghaus, W., "Neue Legierungen mit hoher Koerzitwkraft," *Z. Tech. Physik, 17,* 33–6 (1936).
24. Jonas, B., and van Emden, H. J. M., "New Kinds of Steel of High Magnetic Power," *Philips Tech. Revs., 6,* 8–11 (1941).
25. Kato, Y., and Takei, T., "Permanent Magnet Oxide Magnet and Its Characteristic," *J. Inst. Elec. Engrs.,* (Japan), *53,* 408–12 (1933).
26. Kaya, S., "On the Magnetization of Single Crystals of Cobalt," *Sci. Repts. Tohoku Imp. Univ., 17,* 1157–77 (1928).
27. —, "Uniaxial Anisotropy of a Permalloy Crystal," *Rev. Mod. Phys., 25,* 49–53 (1953).
28. Kelsall, G. A., and Nesbitt, E. A., U. S. Pat. 2,190,667 (1940).
29. Kittel, C., "Theory of the Structure of Ferromagnetic Domains in Films and Small Particles," *Phys. Rev., 70,* 965–71 (1946).
30. —, Nesbitt, E. A., and Shockley, W., "Theory of Magnetic Properties and Nucleation in Alnico 5," *Phys. Rev., 77,* 839–40 (1950).
31. Kittel, C., and Galt, J. K., "Solid State Physics," Vol. III, Academic Press Inc., (1956).
32. Kiuti, S., "An X-Ray Investigation on the Ternary Equilibria in the Fe-Ni-Al System," *Sci. Repts., Tohoku Imp. Univ., 29,* 747–794 (1941).
33. Koch, A. J. J., Steeg, V. D., and de Vos, K. J., "A Contribution to the Study of Permanent Magnet Alloys of the Fe-Co-Ni-Al Type," Proc. of the Conf. on Magnetism and Magnetic Materials, Boston (1956).
34. Koster, W., "Mechanische und magnetusche Ausscherdungshartung der Eisen-Kobalt-Wolfram und Eisen-Kobalt-Molybdenum Legierungen," *Arch. Eisenhuttenw., 6,* 17–32 (1932).
35. Kronenberg, K. J., "Zur Frage magnetisch gerichteter Gefuge in Dauermagneten," *Z. Metallkunde, 45,* 440–7 (1954).
36. Libsch, J. F., Both, E., Beckman, G. W., Warren, D., and Franklin, R. J., "Effect of Annealing in a Magnetic Field Fe-Co and Fe-Co-Ni Alloys," *Trans. Am. Inst. Mining Met. Engrs., 188,* 287–96 (1950).
37. Luborsky, F. E., Mendelsohn, L. I., and Paine, T. O., "Reproducing the Propperties of Alnico Permanent Magnet Alloys with Elongated Single-Domain Cobalt-Iron Particles," J. Appl. Phys., *28,* 344–51 (1957).
38. Luteyn, A. I., and de Vos, K. J., "Permanent Magnets with $(BH)_{max}$ Values Over Ten Million Gauss Oersteds," *Philips Res. Repts., 11,* 489–90 (1956).

39. Martin, D. L., "Processing and Properties of Cobalt-Platinum Permanent Magnet Alloys," Conf. on Magnetism and Magnetic Materials, A.I.E.E., Boston (1956).
40. Masumoto, H., "On the Thermal Expansion of the Alloys of Iron, Nickel and Cobalt," *Sci. Repts. Tohoku Imp. Univ.*, **20**, 101–23 (1931).
41. —, "Thermal Expansion of Alloys of Co, Fe and Cr and a New Alloy, Stainless Invar," *Sci. Repts. Tohoku Imp. Univ.*, **23**, 265–80 (1934).
42. McCaig, M., "Magnetostriction of Anisotropic Permanent Magnet Alloys," *Proc. Phys. Soc.*, (London), **B62**, 652–6 (1949).
43. Mendelsohn, L. I., Luborsky, F. E., and Paine, T. O., "Permanent Magnet Properties of Elongated Single-Domain Iron Particles," *J. Appl. Phys.*, **25**, 1274 (1955).
44. Mishima, T., U. S. Pat. 2,027,996, Aug. 27, 1931.
45. —, "Nickel-Aluminum Steel for Permanent Magnets," *Ohm*, **19**, 353 (1932).
46. Myers, H. P., and Sucksmith, W., "Spontaneous Magnetization of Cobalt," *Proc. Roy. Soc.*, **207**, 427–46 (1951).
47. Neel, L., "Propriétés d'un ferromagnétique cubique en grains fins," *Comp. rend.*, **224**, 1488–90 (1947).
48. —, "Anisotropic magnétique superficielle et surstructures d'orientation," *J. Phys. radium*, **15**, 225–39 (1954).
49. Nesbitt, E. A., U. S. Pat. 2,298,225 (1942).
50. —, "Vicalloy, A Workable Permanent Magnet Alloy," *Metals Tech.*, **13**, No. 1973, 1–11 (1946).
51. Nesbitt, E. A., and Heidenreich, R. D., "Physical Structure and Magnetic Anisotropy of Alnico 5," *J. Appl. Phys.*, **23**, 366–71 (1952).
52. —, "Physical and Magnetic Structure of Mishima Alloys," *Revs. Modern Phys.*, **25**, 322 (1953).
53. Nesbitt, E. A., and Williams, H. J., "Shape and Crystal Anisotropy of Alnico 5," *J. Appl. Phys.*, **26**, 1217 (1955).
54. Nesbitt, E. A., Williams, H. J. and Bozorth, R. M., "Factors Determining the Permanent Magnet Properties of Single Crystals of Fe$_2$NiAl," *J. Appl. Phys.*, **25**, 1014 (1955).
55. Nesbitt, E. A., and Heidenreich, R. D., "Magnetic Annealing in Perminvar II Magnetic Properties," *J. Appl. Phys.*, **30**, 1000 (1959).
56. Newkirk, J. B., Smoluchowski, R., Geisler, A. H., and Martin, D. L., "Phase Equilibria in an Ordering Alloy System," *J. Appl. Phys.*, **22**, 290 (1951).
57. Oliver, D. A., and Shedden, J. W., "Cooling of Permanent Magnet Alloys in a Constant Magnetic Field," *Nature*, **142**, 209 (1938).
58. Ruder, W., U. S. Pat. 1,968,569, June 3, 1933.
59. Schnettler, F. J., and Monforte, F. R., "Effect of Cobalt on the Relaxation Frequency of Nickel-Zinc Ferrite," *J. Appl. Phys.*, **29**, 477–8 (1958).
60. Scott, H., "Expansion Characteristics of Low-Expansion Nickel Steels," *Trans. ASST*, **13**, 829 (1928).
61. —, "Recent Developments in Metals Sealing into Glass," *J. Franklin Inst.*, **220**, 773 (1935).

62. Seljesater, K. S., and Rogers, B. A., "Magnetic and Mechanical Hardness of Dispersion Hardened Iron Alloys," *Trans. ASST,* **19,** 553 (1932).
63. Stoner, E. C., and Wohlfarth, E. D., "Interpretation of High Coercivity in Ferromagnetic Materials," *Nature,* **160,** 650 (1947).
64. —, "Mechanism of Magnetic Hysteresis in Heterogeneous Alloys," *Phil. Trans. Roy. Soc.,* **240,** 599 (1948).
65. Sucksmith, W., and Thompson, J. E., "Magnetic Anisotropy of Cobalt," *Roy. Soc. London,* **225,** 362 (1954).
66. Taniguchi, S., "Theory of Uniaxial Ferromagnetic Anisotropy Induced by Magnetic Annealing in Cubic Solid Solutions," *Sci. Repts. Research Insts. Tohoku Univ.,* **A7,** 269 (1955).
67. Volk, K. E., Dannohl, W., and Masing, G., "Die Entmischungsvorgänge in Kobalt-Kupfer-Nickel-Legierungen im festen Zustand," *Z. Metallkunde,* **30,** 113–22 (1938).
68. Weiss, P., Forrer, R., and Birch, F., "Sur l'aimantation à saturation des nickel-cobalts et les moments atomiques du nickel et du cobalt," *Comp. rend.,* **189,** 789 (1929).
69. Weiss, P., and Preuss, A., "Magnetic Properties of Fe-Co Alloys," *Trans. Faraday Soc.,* **8,** 154 (1912).
70. White, J. H., and Wahl, C. V., U. S. Pat. 1,862,559. (Appl. 8/14/31).
71. Williams, H. J., Heidenreich, R. D., and Nesbitt, E. A., "How Cobalt Ferrite Heat-Treats in a Magnetic Field," *J. Appl. Phys.,* **27,** 85–89 (1956).

Chapter 9

COBALT ALLOYS IN HIGH-TEMPERATURE, HIGH-STRENGTH SERVICE

C. R. WHITTEMORE

Deloro Smelting and Refining Company, Ltd.
Deloro, Ontario, Canada

The utilization of cobalt in the alloy field is outlined in Table 9.1; general classifications and consumption data are based on the United States Bureau of Mines Statistics for the years 1956–1959.

TABLE 9.1. COBALT CONSUMED IN THE UNITED STATES BY USES (Percentage Basis)

	1956	1957	1958	1959
High speed and other steels	4.5	3.8	2.6	10.1
Permanent and soft magnets	29.2	31.6	31.0	30.5
Co-Cr-W-Mo alloys	33.9	33.2	31.1	25.0
Hard facing alloys and cemented carbides	9.1	8.3	6.8	8.1
Other metallic uses	3.8	2.5	3.3	4.7
Chemical	19.5	20.5	25.2	21.6
Total pounds	9,562,260	9,156,617	7,542,000	5,027,350

About 1875, Elwood Haynes began his research on stainless metals, and in 1899 developed an alloy of cobalt and chromium which resisted chemical fumes and possessed great hardness up to visible redness. It could not be cold-worked, but was malleable at a bright orange heat. By 1908, he had developed a cutting alloy with an edge equal to that of tempered steel. To the cobalt-chromium-base alloy were added tungsten, molybdenum, and carbon to produce cutting tools superior to high-speed steel-tools. This gave the cobalt-chromium-tungsten alloys a field of their own, and they were termed "stellites" from the Latin word "STELLA" meaning star. The Co-Cr-W high-carbon tool alloy was the preferred cutting tool during World War I, as tungsten carbide was during World War II.

Application of the alloy in rod form, by oxy-acetylene welding, to the edges of hot-blanking and trimming dies initiated the process now known as "hard facing."

213

COBALT IN FERROUS ALLOYS

The iron-cobalt equilibrium diagram shows that cobalt is entirely miscible with gamma iron and forms solid solutions with alpha iron to about 80 per cent cobalt.[7] In general, the solid solubility of any element in ferrite produces increased strength and hardness on the one hand; decreased elongation and reduction of area on the other.

The tendency of cobalt to form carbides is slightly less than that of iron. Cobalt is the only alloying element that reduces the hardenability of steel. Its principal function is to resist softening at elevated temperature when dissolved in ferrite.

Cobalt exhibits a definite γ-field which broadens in the presence of chromium, thus making it possible to increase the hardenability of chromium steels.

Cobalt decreases appreciably certain forms of brittleness, probably by action on grain boundaries.

The effect of cobalt on the T-T-T curves does not always result in a decrease in the incubation period. For instance, in low-carbon or chromium steels it has been shown that cobalt delays the beginning of austenite decomposition.

High-speed Steels

Cobalt is an essential constituent of a group of tungsten tool steels capable of heavy cuts and feeds at high speeds in the machining of steels and nonferrous metals.[32,42,49,72 76,78,105,142] These steels consist basically of 18 per cent tungsten, 4 per cent chromium, 1 per cent vanadium, 5–12 per cent cobalt, and 0.5–0.8 per cent carbon. In general, the cutting ability is proportional to the cobalt content up to 13 per cent cobalt. Cobalt dissolves in tungsten in amounts up to 30 per cent, and a tungsten-cobalt compound is precipitated upon reheating, thus improving the plain tungsten tool steels.

The addition of cobalt to molybdenum high-speed steels also improves their properties.

Glass-to-Metal Seals

The primary problem with glass-to-metal seals is the difference in thermal expansion of the metal in relation to the glass.[2,97,102,118,121,146] In general, it may be said that glasses and metals which are to be joined should not differ in their expansion coefficients by much more than $1 \times 10^{-6}/°$ C.

The iron-nickel-cobalt alloys used extensively for glass-to-metal seals have low expansivity at temperatures less than their characteristic inflection temperatures and greater expansivity at higher temperatures. Hence, by blending, the inflection temperature of iron-nickel-cobalt materials can be made to coincide with the annealing range of certain glass compositions, and expansion properties can be made to equal or approach those of the glasses.

Nominal chemical compositions of such alloys are 54 per cent iron, 28 per cent nickel, and 18 per cent cobalt. They have transition temperatures of about 435° C (815° F), and expansivities between 25° and 325° C (77° and 617° F) of 4.0 $\times$ $10^{-6}/°$ C.

Rodar has a nominal composition of 29 per cent nickel, 17 per cent cobalt, 0.30 per cent manganese, 0.06 per cent carbon, 0.20 per cent silicon, 53.5 per cent iron. Tensile strength is 80,000 psi with an elongation of 30 per cent in 2 ins. and Brinell 156. In the temperature range 30–300° C, the average thermal expansion is 4.41–5.17 in./in./° C $\times$ 10^{-6}.

The British patent No. 795,980, issued to Philco Corporation, discloses the removal of superficial oxide films from nickel-cobalt-iron alloys used for glass-to-metal seals. The oxide is removed by a hot aqueous solution of sulfuric acid containing 75 g ammonium sulfate per 100 ml acid.

Low-expansion Alloys

P. Hidnert and R. Kerby of the National Bureau of Standards confirmed that the thermal expansion of certain cobalt-iron-chromium alloys is extremely low and nearly constant between 20° and 60° C. An alloy containing 36.6 per cent iron, 8.9 per cent chromium, and 54.5 per cent cobalt has a coefficient of expansion less than 1 $\times$ $10^{-6}/°$ C in the range 20° to 60° C. The low expansion of such alloys is sensitive to small variations in chemical composition; some alloys undergo a transformation on cooling at low temperatures.

Superinvar (Fe 63.5 per cent, Ni 31.5 per cent, Co 5 per cent) and Stainless Invar (Fe 36.5 per cent, Cr 9.5 per cent, Co 54 per cent) have a very low coefficient of thermal expansion, which may be considered zero in the case of the second alloy. These alloys are used in geodesic instruments, length standards, high precision variable condensers, etc.

Alloys for Corrosion and Oxidation Resistance

The development of the gas turbine gave impetus to investigations of the effect of alloying elements in steel on improved performance at elevated temperatures. Bollenrath, Cornelius, and Bungardt, in 1938, described a range of iron-nickel-chromium-cobalt-tungsten-molybdenum alloys for gas turbine blading.[23] These alloys contained 10–18 per cent chromium, 25–40 per cent nickel, 20–35 per cent cobalt, 0–8 per cent tungsten, 0–8 per cent molybdenum, and 0–3 per cent titanium or 2–8 per cent columbium.

Bardgett and Bolsover[14] investigated a forgeable alloy steel, referred to as "Multi-Alloy," containing (in per cents) 0.25 carbon, 1.63 manganese, 1.03 silicon, 46.52 nickel, 20.5 chromium, 2.73 molybdenum, 3.33 cobalt, 2.92 columbium, 3.52 tungsten, and 1.2 titanium. At 800° C (1472° F) and with a stress of 5000 psi, the creep strain at 300 hours was 0.20 per cent. Steels containing 6–7 per cent cobalt, 0.2–0.43 per cent carbon, 14.3 per cent chromium, 18 per cent nickel, 3.85 per cent molybdenum, 3.85 per cent copper, and 0.75 per cent titanium were used with air/gas ratios of 2/1, 4/1, and 6/1 at temperatures up to 750° C (1382° F) with satisfactory scaling rates.

Valve-stem tips for aero engines contain 1.27–1.43 per cent carbon, 11.75–13.75 per cent chromium, 2.7–3.3 per cent cobalt, 0.6 per cent nickel, and 0.5–0.85 per cent molybdenum, with a Rockwell hardness of C52.

Union Minière du Haut Katanga found that an alloy containing 47–50 per cent cobalt, 27 per cent chromium, 23 per cent iron, less than 0.1 per cent carbon, and an optional 3 per cent molybdenum has excellent resistance to oxidation in air at 1200° C and good mechanical strength at elevated temperatures. Water-quenching from 1100° C improves the mechanical strength and corrosion resistance. By increasing the carbon to 1.2–2.0 per cent, high abrasion resistance is obtained. The mechanical properties are illustrated below.

No.	Tensile psi	Yield psi	Elong. 1 in., %	Reduction of Area, %	Rockwell "C"
1	72,300	52,100	34.0	46.0	60
2	75,400	51,200	31.0	35.0	67

With a stress of 20,000 psi and at 1500° F, the life to rupture was 32.1 hours. Elongation in 2 in. was 45.5 per cent.

The low carbon alloy is capable of being rolled or forged, and components quenched from 1150° C show good mechanical strength and corrosion resistance. A 12-day corrosion test of this wrought alloy in SO_2-saturated sulfuric acid gave the following results:

H_2SO_4 %	Temp °C	Loss in Wt, mg/cm^2/day	
		Quenched	Unquenched
98.3	80	0.14	0.2
93.5	60	1.25	1.51
10.0	50	2.0	13.7
0	40	0.7	0.65

TABLE 9.2. COBALT-BASE HARD FACING ALLOYS

Trade Designation	No.	C	Co	Cr	Mo	W	Si	Mn	Ta	Hardness Rockwell "C"		Tensile, psi	Compressive, psi	Elongation
										Oxyacetylene	Arc			
Stellite	1	2.45	50	33	...	13	0.80	0.60	...	55	51	47,000–89,000	256,000	Nil
Stellite	6	1.0	64	26	...	5	0.80	0.60	...	40	37	105,000–130,000	220,000	1.0
Stellite	12	1.80	58	29	...	9	0.80	0.60	...	45	41	76,000–120,000	193,000	Nil
Chapman Valve	CV	0.35	60	30	5.0	...	0.30	0.70	3.0					

HARD FACING ALLOYS

The cobalt content of hard facing alloys may range from 10 to 65 per cent cobalt in combination with iron, chromium, tungsten, molybdenum, carbon, etc. The predominant element, cobalt or iron, is used here as the base classification.

Variations in chemical composition determine the physical and chemical properties,[36] and are illustrated in Table 9.2. Elements such as carbon, boron, silicon, manganese, aluminum, titanium, etc., present in amounts under 5 per cent, have a marked effect on properties. Nickel frequently replaces part of the cobalt.

Hardness is not the only criterion of wear resistance; structure and corrosion resistance are important.

Table 9.2 lists well-known commercial cobalt-base alloys for hard facing by oxy-acetylene or electric arc deposition.[45,73,86,126] These alloys are resistant to abrasion, heat, impact, and corrosion in varying degrees according to their composition. Alloy No. 1 has high abrasion and heat resistance but low impact resistance, while Alloy No. 6 has high impact and heat resistance and medium resistance to abrasion. The alloys have a low coefficient of friction and take a high polish. Stellite No. 6 retains its hardness up to 1600° F, grades 1 and 12 up to 1800° F, whereas a cobalt-vanadium high-speed steel drops from 70 Rockwell "C" to 35 Rockwell "C" in the range of 850–1400° F.

Table 9.3 gives the corrosion resistance of the "Stellite" alloys and the

TABLE 9.3. CORROSION RESISTANCE OF STELLITE ALLOYS
Loss in Wt, mg/dm^2/day

Reagent	Strength, %	Stellite No., 1	Stellite No., 6	Stellite No., 12	Stainless Steel, 18/8/3
Nitric acid	5	0	0.6	0.3	3.3
	20	2.7	1.3	2.4	1.9
	50	2.7	3.5	2.2	2.2
Sulfuric acid	10	0	1.9	0.7	1.2
	30	1.1	X	X	58.0
	55	0	X	X	Y
	74	0.8	X	X	246
Hydrochloric acid	2	2.2	406	152	184
	10	488	965	853	325
	20	283	Y	546	319
	37	151	Y	540	...

X denotes that variable results may be expected.
Y denotes that the corrosion rate is in excess of 1000 mg/dm^2/day.

rates of attack in three common mineral acids at different concentrations at room temperature.

It is now practical to metal-spray onto carbon and low alloy steel components, cobalt-base alloys that are finely powdered and formulated for applying[71] by means of a spray gun or pistol. The sprayed metal is held in contact with the metal surface by a mechanical bond which is acceptable for some applications. In other applications, the sprayed metal is subsequently fused and metallurgically bonded with the base metal. To effect such a bond, the alloy must be at the fusion temperature, which is indicated by the ability of the alloy to glisten or glaze. This property depends on surface tension, a wide plastic range, and freedom from oxide.

The following cobalt-base powder alloys are covered by British Patent 809,088.

	Composition							Deposit Hardness, DPH	Approx. M.P. °C.
Alloy	Co	Ni	Cr	W	C	B	Si		
Stellite SF 1	45	13	19	13	1.0	2.5	3.0	600	1125
Stellite SF 6	50	13	19	8	1.0	1.5	2.5	425	1170
Stellite SF 12	52	13	19	9	1.0	1.5	2.5	500	1140
Stellite SF 20	42	13	19	15	1.5	3.0	3.0	750	1050

Applications comprise pump shafts, sleeves, pump plungers, pyrometer sheaths, edges of fan blades, etc.

In the field of iron-base hardfacing alloys that are resistant to abrasion, oxidation at medium temperatures (1000° F), and mild corrosion, the compositions shown in Table 9.4 are typical.[11,36,144]

TABLE 9.4. IRON-BASE HARD FACING ALLOYS

No.	C	Cr	W	Mo	Co	Fe	Ni	Others	Hardness, Rockwell "C"
1	3.00	17.0	...	16.0	6.2	55.0	...	V-1.90	60–62
2	2.50	14.0	6.0	9.0	18.0	50.0	...	...	55–60
3	3.50	18.5	1.2	11.9	9.4	55.0	0.6	...	62–64
4	2.75	24.5	13.3	0.6	14.8	43.0	...	V-1.5	52–54
5	1.30	5.7	4.0	7.0	10.5	70.0	...	V-1.7	63–65
6	0.75	...	...	...	34.0	20.0	36.0	Si-4.0 B-3.0	32–35

Alloy 6 withstands heat, wear, and corrosion, particularly lead oxide corrosion; these properties are required for internal combustion engine valves.

AUSTENITIC IRON-COBALT ALLOYS

Austenitic iron-cobalt alloys are the outgrowth of United States government research undertaken during World War II for the purpose of finding materials for operation of components stressed above 1200° F (650° C).

These alloys are basically highly alloyed wrought stainless steels containing 50–15 per cent iron. The metals Co, Ni, and Cr replace iron and are further stabilized by small amounts of W, Mo, and Cb. They are made precipitation hardenable by the addition of Al and Ti, these elements having been found the most effective in small quantities. Carbon is kept under 0.10 per cent.

Precipitation hardening increases resistance to deformation because the precipitated particles are fine and uniformly distributed to produce uniformity in hardness and stability under loading at high temperature.

Alloys in this class, such as "Refractaloy" 26, K-42-B, and N-155 (Multimet), are given in Table 9.5. Alloy N-155 (Multimet), with a carbon content of 0.20 max, and other elements with this wrought composition are used for investment castings.

Tensile properties are as follows:

Temp °F	Ultimate tensile, psi	Elongation, %	Reduction of Area, %
70	96,000–106,000	25–35	16–26
800	70,000–76,000	26–37	24–37
1000	67,500–72,500	25–32	20–30
1200	60,000–66,000	28–37	25–34
1350	53,000–61,000	18–26	22–28
1500	48,000–53,500	15–25	18–28

Cobalt as an alloying element (2–10 per cent) in chromium stainless steels has been found to have a favorable influence on their resistance to over-all corrosion and intergranular corrosion after heat treatment at 475–500° C for 100–1000 hours.[37]

NICKEL-COBALT-BASE ALLOYS

Increased efficiency of jet engines is a function of the operating temperature which requires higher stress-rupture strength. A desirable value for stress-rupture is 20,000 psi at 1800° F for 100 hours. The nickel-base casting alloys are presently developing 18,000 psi, the cobalt-base somewhat less.

Table 9.6 shows the nominal compositions of commercial nickel-cobalt-base alloys, all of which are age-hardenable. They contain various amounts of aluminum, titanium, and carbide-forming elements. Tables 9.7, 9.8, 9.9 give the heat treatment and properties of these alloys.

TABLE 9.5. AUSTENITIC IRON-COBALT ALLOYS

Temp °C	°F	Tensile, Ultimate psi	Elongation %	Stress-Rupture, psi			Creep Strength psi 0.5% plastic strain	
				10 hr	100 hr	1000 hr	100 hr	1000 hr

Refractaloy 26; A.M.S. 5760 (Wrought)*

37 Ni, 20 Co, 18 Cr, 17 Fe, 3 Mo, 2.8 Ti, 0.8 Si, 0.7 Mn, 0.2 Al, 0.05 C

Temp °C	°F	Tensile, Ultimate psi	Elongation %	10 hr	100 hr	1000 hr	100 hr	1000 hr
20	70	154,000	19.0	...	...	...		
650	1200	136,000	15.0	...	82,000	65,000	70,000	63,000
700	1300	120,000	5.0	...	60,000	46,000		
760	1400	106,000	6.0	...	42,000	31,000		
816	1500	71,000	29.0	...	19,000	12,000	20,000	13,000

*Heat Treatment: 2100°F—1 hr oil-quenched; 1500°F—20 hr air-cooled, 1350°F—20 hr air-cooled.

K-42-B (NDRC 77)

42 Ni, 22 Co, 18 Cr, 13 Fe, 2.6 Ti, 0.7 Mn, 0.7 Si, 0.2-0.6 Al, 0.05 C

Temp °C	°F	Tensile, Ultimate psi	Elongation %	10 hr	100 hr	1000 hr	100 hr	1000 hr
649	1200	117,000	9.0	76,000	65,000	39,000	24,000 (a)	33,000 (b)
732	1350	97,000	4.0	50,000	37,000	26,000	7,500 (a)	13,500 (b)
816	1500	54,000	10.0	22,000	16,000	10,000		
871	1600	29,000	45.0	...	...	...		

TABLE 9.5. (Cont.)

N-155 (Haynes Multimet) - Forged; A.M.S. 5532b
21 Cr, 20 Co, 20 Ni, 3 Mo, 1.2 Cb + Ta, 2.5 W, 0.15 N, 0.08–0.16 C, Bal Fe

Temp °C	°F	Tensile, Ultimate psi	Elongation %	Stress-Rupture, psi 10 hr	100 hr	1000 hr	Creep Strength psi
20	70	142,700 (x)	16.0				
20	70	121,400 (y)	36.0				
650	1200	89,500 (y)	29.0	78,000 (x)	60,000 (x)	49,000 (x)	
650	1200	...	...	62,000 (z)	52,000 (z)	43,000 (z)	

(x) Bar stock, 1-in. diameter as forged.
(y) Bar stock, 1-in. diameter heated 1 hr at 2320°F, water-quenched; heated 24 hr at 1500°F, air-cooled.
(z) Bar stock, 1-in. diameter heated 1 hr at 2280°F, water-quenched; reheated 4 hr at 1500°F, air-cooled.

Temp °C	°F	Tensile, Ultimate psi	Elongation %	Stress-Rupture, psi 10 hr	100 hr	1000 hr	Creep Strength psi
732	1350 (d)	...	...	36,000 (z)	28,000 (z)	22,000 (z)	15,000 (c) 0.00007 (e); 50 hr

S-590 A.M.S. 5533, 5770 (Forged)
26 Fe, 20 Co, 20 Cr, 20 Ni, 4 Mo, 4 W, 4 Cb, 1.5 Mn, 0.4 Si, 0.4 C

Temp °C	°F	Tensile, Ultimate psi	Elongation %	Stress-Rupture, psi	1000 hr	10,000 hr
20	70	138,000	24		...	...
650	1200	98,000	25	...	40,000	29,000
700	1300	80,000	30	...	27,000	20,000
760	1400	66,000	32	...	20,000	14,000
816	1500	53,000	27	...	15,000	10,000

(a) Stress for creep rate of 0.0001% per hr
(b) Stress for creep rate of 0.001% per hr
(c) Stress for 12,000 hr
(d) Bar heated 1 hr 2200°F, water quenched, heated 50 hr 1860°C, air-cooled
(e) Creep rate percent per hr at 2000 hr

TABLE 9.6. COMPOSITION OF NICKEL-COBALT-BASE ALLOYS

Alloy	C	Mn	Si	Cr	Ni	Co	Mo	W	Ti	Al	Fe	B
Udimet 500 cast	0.07	0.1	0.3	18.0	63.5	18.0	4.5	...	3.0	3.0	0.5	...
M-252	0.15	0.5	0.65	19.0	52.0	10.0	10.0	...	2.5	1.0	5.0	...
Inconel 700	0.15	0.1	0.2	15.0	45.0	28.0	3.0	...	2.2	3.0	7.0	...
Nimonic 90	0.08	0.5	0.5	20.0	58.0	18.0	...	...	2.3	1.4	3.0	...
Nimonic 95	0.10	0.5	0.5	20.0	54.0	18.0	...	...	3.0	2.0	3.0	...
Nimonic 100	0.25	0.3	0.3	11.0	56.0	20.0	5.0	...	1.5	5.0	1.0	...
Udimet 500	0.10	0.75	0.75	18.0	50.0	8.0	4.0	...	3.0	3.0	4.0	...
Udimet 600	0.10	0.75	0.75	18.0	49.0	16.0	4.0	...	3.0	4.0	4.0	0.40
Udimet 700	0.15	0.75	0.75	15.0	50.0	19.0	5.0	...	3.5	4.2	1.0	0.10
X-40	0.50	0.12	0.55	24.5	11.0	55.3	...	7.1	...	...	0.9	...

TABLE 9.7. HEAT TREATMENT OF NICKEL-COBALT-BASE ALLOYS

Alloy		Solution Treatment			Aging	
	Time, hr	Temp, °C	Quenching	Time, hr	Temp, °C
M-252		4	1070	air	15	760
Inconel 700		2	1175	air	4	875
Nimonic 90		8	1080	air	16	700
Nimonic 95		8	1080	air	16	700
Nimonic 100		2	1200	air	16	850
Udimet 500		4	1080	air	24	815
Udimet 600		4	1080	air	16	845
Udimet 700		2	1150	air	16	845
X-40			Used without heat treatment			

TABLE 9.8. SHORT-TIME TENSILE PROPERTIES OF NICKEL-COBALT-BASE ALLOYS

Alloy	(1)	20° C		650° C		870° C	
		Ultimate, psi	Yield, psi	Ultimate, psi	Yield, psi	Ultimate, psi	Yield, psi
M-252		174,100	...	160,000	98,600	70,000	60,100
Inconel 700	W	171,600	94,300	145,800	91,600	84,500	55,700
Nimonic 90	W	179,900	113,000	134,200	95,900	54,300	41,400
Nimonic 95	W	184,800	117,100	135,900	98,600	57,100	47,300
Nimonic 100	W	182,900	119,000	157,300	111,500	73,000	47,300
Udimet 500	W	197,200	...	174,100	...	100,100	...
Udimet 600	W	190,000	130,700	197,900	130,100	103,000	97,200
Udimet 700	W	204,100	140,300	197,900	121,700	100,100	93,000
X-40	C	...	...	117,100	47,000	68,200	31,000

W—wrought or rolled
C—cast

The Nimonic series shows the effect of cobalt, aluminum, and titanium on high temperature properties.[88]

Papers have appeared on cobalt in stainless steels,[3,19,21,37] thermal fatigue,[31] the Fe-Cr-Co-C system,[38] ferromagnetic Co-Ni-base alloy,[34] austenitic solid solutions,[53] sheet material,[120] elastic limit,[115] and various heat-resistant alloys.[44,59,67,93,116,122,123,134,135,140]

COBALT-BASE ALLOYS*

As noted in regard to hard facing, cobalt-base alloys have excellent wear resistance and, in addition, are oxidation- and corrosion-resistant in various corrosive media and elevated temperature conditions.

*The literature on this subject is voluminous. The reader is referred to the following, specifically: 4, 8, 9, 13, 15, 17, 18, 20, 24, 25, 27, 29, 30, 35, 43, 51, 54, 61, 63, 64, 66, 68, 69, 74, 80, 82, 83, 87, 89, 90, 91, 94, 95, 96, 98, 99, 100, 103, 104, 111, 112, 114, 127, 128, 129, 131, 132, 136, 141, 145, 148.

TABLE 9.9. STRESS-RUPTURE OF NICKEL-COBALT-BASE ALLOYS IN 100 AND 1000 HOURS
(lbs per sq in.)

Alloy	Temp.	650°C		780°C		815°C		870°C		980°C	
	Time, hr	100	1000	100	1000	100	1000	100	1000	100	1000
M-252		94,400	74,300	61,500	44,400	34,300	18,600	20,000	11,500	...	...
Inconel 700		100,100	88,700	68,500	54,300	42,900	30,000	28,600	18,600	5,700	...
Nimonic 90		80,100	67,200	54,300	35,700	28,600	17,140	15,700	8,600	...	...
Nimonic 95		...	...	55,700	38,600	32,800	20,000	21,500	11,500	...	...
Nimonic 100		...	...	...	...	40,000	28,600	28,600	18,600	10,000	2,860
Udimet 500		...	...	71,500	61,500	44,400	31,400	30,000	21,500	5,700	...
Udimet 600		...	...	85,900	64,400	51,500	37,200	35,700	24,300	11,500	...
Udimet 700		...	...	87,100	73,000	55,700	42,900	38,600	28,600	15,700	...
X-40		...	...	48,000	38,000	29,000	21,700	16,800	12,000	14,500	6,700

Early applications (1931–2) included hard facing the seating surfaces of internal-combustion engine valves, and hot-trimming dies requiring resistance to deformation and oxidation at elevated temperature.[12] About the same time, a Co-Cr-W-C alloy was developed which served as a pressing die for handling the corrosive and abrasive mix used in dry-cell batteries.

In 1933, the Austenal Laboratories and the Union Carbide Corporation developed an alloy containing 64 per cent cobalt, 30 per cent chromium, 5 per cent molybdenum and 0.45 per cent carbon (Austenal trademark "Vitallium") for dental prosthesis and the manufacture of parts for osteosynthesis.

The development of the General Electric turbosupercharger for improving gas turbine efficiency, and the accompanying demand for materials able to withstand a severe combination of stress and temperature, led to the utilization of cobalt-base alloys in jet engine components such as nozzle guide vanes, turbine discs, and turbine buckets and ordnance requirements.

The alloys are available in the form of bar, sheet, forgings, and castings.

Table 9.10 tabulates a number of compositions of commercial "stellites" which are used in cast and wrought forms.[84,85]

High Temperature Alloys

Table 9.11 summarizes the chemical compositions and physical properties of present-day cobalt-bearing alloys for high temperature service.

The age-hardening of cobalt-base alloys that are low in carbon is based on solution treatment and precipitation at temperatures of 538–871°C (1000–1600°F) and times of 8–100 hours. Impact values of all cast cobalt-base alloys are lower at room temperature than they are at 816°C (1500°F), but the impact values of wrought alloys are higher. Hot fatigue tests at 649°C (1200°F) indicate that cast alloys are somewhat inferior to wrought alloys.

Future High Temperature Alloys

Improvements in high temperature service of cobalt-base alloys are to be sought in a better knowledge of the behavior of dislocations and vacancies. To reduce creep rate at elevated temperatures, the movement of dislocations under stress must be kept to a minimum. This is effected by precipitation hardening, whereby the precipitated band becomes a barrier to dislocation movements. Cottrell has suggested that "the greatest creep resistance should be obtained by using two distinct precipitating substances, one already precipitated before the creep deformation, in order to raise the initial elastic limit and reduce initial creep, and one held back in supersaturated

TABLE 9.10. COMPOSITION OF COBALT-BASE ALLOYS

% wt

	Co	Cr	Mo	W	Fe*	Ni	C	Si*	B	Hardness Rockwell "C"
Cast Alloys										
No. 1 Welding rod	50.0	33.0	...	13.0	2.0	...	2.0	1.0	...	54–56
No. 6 Welding rod	64.0	25.5	...	4.75	2.5	...	1.0	1.75	...	39–42
No. 12 Welding rod	58.0	29.0	...	9.0	1.5	...	1.85	1.50	...	48–51
Cutting alloys	42–48	30.5–35.5	...	15–19	1.5	...	1.75–2.7	1.50	...	59–68
Battery castings	50–65	28–32	...	5–15	1.5	...	0.75–1.25	1.00	...	40–50
Valve inserts	45–48	30.5	...	12.5	2.0	...	2.40	0.50	...	55–60
Wear resisting	51–53	30–32	...	10–11	2.0	...	1.70	0.60	...	53–58
A.M.S. 5385										
Haynes No. 21	50–55	27.0	5.5	...	3.0	2.0	0.25	1.0	.007	32–34
A.M.S. 5375										
Haynes No. 23	63–69	25.0	1.0	5.0	2.0	1.5	0.45	1.0	...	32–34
A.M.S. 5378										
Haynes No. 27	31–35	24.5	5.5	...	2.0	32.0	0.40	1.0	...	21–24
A.M.S. 5380										
Haynes No. 30	46–49	26.0	6.0	...	2.0	15.0	0.45	1.0	...	25–30
A.M.S. 5382										
Haynes No. 36	51–53	25.0	...	7.5	2.0	10.5	0.50	1.0	...	32–34
Haynes-HE1049	51–53	18.5	...	14.5	2.0	10.0	0.40	0.60	.05	...
A.M.S. 5387	55–57	29.0	1.5	4.5	3.0	3.0	1.2	1.50	...	...

*Maximum.
Manganese is 1.5% max. in all alloys.

	Co	Cr	Mo	W	Fe*	Ni	C	Si*	B	Hardness Rockwell "C"
Wrought Alloys										
Haynes 6B	59.0	30.0	...	4.5	1.5	1.0	1.10	0.70	...	42–45
Haynes 6K	58.0	31.0	...	4.5	1.5	1.0	1.60	0.70	...	46–49
Haynes 25	49.0	20.0	...	15.0	2.0	10.0	0.10	0.70	...	30–38

TABLE 9.11. SUMMARY OF COMMERCIAL COBALT-BEARING ALLOYS FOR HIGH TEMPERATURE SERVICE

Temp °C	°F	Tensile, Ultimate psi	Elongation %	Stress-rupture, psi 10 hr	100 hr	1000 hr	Creep Strength psi			
						S-816 (NDRC 76)				
					42 Co, 20 Cr, 20 Ni, 4 W, 4 Cb, 4 Mo, 3 Fe, 1.3 Mn, 0.60 Si, 0.40 C					
649	1200	112,000	22.0	75,000	62,000	48,000	29,000(a)		42,000(b)	
732	1350	98,000	23.0	49,000	37,000	29,000	19,000(a)		26,000(b)	
816	1500	73,000	23.0	30,000	24,000	18,000	12,000(a)		16,000(b)	
871	1600	51,000	17.0	20,000	14,500	10,500	5,000(a)		9,800(b)	
927	1700	44,500	15.0	...	10,000	5,800				
982	1800	25,500	20.0	8,800	5,300	3,800				
					Cast Haynes Stellite No. 21 (NDRC 10 or Modified Vitallium)					
					60 Co, 27.5 Cr, 5.5 Mo, 2.5 Ni, <2.0 Fe, 1.0 Mn, 0.60 Si, <0.35 C					
649	1200	71,000	18.4	70,000	51,000	42,000	10,000(c)	0.0_313 (d)	0.0_31 (e)	0.0_48 (f)
732	1350	68,600	9.5	...	36,000	27,500	15,000(c)	0.0_33 (d)	0.0_319(e)	0.0_31 (f)
816	1500	65,700	17.4	...	24,000	14,200	7,000(c)	0.0_322 (d)	0.0_31 (e)	0.0_465(f)
871	1600	41,600	19.3	...	16,700	13,200	7,000(c)	0.0_3125(d)	0.0_444(e)	0.0_444(f)
982	1800	33,300	35.0	12,500	9,400	6,500	10,000(c)	0.0_333 (d)	0.0_313(e)	0.0_313(f)

Haynes No. 25 (L-605)
50 Co, 20 Cr, 15 W, 10 Ni, <2 Fe, 1.5 Mn, 0.50 Si, 0.10 C

Temp (°C)	Temp (°F)									
816	1500	50,000	15.0	30,000	22,500	17,000	9,000(c)	0.0_348(d)	0.0_337(e)	0.0_435(f)
871	1600	...	...	23,000	16,500	12,000	12,000(c)	0.0_21(d)	0.0_46(e)	
927	1700	30,000	...	17,500	11,000	7,200	8,000(c)	0.0_38(d)	0.0_333(e)	
982	1800	21,000	16.0	11,500	7,200	4,500	6,000(c)	0.0_343(d)	0.0_333(e)	
							4,000(c)	0.0_388(d)	0.0_276(e)	

Haynes No. 23 (NDRC 63; AMS 5375)
64.5 Co, 26 Cr, 1.5 Ni, 5.5 W, <2 Fe, 0.40 C

Temp (°C)	Temp (°F)								
...	Room	111,000	8.7	...	...				
538	1000	77,100	14.8	...	...				
649	1200	66,500	11.5	58,000	47,000	...			
816	1500	64,000	19.4	27,200*	21,800	17,000	12,000(c)	0.0_3285(d)	0.0_311(e)
927	1700	37,500	7.0	14,000	11,500	12,500			
982	1800	33,100	32.0	8,600	5,400				

Haynes No. 27 (NDRC 60; AMS 5378)
> 30.0 Co, 26.0 Cr, 6.0 Mo, <2.0 Fe, 0.50 C, Bal. Ni

Temp (°C)	Temp (°F)									
...	Room	90,800	12.7	...	...	...				
538	1000	63,600	16.0	...	...	...				
649	1200	63,400	14.0	58,000	55,000	46,000				
816	1500	55,400	21.3	29,200*	23,400	18,400	12,000(c)	0.0_319(d)	0.0_318(e)	0.0_48(f)
927	1700	43,000	23.0	16,000	12,000	8,600				
982	1800	33,400	24.0	12,500	9,300	6,800				

Aged 50 hr at 816°C (1500°F).

TABLE 9.11. (Cont.)

Haynes 31 (X 40); A.M.S. 5382 (Cast)

56 Co, 25.6 Cr, 10 Ni, 7.3 W, 0.6 Fe, 0.5 C

Temp °C	°F	Tensile, Ultimate psi	Elongation %	Stress-rupture, psi 10 hr	100 hr	1000 hr	Creep Strength psi
20	70	130,000	8.0	...	...	...	
538	1200	92,000	15.0	...	56,000	45,000	
760	1400	72,000	11.0	...	38,000	30,000	
870	1600	50,000	18.0	...	22,000	17,000	
980	1800	30,000	30.0	...	9,000	7,000	

G-32-B

45.5 Co, 18.8 Cr, 12.5 Ni, 2.00 Mo, 1.30 Cb, 2.80 V, 0.30 C, 0.40 Mn, 0.40 Si, bal. Fe
Solution treated at 1280°C (2336°F), 10 min. and oil-quenched. Aged 46 hr at 750°C (1382°F)

Temp °C	°F	Tensile, Ultimate psi	Elongation %	30 hr	100 hr	1000 hr	Stress (creep rate 10^{-5}/hr)
...	Room	143,360	10.0	...	...	...	
700	1292	...	...	50,880	46,640	39,220	38,160
750	1382	...	...	44,520	38,160	31,800	30,740
800	1472	...	...	33,920	27,560	21,200	21,200
850	1562	...	...	25,440	21,200	14,840	15,900

Nimonic 90

18 Co, 18 Cr, 1.0 Fe, 0.10 C, 2.0 Ti, 1.5 Al, Ni Bal.

				100 hr	300 hr	1000 hr
...	Room	156,880	39.0	...	...	...
649	1200	...	...	72,080	66,780	60,420
704	1300	110,240	20.0	58,300	51,940	45,580
749	1380	97,520	15.0	42,400	37,100	31,800
816	1500	72,080	8.0	26,500	22,260	16,960

M-252 (Wrought)

10 Co, 19 Cr, 51.6 Ni, 9.7 Mo, 1.0 Al, 2.5 Ti, 0.01 B, 5.0 Fe, 0.5 Mn, 0.5 Si, 0.15 C

				100 hr	300 hr	1000 hr
20	70	180,000	16.0	...	...	...
538	1000	178,000	15.0	...	...	...
650	1200	168,000	11.0	...	98,000	79,000
760	1400	137,000	10.0	69,000	52,000	38,000
870	1600	74,000	18.0	34,000	23,000	13,500

René 41 (Cast)

19 Cr, 11 Co, 9.75 Mo, 1.65 Al, 2.5 Fe, 0.30 Mn, 0.30 Si, 0.003 B, 0.10 C, Ni Bal.

				100 hr	300 hr	1000 hr
650	1200	100,000(f)	3.0	...	...	...
900	1650	... (g)	...	25,000 (25 hr)	...	...

f - Solution treat at 1950°F plus re-solution at 1950°F for 30 min; rapid air cool; age at 1400°F for 16 hr; air cool.

g - Solution treat at 1950°F plus re-solution at 2150°F for 30 min; rapid air cool; age at 1650°F for 4 hr; air cool.

TABLE 9.11. (Cont.)

Temp °C	Temp °F	Tensile, Ultimate psi	Elongation %	Stress-rupture, psi 10 hr	100 hr	1000 hr	Creep Strength psi
						René - (Sheet)	
20	70	170,000	30.0	...	...	...	
760	1400	140,000	3.0	...	...	...	
900	1650			25,000 (20 hr)			

W.I. - 52 (Tungsten Institute)

64.1 Co, 20 Cr, 11 W, 1.5 Cb, 1.5 Ni, 1.0 Fe, 0.3 Mn, 0.2 Si, 0.4 C

Temp °C	Temp °F	Tensile, Ultimate psi	Elongation %	10 hr	100 hr	1000 hr	Creep Strength psi
20	70	110,000	2.5	...			
870	1600				24,000	20,000	
930	1700				19,000	15,000	

G. E. Alloy J-1570 (Vacuum Melted)

38.8 Co, 28 Ni, 20 Cr, 7 W, 2 Fe, 4 Ti, 0.2 C

Temp °C	Temp °F	Tensile, Ultimate psi	Elongation %	10 hr	100 hr	1000 hr	Creep Strength psi
20	70	150,000	10.0	...	...	...	
650	1200	132,000	12.0	...	95,000	78,000	
700	1300	118,000	8.0	...	78,000	63,000	
760	1400	100,000	9.0	...	55,000	43,000	
816	1500	82,000	14.0	...	33,000	24,000	
870	1600	53,000	25.0	...	23,000	16,000	
930	1700	35,000	40.0	...	14,000	8,000	

Physical tests on hot-rolled bar, in fully heat-treated condition. Heat treatment consists of heating to 1052–1179°C (1925–2115°F) for 8–12 hr followed by air-cooling, reheating to 704°C (1300°F) for 12–16 hr and cooling in air.
*Aged 50 hr at 816°C (1500°F).

Symbols:

(a) Stress for creep rate of 0.0001% per hr   (d) Creep rate per hr at 500 hr
(b) Stress for creep rate of 0.001% per hr   (e) Creep rate per hr at 1000 hr
(c) Stress for 1800–2000 hr   (f) Creep rate per hr at 2000 hr

solution, ready to precipitate in dislocations and prevent them from climbing." This may be the basis for further development of cobalt-base alloys.

Figure 9.1 shows, diagramatically, the temperature limitations of present and future materials used for turbojet and ramjet engines.[46]

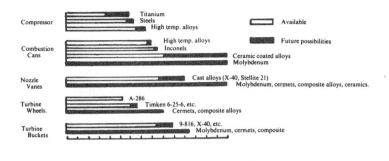

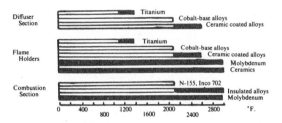

Figure 9.1. Temperature limitations of present and future materials for turbojet engine components and ramjet components.

Microstructural Constitution

Cobalt-base alloys are naturally complex in structure since they contain carbon, chromium, tungsten and/or molybdenum, which form primary and complex hard carbides in a relatively ductile Co-Cr matrix.[33] The microhardness of the carbides will be 55–60 Rockwell "C"; of the matrix, 35–40 Rockwell "C" in a sand casting.

The addition of minor quantities of the elements boron, zirconium, titanium, aluminum, etc., makes the alloy even more complex, but some of the elements have been found to improve hardness values at high temperatures.[1]

The principal intermetallic compounds formed in the cobalt-alloy systems are complex carbides of the M_7C_3, $M_{23}C_6$, and M_6C types. These are believed to function as dispersoids, acting as "blockers" in the retardation of dislocation movements, slip, and plastic flow.

Minor amounts (0.007–0.150 per cent) of certain elements such as boron improve the stability of the cobalt alloy.

Elsea and McBride investigated the effect of nitrogen, iron, and nickel on the alpha-beta transformation and gamma precipitation.[56] With 20 per cent chromium, nitrogen contents of 0.01–0.07 per cent lower the alpha-beta transformation temperature over a fairly constant width of field. The 30 per cent chromium alloy and nitrogen contents of 0.01–0.14 per cent show a lowering of the alpha-beta transformation temperature with the width of field widening with increasing nitrogen. The amount of gamma precipitate increases as the nitrogen content increases.

Iron contents of 1–6 per cent in a 20 and 30 per cent chromium alloy lower the alpha-beta transformation temperature with the width of field widening. Gamma precipitation was observed only in the cobalt alloy containing 32 per cent chromium and 6 per cent iron. Nickel contents of 1–14 per cent have an effect on the alpha-beta transformation range similar to that of iron. Increasing amounts of nickel raise the gamma precipitation temperature until gamma and alpha coexist.

The intermediate phases in the ternary alloy systems Cr-Co-Ni, Cr-Co-Fe, and Cr-Co-Mo in the 1200°C isothermal sections have been investigated with respect to the occurrence of σ-phase in alloys of the transition elements.[41,42] In the Cr-Co-Ni- and Cr-Co-Fe-phase diagrams at 1200°C, the Cr-Co-σ-phase forms elongated fields extending into the ternary systems, suggesting that nickel and iron are capable of partially replacing cobalt. At 800°C, the σ solid solution field extends all the way from the Cr-Co-σ-phase to the Cr-Fe-σ-phase across the Cr-Co-Fe ternary diagram, so that iron and cobalt are completely replacing each other.

In the Cr-Co-Mo system at 1200°C, the Cr-Co-σ-phase forms an elongated field of ternary solid solutions, indicating that molybdenum is capable of partially replacing chromium in the σ-phase.

These phase changes may be attributed to electron vacancy concentrations. A condition for the occurrence of the σ-phase appears to be the attainment of a range of electron vacancy numbers per atom intermediate between that in the face-centered cubic transition elements—nickel, cobalt, and iron—and in the body-centered cubic transition elements—chromium and molybdenum.

In cobalt-chromium alloys, the α–β transformation is little affected by tungsten, but molybdenum tends to raise it.[62] Both elements tend to promote the formation of γ-phase, molybdenum being the more potent. X-ray diffraction studies in the Co-Cr-Mo alloys show molybdenum in solution in both γ and the two cobalt-rich terminal solid solutions, α and β.

Nisbet and Hibbard[114a] have rationalized, on the basis of the principles of alloying, the effect of hardening element additions (Ta, W, Mo, Zr, Ti,

Al, Be, C) on the high temperature properties of Fe-Cr-Co-Ni base-alloys. The authors conclude that the strength of these alloys can be rationalized on the basis of strengthening effects related to fundamental characteristics of the components and possible phase relationships. Factors influencing ductility are: alloy content, crystal structure, temperature at which fracture occurs, temperature of precipitation hardening, temperature of allotropic transformation, deoxidation practice, and recrystallization. In the design of high temperature alloys, the base alloy should comprise solid solutions saturated as nearly as possible with the most effective solution-hardening elements, i.e., large differences in atomic diameter, valency, compressibility, and minimum solubilities. Solution-hardening elements not only raise the base strength, but also increase the amount of strain-hardening and raise the recrystallization temperature, thus counteracting a lowered melting point.

The ternary alloys of titanium-carbon-cobalt and titanium-chromium-cobalt have been investigated with respect to mechanical properties, structure and transformation range, response to heat treatment, and aging.[39] Up to 3 per cent, cobalt is soluble in alpha or beta titanium. Carbon lowers the beta solvus line in the Ti-Co-C alloys. Cobalt is not beneficial to Ti-Cr alloys.

The intermediate phase Ti_2Co is face-centered cubic with 96 atoms per unit cell; TiCo is body-centered cubic.[50] In the titanium-cobalt system, the intermediate phase, rich in cobalt, is $TiCo_2$, hexagonal in structure.

Microstructural constitution has been considered for alloys of cobalt and copper,[16] chromium,[57] chromium and iron,[22,38] vanadium,[48] and tungsten carbide.[77]

MISCELLANEOUS ALLOYS

Spring Alloy

The alloy trademarked "Elgiloy," manufactured by the Elgin National Watch Company, has a nominal composition; in per cent, 40 cobalt, 20 chromium, 15 nickel, 7 molybdenum, 2 manganese, 0.04 beryllium, 0.15 carbon, and balance iron.[130,143] Elgiloy was developed primarily for watch springs, but because of its outstanding properties of corrosion resistance, high and low temperature performance, and non-magnetic behavior, it is used for fountain pen nibs, instrument springs, communication equipment, instrument pivots, medical and dental equipment, special valves, etc.

Elgiloy springs deliver more torque (120 per cent) than comparable carbon steel. Fatigue resistance is 190 per cent, and resistance to set 370 per cent of spring steel.

Physical and mechanical properties are as follows:

Physical Constants		Mechanical Properties	
Specific gravity	8.3	Ultimate, psi	368,000
Coefficient linear expansion		Yield, psi	280,000
per °C (0–50°C)	12.7×10^{-6}	Proportional limit,	
Thermoelasticity per °C		psi	233,000
(0–50°C)	39.6×10^{-5}	Hardness,	
Electrical resistance, ohms/		Rockwell	C59
circular mil. ft	600		
Modulus of elasticity, psi	29,500,000		
Magnetic qualities	nonmagnetic		

The resistance of Elgiloy to atmospheric and chemical corrosion is superior to that of the best stainless steels.

As rolled, Elgiloy is hard and stiff but capable of being sheared, formed or coiled, and punched. It can be soldered, brazed, and welded; but it machines with difficulty because of work-hardening.

Maximum spring properties and corrosion resistance are obtained by heat treatment consisting of aging at proper temperatures and intervals.

Cobenium is the name of a similar heat-resistant spring alloy marketed by Wilbur B. Driver Company.

Constant Modulus Alloys

Alloys which have a modulus of elasticity which varies little with temperature are Co-Elinvar (Co 57–60 per cent, Fe 25–35 per cent, Cr 8–15 per cent) and Velinvar (Co 56–63 per cent, Fe 29–34 per cent, V 7–10 per cent). They are used in the manufacture of hair-springs for precision instruments and chronometers.

Dental and Surgical Alloys

The cobalt-chromium-base alloys used in dental and surgical applications are not attacked by body fluids and hence do not set up an emf in the body which would cause irritation of the tissues.

Typical dental and surgical alloys are as follows:

Alloy	C	Co	Cr	Mo	Fe	Si	Mn	Ni	V	Be
A	0.46	62.7	29.3	5.6	0.80	0.30	0.60	...	2.0	...
B	0.55	61.0	30.0	5.8	1.00	0.50	0.75	...	...	...
C	0.20	57.8	18.0	2.0	0.50	0.50	...	14.0	7.0	...
D	0.50	63.7	27.5	5.3	1.80	0.10	0.10	...	...	...
E	0.20	27.5	27.5	5.3	1.60	0.40	0.70	35.7	...	1.20
F	0.40	67.9	24.0	5.3	1.50	0.30	0.60	1.4	...	...

Electrical Resistance Alloys

The "Kanthal" alloys containing 20–30 per cent chromium, 5–6 per cent aluminum, 1.5–3.0 per cent cobalt, and balance iron are used in the manufacture of electrical resistances which must withstand temperatures above 1350° C. They are not affected by sulfur-bearing atmospheres.

"Konel," "Cobanic," and "Hilanic," which contain cobalt, nickel, iron, and titanium, are used in the manufacture of radio-tube filaments since they have high electrical resistivity and good heat resistance.

Miscellaneous Applications

Other workers have discussed cobalt alloys in stainless steels,[37,47] microtomes,[65] springs,[106] and engineering materials.[5,124]

MANUFACTURING PROCESSES

Processing highly alloyed cobalt-bearing alloys into finished components necessarily requires a number of different methods and techniques which are dictated by the properties of the particular alloy.

The alloy may be cast to shape, or cast in ingots for forging or pressing for processing into bar stock, sheet, etc.

Casting components of alloys having a high Cr, W, or Mo content is the most economic method for fabrication. Even with alloys which have good forming properties, the wear of the dies may be severe and result in high cost.

Cast components have proved capable of withstanding stresses at high temperature, even though a cast structure does not have the directional properties of wrought material. A most important factor in casting is grain size, which may be controlled to some extent by the degree of superheat, pouring temperature, mold temperature, shape of casting, and method of casting.[70]

Melting

Melting equipment and techniques continue to improve as a necessary part of the development of superalloys. Many of the alloys contain appreciable amounts of aluminum, titanium, boron, etc. which are reactive with nitrogen, oxygen, and hydrogen. Conventional air melting in induction or arc furnaces will not permit the effective use of these reactive metals. Slags are not sufficient protection and tend to decrease cleanliness, therefore techniques involving vacuum or inert atmospheres have been commercially developed. Induction melting of heats from 25 to 5000 pounds in vacuum, and consumable electrode vacuum remelting of ingots up to 15,000 pounds are proved methods.

Conventional melting of prime metals and master alloys for cast components is effected in high frequency induction melting furnaces or indirect-arc furnaces without the use of slags but with the addition of deoxidants. The induction furnace may range in size from 20 kw to 200 kw, with frequencies of 3000–20,000 cycles. Low frequencies for furnaces over 50 kw are supplied by motor generators or an inductor alternator, while higher frequencies for 20–50 kw are furnished by a spark-gap converter.

The refractory material for the crucible may be magnesite or zirconium silicate. Induction furnaces up to 50 kw use a pre-formed crucible which rests on and is supported at the sides with a backing of refractory insulating powder of magnesia or zirconia. A mica sheet is placed on the inside of the coil for electrical insulation and retention of the dry insulating powder. Induction furnaces in excess of 50-kw capacity use a monolithic lining made *in situ* since the larger sizes of pre-formed crucibles do not stand the severe thermal strains imposed on them. The monolithic lining is formed by plastering the inner surface of the coil with a cement of the same composition as that to be used for the inner lining or crucible. One-eighth thickness of asbestos cloth is placed against the coil and a second layer of cement, approximately 3/8 inch thick, is plastered over the asbestos. These layers are thoroughly dried for 24 hours by suspending a 3-kw heater inside the shell. Dry refractory is rammed in the bottom and a cylindrical sleeve made of "Transite" or steel located on top to form the crucible. Dry refractory cement is then poured in layers between the coil and the former and rammed. The removal of the former and the curing of the refractory is accomplished by slowly melting a charge of metal.

The high frequency induction furnace stirs the charge by electrodynamic effects; this accounts for the homogeneity of complex alloys. The furnace can also carry out melting in the complete absence of any carbonaceous material; this is important in melting precipitation-hardening alloys.

The indirect-arc rocking type of furnace, e.g., Detroit, which has a conical or cylindrical shell, is lined with insulating and magnesite refractory, the latter forming the hearth on which melting takes place. The lining may be a preformed refractory crock or a rammed lining. Two horizontal electrodes enter this furnace, one from either end, so that the arc is struck at the centre of the melting chamber. The metal is not part of the electrical circuit.

Vacuum Melting

Two vacuum melting processes are now in commercial use: (1) induction; (2) consumable-electrode arc melting under vacuum or in a protective atmosphere.[6,10,28,52,55,58,108–110,113,125,138,139]

The induction method consists of melting in a vacuum chamber, using a conventional induction furnace with a magnesia or zirconia crucible. The consumable-electrode remelting process uses air-melted electrodes of the alloy and consumably remelts them in a copper, water-cooled crucible under vacuum or argon.

Quality improvements in vacuum melting as compared with air melting are as follows: (a) improved cleanliness, (b) decreased gas content, (c) higher mechanical properties, (d) improved soundness, (e) better hot and cold workability, (f) improved magnetic properties, (g) production of new metals and alloys which cannot be made economically or with any degree of consistency by present conventional methods. These improvements are attainable in some alloys by induction melting, in others by consumable-electrode melting or a combination of the two processes.

The following values compare the vacuum melted gas level of superalloys with the electric arc process.

Melting Process	Hydrogen	Oxygen	Nitrogen
Arc melt under slag	5–15 ppm	10–200 ppm	50–600 ppm
Vacuum melt, induction	< 1-2	5–125	20–200
Vacuum melt, consumable-electrode arc	< 1-2	10–100	20–200

Chemical and physical improvements may be classified as cleanliness-sensitive, chemistry-sensitive, and segregation-sensitive.

The property of cleanliness-sensitivity is evidenced by improvement of room temperature fatigue strength as gross inclusions, which act as stress raisers, are eliminated. Stress-rupture life is sensitive to the chemistry of the alloy, and minor additions, e.g., titanium, aluminum, zirconium, etc., are more closely controlled. Segregation-sensitivity is a problem with alloys containing high density elements and is minimized by consumable-electrode melting.

Improvements in high temperature properties of superalloys may not be due so much to the melting process itself as to minor but significant chemistry modifications, e.g., the elimination of manganese and silicon by the utilization of vacuum melting. The effective use of titanium, aluminum, and zirconium in increasing high temperature strength was made possible by vacuum melting.

The evaluation of air and vacuum melting is indicated in the following tabulation, which gives the temperature ratings based on 100-hour rupture life at 20,000 psi.

Alloy	Air Melted °F	Vacuum Melted °F
J-1570	...	1650
Udimet 500	...	1670
Waspaloy	1570	1630
M-252	1570	1625

Investment Casting

This process involves the use of a pattern, in wax or plastic, which is a positive replica of the part, with appropriate wax and metal shrinkage allowance.[75,92,147]

The steps in the process are as follows:

(a) A pattern die is machined from steel, brass or aluminum. Alternatively, a master pattern is made in brass or aluminum and from it a mold is made in one or more parts and embedded at the parting line in a suitable refractory material. A soft low melting point nonferrous alloy is cast against the exposed pattern. Shrinkage allowances are made for the metal to be cast and for the wax or plastic.

(b) The wax or plastic is injected into the die to produce the component with or without the gating. The patterns are assembled or gated into suitable form and size.

(c) The assembly is pre-coated in a slurry of refractory material, such as silica flour suspended in a water-alcohol-ethyl silicate solution, of a consistency to produce a dense and uniform coating on the part after drying.

(d) The coated assembly is placed in a mold and invested or enveloped with a refractory material.

(e) The invested mold is allowed to air-set for 8–36 hours; the wax is melted out at 300–400° F (polystyrene patterns are dried at 150–160° F) and then completely burned out at 1600–1850° F.

(f) The metal is cast into the cavity by (1) static pouring, (2) pressure casting, (3) vacuum melting and casting, or (4) centrifugal casting.

(g) Severance operations and cleaning follow normal procedures.

Investment casting techniques developed in the dental and jewelry trades were adapted to the production of turbosupercharger blades in 1940. Thus, a "precision" process was applied to machine components to provide a new method of fabrication.

Forming

Techniques of forging, rolling, and forming require close temperature control in the range for hot-working and in the degree of reduction.[79,107,137]

In pressing or forming, the number of anneals usually equals the number of draws. The steps involved depend on the particular alloy selected. The following alloys are illustrative.

Waspaloy has a narrow hot-working range and is "stiff" under the forging hammer. Forging should start at 2150° F maximum furnace temperature and finish at 1850° F minimum metal temperature. Furnace atmosphere should be neutral or slightly oxidizing. The alloy is austenitic under all conditions. Heavy section forgings should be equalized in a furnace before cooling.

To cold form, the thin sections require solution treatment at 1975° F for 4 hours, air-cooling, and intermediate "in process" anneals to nullify work-hardening.

René 41 has a critical heating and cooling rate; the alloy will age-harden on cooling from 1800° F, as shown by the following values for annealed material when air-cooled and water-quenched.

	2150° F Air-Cooled	2150° F Water-Quenched
Tensile, psi	195,000	130,000
0.2% yield, psi	160,000	65,000
Elongation	31%	50%
Hardness, Rockwell	C-43	B-93

It is essential that the heating and cooling rates during the annealing cycle be rapid. Minimum annealing temperature is 1950° F.

Multimet alloy shows a decrease in ductility in the range 1200–1800° F, but is forgeable in the range 1900–2200° F. It is preferable to cold-form sheet material, but annealing between operations is required to avoid cracking.

"Haynes" alloy No. 25 (L-605) has good hot workability and cold-working characteristics, and may be fabricated into parts by hot-forging, cold-forging, stamping, drawing or bending. For cold-working, the alloy is first solution-treated at 2200–2275° F.

Joining

High alloy materials capable of being fabricated in the wrought form are usually of the austenitic type and, in general, can be joined by all of the methods applicable to the austenitic stainless steels.[26,40,60,81,101,119] Some alloys exhibit characteristics that are peculiar to that alloy composition. "Multimet" alloy is subject to microfissuring if proper welding techniques are not used. Ductility falls sharply at 1700° F, hence this point must be passed through as quickly as possible by (a) using stringer beads, (b)

TABLE 9.12. SUPERALLOYS IN ORDER OF DECREASING MACHINABILITY

Alloy	Type	Nominal Chemical Composition									
		C	Co	Ni	Cr	W	Mo	Cb/Ta	Ti	Al	Fe
Therlo; Kovar A; Rodar;	Iron Base	...	17	29	...	...	...	...	...	...	54
G-18-B		0.40	10	13	13	2.5	2.0	3.0	...	...	56
K-42-B		0.05	22	43	18	...	...	...	2.5	0.2	13
Refractaloy 26		0.05	20	37	18	...	3	...	2.8	0.2	18
Refractaloy 70		0.05	30	20	20	4	8	...	...	...	15
Refractaloy 80		0.10	30	20	20	5	10	...	...	...	14
N-155		0.15	20	20	21	2.5	3	1	...	...	32.5
S-590		0.43	20	20	20.5	4	4	4	...	...	27.5
Konal	Nickel Base	...	17	72	...	...	...	...	2.2	...	6.25
Nimonic 90		0.10	20	51	20	...	...	...	2	1	5
Inconel 700		0.13	29	46	15	...	3	...	2.2	3.2	0.8
Udimet 500		0.08	19.5	47	19	...	4	...	2.9	2.9	4
M-252		0.15	10	55	19	...	10	...	2.5	1.0	2
Haynes Alloy 25	Cobalt Base	0.15	51	10	20	15	...	...	...	...	...
J-1570		0.20	38	28	20	7	...	...	4	...	2
S-816		0.38	40	20	20	4	4	4	...	...	4
G-34		0.80	45	12	19	...	2	1.3	...	...	20
HS-21		0.25	62	3	27	...	5	...	...	...	...
X40; Haynes 31		0.50	55	10	25	8	...	...	...	...	1.5
Cobenium; Elgiloy		0.15	40	15	20	...	7	Mn 2	...	...	16
Rexalloy 33		2.25	44	...	33	11	...	...	...	...	2.0

quench-welding, (c) maintaining the base material at room temperature, and (d) keeping the interpass temperature at room temperature.

An alloy that is crack-sensitive may be affected by the type of electrode coating. A lime coated electrode has been found to be more effective than a titania type of electrode in eliminating weld cracking in "Multimet."

"Haynes" Alloy No. 25, which has high strength and oxidation resistance at 1800° F, is readily weldable when proper precautions are taken. It is subject to hot-short cracking in the range 900–1300° F where the elongation is 15 per cent compared with 20 per cent at 1900° F.

Machining

Cobalt high temperature alloys are not difficult to machine when in the solution-treated, partially aged, or fully aged condition.[117,133] These alloys work-harden like the austenitic stainless steels, and the machining techniques for stainless are applicable. Cutting tools must have sharp cutting edges, smooth tool-chip contact areas, and rigid mountings. Feeds and speeds are lower than those for austenitic stainless, but the depth of cut should be sufficient to avoid glazing. The cutting fluid should be a good coolant.

Drilling is the most difficult machining operation since the rubbing of the drill causes work-hardening. A sharp drill and positive feed is required. Pilot drills are not practical.

Superalloys are best tapped in the solution-treated condition by a three-flute, high-speed steel gun tap with a hook angle slightly greater than that ordinarily used. A sulfochlorinated type of oil is applied with a brush.

Cut-off is easily accomplished with friction saws and rubber-bonded cut-off wheels.

Turning and facing operations are the least difficult. High-speed steel, stellite-type cast alloy, and carbide tools are used. For intermittent cuts, high-speed steel and reduced speeds are required..Finishing cuts should be made well below the work-hardened surface left by the roughing operation. Stress relieving may be required after roughing operations.

Table 9.12 lists a number of superalloys in order of their decreased machinability.

References

1. Adkins, E. F., and Jaffee, R. I., "Application of Dispersion Hardening to Cobalt," *Cobalt,* No. 3, 27–30 (1959).
2. Anonymous, "Glass-to-Metal Seals. Applications of Iron-Nickel-Cobalt Alloys," *Metal Ind.,* **75,** 263–66, 292–3 (1949).
3. —, "Cobalt versus Titanium Stabilized Stainless Steel," *Metal Progr.,* February, 116 (1953).

4. —, "Aircraft Materials—Present and Future," *Materials & Methods,* **45,** No. 5, 126–30 (1957).

5. —, "The Uses of Cobalt," *Cobalt,* No. 1, 5–12 (1958).

6. —, "Vacuum Melted High Temperature Alloys," *Metal Industry,* Jan. 24, 63–5 (1958).

7. American Society for Metals "Metals Handbook," Cleveland, Am. Soc. for Metals, 1948.

8. A.S.M. Staff, "Approximate Strength of Important Jet Engine Alloys (Round Test Bars)," *Metal Progr.,* **60,** 80B (1951).

9. A.S.T.M. "Symposium on Materials for Gas Turbines," *Am. Soc. Testing Materials,* **199,** (1946).

10. Austenal, Inc., "Investment Caster Uses Vacuum," *Steel,* Nov. 25, 96–99 (1957).

11. Avery, H. S., "Hard Facing Alloys for Steel Mill Use," *Iron Steel Engr.,* **26,** Sept. (1951).

12. Badger, F. S., "High Temperature Alloys, 1900–1958," *J. Metals,* **10,** 512–16 (1958).

13. —, and Fritzlen, G. A., "Nickel- and Cobalt-Base Alloys," A.S.M. Conference on Metals for Supersonic Aircraft and Missiles (1958).

14. Bardgett, W. E., and Bolsover, G. R., "Special Steels for Gas Turbines," Iron Steel Inst., July, 135–48 (1952).

15. Beattie, H. J., and Versnyder, F. L., "Microconstituents in High Temperature Alloys," *Am. Soc. Metals,* Preprint 1, Oct. (1952).

16. Becker, J. J., "Precipitation and Magnetic Annealing in Cu-Co Alloy," *J. Metals,* **212,** No. 1, 138–44 (1958).

17. Betteridge, W., "Treatment of Nimonic Alloys," *Metal Treatment,* **26,** 45–52 (1959).

18. Bieber, C. G., U. S. Pat. 2,570,193, Oct. 9, 1951.

19. Binder, W. O., and Franks, R., U. S. Pat. 2,624,671, Jan. 6, 1953.

20. Binder, W. O., and Spendelow, H. R., "New Cobalt-Base Alloy for High Temperature Sheet," *Metal Progr.,* **57,** 321–6 (1950).

21. Binder, W. O., and Weisert, E. D., "Some Notes on the Oxidation Resistance of Boron-Containing Cr-Ni-Co-Fe Alloys," *Corrosion,* **9,** 329–32 (1953).

22. Bleyenberghe, P., Van, "Manufacture and Application of a Cobalt-Base Alloy," *Cobalt,* No. 2, 3–10 (1959).

23. Bollenrath, F., Cornelius, H., and Bungardt, W., "The Complex Alloys Co-Ni-Fe," *Metallwirtschaft,* **1,** 755–7 (1938).

24. Boss, G. H., "Approximate Strength of Important Jet Engine Alloys," *Metal Progr.,* **59,** 80B (1951).

25. Buswell, R. W., Jenkins, I., and Pitkin, W. R., "Sintered Alloys for High Temperature Service in Gas Turbines," *Powder Met. Bull.,* **6,** 110–13 (1952).

26. Cape, A. T., "Brazing Alloys for Guided Missiles," *Metal Progr.,* **74,** No. 3, 99–104 (1958).

27. Chaston, J. C., and Child, F. C., "Some Cobalt-Rich Alloys for High Temperature Service," Iron Steel Inst. Spec. Rept., No. 43 (1952).

28. Child, H. C., and Harris, G. T., "Vacuum Melting of Steels," *J. Iron Steel Inst.,* **190,** 414–31 (1958).

29. Clark, F. H., "Metals at High Temperatures," New York, Reinhold Publ. Corp., 1950.
30. Clark, W. C., U. S. Pat. 2,536,033, Jan. 2, 1951.
31. Clauss, F. J., and Freeman, J. W., "Thermal Fatigue of Ductile Materials," (S-816). Nat. Adv. Com. for Aeronautics Tech. Note 4160 and 4165 (1958).
32. Climax Molybdenum Co., "Molybdenum in Steel and Iron Alloys," New York, Climax Molybdenum Co. (1948).
33. Cobalt Information Center, "Cobalt and Its Alloys. Allotropy and Phase Diagrams," Cobalt Information Center, Columbus, Ohio (1956).
34. Cochardt, A., "Development of a Ferromagnetic Cobalt-Nickel-Base High Temperature Alloy," *Trans. Am. Soc. Metals.*, **52**, 15 p. (1960).
35. Comstock, G. J., and Shaw, J. D., "Properties of Cobalt-Nickel-Chromium Alloys Made by Powder Metallurgy," from "Physics of Powder Metallurgy," pp 372–86, New York, McGraw-Hill Book Company, 1951.
36. Cornelius, H., "Influence of Composition of Facing Alloys Upon their Properties," *Arch. Eisenhüttenw.*, **15**, 47–58 (1941).
37. Coutsouradis, D., "Corrosion Resistance of Some Stainless Steels Alloyed with Cobalt," *Cobalt*, No. 5, 3–14 (1959).
38. —, and Habraken, L., "The Fe-Cr-Co-C Quaternary System," *Cobalt*, No. 4, 3–27 (1959).
39. Craighead, C. M., Simmons, O. W., and Eastwood, L. W., "Titanium Binary Alloys," *J. Metals*, **188**, 485–513 (1950).
40. Culbertson, R. P., "Weldability of Wrought High Alloy Materials," *Materials & Methods*, 98–102, Feb. (1955).
41. Darby, J. B., and Beck, P. A., "Intermediate Phases in the Cr-Mo-Co System at 1300° C," *J. Metals*, **7**, 765–6 (1955).
42. Das, D. K., Rideout, S. P., and Beck, P. A., "Intermediate Phases in the Mo-Fe-Co, Mo-Fe-Ni, and Mo-Ni-Co Ternary Systems," *J. Metals*, **4**, 1071–75 (1952).
43. Davis, E. A., and Manjoine, M. J., "Effect of Shape of Notch on Rupture Strength of High Temperature Alloys," *Am. Soc. Testing Mat.*, Preprint, **78**, (1952).
44. Decker, R. F., and Freeman, J. W., "Mechanism of Beneficial Effects of Boron and Zirconium on Creep-Rupture Properties of a Complex Heat-Resistant Alloy," Nat. Adv. Com. for Aeronautics Tech. Note 4286 (1958).
45. Deloro Stellite Limited, "Hard Facing with Stellite," *Machinery*, **80**, 179–88 (1952).
46. Demerjian, S. G., "Which Alloys for Jet Hot Spots," *Materials & Methods*, 116–18, Oct. (1955).
47. Dewees, N. B., "Wear of Cobalt-Base and Stainless Materials in High Purity Water," *Am. Soc. Lubrication Engrs.*, Preprint, 57LC-I (1957).
48. Duwez, P., "The Crystal Structure of V_3Co," *J. Metals*, **3**, 564 (1951).
49. —, and Martens, H., "Phase Relationships in the Iron-Chromium-Vanadium System," *Trans. Am. Soc. Metals*, **44**, 484–94 (1952).
50. Duwez, P., and Taylor, J. L., "The Structure of Intermediate Phases in Alloys of Titanium and Iron, Cobalt and Nickel," *Trans. A.I.M.E.*, **188**, 1173–6 (1950).

51. Dym, J. B., and Badger, T., "Cast Alloys Vary in Cutting Efficiency," *Am. Machinist,* 109–11, Nov. 20 (1947).

52. Dyrkacz, W. W., "Quality Improvement in Stainless Steels and Superalloys by Vacuum Melting," *Metal Progr.,* May, 138–41 (1959).

53. Eberle, F., Hoke, J. H., Rozic, E. J., and Leyda, W. E., "The Strengthening of Austenitic Solid Solutions," Wright Air Develop. Centre Tech. Rept., 52–28 (1958).

54. Edwards, A. R., "New High Temperature Alloys," *Australasian Engr.,* 42–7, June (1952).

55. Electrochemical Society, "Vacuum Melting of High Alloy Materials," Electrochemical Society, Boston, 1954.

56. Elsea, A. R., and McBride, C. C., "Cobalt-Chromium Alloys," *Trans. A.I.M.E.,* **188,** 154–61 (1950).

57. Elsea, A. R., Westerman, A. B., and Manning, G. K., "The Cobalt-Chromium Binary System," *Trans. A.I.M.E.,* **180,** 579–603 (1948).

58. Everhart, J. L., "Vacuum Melted Metals and Alloys. Why Use Them," *Materials in Engineering Design,* August, 89–97 (1959).

59. Ewing, J. F., and Freeman, J. W., "Influence of Hot Working Conditions on the High Temperature Properties of Heat-Resisting Alloys," *Bull. T. R.,* 549, Am. Soc. Test. Mat. (1956).

60. Feduska, M., "High Temperature Brazing Alloy-Base Metal Wetting Reactions," *Welding J.,* **38,** 122S–131S (1959).

61. Fieldhouse, I. B., Hedge, J. C., Long, J. L., and Waterman, T. E., "Thermal Properties of High Temperature Materials," Technical Rept. 57–487, U. S. Office of Technical Services, PB 131718, (1958).

62. Fletcher, E. E., and Elsea, A. R., "Effects of Tungsten or Molybdenum upon the Alpha-Beta Transformation and Gamma Precipitation in Cobalt-Chromium Alloys," *Trans. A.I.M.E.,* **191,** 897–902 (1951).

63. —, —, "Effect of Nitrogen and Manganese on Structure and High Temperature Properties of Cast X-40 Alloy," *Trans. Met. Soc. A.I.M.E.,* **215,** No. 6, 917–25 (1959).

64. Foley, F. B., U. S. Pat. 2,543,841, March 6, 1951.

65. Fordham, S., Hallpike, M., and Riddihough, M., "Notes on the Technique of Temporal Bone Microtomy," (Stellited Knives), *British Medical Bull.,* **12,** 93–100 (1956).

66. Fountain, R. W., and Forgeng, W. D., "Phase Relations and Precipitation in Cobalt-Titanium Alloys," *Trans. Met. Soc. A.I.M.E.,* **215,** No. 6, 998–1008 (1959).

67. Franks, R., and Binder, W. O., Canadian Pat. 460,263, 460,274, 460,275, Oct. 11, 1949.

68. Freeman, J. W., Ewing, J. F., and White, A. E., "Influence of Chemical Composition on Rupture Properties at 1500° F of Forged Cr-Co-Ni-Fe- Base Alloys," Nat. Adv. Comm. Aeronautics. Tech. Note 2745 (1952).

69. Frey, D. N., Freeman, J. W., and White, A. E., "Fundamental Effects of Cold Work on Some Cobalt-Chromium-Nickel-Iron-Base Creep-Resistant Alloys," Nat. Adv. Comm. Aeronautics Tech. Note 2586 (1952).

70. Gadd, E. R., "Precision Casting Turbine Blades. High Temperature Steels and Alloys for Gas Turbines," Iron Steel Inst. Sp. Rept. No. 43 (1952).
71. Gault, J. R., and Ironside, D. A., "The Spray Fuse Hard Facing Process for 'Stellite,' Cobalt Base Powders," *Machinery,* Jan. 28, (1959).
72. Gill, J. P., *et al.,* "Tool Steels," Cleveland Am. Soc. for Metals, 1944.
73. Grainger, G., "Hard Facing with Cobalt-Base Alloys," *Cobalt,* No. 3, 3–15 (1959).
74. Grant, N. J., Kates, L. W., and Hamilton, N. E., "Development and Evaluation of Cast Turbine Rotors," *Foundry,* 78, 86–93, 234–9 (1950).
75. Gresham, H. E., and Dunlop, A., "Investing Casting Nozzle Guide Vanes," Iron Steel Inst. Spec. Rept. No. 43 (1952).
76. Grossman, M. A., and Bain, E. C., "High Speed Steel," New York, John Wiley and Sons, Inc., 1931.
77. Gurland, J., and Norton, J. T., "Role of the Binder Phase in Cemented Tungsten Carbide-Cobalt Alloys," *J. Metals,* 4, 1051–56 (1952).
78. Habraken, L., and Coutsouradis, D., "Cobalt in Steels. What Improvements May be Expected," *Cobalt,* No. 2, 11–12 (1959).
79. Haley, H. E., "Fabricating High Strength Superalloys," *Metal Industry,* 94, 11–12, 203–6, 229–32 (1959).
80. Harder, O. E., and Roberts, D. A., "Cobalt-Chromium-Nickel-Base Alloy," Canadian Pat. 480,487, 480,488, and 480,489, Jan. 22, 1952.
81. Harkins, F. G., "Process Control for Resistance Welding under Government Specifications," *Welding J.,* 31, 567–74 (1952).
82. Haynes, E., "Alloys of Chromium and Other Metals," *Trans. A.I.M.E.,* XLIV, 573–9 (1912).
83. —, "Stellite and Stainless Steel," *J. Western Soc. Engr.,* 35, 467–82 (1919–20).
84. Haynes Stellite Co., "Haynes Alloys for High Temperature," Kokomo, Ind. (1951).
85. —, "Investment Cast Wear-Resistant Alloys," Kokomo, Ind. (1958).
86. —, "Hard Facing Manual," Kokomo, Ind. (1959).
87. Hehemann, R. F., and Ault, G. M., "High Temperature Materials," A.I.M.E. Cleveland Conf., April, 1957.
88. Henry Wiggin & Co., Ltd., "The Nimonic Alloys," Birmingham 16, England (1957).
89. Herbenar, A. W., and Heckman, G. R., "Gas Turbine Materials," Paper No. 58-A-46B, A.S.M.E. Gas Turbine Progress Rept. (1958).
90. Hoffman, C. A., and Gyorgak, C. A., "Investigation of Effects of Grain Size upon Engine Life of Cast A.M.S. 5385 Gas Turbine Blades," Nat. Adv. Comm. for Aeronautics Res. Mem. E53D06 (1953).
91. Hoppin, G. S., and Bamberger, E. N., "Effects of Hydrogen Brazing on Properties of High Temperature Alloys," *Welding J.,* 38, No. 4, 194S–201S (1959).
92. Investment Casting Institute, "How to Design and Buy Investment Castings," Investment Casting Institute, Chicago (1959).
93. Jessop, Wm. & Sons, Ltd., Brit. Pat. 670,560, April 23, 1952, and 674,023, June 18, 1952.

94. Johnston, J. R., Gyorgak, C. A., and Weeton, J. W., "Engine Performance of (Cobalt-Base) Alloy 73J Turbine Blades Cast to Predetermined Grain Size," Nat. Adv. Comm. for Aeronautics Res. Memo., E54 E05 (1958).

95. Kamen, E. L., and Beck, P. A., "Survey of Portions of the Cobalt-Chromium-Iron-Nickel Quaternary System," Nat. Adv. Comm. Aeronautics Tech. Notes 2603 and 2683 (1952).

96. Kinsey, H. V., "High Temperature Alloys for Gas Turbines," Can. Metals, 28–30, October (1952); 20–24, December (1952).

97. Kohl, W. H., "Materials Technology for Electron Tubes," New York, Reinhold Publ. Corp., 1951.

98. Korchynsky, M., and Fountain, R. W., "Precipitation Phenomena in Cobalt-Tantalum Alloys," Trans. Met. Soc. A.I.M.E., 215, No. 6, 1033–43 (1959).

99. Lampson, F. K., Tsareff, T. C., and Green, A. W., "Thermal-Shock Testing under Stress of Certain High Temperature Alloys," Proc. Am. Soc. Testing Mat., 57, 965–76 (1957).

100. Lane, J. R., and Grant, N. J., "Carbide Reactions in High Temperature Alloys," Trans. Am. Soc. Met., 44, 113–37 (1952).

101. Lardge, H. E., "Welding of Heat-Resistant Alloys in Sheet Form," Iron Steel Inst. Sp. Rept. No. 43 (1952).

102. Mairs, K. H., "Fe-Ni-Co Alloys for Glass-to-Metal Seals," J. Metals, 4, 460–4 (1952).

103. Manjoine, M. J., "Effect of Rate of Strain on the Flow Stress of Gas Turbine Alloys at 1200° and 1500° F," Proc. Am. Soc. Testing Mat., 50, 931–48 (1950).

104. Manly, W. D., and Beck, P. A., "Survey of the Chromium-Cobalt-Nickel-Phase Diagram at 1200°C," Nat. Adv. Comm. Aeronautics Tech. Note 2602 (1952).

105. Martin, D. L., and Geisler, A. H., "Constitution and Properties of Cobalt-Iron-Vanadium Alloys," Trans. Am. Soc. Metals, 44, 461–83 (1952).

106. Mehan, R. L., "Irradiation of Haynes-25 and Inconel X Compression Springs in High Temperature, High Pressure Water," Am. Soc. Mech. Engr. Paper, 58-A-94 (1958).

107. Mihalisin, J. R., and Iwanski, J. S., "Response of a Complex Superalloy to Heat Treatment," Trans. Met. Soc. A.I.M.E., 215, No. 6, 912–16 (1959).

108. Miller, J. R., "Vacuum Melting Improves Investment Casting," J. Metals, 10, 522–4 (1958).

109. Moore, J. H., "Development of Commercial Vacuum Furnaces for Melting Metals and Alloys," Metal Progr., Sept. 161–6, Oct. 103–5 (1953).

110. Moore, W. F., and Kiesler, A. J., "Influence of Vacuum Melting on the Mechanical properties of Heat-resisting Materials," Foundry Trade J., 104, 2175, 741–5 (1958).

111. Morral, F. R., "Alloys for the Aircraft Industry—Role of Cobalt," Cobalt, No. 2, 23–36 (1959).

112. Muscatell, F. L., Reynolds, E. E., Dyrkacz, W. W., and Dalheim, J. H., "Thermal Shock Resistance of High Temperature Alloys," A.S.T.M. Proc., 57, 947–62 (1957).

113. National Advisory Committee for Aeronautics, "Evaluation of Two High-Carbon Precision- Cast Alloys at 1700° and 1800° F by Rupture Test," Tech. Note No. 1130 (1946).

114(a). Nisbet, J. D., and Hibbard, W. R., "A Rationalization of Measured High Temperature Properties of Fe-Cr-Co-Ni Alloys," *J. Metals,* Sept. 1953; *Trans. A.I.M.M.E.,* v 197, p. 1149–1165, 1953.

114. —, "Resistance of Six Cast High Temperature Alloys to Cracking Caused by Thermal Shock," Tech. Note 2037 (1950).

115. Nohl, H., Lux, B., and Siegfried, W., "Effects of Addition Elements on the Elastic Limit of Co-Ni-Cr-Base Alloys," *Revue Métallurgie,* **56,** 19–29 (1959).

116. Ocott, E. L., "U. S. Pat. 2,462,665, Feb. 22, 1949.

117. Olofson, C. T., and Morral, F. R., "Machining of Cobalt-Containing Alloys," *Cobalt,* No. 5, 15–24 (1959).

118. Partridge, J. H., "Glass-to-Metal Seals," Society of Glass Technology, Sheffield, England (1949).

119. Perriton, R. C., and Phillips, R. T., "Welding Certain Heat- and Corrosion-Resisting Alloys," *Welding J.,* **26,** No. 3, 98–102 (1958).

120. Preston, D., "Investigation of High Temperature Sheet Materials," *A.S.T.M.,* Preprint, 85 (1952).

121. Redston, G. D., and Stanworth, J. E., "Iron-Nickel-Cobalt Alloy for Sealing to Glass," *J. Sci. Instruments,* **23,** 53–7 (1946).

122. Reynolds, E. E., "The Influence of Chemical Composition on the Rupture Properties at 1200° F (648° C) of Wrought Chromium-Nickel-Cobalt-Iron-Molybdenum-Tungsten-Niobium Alloys," Univ. Microfilms Publ. No. 2451 (1951).

123. —, Freeman, J. W., and White, A. E., "Influence of Chemical Composition on Forged Modified Low-Carbon N-155 Alloys in Solution-Treated and Aged Condition as Related to Rupture Properties at 1200°F," Nat. Adv. Comm. Aeronautics Tech. Note 2449 (1951).

124. Rheingans, W. J., "Resistance of Materials to Cavitation Damage," Report of Cavitation Symposium, Am. Soc. Mech. Eng. (1956). Materials in Design Engineering, v 48, Sept. 102–106 (1958).

125. Richmond, F. M., "Progress in Vacuum Melting Opens New Horizon," *Steel,* **17,** No. 4, 1–4 (1955).

126. Riddihough, M., "Hard Facing by Welding," Deloro Stellite Ltd., Shirley, Birmingham, England, 1955.

127. —, "Properties of Cobalt Investment Cast Alloys," *Foundry Trade J.,* Nov. 5, 421–428 (1959).

128. Roller, D., and Andrews, C. R., "Effect of Molten Boron Oxide on Selected High Temperature Alloys," *Corrosion,* **15,** 85t–96t (1959).

129. Rolls-Royce, Ltd., British Pat. 666,401, Feb. 13, 1952.

130. Rose, K., "Highly Corrosion-Resistant Spring Materials Finds Varied Use," *Materials & Methods,* **32,** 54–5 (1950).

131. Schmucker, R. A., Preusch, C. D., and Bowne, L. F., U. S. Pat. 2,551,170, May 1, 1951.

132. Servi, S. I., and Grant, N. J., "Creep and Stress Rupture as Rate Processes," *J. Inst. Metals*, **80,** 33–7 (1951–52).
133. Shaw, M. C., and Smith, P. A., "Metallurgical Considerations in Machining, Physical Characteristics of Cast Alloys and Carbides," *Am. Machinist,* Oct. 15, 130–2 (1951).
134. Siegfried, W., and Eisermann, F., "A Turbine-Blade Alloy Castable and Low in Cobalt and Columbium," *Metal Progr.,* January, 141–6 (1955).
135. Skues, C., Giffard, J. A., and Stokes, C., British Pat. 616,207, Jan. 18, 1949.
136. Smeltzer, W. W., "Oxidation of Nickel-Cobalt Alloys in the Range of Curie Temperatures," *Acta Metallurgica,* **7,** 191–8 (1959).
137. Staff Report, "Better Ways to Fabricate High Temperature Materials," *Metal Progr.,* May, 97–101 (1958).
138. Stutzman, M. J., "Studies and Comparison of the Properties of High Temperature Alloys Melted and Precision Cast Both in Air and in Vacuum," Wright Air Development Centre Tech. Rep. 57–678, December (1957).
139. —, Ibid, March (1958).
140. Sykes, C., and Shirley, H. T., "Scaling of Heat-Resisting Steels," Iron Steel Institute Sp. Rept. No. 43 (1952).
141. Urbain, M., "High Temperature Alloys," *Cobalt,* No. 1, 13–31 (1958).
142. Vanadium Corporation of America, "Vanadium Steels and Irons," pp 140–7, New York, Vanadium Corporation of America, 1937.
143. Waindle, R. F., "New Uses for Cobalt-Base Spring Alloy," *Metal Progr.,* **56,** 808–11 (1949).
144. Wallace, E., "Hard Facing by Rod and Metal Powders," *Welding and Metal Fabrication,* **27,** No. 1, 5–13 (1959).
145. Weeton, J. W., and Signorelli, R. A., "An Investigation of Lamellar Structures and Minor Phases in Eleven Cobalt-Base Alloys before and after Heat Treatment," Nat. Adv. Comm. for Aeronautics Tech. Note 3109 (1954).
146. Went, J. J., Canadian Pat. 486,768, Sept. 23, 1952.
147. Whittemore, C. R., "Cobalt-Base Alloys-Casting," *Canadian Metals,* 33–4, Jan. (1956).
148. Yaker, C., and Hoffman, C. A., "Effect of Solution Treatment Followed by Aging Treatment on Life of Small Cast Gas-Turbine Blades of a Cobalt-Chromium-Base Alloy," Nat. Adv. Comm. for Aeronautics Tech. Note 2320 (1951).

Chapter 10

TOOL STEELS, AND OTHER METALLURGICAL APPLICATIONS

TOOL STEELS

Although less than 1 per cent of the world's steel output takes the form of tool steels, the importance of these materials is evidenced by the fact that they are utilized by nearly every industry for such operations as blanking, cutting, drawing, extruding, forming, and rolling. The general subject of tool steels is covered fully in various reference books.[1,2,8,14,21] In Seabright's book,[21] for example, extensive tables provide information about the chemical composition of representative tool steels, steels recommended for various applications, and suppliers. Cobalt, one of the alloying elements, appears in several categories of tool steels. In general, red-hardness properties increase, and toughness decreases as cobalt content increases.

High Carbon, High Chromium Steels

These steels, containing 1–2.5 per cent carbon and 11–12.5 per cent chromium, have high wear resistance and excellent nondeforming properties, and are used extensively for dies. They can be divided into two principal classifications—air hardening and oil hardening. They can also be grouped by carbon content—the original 2–2.5 per cent carbon, and a modification containing 1–1.5 per cent for improved machinability and minimized brittleness. Small amounts of cobalt, molybdenum, nickel, silicon, tungsten, and vanadium are often added to these die steels, but the specific effect of cobalt and most of the other alloying elements is not fully known.

Some examples of cobalt-containing die steels have the following compositions:

C	Si	Mn	Cr	Mo	W	Co	V	Ni
1.40	0.25	0.30	12.00	0.80	...	3.50	...	...
1.50	0.25	0.30	12.00	0.80	...	0.40	0.85	...
1.54	0.25	0.30	11.68	0.63	...	0.44	0.79	...
1.70	0.50	0.60	14.00	1.25	...	4.00	1.20	1.00
2.16	0.25	0.30	12.38	...	...	0.59	0.90	...
2.20	0.25	0.30	12.00	...	...	0.50	0.80	...
2.50	1.00	1.20	14.00	0.30	2.00	1.00	1.25	1.00

251

Cobalt is sometimes added to chromium-tungsten die steels, used for hot-working operations, since it increases wear resistance and hardness at high temperature. Commercial types of cobalt-bearing hot-work steels suitable for extrusion mandrels, die casting and extrusion dies, hot punch tools, forging die inserts, press forging dies, shear blades, and intermittent water-cooled jobs (e.g., shell piercing tips) have the following compositions:

C	Si	Mn	Cr	Mo	W	Co	V	Ni
0.35	1.00	0.30	5.00	0.30	4.50	0.50	0.30	...
0.45	1.00	0.75	5.00	1.00	3.75	0.50	0.50	...
0.40	0.25	0.35	4.25	0.40	4.25	4.25	2.20	...
0.50	0.35	0.35	3.50	1.00	12.00	2.00	0.60	2.25
0.60	1.75	0.75	7.50	1.00	7.50	0.60	0.60	0.50
0.60	1.10	1.25	7.50	3.00	1.75	0.60	1.00	2.00

A modification of the usual high carbon, high chromium steels has been employed in Germany for hot wire-drawing gages, pyrometer sheaths, and similar applications where high resistance to abrasion and heat are required. It contains 2–3 C, 0.1–0.6 Si, 0.2–1.0 Mn, 25–30 Cr, and 3.5–4.0 Co.

High Speed Steels

High speed steels were developed shortly after the turn of the century, when it was found that tungsten tool steels were greatly improved by a heat treatment far in excess of temperatures previously considered beneficial. These steels, containing approximately 0.5–0.8 per cent carbon, 18 per cent tungsten, 4 per cent chromium, and 1 per cent vanadium, retained their cutting edge and hardness for long periods of time even at a dull red heat. Machine tools made from such steels could be operated at high speeds, and the time thus saved had far-reaching effects on the industrial economy. The addition of 5–12 per cent cobalt to these steels allowed a greater red hardness and enabled the tools to be used more effectively on hard materials at high speeds. Cobalt high speed steels are used extensively in single point cutting tools where deep cuts and fast speeds are required, or where the material is hard and scaly or produces discontinuous chips.

Cobalt in high speed tools raises the melting point and permits the use of higher heat-treating temperatures without appreciable grain growth. This allows a greater solution of carbon, chromium, tungsten, and vanadium in the austenite, which, together with the cobalt present in the matrix, gives a greater amount of retained austenite. Secondary hardness and red hardness are likewise increased.

The beneficial effect of cobalt on the cutting endurance of lathe tools is greatly increased by the use of a high quenching temperature, around

1320° F. Cobalt slightly increases the brittleness of high speed steel after quenching and tempering. Cobalt and molybdenum both increase the tendency towards decarburization during the heating cycle, and most cobalt tool steels should be ground to a considerable depth before use.

Tarasov reported that cobalt did not appear to have any definite effect on the grindability of high speed steels.[22]

Cobalt, when added to steel in the 1 per cent carbon range, raises the M-point (point at which the austenite-martensite transformation begins) 20–25° F for each 1 per cent Co. The carbide-forming tendency of cobalt is less than that of iron; the metal is largely dissolved in solid solution. Cobalt forms only one carbide in steel, Co_3C, whereas the more important high speed steel alloying elements, vanadium, tungsten, chromium, and molybdenum, have strong carbide-forming tendencies.

Typical compositions of high speed steels, classified in the simple manner suggested by Gill and associates,[8] are given in Table 10.1. Differences

TABLE 10.1. COMPOSITION OF HIGH SPEED STEELS

Steel Type	C	W	Mo	Cr	V	Co
Tungsten	0.50–0.95	14.00–18.00	0–0.80	4.00	1.00–3.00	...
Tungsten-cobalt	0.75	18.00	0–0.75	4.00	1.00	5.00
	0.75	18.00		4.00	2.00	8.00
	0.85	18.75	0.80	4.10	1.90	12.00
	0.75	14.00		4.00	2.00	5.00
	1.55	12.50		4.75	5.00	5.00
	0.75	20.00		4.25	1.75	12.00
Molybdenum	0.75–0.80	0–1.50	8.25–8.50	4.00–4.25	1.00–2.00	...
Molybdenum-cobalt	0.75	...	4.00	3.50	1.00	2.00
	0.82	1.50	8.50	3.75	1.25	5.00
	0.80	1.50	8.50	4.00	2.00	8.00
	0.90	1.45	8.70	3.75	2.05	8.25
Tungsten-molybdenum	0.80–1.25	5.75	4.50–4.75	4.00–4.25	1.50–4.00	...
Tungsten-molybdenum-cobalt	1.25	10.00	2.50	4.25	4.30	5.50
	0.80	5.75	4.75	4.00	1.50	5.00–8.00
	1.55	6.50	3.00	4.75	5.00	5.00
	0.85–0.88	6.00	5.00–6.00	4.00–4.10	1.90–2.00	9.00
	0.95	6.50	10.00	4.75	2.50	9.00

TABLE 10.2. HEAT-TREATING TEMPERATURES FO
HIGH SPEED STEELS IN SEMI-MUFFLE FURNACES

Steel Type	Hardening Temperature, °F	Tempering Temperature, °F
Tungsten	2300-2350	1050-1075
Tungsten-cobalt	2325-2375	1000-1050
Molybdenum	2200-2220	1025
Molybdenum-cobalt	2200-2220	1025
Tungsten-molybdenum	2220	1050-1075
Tungsten-molybdenum-cobalt	2220	1025

in heat treatment and physical properties are given in Tables 10.2, 10.3, 10.4, and 10.5, abstracted from the book of Gill, *et al.* In addition to the elements shown in Table 10.1, high speed steels ordinarily contain 0.25 per cent silicon and 0.25 per cent manganese.

TABLE 10.3. STATIC TORSION TESTS ON QUENCHED AND
TEMPERED HIGH SPEED STEELS

Steel Type	Hardness at Room Temperature, Rockwell C	Ultimate Torque, in.-lb	Ultimate Deformation, °
Tungsten	64.3-66.0	455-475	145-160
Tungsten-cobalt	64.9-65.8	420-430	100-135
Molybdenum	65.5	460	150
Tungsten-molybdenum	65.5-66.3	425-465	125-180

Heat treatment recommendations for the 18W 4Cr 2V high speed steel containing 8 per cent cobalt are given below.[3] This steel is used in heavy-duty turning, boring, planing, form cutting, and slotting, and usually in-

TABLE 10.4. HOT-HARDNESS (MUTUAL INDENTATION): HIGH
SPEED STEELS TREATED FOR MAXIMUM HARDNESS
BEFORE TESTING

Steel Type	1100 °F Test, Brinell No.	1200 °F Test, Brinell No.	Room Temperature, Rockwell C
Tungsten	440-480	337-355	65.5-66.0
Tungsten-cobalt	520	400	65.0
Molybdenum	458-475	308-313	65.0-66.8
Tungsten-molybdenum	465	342	65.5
Tungsten-molybdenum-cobalt	500	390	66.0

TABLE 10.5. HOT-HARDNESS BY HOT ROCKWELL METHOD

Steel Type	Hardness at Room Temperature Before Testing, Rockwell C	Hot-Hardness		
		1000°F	1050°F	1100°F
Tungsten	64.0-66.3	58.0-60.2	56.5-57.8	54.5-56.2
Tungsten-cobalt	66.2-67.2	60.2-62.0	59.5-61.4	58.7-59.6
Molybdenum	65.3	58.0	57.0	55.5
Tungsten-molybdenum	65.3-65.4	58.0-59.0	57.0-57.5	55.9-56.7

volves heavy cutting and feeding at high speeds on hard, gritty, or scaly metals as well as the machining of austenitic stainless steels.

Forging. Preheat, preferably in a separate furnace, to 1200–1300° F (650–705° C). Bring up to 2000–2100° F (1095–1150° C) until uniform. Do not forge below 1650–1750° F (900–955° C). Cool slowly in furnace, or in dry ashes or mica; then anneal.

Annealing. Heat slowly to 1600–1650° F (870–900° C). Soak 1–2 hr/in. thickness. Pack anneal to minimize decarburization. Cool slowly in furnace at 50° F (28° C)/hr minimum.

Hardening. Preheat at 1550–1600° F (840–870° C). Transfer to a high heat furnace at 2350–2425° F (1285–1330° C). Use the lower side of this range when heating in molten salt. Hold the work at the hardening temperature just until it becomes heated through. Quench in oil or a 1000–1100° F (540–595° C) salt bath.

Tempering. Double draw at 1025–1050° F (550–565° C) for maximum hardness. Double draw above 1050° F (565° C) if increased toughness is required. Hold work at temperature for 1–2 hr/in. of section.

The heat treatment for various types of tool steels is well covered in the section on these materials in the "Metals Handbook" of the American Society for Metals,[1] and by Seabright.[21]

Perrault[20] mentions the difficulties encountered in France during World War II when the supply of cobalt for high speed steels was scarce. It was found, for example, that machining of certain railroad equipment was possible only with cobalt-containing tools, and the regulations prohibiting the use of cobalt for anything but permanent magnets had to be revised to allow the production of tools containing 10 per cent cobalt for these purposes.

Russian workers have reported[19] that a high speed steel having the following composition (in percentages), C 0.78, W 18, Mn 0.5, Cr 4, V 1.5, and Co 18, gave an impressive performance. A cutting tool of this super-cobaltic material was still in good condition after undergoing a test one hundredfold longer than that which dulled a 6 per cent cobalt tool steel.

VALVE STEELS

The valves of internal combustion engines demand a steel which will retain its structure and mechanical properties at elevated temperatures, and
resist corrosion and oxidation from exhaust gases. Many alloy steels have
been used for this purpose, among them a few cobalt-containing varieties
illustrated in Table 10.6.[20]

TABLE 10.6. COMPOSITION OF COBALT-CONTAINING VALVE STEELS

C	Si	Cr	Mo	V	Ni	Co
0.95	0.4	18.5	1.0	...	...	2.0
1.0–1.5	...	11.0–14.0	0.5–0.9	0.2–0.3	...	2.5–3.5
1.21	0.31	13.16	0.64	...	0.59	4.88
1.78	0.40	13.06	1.14	...	0.11	2.40
0.40	3.0–4.0	2.0–10.0	...	...	...	0.5–3.0

LOW-EXPANSION ALLOYS

A very low coefficient of expansion is sometimes required in a metal component. For a long time a nickel-steel containing 36 per cent Ni, called
"Invar," filled this role. In 1929, Masumoto replaced some of the nickel
with cobalt to give an alloy containing 63.5 per cent Fe, 31.5 per cent Ni,
and 5 per cent Co, which had a lower expansion coefficient than invar. Several years later, Masumoto developed a "stainless invar" having the following composition: 36.5 per cent Fe, 9.5 per cent Cr, and 54 per cent Co. The
coefficient of expansion of this alloy is practically zero. By slightly altering
this composition to give 37 per cent Fe, 9 per cent Cr, and 54 per cent Co, a
negative coefficient of expansion is obtained, the alloy contracting very
slightly at elevated temperatures.

CARBON STEELS AND LOW ALLOY STEELS

Houdremont and Schrader[15] investigated the addition of 0–7 per cent
cobalt to a steel containing 0.9 per cent carbon, and found that cobalt diminishes the depth of hardening. Davenport[6] determined the isothermal
transformation diagrams of 0.95 per cent C steels containing 0, 1, and 2 per
cent cobalt, and showed that cobalt increases the rate of decomposition of
austenite. Hawkes and Mehl[12] confirmed these results with steels containing
0–7.5 per cent cobalt, and demonstrated that cobalt increases the rate of
the austenite-pearlite transformation by action on both the rate of nucleation and that of grain growth. They concluded that cobalt was the only
element which raised the temperature range over which martensite forms in

homogeneous austenite. Hagel, Pound, and Mehl[11] showed that cobalt increases the free energy of the austenite-pearlite transformation. Houdremont[14] attributed the influence of cobalt on the T-T-T curves to the fact that cobalt increases the diffusion rate of carbon, but other workers[10,12] have reported conflicting results.

Habraken and Coutsouradis[10] found that few appreciable modifications were brought about in the properties of low carbon steels and 0.4 per cent C structural steels by the addition of cobalt. They also investigated the effect of 0–5 per cent cobalt on low alloy steels containing 0.05–0.10 per cent C, 2.25 per cent Cr, and 1 per cent Mo, and found a decrease in certain forms of brittleness, probably due to grain-boundary phenomena. For instance, when this steel was austenized at 975° C for 2 hr, air-cooled and tempered at 675° C for 6 hr, and air-cooled, the impact strength in kg/cm rose from 4.9 without cobalt to 29 with an addition of 0.25 per cent Co.

CAST IRON

It has been reported in some early metallurgical reference books that cobalt up to 2 per cent in cast iron has no marked effect on the mechanical properties but increases its resistance to corrosion in dilute sulfuric acid. Bokhovkin[4] studied the effect of 1–5 per cent cobalt on white cast iron containing 4 per cent C and 1.2 per cent Si. He found the maximum corrosion resistance at 2 per cent cobalt, and attributed this to the bonding of cobalt with silicon and carbon.

Kalmus and Blake[16] investigated the effect of additions of 0.25–3 per cent cobalt, nickel, and copper on the corrosion of a high-grade commercial ingot iron containing 0.01 per cent carbon. They found that the resistance to atmospheric and sulfuric acid attack was lower for the alloyed compositions, but little difference was observed between cobalt, nickel, and copper additions.

BERYLLIUM COPPER

Beryllium copper is an alloy possessing valuable properties of high strength, good electrical and thermal conductivity, high fatigue resistance, low modulus of elasticity, good corrosion resistance, non-magnetic and non-sparking behavior, and ability to be softened or hardened by simple heat treatment processes. Its unique properties render it suitable for such applications as small springs, diaphragms, bellows, Bourdon tubes, welding electrodes, dies, and non-sparking tools.

There are two commercial types of beryllium copper alloys. The typical one contains about 1.5–2.7 per cent beryllium and a small quantity, usually about 0.50 per cent, of cobalt to improve the response to heat treatment.

Low beryllium copper, less strong and hard than the ordinary alloy, contains about 2.6 per cent cobalt and only about 0.4 per cent beryllium, and is employed where higher conductivity or a better retention, at elevated temperatures, of the strength and hardness imparted by heat treatment are desired. Sometimes nickel is substituted for cobalt in both these alloys, but the latter is preferred.

Reliable information on these alloys is summarized in an excellent booklet, containing 70 references, available from the Copper Development Association.[5] In low beryllium copper containing 2.6 per cent cobalt and 0.4 per cent beryllium, the cobalt has a direct precipitation hardening action on the copper as does beryllium in ordinary beryllium copper. In fact, cobalt-copper without any beryllium addition is capable of precipitation hardening.

With typical beryllium copper containing about 2 per cent beryllium and 0.5 per cent cobalt, the object of the cobalt addition is to make the time of heat treatment less critical. In the absence of cobalt or nickel, maximum hardness is very rapidly passed, and over-aging occurs. The reason for this has not yet been established. One theory proposes that the cobalt has a blocking action on the diffusion of beryllium and decreases the rate of agglomeration of the beryllium-rich phase. Another theory postulates that over-aging is the result of discontinuous precipitation at the grain boundaries, and that it is, therefore, encouraged by the commencement of recrystallization. Cobalt is found to slow up the rate of recrystallization and, consequently, the rate of over-aging.

GOLD ALLOYS

Molten gold, unlike silver, can be mixed in all proportions with cobalt. The freezing point curves have two branches meeting at a eutectic at 997° and 90 per cent gold.[17] Solid solutions containing 0–5.5 and 96.5–100 per cent cobalt are formed. Cobalt whitens gold, and for certain jewelry purposes where hardness and ease of polishing are important the following composition has been recommended: 4 Co, 10 Ag, 11 Cu, and 75 per cent Au.[20]

BRASSES AND ALUMINUM BRONZES

The addition of 0.5 per cent cobalt to 80:20 brass wire raises the tensile strength nearly 20 per cent.[18] Guillet[9] found that the addition of 2–3 per cent cobalt to brasses increased the hardness, and that this hardness persisted even when the temperature was carried to 700°C. At this temperature, such brasses have a Brinell hardness of 90, a strength of 55,000 psi, and an elongation of 25 per cent.

The effect of cobalt additions on aluminum bronzes has been noted by Haworth and Hume-Rothery.[13]

LIGHT METALS

Studies have been made on the effect of cobalt additions to aluminum[7] and magnesium,[23] but such alloys have not attained any commercial importance.

References

1. American Society for Metals, "Metals Handbook," Cleveland, Ohio, 1948.
2. American Society of Tool Engineers, "Tool Engineers Handbook," New York, McGraw-Hill Book Company, 1949.
3. Atlas Steels Limited, "Technical Data, Atlas Tool Steels," Welland, Canada, 1959.
4. Bokhovkin, I. M., "The Effect of Cobalt on the Corrosion of White Cast Iron," *Trudy Arkhangel'sk Lesotekh. Inst.,* **16,** 79–84 (1955). *Chem. Abst.,* **52,** 10850 (1958).
5. Copper Development Association, "Beryllium Copper," London, 1958.
6. Davenport, E. S., "Isothermal Transformation in Steels," Trans. Am. Soc. Metals, Campbell Memorial Lecture (1939).
7. Fink, W. L., and Willey, L. A., "Aluminum-Cobalt," from American Society for Metals, "Metals Handbook," **1948,** p 1158.
8. Gill, J. P., Rose, R. S., Roberts, G. A., Johnstin, H. G., and George, R. B., "Tool Steels," Cleveland, Ohio, American Society for Metals, 1944.
9. Guillet, L., "Les Laitons au Cobalt," Paris, Cuivre et Laiton, March 15, 1931.
10. Habraken, L., and Coutsouradis, D., "Cobalt in Steels," *Cobalt,* No. 2, 11–22 (1959).
11. Hagel, W. C., Pound, G. M., and Mehl, R. F., "Calorimetric Study of the Austenite-Pearlite Transformation," *Acta Metallurgica,* **4,** 37–46 (1956).
12. Hawkes, M. F., and Mehl, R. F., "The Effect of Cobalt on the Rate of Nucleation and the Rate of Growth of Pearlite," *Am. Inst. Min. Met. Eng. Trans.,* **172,** 467–92 (1947).
13. Haworth, J. B., and Hume-Rothery, W., "The Effect of Four Transition Metals on the α-β-Brass Type of Equilibrium," *Phil. Mag.,* **43,** 613–31 (1952).
14. Houdremont, E., "Handbuch der Sonderstahlkunde," Verlag Stahleisen, Dusseldorf, and Springer Verlag, Berlin, Gottingen, and Heidelberg, Vol. II, 1956.
15. —, and Schrader, H., "Ueber die Wirkung des Kobalts in Kohlenstoffstahl unter Berucksichtigung technischer legierter Kobaltshle, insbondere des Schnelldrehstahles," *Kruppsche Monatshefte,* **13,** 1–54 (1932).
16. Kalmus, H. T., and Blake, K. B., "Cobalt Alloys with Non-Corrosive Properties," Ottawa, Can. Dept. Mines, 1916.
17. Koster, W., and Horn, E., "Der Einfluss der Elemente Silber, Gold, Kadmium, Gallium, Indium, Germanium, Wismuth, Selen und Tellur auf die polymorphe Umwandlung des Kobalts," *Z. Metallkunde,* **43,** 333–34 (1952).

18. Mellor, J. W., "A Comprehensive Treatise on Inorganic and Theoretical Chemistry," Vol. **XIV,** London, Longmans. Green and Co., 1935.
19. Perel'man, F. M., Zvorykin, A. Y., and Gudima, N. V., "Kobal't," *Akad. Nauk S.S.S.R.,* 1949.
20. Perrault, R., "Le Cobalt," Paris, Dunod, 1946.
21. Seabright, L. H., "The Selection and Hardening of Tool Steels," New York, McGraw-Hill Book Company, 1950.
22. Tarasov, L. P., "Grindability of Tool Steels," *Trans. Am. Soc. Metals,* **43,** 1144–74 (1951).
23. Wetherill, J. P., "Magnesium-Cobalt Alloys," *Metals and Alloys,* **6,** 153–5 (1935).

Chapter 11

CEMENTED CARBIDES

Although the amount of cobalt used in the production of cemented carbides is very much less than that used for the manufacture of magnets or high temperature alloys, the great importance of these carbides in the industrial economy of the world merits a special chapter.

At the end of the last century, Moissan made tungsten carbide and pointed out its exceptional hardness. Some cutting tools of this material were produced in Germany during World War I, but their usefulness was limited by extreme brittleness until about 1923, when cobalt was introduced as the metal matrix to contain and bind the hard carbide particles.[21] Continuous development since then has given a wide range of cemented carbides or "hard metals," used extensively for cutting tools, wire drawing and other dies, rock drills, stamping matrices, masonry saws, nozzles, and many other applications where great hardness and wear resistance are required.

The advantages of these materials can be illustrated by the fact that a high-speed steel lathe tool will cut a medium hard steel at the rate of 120–180 ft/min, whereas a tungsten carbide tool increases the rate to 600 ft/min. Russian investigators,[20] measuring stock removal with different lathe tools and assigning a productivity index of 100 for high-speed steel, found the index for cemented carbide to vary from 250 to 500. A general survey of the field of cemented carbides has been given by Sykes,[28] Rose,[23] and Goetzel.[11]

Tungsten carbide powder is made by heating pure tungsten powder and carbon at 1500–1600° C, and grinding the resulting product. The latter should have a total carbon content of 6.05–6.20 per cent and a free carbon content not above 0.1 per cent. Cemented carbides which are used for machining steel often contain a mixture of tungsten carbide and titanium carbide, the latter preventing a cratering effect when the hard metal is composed of tungsten carbide and cobalt only. Sometimes other carbides, such as tantalum, are incorporated with tungsten carbide.

Cobalt is far superior to any other substance as the binding agent or matrix for tungsten carbide and for all hard metals where the dominant carbide is tungsten. In cemented carbide production, the grain size and the ratio of cobalt to tungsten carbide may vary widely, depending on the intended use. In general, increasing cobalt content decreases the hardness and increases the toughness of the cemented carbide. For machining abrasive materials and cast iron, fine-grained tungsten carbide containing 4–10 per cent cobalt is prepared. For applications where more toughness is required, (e.g., large drawing dies or mining tools) coarser grained carbide having 6–30 per cent cobalt is produced. Hard metal for machining steel may have an addition of titanium carbide up to around 15 per cent, or small quantities of tantalum or other carbides may be used.

The various carbides and the cobalt metal, weighed out in the desired proportions, are placed in small mills using hard metal balls. A liquid such as acetone is added, and the charge is rotated for several days to mix the cobalt metal thoroughly with the carbides. The grain size of the tungsten carbide in the final hard metal is determined largely by the grain size of the tungsten metal powder originally used, but it is influenced to a certain extent by the variables in milling the carbide and cobalt. Cobalt is usually added in the form of metal powder, but cobalt oxide may be employed, the latter passing to metal in the subsequent reducing step.

After mixing by milling, the settled powder is separated from the liquid and reduced at 600° C with hydrogen to eliminate traces of oxide which may have formed in milling. The carbide powder is mixed with a solution of paraffin wax in carbon tetrachloride, or camphor in ether, to improve its pressing properties. It is pressed in steel or carbide-lined dies at a pressure of 10–30 tons/sq in. into various forms: pellets, bars, briquettes, tubes, tips, etc. These shapes are packed in carbon powder and pre-sintered at 750° C under hydrogen, checked for dimensions, and ground or machined, if necessary, before the sintering operation.

The shaped carbide pieces are packed in carbon, sintered in a hydrogen atmosphere, and removed from the furnace when cold. The sintering temperature is quite critical and differs for the various grades of carbide from about 1300° C for 20 per cent cobalt to about 1600° C for those containing titanium carbide. During the sintering process, the cobalt metal melts and dissolves about 14 per cent of the tungsten carbide, all but 1 per cent of which is reprecipitated on cooling. The cemented carbide shapes attain their final density and hardness after the 20 per cent shrinkage which occurs during sintering.

Sometimes alumina with a little carbon powder is used instead of carbon for packing carbide tips in sintering. The carbon-packed tips have a slightly harder surface layer, the result of a superficial migration of cobalt from the surface, or the formation of a little cobalt carbide in this layer. Free tungsten is sometimes added to hard metal powder to increase abrasion resistance. Some may become incorporated in the cobalt bond, but most react with tungsten carbide to form W_2C, which is harder than the saturated form but more brittle.

Instead of cold-pressing and sintering, a hot-pressing method can be employed for carbide shapes. A graphite mold containing carbide powder is heated to sintering temperature by high frequency current or by using the mold as a resistor, and the powder is compressed by a plunger. Since all shrinkage takes place in the direction of pressing, very close tolerance can be maintained on the finished shapes.

Test bars are pressed and sintered after milling the tungsten carbide and cobalt, and before continuing with the commercial operations of pressing and sintering. One of the test pieces is fractured. A slightly rugged surface is satisfactory, whereas a very smooth fracture indicates brittleness, unavoidable with a very low cobalt content. Density and hardness are determined with another test piece; polished surfaces are prepared by grinding on a diamond wheel and polishing with diamond paste. The polished test piece is examined at 100 magnifications for porosity, and at 1500 magnifications for microporosity, intergranular porosity, and distribution of cobalt around the grain boundaries. The specimen is then etched in 10 per cent alkaline potassium ferricyanide, which reveals the cobalt bond as light yellow and leaves the gray tungsten carbide unattacked. For samples containing titanium carbide, an etch with nitric and hydrofluoric acid attacks the cobalt bond and imparts a slight pink color to the titanium phase. The grain size is checked against standard charts.

The physical properties of some commercial cemented carbides are given in Table 11.1.[3]

Hardness, compressive strength, thermal conductivity, modulus of elasticity, and corrosion resistance decrease with increasing cobalt in the carbide. Transverse rupture, impact strength, and endurance limit increase with increasing quantities of cobalt binder.

Transverse rupture strength exhibits unique behavior in that it reaches a maximum between 15 and 20 per cent cobalt, and then decreases with further additions of the binder. A study by Gurland and Bardzil[15] showed that transverse rupture strength attains a maximum for values of the mean free path between tungsten carbide particles of 0.3–0.6 microns. This strength increases as the film of cobalt becomes thinner, but is eventually reduced by increased amounts of the brittle phase and incomplete dispersion of the tungsten carbide grains. The fracture originates in, and proceeds through, the carbide grains, tending to avoid the cobalt.

The principal difference in fracture between alloys of high and low binder contents is found in the relative proportion of failures at the carbide-to-carbide grain boundaries. These are much more numerous in low-cobalt

TABLE 11.1. PHYSICAL PROPERTIES OF CEMENTED CARBIDES

Composition	Density, g/ml	Hardness, V.P.N.	Transverse Rupture, lb/in.^{2}	Compressive Strength, lb/in.^{2}	Coefficient Thermal Expansion, per °C	Thermal Conductivity, cal/cm^2/cm/sec/°C	Specific Heat	Electrical Resistance at 20°C, micro ohms/cm^3
Cobalt 4%. Fine-grained tungsten carbide 96%.	15.05	1800	160,000	780,000	5×10^{-6}	0.20	0.05	21.0
Cobalt 6%. Fine-grained tungsten carbide 94%.	14.80	1650	220,000	750,000	5×10^{-6}	0.19	0.05	20.0
Cobalt 6%. Coarse-grained tungsten carbide 94%.	14.80	1400	260,000	680,000	5×10^{-6}	0.19	0.05	20.0
Cobalt 10%. Coarse-grained tungsten carbide 90%.	14.35	1300	290,000	620,000	6×10^{-6}	0.16	0.05	18.0
Cobalt 7%. Titanium carbide 5%. Medium-grained tungsten carbide 88%.	13.35	1500	210,000	630,000	5.5×10^{-6}	0.15	0.05	25.0
Cobalt 8%. Titanium carbide 15%. Medium-grained tungsten carbide 77%.	11.10	1500	195,000	590,000	6×10^{-6}	0.09	0.06	43.0

alloys. In the latter, smaller tungsten carbide grain size at constant composition leads to a decrease in strength, the result of an increased area of carbide-to-carbide contact. The grain boundaries themselves may be weak, or their failure may be due to stress concentrations induced by the uneven distribution of the binder phase. The authors recorded that impact strength increases with cobalt content, and the effect of grain size is relatively small, while the hardness of cemented carbide varies with the interparticle distance according to an exponential relation.

Tretyakov[29] suggested, as an explanation for the discontinuous parallelism between hardness and tensile strength, that cobalt is striated in the lattice in layers, and that microplasticity is lost in alloys with cobalt below 18 per cent because of the increased strain.

A popular drilling crown for hard service in the mining and petroleum industries consists of industrial diamonds, either whole stones or fragmented boart, set in a tungsten carbide matrix. The latter is bonded with 5–20 per cent cobalt, depending on the type of rock to be drilled. The fact that cobalt metal, high cobalt alloys, and cobalt-bonded tungsten carbide hold the diamonds exceptionally well, would indicate that diamond is readily wetted by cobalt, and that the resulting attachment is strong.[8,30]

It has been demonstrated[7] that tungsten carbide-cobalt compacts of superior hardness and slightly increased density can be made by the electric-resistance sintering of pre-sintered mixtures of tungsten carbide and cobalt. A change of the major binder phase from an elemental to a ternary compound, probably Co_3W_3C, has been offered as the primary reason for the increased hardness of the electric-resistance sintered compacts. Control of close dimensions and quality, however, is difficult to attain.

The usual concept of a cemented carbide is that the tungsten carbide forms the frame in the structure, and that the cobalt binder merely serves to transmit the intrinsic strength of one tungsten carbide crystal to its neighbor throughout the hard metal, with the softer component minimizing the danger of rupture along the grain boundaries. A different theory has also been proposed,[2] wherein the cemented carbide is regarded as being made up of macroscopic cobalt crystals containing many thousands of small tungsten carbide particles which impose stresses and dislocations on the crystal lattice, and provide a metal of very high strength. In other words, the primary component is not the tungsten carbide but the cobalt matrix.

Steinitz[26] stated that cobalt and tungsten carbide behave like two substances in a binary system. Rautala and Norton[22] found, in addition to the η-phase, Co_3W_3C, two double carbides, $Co_3W_6C_2$ and $Co_3W_{10}C_4$, which have, respectively, cubic symmetry and a hexagonal lattice. Norton[18] observed that the films of cobalt surrounding the carbide grains are in a condition of restraint, and that the high strength of the aggregate is the result. The cobalt is not in bulk, and is not subject to plastic flow because of the high state of residual stress—the result of a wide difference in thermal expansion between Co and WC—existing in the sintered body at normal temperature.

Gurland and Norton[16] concluded that the effectiveness of cobalt as a binder is due to the relatively low melting temperature of the Co-WC solid solution, the solubility of WC in Co, and the wetting of carbide particles by the liquid binder. Densification of cemented tungsten carbide-cobalt alloys occurs as the result of a rearrangement of the carbide particles; the surface tension forces of the binder, which tend to eliminate pores in the compact, yield a dense packing. Densification is also promoted by the disappearance of small grains and the growth of large grains of tungsten carbide. The resulting structure is one of carbide particles embedded in a cobalt-rich matrix, and a continuous skeleton of tungsten carbide is prevented from forming during the sintering treatment. The high strength and lack of ductility of cemented carbides can be attributed to the mechanical restraint exerted by the carbide particles on the thin films of the binder, the yield strength of which is correspondingly increased, and to the complex state of stress resulting from the presence of residual stresses of thermal origin. Gurland and Norton determined the ability of liquid cobalt to wet tungsten carbide by measuring the angle of contact of a drop of cobalt on a solid tungsten carbide surface. The angle was practically zero; hence, the wetting power of cobalt for tungsten carbide is very high.

Gurland[12] studied the effect of carbon content on the structure and properties of cemented tungsten carbide. Examination of the ternary diagram W-Co-C shows that two phases, WC and a cobalt-rich solid solution β, appear in the sintered structure if the carbon composition corresponds very closely to the theoretical carbon content of WC, i.e., 6.12 per cent C. Small deviations from the ideal carbon content result in the appearance of either graphite or the double carbide W_3Co_3C, i.e., the η-phase. The latter occurs as a stable phase in a narrow temperature range during the sintering of slightly carbon-deficient WC-Co alloys. The properties of sintered compacts are strongly influenced by the carbon content of WC-Co alloys. A deficiency of carbon will have a more detrimental effect than an excess, since the former produces the η carbide which reduces the strength by displacing the binder from the sintered structure. The grain size of WC in the sintered compact increases with sintering time, sintering temperature, amount of binder, carbon content, and inhomogeneity of particle size distribution. The rate of grain growth decreases with larger initial grain size of the carbide powder. The major part of grain growth occurs isothermally and is characterized by the disappearance of the smallest grains of WC and an increase in number and size of the largest. Carburization of a carbon-deficient alloy during sintering produces non-uniform grain growth, associated with the disappearance of the η-phase.

Norton[19] observed that at 1500° C cobalt is evaporated from cemented carbides if the pressure is 1 μ, and that very hard alloys can be produced in this way. In the ternary system W-C-Co, too much carbon means free graphite, which is undesirable; too little carbon leads to the formation of W_3Co_3C, which is worse.

Shooter[25] reported that the presence of cobalt in cemented carbides had little or no effect on their frictional properties. Shaw and Smith[24] stated that the tendency of a cemented carbide to weld to steel increased with an increase in cobalt content. Kochanovska[17] reported that sintering a cobalt powder containing 90 per cent cubic and 10 per cent hexagonal at 1300° C increased the content of hexagonal considerably. After sintering with 20 per cent tungsten carbide, all cobalt was in the cubic state, and it appeared that 0.4 per cent WC, which remained in solid solution in the cobalt, stabilized the cubic form. It was proposed that the presence of hexagonal cobalt in Co-WC compacts would serve as an indicator of incomplete sintering or incorrect heat treatment.

Titanium carbides with cobalt binder have been reviewed.[1,6,9,11,23] Cobalt content ranges from 5 to 30 per cent for 95–70 per cent titanium carbide compositions. Blumenthal[5] reported that, contrary to general belief, the presence of a film of TiO_2 around the particles of TiC promotes cobalt infiltration. Eremenko and Lesnik[10] found that the eutectic mixture at 1360° C contains 6 per cent TiC, and that the cobalt-rich solid solution at this temperature has 1 per cent TiC. Titanium carbide dissolved in cobalt seems to stabilize the cubic modification of the latter.

Ternary boride compounds Mo_2CoB_2 and Mo_2CoB_4, having desirable properties as an ingredient in cutting tools, have been described.[27]

Gurland[13] has compared the strength of sintered carbides WC, TiC, TaC, CbC, VC, and ZrC having binder contents of 10 and 37 volume per cent cobalt. The transverse rupture strength is shown in Table 11.2. Zirconium

TABLE 11.2. STRENGTH OF SINTERED CARBIDES

Carbide	Average Transverse Rupture Strength, $\times 10^3$ psi	
	Volume % Co	
	10	37
WC	241	346
TaC	163	269
TiC	162	254
CbC	132	205
VC	83	183
ZrC	37	113

carbide showed considerable porosity, and an unidentified light-gray constituent was observed around the carbide grains. When transverse rupture strengths are plotted against elastic moduli of these carbides, a fair relation is observed, the strength increasing with the elastic modulus.

Gurland[14] studied temperature stresses in WC-Co alloys ranging from 5 to 37 volume per cent cobalt. The stresses in the carbide constituent were calculated from elastic theory and measured by X-ray diffraction techniques. Compressive stresses act on the dispersed carbide phase of high binder compositions, whereas tensile stress components predominate in alloys with low cobalt content. The compressive strength on WC is beneficial, the tensile component undesirable since the carbide is stronger in compression than in tension.

ETCHING REAGENTS FOR CEMENTED CARBIDES

The standard etchant for cemented carbides is equal parts 10 per cent KOH and 10 per cent potassium ferricyanide, $K_3Fe(CN)_6$.[4] Immersion in the boiling solution is usually 1–5 minutes. The cobalt phase is not attacked and appears as white or light-yellow patches among the grains of tungsten carbide. The strength of the alkaline ferricyanide, and the ratio of constituents, as well as the immersion period, can be varied to suit the product.

When titanium carbide is present, the preferred etching agent is a mixture of nitric and hydrofluoric acids—for example, 1.5 parts concentrated HF to 1 part HNO_3—which quickly attacks the cobalt bond and gives a faint pink color to the titanium carbide.

Another agent for cemented carbides is phosphoric acid with 5 per cent concentrated nitric acid. The cobalt phase can be dissolved by boiling for a sufficient time in concentrated HCl; subsequent boiling in solutions of ammonium persulfate and $H_2SO_4 + H_2O_2$, respectively, reveals the carbides.

If desired, cemented carbides may be etched electrolytically, with or without previous electrolytic polishing; generally, however, a simple chemical etching is satisfactory for most products.

References

1. Barksdale, J., "Titanium," New York, Ronald Press, 1949.
2. Bell, G. R., "Pressing and Sintering Metal Powders," *J. Chem. Met. Mining Soc. S. Africa,* **56,** 259–76 (1956).
3. Berry, B. E., "The Manufacture of Cemented Tungsten Carbide," *Murex Rev.,* **1,** 165–83 (1951).
4. Bleecker, W. H., "A Metallographic Technique for Cemented Carbides," *Iron Age,* **165,** 71–4 (1950).

5. Blumenthal, H., "Preliminary Results on the Infiltration of Titanium Carbide with Cobalt," *Powder Met. Bull.,* **6,** 186–8 (1953).
6. Campbell, J. B., "Metals and Refractories Combined in High-Temperature Structural Parts," *Materials & Methods,* **31,** 59–63 (1950).
7. Cotter, P. G., Kohn, J. A., and Potter, R. A., "Improved Tungsten Carbide-Cobalt Compacts by Electric-Resistance Sintering," *U. S. Bur. Mines Rept. Invest.,* **5100** (1955).
8. Custers, J. F. H., Elliott, C. R., and Young, R. S., "Fundamentals of Diamond Drilling," *J. Chem. Met. Min. Soc. S. Africa,* **52,** 38–92 (1952).
9. Engel, W. J., "Bonding of Titanium Carbide with Metal," *Metal Progr.,* **59,** 664–7 (1951).
10. Eremenko, V. N., and Lesnik, N. D., "The Reaction of Titanium Carbide with Cobalt," *Voprosy Poroshkovoi Met. i Prochnosti Materialov, Akad. Nauk Ukr. S.S.R.,* **1956,** No. 3, 73–80. *Chem. Abst.,* **51,** 7273 (1957).
11. Goetzel, C. G., "Treatise on Powder Metallurgy, Vol. 1," New York, Inter-Science Publishers, Inc., 1949. Vol. II, Ibid, 1950.
12. Gurland, J., "A Study of the Effect of Carbon Content on the Structure and Properties of Sintered WC-Co Alloys," *J. Metals,* **6,** 285–90 (1954).
13. —, "Comparison of the Strength of Sintered Carbides," *J. Metals,* **9,** 512–13 (1957).
14. —, "Temperature Stresses in the Two-Phase Alloy, WC-Co," *Trans. Am. Soc. Metals,* **50,** 1063–71 (1958).
15. —, and Bardzil, P., "Relation of Strength, Composition, and Grain Size of Sintered WC-Co Alloys," *J. Metals,* **7,** No. 2, Section 2, 311–15 (1955).
16. Gurland, J., and Norton, J. T., "Role of the Binder Phase in Cemented Tungsten Carbide-Cobalt Alloys," *J. Metals,* **4,** 1051–56 (1952).
17. Kochanovska, A., "Effect of Impurities on Allotropic Transformations of Cobalt," *Czechoslov, J. Phys.,* **5,** 279–80 (1955). *Chem. Abst.,* **49,** 12908 (1955).
18. Norton, J. T., "Some Observations on the Role of the Binder in Cemented Refractory Alloys," *Powder Met. Bull.,* **6,** 75–8 (1951).
19. —, "Interaction Between Metals and Atmospheres During Sintering," *J. Metals,* **8,** 49–53 (1956).
20. Perel'man, F. M., Zvorykin, A. Y., and Gudima, N. V., "Kobal't," *Akad. Nauk S.S.S.R.,* 1949.
21. Perrault, R., "Le Cobalt," Dunod, Paris, 1946.
22. Rautala, P., and Norton, J. T., "Tungsten-Cobalt-Carbon System," *J. Metals,* **4,** 1045–50 (1952).
23. Rose, K., "Cemented Carbides," *Materials & Methods,* **29,** 73–84 (1949).
24. Shaw, M. C., and Smith, P. A., "Physical Characteristics of Cast Alloys and Carbides," *Machinist,* **95,** 1790–2 (1951).
25. Shooter, K. V., "Frictional Properties of Tungsten Carbide and of Bonded Carbides," *Research,* **4,** 136–9 (1951).
26. Steinitz, R., "Phase Diagrams Play an Important Role in Powder Metallurgy," *J. Metals,* **5,** 891–4 (1953).
27. —, and Binder, I., "New Ternary Boride Compositions," *Powder Met. Bull.,* **VI,** 123–5 (1953).

28. Sykes, W. P., "Cemented Tungsten Carbide Alloys," *Trans. Am. Inst. Mining Met. Eng.,* **128,** 76–89 (1938).
29. Tretyakov, V. Y., "Properties and Production of Metal Ceramic Tungsten Carbide Cobalt Alloys," *Technik,* **12,** 733–5 (1957). *Chem. Abst.,* **52,** 6102 (1958).
30. Young, R. S., "Production and Properties of Cobalt," *Chemical Age,* **LXIII,** 193–5 (1950).

Chapter 12

ELECTROPLATING COBALT

In the early part of the century, the rapid increase in cobalt production from new Canadian deposits and the unsatisfactory behavior of nickel plating in outdoor exposure led to many laboratory investigations of cobalt electrodeposition. Some of these appeared promising, initially, but the relative scarcity of cobalt, and the other demands for this metal have kept its price high in comparison with nickel or chromium. Since cobalt oxidizes more easily than nickel or chromium, it is less suitable for coating objects exposed to heat. The satisfactory development of thin films of chromium able to prevent tarnishing of an underlying, thicker, corrosion-resistant layer of electrodeposited nickel finally deterred most research into the deposition of cobalt alone.

Careful pioneer work on cobalt plating was done by Watts,[48] and Kalmus and associates;[26] more recent investigations are given in standard reference books[4,15,22,32] and in individual papers.[14,20,28,40,41,43] Like nickel, electroplated cobalt has a steel-gray appearance, but the latter has a faint bluish tinge. Cast or rolled anodes have been used successfully in cobalt electroplating. Typical bath compositions and operating conditions are as follows:[22]

Bath No.	Composition	oz/gal.	g/l	pH	Current Density, amp/ft^2	Temp
1	$Co(NH_4)_2(SO_4)_2 \cdot 6H_2O$	23	175	5.5	4–39	Room
2	$CoSO_4 \cdot 7H_2O$	67	504	5	35–163	Room
	NaCl	2	14			
	H_3BO_3	6	45			
3	$CoSO_4 \cdot 7H_2O$	67	504	5.2	28–47	Room
	NaF	2	14			and
	H_3BO_3	6	45			up
4	$CoCl_2 \cdot 6H_2O$	7–80	50–600	. . .	20–140	Room
	NH_4HF_2	1–16	10–120			and
	H_3BO_3	6	45			up
5	$Co(NH_4)_2(SO_4)_2 \cdot 6H_2O$	23	175	Slightly	. . .	Room
	$NH_4C_2H_3O_2$	3.5	26	acid		and
	CH_3COOH	0.1	1			up
	HCOOH, 38%	0.35	2.6			
	$CdSO_4$	0.02	0.18			

271

The Brinell hardness of cobalt deposits has been reported to vary between 270 and 311,[32] compared with that of nickel which ranges from 180 to 420.

The electrical resistance of cobalt has been reported to range approximately from 5×10^{-6} to 15×10^{-6} ohm/ccm,[32] a variation which is not surprising in view of the fact that this property is influenced by impurities as well as preheating and annealing treatments. For highly purified cobalt heated several hours *in vacuo*, electrical resistivity at 20° C may be taken as 6.3×10^{-6} ohm/ccm. The temperature coefficient of the resistance between 0 and 100° C is about 0.006/° C,[13] values of 0.0032–0.0066[32] having been reported in the literature. The electrical resistance of cobalt is greatly increased by the presence of impurities, less than 0.5 per cent often trebling the resistance.

In the electrochemical series, cobalt occupies a position between thallium and nickel, the standard electrode potential for $Co \rightarrow Co^{++}$ at 25° C being $+0.278$ volt. The deposition potential of cobalt from solutions of sulfate and chloride in different acidities, temperatures, and current densities has been noted by Mellor.[32] In N-$CoSO_4$ at 15° C, the effect of current density varies with acidity, as shown in Table 12.1.

TABLE 12.1. DEPOSITION POTENTIAL OF COBALT AT DIFFERENT CURRENT DENSITIES AND ACIDITIES

Current Density, amp $\times 10^{-4}$/sq cm	Deposition Potential, volts		
	0.1 N H_2SO_4	pH 4	pH 6
1.4	-0.31	-0.49	-0.56
80	-0.57	-0.62	-0.64

The effect of current density and temperature on deposition potentials of normal solutions of cobalt chloride and sulfate is illustrated in Table 12.2.

TABLE 12.2. DEPOSITION POTENTIAL OF COBALT SOLUTIONS AT DIFFERENT CURRENT DENSITIES AND TEMPERATURES

Current Density, amp $\times 10^{-4}$/sq cm	Deposition Potential, volts			
	N-$CoCl_2$		N-$CoSO_4$	
	1° C	50° C	1° C	50° C
1.4	-0.413	-0.335	-0.405	-0.324
45.5	-0.474	-0.354	-0.486	-0.374

The effect of temperature and acidity on deposition potentials of N-$CoCl_2$ is indicated in Table 12.3.

TABLE 12.3. DEPOSITION POTENTIAL OF COBALT AT DIFFERENT ACIDITIES AND TEMPERATURES

	Deposition Potential, volts	
Acidity	1°C	50°C
Neutral	−0.474	−0.354
0.5% H_3BO_3	0.153	−0.004
0.03 N HCl	0.125	0.070

The cathodic or hydrogen overvoltage for a cobalt electrode in $N-H_2SO_4$ has been given as 0.22–0.29 volt at 20°C by various workers. Table 12.4 gives the cathodic overvoltage of cobalt with varying current densities in normal solutions of the following salts.

TABLE 12.4. CATHODIC OVERVOLTAGE OF COBALT

	Current Densities, milliamp/cm^2							
	2	6	10	20	50	100	200	400
$CoSO_4$	0.50	0.48	0.48	0.48	0.50	0.51	0.51	0.49
$Co(NO_3)_2$	0.26	0.38	0.45	0.57	0.73	0.72	0.69	0.64
$CoCl_2$	0.31	0.30	0.31	0.32	0.35	0.38	0.44	0.53
H_2SO_4	0.27	0.28	0.28	0.27	0.27	0.26	0.26	0.25
NaOH	0.25	0.28	0.28	0.29	0.29	0.29	0.30	0.30

The cathodic overvoltage of cobalt is similar to that of nickel, but is more constant.[32,35] At very high current densities, rapid increases of overvoltage occasionally take place. The effect is a surface one, since cleaning the surface restores the normal overvoltage.

Cobalt becomes passive under certain conditions of electrolysis. Literature regarding this passivity is voluminous; it is also confusing because of the number of variables affecting the oxide film or surface modification formed by metals under conditions of passivity. Cobalt does not become passive at the low current densities required of nickel or iron.

The oxygen or anodic overvoltage of cobalt for varying current densities in normal solutions of the following salts is given in Table 12.5.

TABLE 12.5. ANODIC OVERVOLTAGE OF COBALT

	Current Densities, milliamp/cm^2							
	2	6	10	20	50	100	400	1200
$CoSO_4$	0.02	0.03	0.03	0.04	0.05	0.06	0.06	0.08
$Co(NO_3)_2$	0.11	0.11	0.09	0.06	0.00	0.00	0.02	0.02
$CoCl_2$	0.03	0.02	0.00	0.02	0.03	0.02	0.03	0.07
NaOH	0.58	0.60	0.59	0.58	0.58	0.57	0.56	0.54

The anodic behavior of cobalt has been studied by El Wakkad and Hickling.[17] They found that CoO is formed first but is oxidized to Co_2O_3 when the surface is only partly covered with the lower oxide. In the passivation of a cobalt anode, the Co_2O_3 forms a protective layer, essentially one molecule thick, which is further oxidized to CoO_2 before oxygen evolution commences. The standard Co_2O_3/CoO_2 potential is $+0.58$ volt.

Co^{++} is oxidized in a very acid medium to Co^{+++} at a potential of $+1.808$ volts.[16] CoO_2, which decomposes to form $Co(OH)_3$ and O, is formed at the time of the anodic oxidation of cobalt in alkaline solution. In very alkaline solutions, cobalt dissolves as CoO_2H^-.[16]

The crystal structure of electrodeposited cobalt has been reported.[1,36] With $CoSO_4$ at current density of 0.005–0.1 amp/cm² and pH 1.2–7, for low current density and high pH the deposits were almost completely hexagonal and close-packed. Other current and pH conditions gave rise to mixtures of hexagonal and face-centered cubic forms. The cubic structure was deposited from a solution of $CoSO_4$ and $Co(NH_4)_2(SO_4)_2$ at pH 1.7–5 and current density of 0.01–0.1 amp/cm². A high pH favored the formation of the hexagonal form, independent of the nature of the base metal, either copper, iron, or cobalt.

Since World War II, production of electrolytic cobalt has commenced in the Belgian Congo, Northern Rhodesia, and Canada. During and since the war, many studies of the electrodeposition of cobalt have been carried out by the U. S. Bureau of Mines[11,20,39,40,41,42] as part of its broader investigations into the extractive metallurgy of domestic cobalt ores. Electrolytic cobalt is, or can be, commercially produced from sulfate solutions containing 10–40 g/l Co, varying in pH from about 1.5 to 6 and in current density from 15 to 45 amp/ft², with or without the addition of substances to the electrolyte such as 50 g/l boric acid and 5 g/l sodium fluoride. The conditions employed depend on the composition of the feed solution and on other factors affecting the economics of the operation. One factor now apparently agreed on is the plating temperature, around 60° C. This higher temperature increases current efficiency, improves the physical properties of the deposit, and permits a wider range of impurities to be tolerated in the electrolyte.

Churchward, Shelton, and Knickerbocker[11] investigated the effect of impurities in a standard electrolyte containing 20 g/l cobalt as $CoSO_4$, 50 g/l boric acid, and 5 g/l NaF at 25 amp/ft² using lead anodes and stainless steel cathodes. The maximum tolerance for metallic impurities in the production of satisfactory 7-hour cobalt electrodeposits was (in mg/l): Zn 10, Cd 1, As^{III} 3, As^{V} 1, Sb^{III} 10, Hg^{II} 1. Tri- and hexavalent chromium, in concentrations up to 100 mg/l, were only slightly harmful, while nickel, copper, iron, and manganese were not found to be deleterious. When the beneficial effect of a bath temperature of 60° C was realized, later work by the Bureau[42] indicated that 100 times as much zinc could be tolerated. This has been substantiated by the fact that Union Minière produces electrolytic cobalt in the presence of 0.1 g/l zinc.

The conductivity –pH relationship of the standard Bureau electrolyte containing, per liter, 20 g Co as cobalt sulfate, 50 g boric acid, and 5 g sodium fluoride, may be expressed by the equation

$$2.44C = 10^{-pH} + 0.064 + 0.00125 (T - 29.6)$$

where T is degrees centigrade. The mole-per cent of hydrogen released at the cathode is approximately equivalent to the percentage of the total current carried by the hydrogen ions.[41]

The specific viscosity of a cobalt sulfate electrolyte containing about 50 g/l boric acid and 5 g/l sodium fluoride can be calculated from the formula

$$u = 1.468^k$$

u being the specific viscosity at 30° and k the normality of the electrolyte in cobalt. For pure cobalt sulfate solutions at 25° C, the formula becomes $u = 1.352^k$.

The temperature coefficient of specific viscosity for an electrolyte containing 5 g sodium fluoride, about 20 g cobalt/l, and boric acid to 50 g/l or saturation, whichever is smaller, can be estimated to 0.1 per cent by Meyer's formula

$$u = 1.231 + 2.043 \times 10^{-3} T$$

where T is temperature in degrees centigrade. The formula gives an estimate to within less than 1 per cent of the specific viscosity of electrolytes over a fairly wide range of bath temperatures and cobalt concentrations.

The conductivity of pure $CoSO_4$ solutions varies with concentration in the electrolyte in the following manner:[41]

$CoSO_4$, g/l	2.95	5.89	14.74	20.63	29.47;
Conductivity, ohms/cm	0.00514	0.00878	0.01765	0.02275	0.02930.

Torrance[47] reported that cobaltic oxide, Co_2O_3, can be deposited on the anode from a faintly acid solution. The Sand revolving-diaphragm electrode was used to separate the cathode from the cobalt solution, thus inhibiting the deposition of cobalt as metal. The anolyte, which was cobalt solution, had to be buffered with sodium acetate. The catholyte was 2N nitric acid. Cobaltic oxide is not deposited from a solution with acidity much stronger than pH 3.5, and adherent deposits could not be obtained much above 0.0556 g cobaltic oxide. Others have noted the deposition of very small quantities of Co_2O_3, or possibly CoO_2, on lead anodes at high current density.[16,39]

The electrodeposition of cobalt from coordination compounds has been studied.[29] In a series of cobaltic and cobaltous ammines, the nature of the coordinating groups and the stability of the complex ions were more important in plating than pH variations.

Cobalt has been deposited from a fluoborate bath which is made by dissolving cobalt carbonate in fluoboric acid to give a concentration of 116–154 g/l cobalt fluoborate.[18] Boric acid at 15 g/l is added and plating carried out at 45–50° C, pH 3.5, and cathode current density 50–60 amp/sq ft. The tensile strength of the deposit is increased by increasing the concentration of fluoborate, by adding gelatin to the solution, and by dipping the brass strip in 3 per cent NaCN and 1:20 HCl solution after bright dipping.[19] The internal stress of the cobalt deposit is lowered by increasing its thickness, and by raising the current density and bath temperature.

Cobalt plating from a 2M oxalate solution at pH 4, 1.8 volts, and 95–100° C, has been reported.[28] At other temperatures, the deposit is contaminated with carbon.

The life of lead storage batteries is decreased by the presence of small quantities of cobalt. This has been attributed to either the adsorption of cobalt which prevents the penetration of the PbO_2 lattice by oxygen, or the oxidizing properties of cobalt compounds and the deposition of metallic cobalt on the negative plate.[3,30]

Cobalt amalgams have been prepared by electrolysis of cobalt sulfate between cobalt anode and mercury cathode. Both cubic and hexagonal cobalt were highly dispersed in mercury.[27] Cobalt powder has been prepared by electrolytic precipitation on a mercury cathode, with subsequent separation of the dispersed particles by partial oxidation.[5]

ELECTRODEPOSITION OF COBALT ALLOYS

Apart from cobalt-nickel plating, which will be discussed in some detail later, interest has been aroused from time to time in the simultaneous deposition of cobalt and another metal. Fink and Hutton[21] found that the cathode product of cobalt-copper deposition was largely dependent on cathode film pH and the ratio of cobalt to copper ion concentration. Clark and Holt[12] obtained bright deposits of cobalt-tungsten alloy from a bath of cobalt sulfate, sodium tungstate, and citric acid in a molar ratio of 1:1:1.5, operation at 70° C, pH 7, and cathode current density 15 amp/dm^2, with anodes of cobalt, tungsten, an alloy of these, or an inert anode. Roy, Udupa, and Dey[38] reported best results with a solution containing 38–39 g/l tungstic acid, 6.8–7.0 g/l CoSO$_4$, and 66 g/l citric acid, with pH maintained at 7–8.5 by addition of ammonia. Others[53] found that the best conditions for electrodeposition were with an electrolyte consisting of 0.05M CoSO$_4$, 0.15M ammonium tungstate, 0.2M sodium tartrate, 0.1M ammonium sulfate, and 2.5M ammonia.

Satisfactory deposits of cobalt-manganese were made from solutions where the anolyte contained 90 g/l CoSO$_4$·7H$_2$O, and the catholyte (in g/l) MnSO$_4$·5H$_2$O 130, (NH$_4$)$_2$ SO$_4$ 130, and NH$_4$SCN 10.[23] An asbestos diaphragm was used, and the bath operated at 20° C, pH 1, cathode current density 20 amp/dm^2, with anodes of graphite or lead. Cobalt and cobalt-molybdenum alloys can be deposited from a caustic-free strongly alkaline bath containing a carbonate and enough soluble cobalt salt to provide the necessary ions.[6] References to electroplating other cobalt alloys have been compiled.[14]

Brenner and associates[6,7,8,9,10] have investigated the electrodeposition of alloys of cobalt and phosphorus, and the plating of cobalt by chemical reduction. For the latter, a typical solution contains (by weight) CoCl$_2$· 6H$_2$O, 3 per cent; NaH$_2$PO$_2$·H$_2$O, 2 per cent; NH$_4$Cl, 20 per cent; and water, 75 per cent. Operation is kept at pH 8–10 by addition of ammonia, temperature is 90–100° C, and sodium hypophosphite is added periodically. Electrodeposition from acid solutions containing phosphites give bright cobalt-phosphorus alloys which are harder than pure cobalt. Deposits having phosphorus up to 1 per cent are strong and ductile, but above this they become brittle. Cobalt deposits containing up to 10 per cent phosphorus are magnetic. Phosphorus alloys may be unstable solid solutions, or mixtures of individual particles of metal and metal phosphides.

ELECTROLYTIC POLISHING

Electrolytic polishing of cobalt has been described by Tegart.[46] Electrolysis is carried out for 0.5–1.5 min at room temperature with a current density of 250 amp/dm^2 and 8–9 volts across the cell, in a series circuit having a stainless steel cathode and a bath of 1 ethyl alcohol/100 HCl. The bluish-green anodic film is soluble in water, and a polished surface with slight grain boundary delineation is obtained. Another procedure is electrolysis at room temperature for 5–10 minutes in orthophosphoric acid of sg 1.35, with cobalt as the cathode and a voltage drop of 1–1.5 volts across the cell, a density of 1–2 amp/dm^2, and a potentiometric circuit. This produces slightly etched surfaces for metallography but strain-free surfaces for magnetic studies. A solid black film forms during treat-ment and should be removed with cotton wool. The current density then rises to 12–16 amp/dm^2. At 1.65–1.70 volts, the anode becomes completely passivated by a thick oxide layer.

Other electrolytic polishing procedures use varying ratios of perchloric and acetic acids, for example, 10 parts of 70 per cent $HClO_4$ to 90 parts glacial acetic acid for 30 seconds at 30 volts and 0.8 amp/in.^{2} For Alnico magnets, a solution of 240 perchloric acid, 750 acetic acid, and 30 water may be used.

COBALT-NICKEL PLATING

Although the deposition of cobalt has never been of importance in the electroplating industry, the addition of cobalt to nickel plating solutions is a widespread practice. In 1936, Weisberg and Stoddard[52] showed that the addition of a cobalt salt, together with sodium formate and formalde-hyde, to the basic nickel bath produced bright deposits of a nickel-cobalt alloy which did not require polishing before chromium plating. Modifica-tions in the bath composition, and continuous removal of impurities have improved the process to give smooth, bright, hard but relatively ductile deposits having low porosity and a high protective value.[34,45,49,50,51] Under optimum plating conditions, articles can, subsequently, be severely de-formed without rupture of the coating.

Anodes for bright nickel-cobalt plating may contain 1–18 per cent cobalt, and it is recommended that bags be used on anodes. Continuous filtration through a press or other filtering device is essential. Continuous purifica-tion by electrolysis of the plating solution is carried out in an auxiliary tank at a low current density, around 2–5 amp/ft^2, to remove Fe, Zn, Cu, Pb, etc. Organic impurities are removed by filtering through activated char-coal or clay. The optimum bath temperature for this process is 60–70° C, and the bath is agitated by air which is free from oil.

Cobalt-nickel baths operate over a wide pH range. For brightest deposits and maximum throwing power, pH values of 3.5–3.7 are recommended, while for the softest, most ductile and easily buffed deposits, a pH of 2.0–2.7 is advisable. Formic acid is useful for pH adjustment. These baths also operate satisfactorily over a wide range of current densities, but for most work a density of 40–60 amp/ft^2 is recommended. With normal anode-cathode spacings and pure solutions, the voltage required for plating at current densities of 40–60 amp/ft^2 is 4–5.

Typical compositions of bright nickel plating solutions containing cobalt salts are:[24,34]

	oz/gal.	g/1
Nickel sulfate	32.0	240
Nickel chloride	4.0	30
Nickel formate	6.0	45
Boric acid	4.0	30
Ammonium sulfate	0.10	0.75
Formaldehyde	0.33	2.47
Cobalt sulfate	0.35, 0.60, or 2.0	2.62, 4.49, or 14.98

Only the content of cobalt sulfate is altered, as shown above, for commercial baths called 1 per cent cobalt, 5 per cent cobalt, and 18 per cent cobalt. The latter bath gives the highest lustre, whitest color, and greatest hardness. The 1 per cent cobalt bath is adapted for a wide range of operating conditions and products such as automobile parts. The 5 per cent solution produces deposits intermediate in characteristics between the 1 and 18 per cent types, and may be used on brass goods for plumbing fixtures.

As ordinarily employed in electrolysis, cobalt-nickel solutions have little leveling power, i.e., the ability to hide polishing lines in an underlying metal. For this reason, they are generally used to plate surfaces which readily take a high polish, such as brass or copper.[45] Weisberg[51] however, has found that a leveling action is given by a solution having the following composition:

	oz/gal.	g/1
Nickel sulfate	48	360
Nickel chloride	4	30
Formic acid	2	15
Boric acid	5.5	40
Formaldehyde, 40% solution	up to 0.35	up to 2.6
Cobalt sulfate	0.4	3

Use of the periodic reverse current in electroplating nickel-cobalt compositions has been described.[2,25,33] Cathodic period is usually 2 seconds or less, and anodic period 1/2–1/25 of a second. The plating is most satisfactory because inferior metal, such as nodules, is depleted by the reverse current. For example, plating for tape recordings is better because of the higher remanence and lower coercivity when an alternating current with rectification on each half-cycle is used for deposition from a bath containing (in g/l) $CoCl_2$, 25–75; $NiCl_2$, 10–75; H_3BO_3, 5–45; o-and/or p-toluene sulfonamide, 1–3; sodium dodecyl sulfate, 0.002–0.003. Operation is at pH 1–5.5, 100–200° F; current density is 100–1400 amp/ft² on the plating cycle and 32–480 amp/ft² on the deplating cycle.[33]

In recent years, bright nickel plating solutions, containing certain complex organic substances in place of cobalt salts have come into use. Organic bright nickel baths are lower in cost but more difficult to control than nickel-cobalt solutions.[45] The latter also possess greater ductility, and are still preferred for many applications. In general, nickel-cobalt deposits are less brittle than nickel deposits of equal hardness, and are particularly useful for electroformed molds and electrotyping.[4,31,37,44]

References

1. Actani, K., "Electrolysis of Aqueous Cobalt Solutions. 1. The Change of State of Electrodeposited Cobalt," *J. Electrochem. Soc. Japan,* **18**, 323–5 (1950). 11. "Crystal Structure of Electrodeposited Cobalt," Ibid, 369–71. *Chem. Abst.,* **45**, 8922 (1951).

2. Anon. "Plating Magnetic Cobalt-Nickel Alloys on Wire," *Iron Age,* **163**, 49 · (1949).

3. Antropov, L. I., Popov, S. Y., Pochekaeva, T. I., and Romenskaya, N. N., "The Influence of Cobalt Sulfate on the Work of Lead Storage Batteries," *Trudy Soveshchaniya Elektrokhim. Akad. Nauk S.S.S.R., Otdel Khim. Nauk,* **1950**, 549–57 (1953). *Chem. Abst.,* **49**, 12161 (1955).

4. Blum, W., and Hogaboom, G. B., "Principles of Electroplating and Electroforming (Electrotyping)," New York, McGraw-Hill Book Company, 1949.

5. Brannland, R., Leffler, J. A., and Faldt, I., "Amalgam-Metallurgical Preparation of Iron, Cobalt, and Nickel Powders," *Svensk. Kem. Tidskr.,* **68**, 380–6 (1956). *Chem. Abst.,* **51**, 979 (1957).

6. Brenner, A., and Burkhead, P. (to Secretary of War), U. S. Pat. 2,653,127, Sept. 22, 1953.

7. Brenner, A., Couch, D. E., and Williams, E. K., "Electrodeposition of Alloys of Phosphorus and Nickel or Cobalt," *Plating,* **37**, 36–42 (1950).

8. —, *et al.,* "Electrodeposition of Alloys of Phosphorus with Nickel or Cobalt," *J. Res. Nat. Bur. Standards,* **44**, 109–19 (1950).

9. Brenner, A., and Riddell, G., "Deposition of Nickel and Cobalt by Chemical Reduction (Electroless Plating)," *J. Res. Nat. Bur. Standards,* **39**, 385–95 (1947).

10. —, *et al.,* U. S. Pat. 2,532,284, Dec. 5, 1950.

11. Churchward, R. E., Shelton, F. K., and Knickerbocker, R. G., "A Study of Impurities in Cobalt Electrowinning," *Trans. Electrochem. Soc.,* **85**, 193–212 (1945).

12. Clark, W. E., and Holt, M. L., "Electrodeposition of Cobalt-Tungsten Alloys from a Citrate Bath," *J. Electrochem. Soc.,* **94**, 244–52 (1948).

13. Cobalt Information Center, "Cobalt Data Sheet," Columbus, Ohio, 1958.

14. —, "Bibliography on Electroplating of Cobalt and Cobalt Alloys," Columbus, Ohio, 1958.

15. Creighton, H. J., and Koehler, W. A., "Electrochemistry. Vol. II. Applications," New York, John Wiley and Sons, Inc., 1944.

16. Deltombe, E., and Pourbaix, M., "Equilibrium Potential/pH Diagram for Cobalt at 25° C," Proc. 6th Meeting Internat. Committee Electrochem. Thermodynamics and Kinetics (Poitiers, 1954) **1955**, 153–66. *J. Inst. Metals,* **23.** *Met. Abstr.,* **663,** (1956).

17. El Wakkad, S. E. S., and Hickling, A., "The Anodic Behaviour of Metals, Part VI. Cobalt," *Trans. Faraday Soc.,* **46,** 820–4 (1950).

18. Fegredo, D. M., and Balachandra, J., "Electrodeposition of Cobalt from Fluoborate Bath," *J. Indian Institute Sci.,* **35B,** 191–201 (1953).

19. —, *et al.,* "Measurement of Internal Stress of Cobalt Deposited Electrolytically from Cobalt Fluoborate Baths," *J. Sci. Ind. Research,* **13B,** 753–5 (1954).

20. Fine, M. M., "Quantitative Electrodeposition of Cobalt," *U. S. Bur. Mines Rept. Invest.,* **3370,** 59–67 (1938).

21. Fink, C. G., and Hutton, J. L., "Why Not a 50:50 Cobalt Copper Solid Solution Alloy. 1. Codeposition of Cobalt and Copper," *Trans. Electrochem. Soc.,* **85,** 119–22 (1944).

22. Gray, A. G., "Modern Electroplating," New York, John Wiley and Sons, Inc., 1953.

23. Gritson, D. N., Vail, E. I., and Moskovets, V. P., "Electrolytic Production of a Manganese-Cobalt Alloy," *Uchenye Zapiski Khar'kov Univ.,* **50.** *Trudy Nauch. Issledovatel. Inst. i Khim. Fakul'teta,* **11,** 273–5 (1954). *Chem. Abst.,* **51,** 1752 (1957)

24. Hanson-Van Winkle-Munning Co., Matawan, N. J., 1945.

25. Jernstedt, G. W., and Ceresa, M., U. S. Pat. 2,470,775, May 24, 1949.

26. Kalmus, H. T., Harper, C. H., and Savell, W. L., "Electroplating with Cobalt," Can. Dept. Mines Rept. 334 (1915).

27. Katoh, N., "X-Ray Study on Cobalt Amalgam," *J. Chem. Soc. Japan,* **64,** 1211–12 (1943). *Chem. Abst.,* **41,** 3338 (1947).

28. Kovalenko, P. N., "Electrodeposition of Cobalt," *Zhur. Priklad. Khim.,* **24,** 951–7 (1951). *Chem. Abst.,* **47,** 5820 (1953).

29. Kramer, M. D., Swann, S., and Bailar, J. C., "The Electrodeposition of Cobalt and Nickel from Coordination Compounds," *Trans. Electrochem. Soc.,* **90,** 55–62 (1946).

30. Krivolapova, E. V., and Kabanov, B. N., "An Investigation of the Corrosion of Lead in Oxidizing Media. 11. The Influence of the Addition of Cobalt Salt, Temperature, and other Factors on the Term of Service of the Positive Electrode of the Lead Storage Battery," *Trudy Soveshchaniya Elektrokhim. Akad. Nauk S.S.S.R., Otdel. Khim. Nauk,* **1950,** 539–48 (1953). *Chem. Abst.,* **49,** 12161 (1955).

31. Ledford, R. F., "Cobalt-Nickel Deposition in Electrotyping," *Plating,* **36,** 560–5 (1949).

32. Mellor, J. W., "A Comprehensive Treatise on Inorganic and Theoretical Chemistry," Vol. XIV, London, Longmans, Green and Co., 1935.

33. Moline, W. E., and Clinehens, R. M., (to National Cash Register Co.), U. S. Pat. 2,730,491, Jan. 10, 1956.

34. Mond Nickel Co., Ltd., "Nickel Plating for Engineers," London, undated.

35. Murtazaev, A., "The Mechanism of Hydrogen Overvoltage on Cobalt in Alkali and Acid Solutions," *Zhur. Fiz. Khim.*, **23**, 1247–56 (1949). *Chem. Abst.*, **44**, 1344 (1950).

36. Okuno, G., "Crystal Structure of Electrodeposited Cobalt," *Bull. Univ. Osaka Prefect.* Ser. A, **4**, 89–100 (1956). Ibid, 101–10. *Chem. Abst.*, **51**, 4790 (1957).

37. Peters, E. I., "Advances in Electrodeposition in the Graphic Arts," *Proc. 37th Ann. Convention Amer. Electroplaters' Soc.*, **1950**, pp 69–84.

38. Roy, D. L., Udupa, H. V. K., and Dey, D. B., "Codeposition of Cobalt and Tungsten from an Aqueous Ammoniacal Citrate Bath," Proc. Intern. Comm. Electrochem. Thermodynam. and Kinet. 8th Meeting, 1958, 469–75. *Chem. Abst.*, **53**, 5913 (1959).

39. Shelton, F. K., "Metallurgical Treatment of Cobalt Ores from the Goodsprings Mining District, Nevada," *U. S. Bur. Mines Rept. Invest.*, **3836** (1946).

40. Shelton, F. K., Churchward, R. E., Stahl, J. C., and Davis, C. W., "Electrolytic Cobalt—A Commercially Feasible Process," *Trans. Electrochem. Soc.*, **91**, 115–31 (1947).

41. Shelton, F. K., Churchward, R. E., Stahl, J. C., and Livingston, G. F., "A Study of Certain Factors in the Hydrometallurgy and Electrodeposition of Cobalt," *U. S. Bur. Mines Rept. Invest.*, **3832** (1945).

42. Shelton, F. K., Stahl, J. C., and Churchward, R. E., "Electrowinning of Cobalt from Cobaltite Concentrates," *U. S. Bur. Mines Rept. Invest.*, **4172** (1948).

43. Soderberg, G., Pinner, W. L., and Baker, E. M., "Cobalt Plating," *Trans. Electrochem. Soc.*, **80**, 579–87 (1941).

44. Spiro, P., "The Production of Electroformed Moulds for Plastics and Die Casting," *J. Electrodepositors' Tech. Soc.*, **23**, 13–32 (1948).

45. Such, T. E., "Bright Nickel Plating Solutions. Their Choice, Control and Operation," Mond Nickel Co., Ltd., London, (1955).

46. Tegart, W. J. M., "The Electrolytic and Chemical Polishing of Metals in Research and Industry," London, Pergamon Press, Ltd., 1956.

47. Torrance, S., "The Electrolytic Separation of Cobalt from Nickel by Deposition as Cobaltic Oxide," *Analyst*, **64**, 109–11 (1939).

48. Watts, O. P., "The Electrodeposition of Cobalt and Nickel," *Trans. Am. Electrochem. Soc.*, **25**, 99–152 (1913).

49. Weisberg, L., "Commercial Electrodeposition of Cobalt-Nickel Alloys," *Trans. Electrochem. Soc.*, **73**, 435–48 (1938).

50. —, "Recent History of Certain Cobalt Nickel Alloy Plating Solutions," *Trans. Electrochem. Soc.*, **77**, 223–31 (1940).

51. —, "Levelling in Cobalt-Nickel Plating Solutions," *Proc. Electroplaters' Soc.*, **37**, 185–91 (1950).

52. —, and Stoddard, W. B., U. S. Pat. 2,026,718, Jan. 7, 1936.

53. Zayats, A. I., and Frantsevich-Zabludovskaya, T. F., "Electrodeposition of Cobalt-Tungsten Alloys," *Ukrain. Khim. Zhur.*, **24**, 585–91 (1958). *Chem. Abst.*, **53**, 9850 (1959).

Chapter 13

COBALT COMPOUNDS IN THE GLASS
AND CERAMIC INDUSTRIES

COBALT IN GLASS

Cobalt has been employed for a long time as a means of imparting a blue color to glass. Glass was first used purely for decorative purposes, in the form of beads; a blue necklace found in Persia, dating from about 2250 B.C., was colored with cobalt. From about 1300 B.C., many decorated glass vessels made in Egypt were colored with cobalt, as was much early Roman glass. Since cobalt is not an impurity ordinarily found in the raw materials used for glassmaking, it is likely that the metal was added intentionally. It must be remembered, however, that not all the blue glasses of antiquity were colored with cobalt.

Some Russian glasses of the eleventh and twelfth centuries were colored with cobalt imported from Iran.[2] In the sixteenth century, cobalt ore in Saxony was roasted to yield a crude oxide termed "zaffre"[18] which was mixed with potassium carbonate and sand, and melted to a glass. This blue glass, called "smalt," was separated from the heavier impurities that settled out at the bottom of the vessel, crushed, and ground to powder. The medieval glassmaker added appropriate quantities of this densely colored smalt to his batch when he wished to have a blue glass. The presence of small quantities of other metals markedly influenced the color of smalt. In spite of its crude form, smalt containing 4–30 per cent CoO has been used in some glass works until quite recently, since the intense coloring power of cobalt requires extreme care in its introduction if the pure oxides are employed.

The presence of only 0.005 per cent cobalt oxide will impart a bluish tint to clear glass. Glassmakers use either CoO or Co_3O_4 in the finely pulverized state as their source of cobalt. The hue and intensity of the cobalt color are not affected by changes in the melting conditions in the glass furnace. Reports on cobalt as a glass coloring agent have been made by Weyl[25,26] and Moore.[19]

The blue is the result of cobalt-oxygen groups, which may be represented as $(CoO_4')^{2-}$. These groups are linked through the four O' ions to the SiO_4' groups as structure-building units, with two alkali ions or one bivalent ion,

283

such as Ca^{2+}, in close association with each $(CoO'_4)^{2-}$ group to ensure local electrical neutrality.[19] The color is influenced only slightly by the associated cations, and is substantially the same as the color given by cobalt in 4-coordination with oxygen in certain crystals containing no alkali and no bivalent cation. The color is not the result of any complex system of alkali or alkaline earths.

Alkali oxides must be present in a cobalt-containing glass to supply the oxygen ions necessary for the formation of $(CoO'_4)^{2-}$ units.[25] In the absence of alkali, cobalt is immiscible in glass melts; for instance, 90 per cent SiO_2 and 10 per cent CoO separate into two liquids on melting. The same is true for B_2O_3:CoO mixtures. Potash glasses give a purer blue than the corresponding soda glasses. All cobalt glasses have a high transmission at the red end of the spectrum, making them suitable for detecting traces of potassium in a flame test even in the presence of sodium. The intense yellow D-lines of sodium at 5889 and 5895 Å are strongly absorbed, whereas the characteristic lines of potassium at 7664 and 7688 Å are transmitted.

When removed from the melt, the surface of cobalt-containing glass cools faster than that of a colorless glass because of increased infrared emission. Fast cooling during the working range shortens the time available for certain molding operations, and thus has the same effect as a high temperature coefficient of viscosity.

Cobalt ions in solution or in crystals cannot be excited to fluorescence, but many cobalt glasses, when irradiated with ultraviolet light, emit a brown to greenish fluorescence. Weyl[25] suggests that this is due to the presence of cobalt atoms.

Most cobalt glasses which are pink at room temperature turn blue on heating, indicating that the average coordination number of cobalt decreases with increasing temperature. There is evidently an equilibrium between the two color centers which depends on the temperature; with cooling, this is frozen in by the increasing viscosity of the glass which makes atomic rearrangements difficult.

The intense coloring effect of cobalt can be understood when it is realized that 0.5 per cent cobalt oxide produces a glass which, with a thickness of 3 mm, transmits a little light in the extreme red but practically none in the rest of the visible spectrum except in the blue, where transmission rises rapidly to as high as 80 per cent in the extreme blue.[19] Small variations in the thickness of the glass will result in appreciable differences in transmission; the glass may appear streaked or spotty.

For the most brilliant blues in delicate work, it is necessary to have raw materials as free as possible from iron and chromium. If copper is present as an impurity, it is recommended that a little alkali nitrate be added to the glass to avoid a greenish color which develops if the melt is made under slightly reducing conditions. Variations in the blue color may, of course, be produced by the deliberate addition of small quantities of other metals, such as copper.

The quantities of cobalt employed to impart a blue color to glass vary with the shade desired. Dark blue bottle glass contains about 18 oz cobalt oxide per ton of batch, while a pastel blue is obtained with 7–8 oz per ton.[17] Pittsburgh Plate Glass Company reported that as much as 7 lb cobalt oxide per ton may be used in structural glasses, and that the goggles used by furnacemen and welders may contain as high as 14 lb cobalt oxide per ton of glass.[22]

Cobalt can give delicate pink colors to certain glasses, such as fused boric oxide glass and the alkali-borate types containing low proportions of alkali. These glasses are all attacked by atmospheric moisture, however, and consequently are of no commercial interest.[19] In these glasses, the cobalt ion is surrounded by 6 oxygens. If alkali is added in sufficient quantity to boric oxide glass, a new absorption band develops in the visible region, and the pink color changes to blue.[1] The Co^{++} ion alters its coordination number with oxygen from 6, with the pink glass, to 4 with the blue.

It has been suggested that under certain conditions in glassmaking, cobalt oxide can be reduced by silicon to free cobalt in the form of a pyrosol.[8] The common cobalt blue of glasses and glazes is virtually unknown in minerals. This would seem to indicate that Co^{++} ions surrounded by oxygen must form at a low temperature, and that the cobalt is removed from the magma when the crystallization of silicates, aluminosilicates, and aluminates commences.[9]

Cobalt in Decolorizing Glass

Cobalt in very small quantities is used extensively for decolorizing glass. As little as 0.02 per cent Fe_2O_3 in glass will produce an appreciable color, and since the natural raw materials for glassmaking—sand and limestone—almost invariably contain iron in amounts not less than this, decolorizing processes are of great importance in the industry. A popular method involves the use of arsenious oxide, sodium nitrate, selenium, and cobalt oxide.[19] The first two compounds are oxidizers, used to decrease the proportion of ferrous iron and increase that of ferric iron, mainly in a colorless form. Selenium, combined with the remaining ferrous iron, gives a faint yellow color, the result of ferrous selenide and the residual colored ferric iron. The introduction of a trace of cobalt oxide neutralizes this yellow tint, and the glass appears colorless. For example, if the finished glass contains 0.05 per cent Fe_2O_3, decolorizing could be effected by the addition of the following reagents, per ton of glass:

Arsenious oxide	1 lb
Sodium nitrate	3 lb
Selenium	0.5 oz
Cobalt oxide	1–1.5 g

Much larger quantities of cobalt are sometimes used to neutralize the yellow. Maryland Glass Company employs about 45 g cobalt oxide per ton of batch,[17] and B. F. Drakenfeld Company[6] uses about 3 per cent cobalt arsenate to neutralize yellow and orange tints.

COBALT IN CERAMICS

Cobalt has been used to give pottery a blue color since ancient times, but its origin is uncertain; the blue of many early glazes which ceramists attributed to cobalt was later found to be the effect of copper.[24] Egyptian earthenware dating from 1300–1200 B.C. was decorated with cobalt, and it is certain that the potters of Persia and Syria made use of cobalt very early in the Christian Era. The use of cobalt in Chinese pottery is authenticated for the T'ang dynasty, 618–906 A.D., and blue decoration on porcelain was highly developed in the Ming dynasty, 1368–1644 A.D.

During the fourteenth and fifteenth centuries, the Chinese used imported cobalt primarily; after this period, however, they turned to their native ore. Despite the fact that it contained manganese and iron, and thus required special washing procedures, later Chinese blue and white porcelain had a higher manganese:cobalt ratio than did early specimens.[10,27] The nondestructive feature of X-ray fluorescence spectroscopy has been of particular value in differentiating the manganese content of early Ming and eighteenth century porcelain.[11]

Reference has already been made to the production, in Europe during the Middle Ages, of a crude cobalt oxide known as zaffre, and the impure potash silica glass colored by cobalt known as smalt, which was made by fusing zaffre with sand and potassium carbonate. After 1756, with the discovery of cobalt deposits in Cornwall, zaffre and smalt, previously imported from Saxony by English pottery manufacturers, became British products. Purer forms of cobalt compounds gradually supplanted smalt; today, the black oxide Co_3O_4 and the gray oxide CoO are the principal sources of cobalt in the ceramic field, together with the chloride, nitrate, phosphate, and sulfate of cobalt.

Cobalt as a Decolorizer

Most of the cobalt consumed in the ceramic industry is used not for producing blue but, rather, white. Small quantities of Fe_2O_3 and TiO_2 in some of the raw materials used for white domestic ware, sanitary ware, and wall tiles impart to these products an ivory tint which must be neutralized by the addition of cobalt. Though these additions are extremely small, the enormous output of whiteware makes this outlet for cobalt the largest in the ceramic field.

Two methods are used for producing white pottery bodies with cobalt compounds.[24] In one, an insoluble body stain is prepared by mixing black cobalt oxide with flint or china clay, calcining the mixture at 1150–1180° C, grinding it wet, and storing it in the slop condition. The latter product is added to each mixing of the body, the proportions being one part cobalt oxide to 5000–30,000 parts clay body. The second method involves using one of the water-soluble salts of cobalt. The danger of specking is eliminated, and the preparation of the body stain is much easier, but soluble salts have several disadvantages. They may be carried to, and concentrated at, the point of greatest evaporation in drying stages, leaving a blue stain on firing. In the firing, water vapor and steam may condense on the ware in cooler parts and dissolve some of the soluble cobalt salt. A loss of cobalt may occur with the press water when filtering the body slip. All these drawbacks can be largely overcome by adding an equivalent amount of sodium carbonate to the solution of the cobalt salt before adding the latter to the body slip, thereby precipitating insoluble cobalt carbonate.

Cobalt is sometimes used to neutralize the yellow which occasionally develops in lead glazes. The tint is usually caused by the presence, in the bisilicate frit, of dissolved lead oxide which has not been converted to the silicate. About 0.005–0.01 per cent cobalt in the glaze will eliminate the yellow.[24]

Cobalt Colors

Cobalt silicate blue, known also as mazarine blue, or royal blue, has a strong violet tint. The orthosilicate of cobalt, $2CoO \cdot SiO_2$, seems to be the only one which is obtainable by direct heating of cobalt oxide and silica. A more intense blue is produced by the compound $CoO \cdot SiO_2$, obtained by the solution of cobalt oxide in melts containing alumino-silicates and borates. The strongest color should be based on the $CoO \cdot Al_2O_3 \cdot SiO_2$ eutectic having the composition 42 per cent Co_3O_4, 20 per cent Al_2O_3, and 38 per cent SiO_2. For more brilliancy, about half the Al_2O_3 is usually replaced by CaO; thus, a typical strong under-glaze blue might have a composition of 42 per cent cobalt oxide, 10 per cent alumina, 20 per cent Cornish stone, 18 per cent flint, and 10 per cent whiting. Addition of 3–5 per cent white lead improves the brilliancy.

Cobalt aluminate, also called matte blue, or Thenard's blue, is turquoise. Like the silicate, it is stable at high temperature and is used extensively for blue coloration of bodies, under-glazes, and on-glazes. It is also a good pigment for high temperature plastics where organic dyes are unsuitable.[14] Cobalt aluminate, $CoO \cdot Al_2O_3$, is a spinel. A series of mixed spinels may be made by heating ZnO or MgO with CoO and Al_2O_3.[24] All these are blue and owe their color to the cobalt spinel present. Cobalt spinel is formed at lower temperatures in the presence of phosphates; cobalt phosphate is used sometimes instead of the oxide. To produce a blue body, the pure blue of the aluminate is usually preferred to the violet blue of the cobalt silicate, and a stain made by calcining cobalt oxide with hydrated alumina and zinc oxide is employed to give 0.5–1.0 per cent CoO in the clay body. The true blue of cobalt aluminate is very difficult to obtain, since it is easily converted to the silicate blue by contact with silica in fluxes and glazes.[24]

Flow blue is obtained by the formation of cobaltous chloride which diffuses into the glaze to give a soft blurred pattern instead of the usual sharp outline.[24] Chlorine evolved from the decomposition by heat of lead chloride or magnesium chloride reacts with cobalt oxide.

A series of colors intermediate between silicate blue and aluminate blue can be obtained by calcining cobalt oxide with materials containing both silica and alumina.[24] Willow blue, for example, is made from 40 per cent cobalt oxide, 45 per cent dry white stone, and 15 per cent flint. The addition of other metal oxides gives various shades of blue, such as Canton, Peacock, Unique, etc. Cobalt stannate is used for blue, particularly in onglaze colors. The orthostannate $2CoO \cdot SnO_2$ is green, but the calcination product corresponding to $CoO \cdot SnO_2$ is a deep blue. A similar shade may be obtained by replacing one molecule of cobalt oxide by magnesia in the orthostannate.

Chrome tin pink and cobalt blue give a series of violet shades, and the addition of manganese compounds to cobalt oxide yields a color known as Mulberry. Chromium oxide and cobalt oxide give jade green, and if zinc oxide and alumina are added to the cobalt-chromium mixture, olive greens and bronze greens are formed. If cobalt oxide and magnesia are calcined together over 1000° C, a red product, probably $MgO \cdot CoO$, is formed which can be stabilized by using glazes high in MgO and Al_2O_3, and low in SiO_2.[24]

Nearly all black colors contain cobalt oxide. For an intense black, a substantial proportion of cobalt is mandatory. For instance, a good underglaze black might contain 36 per cent iron oxide, 32 per cent cobalt oxide, 13 per cent nickel oxide, 12 per cent manganese oxide, and 7 per cent chromium oxide.

Artists' Pigments

Many cobalt compounds are used to color oil paints. Cobalt is not used in water colors, however; the so-called "cobalt blue" of this medium is not a compound of cobalt.

A number of pigments closely resemble the calcined products used for pottery. For example, the fine blue pigment known as Thenard's blue, cobalt blue, azure blue, cobalt ultramarine, or King's blue, is essentially cobalt aluminate.

Violet can be produced with cobalt phosphate, $2CoO \cdot P_2O_5$, which is made by calcining a cobalt salt with sodium phosphate. The same color may be obtained from zinc phosphate or sodium arsenate.

Cereleum, or blue céleste, is produced from oxides of tin and cobalt with calcium sulfate or silica. It is a light blue pigment with a slightly greenish tint, appearing violet under artificial light.

Rinman's green, or cobalt green, probably contains $ZnO \cdot CoO$. This fine pigment may be obtained in various shades of green by calcining a mixture of cobalt sulfate or nitrate and zinc oxide. It can also be produced by precipitating a mixture of solutions of cobalt and zinc salts with sodium carbonate, phosphate, or arsenate, and roasting the residue.

New blue, or turquoise green, is a pigment varying in color from greenish-blue to 'deep turquoise. It is a calcined mixture of cobalt oxide, chromium oxide, and alumina, sometimes prepared by precipitation from salt solution rather than commencing with oxides.

Cobalt magnesia pink, probably $MgO \cdot CoO$, is usually formed by calcining magnesium carbonate with cobalt nitrate.

Cobalt bronze is a violet cobalt ammonium phosphate with a bronze lustre. Cobalt brown is prepared by calcining a mixture of cobalt, ferrous, and ammonium sulfates. Cobalt yellow is potassium cobaltic nitrite.

The nomenclature for cobalt pigments is often confusing. In the early days, colors were prepared by the artist himself or by individual craftsmen; the multiplicity of procedures naturally yielded many shades, often indistinguishable from one another, yet each having a different name. Some color recipes which were developed for the artist have been applied to pottery decoration, with a change of name.

Dyes

Cobalt is a constituent of several metal-containing dyes. A reddish-yellow dye is prepared by coupling diazotised 2-aminophenol-4-sulphonmethylamide to acetoacet-*p*-chloranilide, dissolving the resulting azo dye in dilute sodium hydroxide and heating to 80-85° with aqueous cobaltous sulfate.[4]

Cobalt-containing dyes can be prepared from o-hydroxy-o'-carboxy azo-compounds as well as from azomethines. Examples of these are:

$$\left[\begin{array}{c} N=N \\ CO_{O-Co-O} \\ CO-O \quad O \end{array}\right]^{-} \quad \begin{array}{c} Na \\ + \end{array} \qquad \left[\begin{array}{c} CH=N \\ O-Co-O \\ O \quad O \end{array}\right]^{-} \quad \begin{array}{c} Na \\ + \end{array}$$

Cobalt phthalocyanine, formed by heating phthalonitrile with cobaltous chloride, may be changed by sulfonation into an acid soluble form which can be employed as a vat dye to give bright-blue, light-stable shades.

ENAMELS

Cobalt is employed in the vitreous enameling industry for two purposes: to provide color; to promote adhesion of enamel to steel.

As in the manufacture of pottery, all shades of blue may be imparted to enamels by adding cobalt oxide or salts of cobalt to kaolin, alumina, zinc oxide, copper oxide, and other materials; calcining the mixture; and grinding the product. Cobalt is an important constituent in most black enamels. Cobalt sulfate or nickel sulfate, or both, with the occasional addition of copper sulfate, are employed as mottling agents in the production of gray enameled kitchenware. The amount of cobalt sulfate required is only 0.001–0.002 per cent of the weight of the enamel slip.

It was discovered late in the nineteenth century that increased adherence of enamels to sheet iron was promoted by cobalt and nickel compounds, especially the former. Since then, the inclusion of cobalt oxide in ground coats for sheet iron and sheet steel has become universal. From 0.2 to 3 per cent cobalt oxide may be incorporated with the ground coat,[21] the usual concentration being 0.5–0.6 per cent. The coating is usually 0.003–0.004 in. thick and is fired for 10 minutes at 1520–1600° F.[5] Often, nickel and other oxides are added, together with the cobalt oxide, but the latter is indispensable. The use of lithium cobaltite for this purpose has been patented.[7] A high temperature porcelain enamel for tungsten has the following composition (in parts by weight): zircon, 9; Al_2O_3, 1.5; Co_3O_4, 0.5; $H_2MoO_4 \cdot H_2O$, 0.02; dextrose, 0.3.[16] Presumably, the cobalt is added primarily to promote adhesion.

Many theories have been advanced during the past fifty years on the tendency of cobalt to promote the adherence of enamel to steel,[12,23] but a generally accepted explanation is still lacking. For good adherence, it appears that an iron oxide film is formed on the steel surface before the enamel melts, and that part of this film is dissolved in the enamel. The role of cobalt oxide has been variously described: as an oxygen carrier for the formation of the surface film; as a promoter for solubility of iron oxide in the enamel; as the agent dissolving iron from the base; as the source of metallic cobalt by interaction with metallic iron. X-ray diffraction patterns indicated that the dendrites at the interface between the enamel ground coat and the sheet iron are metallic cobalt.[15] Presumably, the cobalt in the ground coat is reduced in the firing process, while the iron is oxidized. Radioactive CoO has been used in a study of porcelain enamel on sheet iron.[13] A metallic deposit containing cobalt was formed at the enamel-iron interface during firing, and the enamel layer was depleted in CoO near the interface. The amount of deposit and depletion varied directly with the firing temperature. The metallic deposit did not penetrate into the iron base during normal firing. Others have suggested that ground coat adherence is associated with deposition of cobalt, which in turn is dependent on the roughening of the metal surface.[20] It is interesting to note that cobalt oxide does not affect the enamel ground coats used on cast iron.[12]

CERMETS

Cobalt has not attained any importance in the metal-metal oxide mixtures used in high temperature applications. It has been pointed out that the oxide of the metal and the refractory oxide should have similar crystal shapes and lattice parameters.[3] Cobaltous oxide forms a continuous series of solid solutions with MgO.

References

1. Aglan, M. A., and Moore, H., "The Colors of Cobalt in Glass," *J. Soc. Glass Technol.,* **39,** 351–84T (1955).
2. Besborodov, M. A., and Fekhner, M. V., "Chemical Examination of Russian Glasses of the XIth. and XIIth. Centuries," *Doklady Akad. Nauk S.S.S.R.,* **95,** 1037–40 (1954). *Chem. Abst.,* **49,** 682 (1955).
3. Blackburn, A. R., Shevlin, T. S., and Lowers, H. R., "Fundamental Study and Equipment for Sintering and Testing of Cermet Bodies," *J. Am. Ceram. Soc.,* **32,** 81–98 (1949).
4. Bradley, W., "Recent Progress in the Chemistry of Dyes and Pigments," *Roy. Inst. Chem. Lectures, Monographs and Reports,* **1958,** No. 5, 1–94.
5. Clauser, H. R., "Porcelain Enamels," *Materials & Methods,* **31,** 71–82 (1950).
6. Drakenfeld Co., The B. F., Washington, Pa., personal communication, 1946.
7. Ellestad, R. B., and Babbitt, B. R. (to Metalloy Corp.), U. S. Pat. 2,545,424, Dec. 2, 1946.
8. Fanderlik, M., and Schill, F., "The Reduction of Cobalt in Glass," *J. Soc. Glass Technol.,* **32,** 122–6T (1948).

9. Forland, T., and Weyl, W. A., "Distribution of Heavy Metal Ions in Silicates Containing Several Ions of Different Sizes," *J. Am. Ceram. Soc.,* **32,** 267–72 (1949).
10. Garner, H. M., "Imported and Native Cobalt in Chinese Blue and White," *Oriental Art,* **2,** 48–50 (1956).
11. Hall, E. T., "X-Ray Fluorescence Spectroscopy in Chemical Analysis," *Endeavour,* **XVIII,** 83–7 (1959).
12. Hansen, J. E., "Cobalt and Nickel in the Vitreous Enamelling Industry," London, Mond Nickel Co., Ltd., undated.
13. Harrison, W. N., Richmond, J. C., Pitts, J. W., and Benner, S. G., "A Radioisotope Study of Cobalt in Porcelain Enamel," *J. Am. Ceram. Soc.,* **35,** 113–20 (1952).
14. Harshaw Chemical Company, Cleveland, Ohio, personal communication, 1946.
15. Healy, J. H., and Andrews, A. I., "Cobalt Reduction Theory of Sheet Iron Enamels," *Finish,* **7,** No. 12, 22–3 (1950).
16. Horsfall, J. C., "A High Temperature Porcelain Enamel for Tungsten," *Bull. Am. Ceramic Soc.,* **29,** 314–15 (1950).
17. Maryland Glass Company, Baltimore, Md., personal communication, 1946.
18. Mellor, J. W., "A Comprehensive Treatise on Inorganic and Theoretical Chemistry," Vol. XIV, London, Longmans, Green and Co., 1935.
19. Moore, H., "Selenium, Tellurium, Cobalt and Nickel in Glass Making," London, Mond Nickel Co., Ltd., 1956.
20. Patrick, R. F., Porst, E. G., and Spencer-Strong, G. H., "Study of Some Phenomena Associated with the Adherence of Sheet Iron Ground Coats," *J. Am. Ceram. Soc.,* **36,** 305–13 (1953).
21. Perrault, R., "Le Cobalt," Paris, Dunod, 1946.
22. Pittsburgh Plate Glass Co., Creighton, Pa., personal communication, 1946.
23. Priddey, G. C., "The Influence of Cobalt and Nickel in Vitreous Enamel Ground Coats," *Foundry Trade J.,* **80,** 263–8, 271 (1946).
24. Webb, H. W., "Cobalt, Nickel and Selenium in Pottery," London, Mond Nickel Co., Ltd., undated.
25. Weyl, W. A., "Colours Imparted to Glass by Metals. Part VI. The Colours Produced by Cobalt," *J. Soc. Glass Tech.,* **28,** 203–31 (1944).
26. —, "Coloured Glasses," Sheffield, Society of Glass Technologists, 1951.
27. Young, S., "Chinese Blue and White," *Oriental Art,* **2,** 34–45 (1956).

Chapter 14

CATALYTIC BEHAVIOR OF COBALT

Marvin F. L. Johnson
Sinclair Research Laboratories, Inc.
Harvey, Illinois

INTRODUCTION

Catalysts of cobalt or its compounds are applied most widely for hydrogenation reactions in a variety of systems. Cobalt is also considerably important as an oxidation catalyst; for example, as a paint drier.

The well-known catalytic activity of elements of the first transition group reaches a maximum in the triad, iron-cobalt-nickel. Similar maxima in the second and third transition series are also observed. Just as the chemical properties of cobalt are similar to those of iron and nickel, so are its catalytic properties. The differences between these dictate the choice of one over the other in a particular application, since the catalytic chemist is ordinarily concerned not only with activity in the desired direction, but also with side reactions. For this reason, cobalt is an effective Fischer-Tropsch catalyst; iron, on the other hand, is used principally in the synthesis of ammonia from nitrogen and hydrogen. Both are less active in hydrogenation than is nickel.

In order for catalysis to take place over a solid catalyst, some sort of adsorption must occur at the surface; this adsorption must involve an energy comparable to the energies of the bonds being broken and formed. Furthermore, this adsorption must be sufficiently strong to permit the required bond alterations, but must not be so strong that products will not be rapidly removed.

Complete details of the chemistry involved in the adsorption process are by no means completely understood. Since chemical bonds are involved, it is obvious that electronic factors play an important role in determining catalytic activity. Much has been written concerning the electronic factor in heterogeneous catalysis (see Baker and Jenkins[11]). An approach which has been postulated relates chemisorption and catalytic activity to the so-called "d-bond character" as calculated by Pauling.[51] This quantity, which is difficult to measure experimentally, gives the degree of filling of d-orbitals, and is an indication of bond strength. Ethylene hydrogenation data over numerous transition metals were originally correlated with their crystal parameters.[18,19] It was later found that the activity appeared to be a steadily increasing function of the percentage d-character.[21]

Other aspects of the electronic character of catalysts can be related to activity, in certain cases, such as magnetism or conductivity. It seems clear, however, that no single parameter can suffice for a complete explanation of catalytic activity; rather, each method of examining a catalyst provides complementary information. Whereas no clear relationship between percentage d-character and activity for acetylene hydrogenation has been observed,[60] the parallelism with magnetic susceptibility certainly suggests some influence of electronic structure on catalytic activity.

The so-called geometric factor is considered to be of some importance in determining catalytic activity. It was first recognized by Balandin in 1929 (see Trapnell[67]). In brief, the geometric factor requires an optimum spacing of surface atoms relative to the spacings of atoms in the reactant and/or product molecules. It is obvious that this alone cannot be responsible for catalytic activity; if so, there would be no way to account for the inactivity of ionic salts and non-metals. Coincidentally, the electronic and geometric factors are optimized for hydrogenation catalysis by the Group VIII metals.

In the present stage of development of the science of catalysis, it is necessary to rely primarily upon actual catalytic measurements.

PHYSICAL AND CHEMICAL FORMS

As is evident from the foregoing discussion, the activity of solid catalysts is a function of the surface area exposed, since catalysis occurs at surfaces. It is desirable, therefore, to maintain as high a surface area as is consistent with other considerations. A cobalt oxide having a surface area as high as 91 sq m/g* can be prepared by precipitation from a hot cobalt salt solution with sodium carbonate, followed by washing, drying, and calcining at 340°C; the product of such a preparation is mainly Co_3O_4.[40] This can be converted to metal by treatment with hydrogen at a temperature below 500°C. However, as reduction proceeds, a loss of surface area occurs. For example, if the oxide having 91 sq m/g of area at 340°C is reduced, the area will fall to 6 sq m/g; others have observed a decrease from 67 to 3 sq m/g on reduction of cobalt oxide powder at 250°C.[7] An electron microscopic study has shown, in addition, how fine particles of cobaltous oxide, or basic cobalt carbonate, sinter and become enlarged as reduction proceeds.[45]

It may be said, therefore, that pure cobalt metal cannot be produced in the same state of extremely high dispersion as can its oxides, which them-

*Surface areas refer to those determined by means of the well-known BET method.

selves do not have surface areas as high as those, say, of alumina or silica (150–800 sq m/g or more in area). The problem, then, is to find other means of producing a catalyst which has a large amount of exposed cobalt metal surface.

One way is to make a Raney cobalt, quite analogous to the well-known Raney nickel. This is done by preparing an alloy of cobalt and an alkali-soluble metal, such as aluminum, containing 25–50 per cent Co; grinding to a fine powder, and extracting the aluminum by means of caustic alkali. A study of Raney cobalt has been made by Aller,[2] who investigated its preparation and its physical and catalytic properties. Raney cobalt may reduce unsaturated and carbonyl linkages, under mild conditions, but its activity and life are somewhat inferior to Raney nickel. Its properties are somewhat similar to those of Raney nickel, but its surface area is lower; this may account for the lower hydrogenation activity. Care must be taken to ensure that the temperature during alkali extraction does not exceed 15–20° C, otherwise an inactive catalyst will be produced, the result of excessive removal of aluminum necessary for stabilizing the structure.

The more common method of preparing a highly dispersed, catalytically active metal such as cobalt is to employ a support, or carrier. Detailed discussions of the functions, use, and nature of supports may be found elsewhere.[39] Briefly, a catalyst support serves as a base, or framework, for the catalytic component, keeping the fine crystals apart so that they cannot sinter, and making available a high area of active surface accessible to reactants because of the high internal porosity produced. Supports may include hydrous gels, such as alumina or silica, diatomaceous earth (kieselguhr), active carbon, clay, asbestos, pumice, firebrick, and many others. The choice of support depends on the final application of the catalyst. The degree of dispersion of the active cobalt depends on the chemical properties and surface area of the support. In some cases the support should have some catalytic activity; in other cases, it should be completely inert.

The most common method of preparing a supported catalyst is by impregnation. For example, to prepare a cobalt on alumina catalyst, a solution of a cobalt salt is added to the alumina in such quantity that the pores of the alumina are just filled, after which it is dried and calcined. The amount of cobalt added is varied according to the concentration of cobalt in the solution. Thus, the total cobalt to be added is limited by solubility of the salt and the pore volume of the alumina, unless repeated applications are employed. Another drawback of the impregnation method is the lack of uniform distribution of the active cobalt throughout the mass of the support.

A generally more satisfactory way of incorporating cobalt onto a support is by precipitation in the presence of the support. Such a catalyst has been prepared as follows:[64] To a solution of 6360 g of cobalt acetate tetrahydrate in 10 gal. of water was added 1500 g of a diatomaceous earth; after an hour of vigorous stirring, a solution of 3300 g of sodium carbonate in 7 gal. of water was added, over a period of 2–3 hours; after standing overnight, the precipitate was washed several times to remove most of the sodium, to below 0.1 per cent; it was then dried, ground, tabletted, calcined at 370° C, and, finally, activated by reduction with hydrogen at 350–400° C.

Other means of preparation are available;[39] see also the article by Ciapetta and Plank.[23]

In one instance, on precipitation in the presence of diatomaceous earth (kieselguhr), basic cobalt carbonate was deposited primarily in the void space of the kieselguhr, with resultant surface areas appreciably greater than those of the support or the unsupported precipitate.[6] On reduction of these catalysts, the kieselguhr was found to be somewhat effective in preventing the decrease of surface area, but was particularly effective in preventing the decrease in bulk volume of the catalysts.[7]

Anderson et al.,[6] found that the kieselguhr area had no effect on the total area of the catalyst. The density of the catalyst and the distribution of products from a Fischer-Tropsch synthesis were, however, found to be dependent on the exact source of the kieselguhr.[9] Johnson and Ries,[40] working with catalysts prepared in a somewhat different manner, observed in catalysts containing 38–41 per cent Co by analysis, that the catalyst area was higher when the kieselguhr area was higher (see Table 14.1).

TABLE 14.1. THE EFFECT OF KIESELGUHR AREA ON THE AREA
OF KIESELGUHR-SUPPORTED COBALT CATALYSTS

Kieselguhr Area, sq m/g	Catalyst Area, sq m/g	Catalyst Material Area, sq m/g
0.9	92	162
2.2	91	162
4.8	128	212
26	200	330
28	232	375
49	274	467

The figures in the last column represent areas per gram of the nonsiliceous portion of the catalysts, corrected for the contribution of the support area to the total area, assuming additivity. The surface areas resulting from these preparations are apparently many times the areas of the supports. This is believed to be due to the fact that the kieselguhrs were heated with boiling sodium carbonate prior to the addition of the cobalt, a treatment which produces silica sol by alkaline attack of the support. Furthermore, the ease of reduction to cobalt metal is markedly less when the catalyst area is higher because a complex forms between cobalt oxide and silica. This complex, which is the high area material, has been termed "cobalt silicate." Its X-ray diffraction pattern resembles that of a poorly crystallized montmorillonite. The extent of complex formation increases as the support area increases because the extent of alkaline attack is greater.

There can, therefore, be two types of supporting action: (1) dispersion without apparent interaction with support, as with the cobalt-kieselguhr catalysts of Anderson *et al*, [6] or the cobalt on titania of Ries, Johnson, and Melik;[55] and (2) dispersion accompanied by, and related to, an interaction with the support, such as the cobalt hydrosilicate above. The nickel-silica system has been studied much more extensively than has cobalt-silica;[58] much of the information regarding the former can be applied, at least qualitatively, to the cobalt-silica system. The degree of hydrosilicate formation depends, as one might expect, on the exact mode of preparation.

The cobalt-alumina system is another example of an interaction between support and active component. If a high-area alumina is impregnated with a cobalt salt and calcined, say at 500° C, the resulting product will have a deep blue color, characteristic of what is called "cobalt aluminate." This material is much more difficult to reduce to the metal than pure cobalt oxide, particularly at low concentrations of cobalt. A more intimate association between cobalt oxide and alumina may be obtained by co-precipitation, e.g., by the addition of ammonia to a solution containing cobalt and aluminum nitrates. The magnetic and structural properties of such a series, covering the whole range of the cobalt oxide-alumina binary system calcined at 700° C, were studied by Richardson and Vernon.[54] It was concluded that the system has a spinel structure which may be represented by the formula:

$$Co_{xm}^{+2} Al_{yn}^{+3} (\square_t Co_{(1-x)m}^{+3} Al_{(1-y)n}^{+3})O_4$$

where $\square$ represents vacancies. The parameter, x, may be calculated from the measured magnetic moments (μ) by the equation:

$$\mu^2 = x(4.28)^2 + (1 - x)(1.61)^2$$

m is calculated from the cobalt content, n from valence requirements, y and t from consideration of the spinel structure. At low cobalt concentrations, it exists only as Co^{+2} on tetrahedral sites, with lattice vacancies on the octahedral sites.

Practical catalysts of all types are most frequently multi-component; that is, they are mixtures of various chemical constituents rather than a single chemical entity. This will become apparent from subsequent discussions of the various specific uses of cobalt. Some of the early work on the modification and improvement of catalysts, such as cobalt, by incorporation of other components should be credited to Mittasch.[48] It was found, as early as 1913, that the reduction of carbon monoxide with hydrogen under pressure, using a mixture of cobalt oxide with sodium hydroxide as a catalyst, led to the production of hydrocarbons and a mixture of oxygen-containing organic compounds.

HETEROGENEOUS CATALYTIC HYDROGENATIONS

When choosing a catalyst or the conditions for carrying out hydrogenation, the chemist must consider not only hydrogenation activity, but also selectivity—the extent to which side reactions occur. For example, metallic cobalt has the property, in common with other transition elements, of being able to catalyze the breaking of C—C bonds at elevated temperatures. Hence, one must carry out the reaction at a temperature sufficiently low to minimize this side reaction.

Cobalt metal is capable of catalyzing the hydrogenation of olefinic double bonds.[24] Examples of many other types of hydrogenation found in the literature are too numerous to list. Cobalt sulfide is somewhat less active, but has an additional, desirable property of being insensitive to poisoning by sulfur compounds. Cobalt boride has a hydrogenation activity similar to that of Raney nickel. Cobalt has not been very thoroughly investigated as a catalyst for hydrogenation of triple bonds. It is active at 180°C for hydrogenating acetylene to ethane; at higher temperatures, selectivity decreases.[20] As with other catalysts for this reaction, the reactant is so strongly adsorbed that the catalyst is rapidly deactivated.

Cobalt as a catalyst for hydrogenating aromatic compounds has been compared with other types of catalysts by Smith,[61] who has provided a general summary of this reaction. Nickel and cobalt have comparable activities, lower than that of platinum; thus, whereas platinum will hydrogenate benzene at room temperature, elevated temperatures are required with cobalt. There are differences of opinion as to whether nickel or cobalt has the greater activity; this difference could probably be resolved if data on the surface area of the metals were available, permitting comparison on a unit area basis.

Hydrotreating of Petroleum Stocks

Petroleum fractions contain sulfur-, nitrogen-, and oxygen-containing compounds, undesirable because of their effects on corrosivity, odor, stability, and other measures of quality. Sulfur is particularly undesirable, and is a poison in various catalytic processes. Since high-sulfur crude oils are being used more and more, the problem is becoming aggravated. Although non-catalytic processes continue to be used for sulfur removal, catalytic hydrodesulfurization processes are more generally applicable and are becoming more widespread since the advent of catalytic reforming processes, which produce considerable quantities of hydrogen as a by-product.

McKinley[46] has prepared a summary of the technical and scientific details of catalytic hydrodesulfurization. Glossaries of specific processes developed by various companies are also available.[27,68] Hydrodesulfurization is applied to kerosines, stove oils, diesel fuels, fuel oils, catalytic cracking charge stocks, and naphtha feeds for catalytic reformers. In the latter case, the treatment is used to obtain better performance in catalytic reforming by removal of the sulfur and small amounts of arsenic. In some instances, a modified process is applied to whole crudes.

Petroleum sulfur exists in many forms: sulfides, thiols, disulfides, and thiophenes. The purpose of hydrodesulfurization is to convert these compounds into hydrogen sulfide plus one or two hydrocarbons, with as few side reactions as possible. In addition, hydrogenation of diolefins, which tends to produce gums, and of nitrogen and oxygen compounds is usually desirable. For gasoline products, it is preferable to remove sulfur and conjugated di-olefins without hydrogenating high octane aromatics or olefins to lower octane number products. Although olefin hydrogenation under desulfurization conditions is thermodynamically favored, it is possible to operate in such a way that a higher proportion of sulfur compounds is hydrogenated than olefins, perhaps because some olefin hydrogenation ability is poisoned by sulfides. This requires the proper choice of catalyst and conditions.

Although many transition elements can be used for this process, the combination of cobalt and molybdenum oxides supported on alumina, with or without a small amount of silica for stabilization, is most effective and is employed most frequently. This combination of cobalt and molybdenum oxides is superior to either one alone; it is referred to as cobalt molybdate, although cobalt and molybdenum are not necessarily in stoichiometric proportion, molybdenum usually being in excess. There is a known compound, cobalt molybdate. There is no evidence that this compound is formed in the catalyst. These catalysts usually give best performance when pre-reduced and pre-sulfided, giving a mixture of sulfides of cobalt and molybdenum. Even if not pre-sulfided, they become rapidly sulfided when high sulfur stocks are desulfurized, since the thermodynamic requirements for existence of the sulfides are satisfied by very small partial pressures of hydrogen sulfide. In some cases, a definite partial pressure of hydrogen sulfide is required for the maintenance of catalyst activity. It is obvious that a catalytic material which is poisoned by sulfur is useless in such a process, hence the advantage of a catalyst which is active in the sulfided state.

Commercial hydrodesulfurization processes employ either tabletted or extruded catalysts in fixed beds. They operate normally at 100–700 psig and 600–800° F. The oil is, for the most part, in the liquid phase; hydrogen must therefore be dissolved in the liquid and diffused thereby to the catalytic surface.

Processing of this type is currently being applied to lubricating oil stocks. The same cobalt-molybdena-alumina type of catalyst is employed, but at a higher pressure and at a temperature suitable for mild hydrodesulfurization. The oils so produced have lower sulfur content, lower neutralization numbers, better color, less carbon residue, slightly higher viscosity index caused by the opening of heterocyclic rings, improved oxidation stability, and generally better response to inhibitors.

The alumina used as a support is considered to have little acid character, hence does not tend to have the cracking behavior of silica-alumina. In processing heavy residual stocks such as asphalts, cracking is one of the desired reactions since it causes the formation of lower boiling material. Hence, cobalt-molybdenum on an "acid" support, such as silica-alumina, will catalyze hydrocracking in addition to hydrogenation; the general term hydrogenolysis may be employed in this connection. Cobalt-molybdena-alumina catalysts will provide some hydrocracking activity under sufficiently severe conditions. Although hydrocracking processes for residual upgrading have been the subject of much investigation by petroleum companies, no such processes are as yet in operation; some, however, are available for licensing.

Liquid-Phase Coal Hydrogenation

Liquid-phase coal hydrogenation may be catalyzed by impregnated metal salts, among them salts of cobalt.[70] Cobaltous sulfate and ferrous sulfate are not quite as effective as nickelous chloride or stannous chloride. In all cases, the metal is probably converted to the corresponding sulfide under reaction conditions. Cobaltous and ferrous chlorides are much less effective than sulfates; the reason for this is as yet obscure.

AMMINATION OF OLEFINS

Supported cobalt catalysts will promote the reaction between olefins and ammonia at elevated temperatures and pressures, primarily to form nitriles.[64,65] The support cited in a large group of patents in this field is diatomaceous earth, but other supports are also effective. Promotion of the cobalt-kieselguhr system by incorporating magnesia results in some improvements in activity.[66]

AMMONIA SYNTHESIS

Cobalt is a catalyst for the synthesis of ammonia, but it has a lower activity than iron, and its activity declines with time.[34] Hence, it is not used commercially.

CATALYTIC SYNTHESIS OF ALCOHOLS

Whereas modified methanol catalysts, operating with hydrogen and carbon monoxide, produce isobutanol as the main product, those catalysts which contain cobalt produce large amounts of ethanol.[49] For example, a product containing up to 20 per cent ethanol was obtained using a catalyst prepared from $Co(NO_3)_2$, $Zn(MnO_4)_2$, and $KMnO_4$. The higher alcohols produced from such catalysts tend to be unbranched.

FISCHER-TROPSCH SYNTHESIS

In 1902, Sabatier[56] showed that methane could be produced from carbon and hydrogen in the presence of a cobalt catalyst, at atmospheric pressure and at temperatures of 200–300° C. In 1913 and 1914, the hydrogenation of carbon monoxide was accomplished at 100–200 atmospheres and 300–400° C by the use of alkali-activated cobalt and osmium oxides, with the production of liquid products consisting chiefly of oxygenated organic compounds and some aliphatic hydrocarbons.[10] In 1923, Fischer and Tropsch demonstrated that whereas alkalized iron turnings at 400–450° C and 100–150 atmospheres catalyzed the formation of an oily product containing essentially oxygenated compounds, at about 7 atmospheres this catalyst produced mostly olefinic and paraffinic compounds. By 1925, the synthesis of liquid hydrocarbons at ordinary pressures and at 200–250° C was developed; active cobalt or nickel catalysts were used. This was the start of the development of a successful process for the production of hydrocarbons, one which gave rise to a major portion of the gasoline and oil products used by Germany in World War II.

The investigations of Fischer and his co-workers have been reported in many publications.[30–33] The success of their work depended on three main points: maintenance of a constant temperature in a highly exothermic reaction system; elimination of sulfur from the reactant gases; presence of a catalyst, such as cobalt, iron or nickel, with suitable promoters and carriers.

In 1938–1944, the German Fischer-Tropsch plants used the Ruhrchemie process, which employed a 100:5:8:200 Co—ThO$_2$—MgO—kieselguhr catalyst at 180–200°C, 1–10 atm pressure, and a 2–3 stage system with product recovery after each stage. The synthesis gas was fed at the rate of 60–100 volumes per volume of catalyst per hour. The operation and development of this process is described by Hall.[36] About 150 g of hydrocarbons covering a wide range of molecular weight were produced from a cu m of synthesis gas.

The active life of a cobalt catalyst is much greater at 7–20 atm than at atmospheric pressure. Nevertheless, in time, the catalyst must be regenerated because of the action of the traces of sulfur still remaining in the gases even after rigorous purification, of a crystallization of the metal, which decreases the activity of the surface layers, and of a deposition of high molecular weight hydrocarbons on the catalyst. The cobalt used in the catalyst must be at least 99 per cent pure, with the remainder either copper or nickel; small traces of impurities such as calcium oxide or iron are detrimental. The raw gasoline produced by distillation of the liquid product has a relatively low octane number, depending on the boiling range and olefin content which are, in turn, dependent on the exact conditions of operation. Excellent diesel fuel is produced, however.[53]

The synthesis gas is ordinarily a mixture of two volumes of hydrogen and one of carbon monoxide, with inert gases that seldom exceed 20 per cent by volume. It is prepared from coke by a water-gas reaction; enrichment with hydrogen to the H$_2$/CO = 2 level is achieved either by carrying out a water-gas shift reaction with part of the water-gas in which CO + excess steam is converted to carbon dioxide and hydrogen, or by mixing with a high hydrogen gas produced by cracking or reforming coke-oven gas.

Research work carried out at the British Fuel Research Station and at the U. S. Bureau of Mines from 1942–1946 was concerned with the factors influencing the production of active cobalt catalysts. Many of the new tools developed for catalytic research were utilized; later, the emphasis was shifted to iron catalysts. Several novelties in engineering design have appeared since the start of the research work. Rather complete and extensive summaries of the technical and scientific aspects of the Fischer-Tropsch synthesis may be found,[3,4,5,35,38,53,59,62] in particular, the book by Storch, Golumbic, and Anderson.[63] Descriptions of the details of the preparation of catalysts, of certain basic information about these catalysts, and of the kinetics and mechanism of the reaction may be found in these publications.

The Fischer-Tropsch catalyst includes kieselguhr as a carrier, the function of which has been discussed. In addition, promoters are employed which affect performance in a non-additive fashion. Alkali promoters increase the average molecular weight of the products by affecting the chain-growth process. Promoters such as thoria and magnesia, and other oxides that are reduced with difficulty, increase the surface area and may increase the average molecular weight of the product.[5]

Recent research in Fischer-Tropsch has been directed towards utilization of iron catalysts, since iron is cheaper and more readily available. Cobalt catalysts, however, have one advantage: there is virtually no change in composition during synthesis;[8] long life without appreciable disintegration is usually obtained.[37] On the other hand, rather large changes in composition, affecting activity and catalyst disintegration, are observed with iron catalysts.

Since treatment of cobalt catalysts with carbon monoxide results in the formation of cobalt carbides which, under certain conditions, can be hydrogenated, it is not surprising that a mechanism should be advanced for the Fischer-Tropsch synthesis involving the carbide intermediate. Although first suggested by Fischer and Tropsch, a more detailed theory was presented by Craxford and Rideal,[26] who postulated the following steps:

$$Co + CO \longrightarrow Co{-}CO \text{ (chemisorption)}$$

$$Co{-}CO + H_2 \longrightarrow Co{-}C \text{ (surface carbide)} + H_2O$$

$$Co{-}C + H_2 \longrightarrow Co{-}CH_2 \longrightarrow \text{(higher hydrocarbons)}$$

When atomic hydrogen is present on the catalyst, the CH_2 groups are hydrogenated to methane. In the absence of atomic hydrogen—the normal situation—adjacent methylene groups link up with each other to form long paraffin chains. Later work[25] postulated that the portion of the catalyst surface which was in the form of carbide participated in the synthesis, but that the portion which consisted of uncombined cobalt catalyzed the water-gas shift reaction and hydrocracking of the hydrocarbons produced by the synthesis.

The postulates of Craxford stimulated a considerable amount of research regarding the mechanism of the synthesis. As a result, thermodynamic, tracer, and synthesis studies have indicated that bulk-phase cobalt carbide does not participate in the synthesis to a significant extent, nor is it an active catalyst in the synthesis.[63] Hydrogenation of surface carbide can account for only 10–20 per cent of the hydrocarbon product. Several of the details of the Craxford mechanism have proved contrary to experimental evidence.

A mechanism has been proposed involving oxygenated intermediates.[63] In this mechanism, initiation takes place by partial hydrogenation of chemisorbed carbon monoxide to form:

$$\underset{\overset{\|}{Co}}{\overset{H\diagdown\;\diagup OH}{C}}$$

Growth of chains occurs at the end carbons by:

$$\underset{\overset{\|}{Co}}{\overset{H\diagdown\,\diagup OH}{C}}\; +\; \underset{\overset{\|}{Co}}{\overset{H\diagdown\,\diagup OH}{C}}\; \xrightarrow{-H_2O}\; \underset{\overset{\|\;\;\|}{Co\;Co}}{\overset{H\diagdown\quad\diagup OH}{C-C}}\; \xrightarrow{2H}\; \underset{\overset{\|}{Co}}{\overset{CH_3\diagdown\,\diagup OH}{C}}$$

and

$$\underset{\overset{\|}{Co}}{\overset{R\diagdown\,\diagup OH}{C}}\; +\; \underset{\overset{\|}{Co}}{\overset{H\diagdown\,\diagup OH}{C}}\; \xrightarrow[-H_2O]{+2H}\; \underset{\overset{\|}{Co}}{\overset{R-CH_2\diagdown\,\diagup OH}{C}}$$

This mechanism explains many of the characteristics of synthesis products. Its postulates have been essentially substantiated by the work of Kummer and Emmett,[42] who incorporated tagged alcohols into the synthesis gas and delineated the pattern of chain growth from analyses of the resultant hydrocarbon fractions for radioactivity. Although this work employed iron catalysts, the conclusions are believed to be applicable to syntheses over cobalt catalysts.

There is a possibility that chain extension in the Fischer-Tropsch synthesis may involve oxo-type reactions. The oxo catalyst, which cannot initiate hydrocarbon chains from $H_2 + CO$, is believed to be a cobalt carbonyl complex similar to surface carbonyls in the Fischer-Tropsch synthesis.

THE OXO REACTION

The oxo reaction is the catalytic addition of carbon monoxide and hydrogen to an olefin, forming aldehydes which are reduced to primary alcohols in the second stage of the reaction. The process might better be termed "hydroformylation." The catalyst and the reaction are described in detail in several publications.[63,71,72] The general reaction can be represented by:

$$RCH{=}CH_2 + H_2 + CO \xrightarrow{Co} \begin{cases} RCH_2CH_2CHO \\ RCH(CHO)CH_3 \end{cases}$$

It appears that catalysis of the oxo reaction is limited to cobalt. The first catalyst to be tried in the oxo synthesis was the conventional Fischer-Tropsch catalyst, $Co-ThO_2-MgO-$kieselguhr. However, all but the cobalt seem superflous. Although the Fischer-Tropsch synthesis is heterogeneously catalyzed, it is believed that the oxo synthesis is homogeneously catalyzed by the soluble cobalt carbonyls, the efficiency of a solid cobalt catalyst depending on the ease with which it is transformed to the carbonyl. Dicobalt octacarbonyl or cobalt hydrocarbonyl, both of which are soluble in most solvents, are believed to be the essential catalysts. The conditions for the reaction are approximately 75–200° C, 100–300 atmospheres of synthesis gas; reduced metallic cobalt or a cobalt salt may be used as a catalyst, either of which may be converted to a cobalt carbonyl.

Dicobalt octacarbonyl is believed to have the following configuration:

$$
\begin{array}{c}
O \\
\parallel \\
C \\
O{\equiv}C \diagdown \qquad \diagup C{\equiv}O \\
O{\equiv}C{-}\underset{}{Co} \qquad \underset{}{Co}{-}C{\equiv}O \\
O{\equiv}C \diagup \qquad \diagdown C{\equiv}O \\
C \\
\parallel \\
O
\end{array}
$$

It may be prepared by treating a slurry of 15 g of cobaltous carbonate plus 100 ml of benzene with synthesis gas at 250 atm pressure in an autoclave at 130–160° C for 1 hour, then cooling to room temperature before venting the gases; a clear dark solution results. By substituting petroleum ether for benzene, and chilling the product, a crystalline product melting at 51° C (with decomposition) is obtained. It is stable at room temperatures under a small partial pressure of carbon monoxide.

The accepted structure for cobalt hydrocarbonyl, as deduced from electron diffraction data, is as follows:

$$
\begin{array}{c}
O \\
\parallel\!\downarrow \\
C \\
\downarrow \\
O{=}C{=}Co{\equiv}C{-}OH \\
\uparrow \\
C \\
\uparrow \\
O
\end{array}
$$

It has a tetrahedral configuration, with one of the cobalt-carbon bonds shorter than the other three, the result of a triple bond. The above preparation of dicobalt octacarbonyl actually produced cobalt hydrocarbonyl, which decomposes to dicobalt octacarbonyl on release of high pressure gases at room temperature. Cobalt hydrocarbonyl may be prepared from carbon monoxide and an alkaline suspension of cobaltous cyanide, followed by acidification of the resulting solution. Alternatively, a cobalt salt of cobalt hydrocarbonyl may be formed from pyridine and the dicobalt octacarbonyl, and acidified in a stream of carbon monoxide, the product then being collected in a cold trap protected from the air:

$$3Co_2(CO)_8 + 12\,Pyr \longrightarrow 2[Co(Pyr)_6][Co(CO)_4]_2 + 8CO$$

$$2[Co(Pyr)_6][Co(CO)_4]_2 + 8H_2SO_4 \longrightarrow 4HCo(CO)_4 + 2CoSO_4 + 6(PyrH)_2SO_4$$

More recently,[1] observations were made which suggested a heterogeneous mechanism for the oxo reaction, requiring cobalt in an insoluble form. This suggestion was based on an apparent correlation between conversion and concentration of insoluble cobalt originally added as cobalt naphthenate. On this basis, the importance of the carbonyls was related to the constant provision of a fresh, highly active metal surface by carbonyl formation and decomposition.

The essential raw materials for the oxo process in the United States are propylene, butylenes, and their copolymers. The latter, consisting of mixed heptylenes, are the most important, and lead to the production of "isooctyl alcohol," a mixture of at least ten C_8 primary alcohols which are used to make isooctyl phthalate, a plasticizer for polyvinyl chloride. Similar products are made in other countries. In operation, sufficient cobalt naphthenate is added to the heptylenes to give 0.2 per cent cobalt, and the solution is pumped upward through a reactor concurrently with synthesis gas ($1H_2$: $1CO$) at 175° C and 200 atmospheres. The reaction is extremely exothermic; thus, some provision must be made for removing the heat of reaction (e.g., recycle operations).

HOMOGENEOUSLY CATALYZED HYDROGENATIONS

The oxo reaction just described is one example of hydrogenation catalysis by cobalt in solution. Besides the addition of carbon monoxide to the double bond, as in the oxo process, hydrogenation can be accomplished by synthesis gas over a cobalt catalyst.[50] For example, on hydrogenating butyraldehyde at 185° C with reduced cobalt metal under 2000 psi of hydrogen, butanol is produced in the absence of carbon monoxide or in the presence of an additional 1000 psi of carbon monoxide; unchanged butyraldehyde is recovered when using only 300 psi of carbon monoxide along with the 2000 psi of hydrogen. In the latter case, the pressure of carbon monoxide is insufficient to produce the soluble catalyst, but sufficient to poison the active metallic cobalt; at 1000 psi of carbon monoxide, the soluble cobalt catalyst is produced. In general, a double bond will tend to be hydrogenated by synthesis gas under oxo conditions if it is conjugated either with an aromatic ring, another double bond, or a carbonyl group.

Weller and Mills[71] have discussed the activation of molecular hydrogen by homogeneous catalysts involving metal ions. In general, there must be some unfilled electronic levels, not necessarily d-orbitals, with energy sufficiently low to allow formation of a chemical complex with the hydrogen. In addition to the cobalt carbonyls, the cobalt cyanide ion is capable of activating hydrogen, as evidenced by the production of HD when potassium cobaltous cyanide is acidified in the prescence of deuterium gas. Bayston *et al.*[17] found homogeneous activation of hydrogen in solutions of $CoCl_2$ and KCN when $CN/Co > 5$, catalyzed by a small amount of cobaltous hexacyanide ion in equilibrium with cobaltous pentacyanide ion. The cobalt cyanide system has also been studied by Mills *et al.*;[47] they found that the potassium cobaltous cyanide solutions lost activity after one hour, probably because of dimerization.

OXIDATION CATALYSTS

It is well known that salts of heavy metals can be used to catalyze the oxidation of organic compounds. Of these, cobalt is perhaps one of the most useful. Its use as a drying agent for paints will be discussed separately. In addition, it has value as a catalyst for selective oxidation of particular products, both in the laboratory and in industry.

For example, a Scientific Design Company process has been developed for oxidizing alkyl aromatics to aromatic carboxylic acids using a combination of bromine and a heavy metal salt, particularly cobalt or manganese as the catalyst system.[22] A commercial plant operated by Amoco Chemicals Corporation produces phthalic anhydride, isophthalic acid, terephthalic acid, and benzoic acid from mixed xylenes. This process will also be adopted by Imperial Chemical Industries for expansion of its terephthalic acid production to include Terylene polyester fiber and Melinex polyester film. The oxidation of xylenes may be stopped at toluic acid in some cobalt toluate catalyzed processes.

Our understanding of the process of cobalt-catalyzed oxidations of organic compounds by oxygen is largely due to the work of Bawn and his associates[12–16] who have studied various materials in glacial acetic acid and dilute sulfuric acid solvents. The catalysis can be inhibited by certain materials, such as beta-naphthol or benzoquinone. The rates of oxygen consumption in these reactions are functions of the concentrations of the catalyst and hydrocarbon; the kinetic orders, however, vary from system to system. The first step in the process is the conversion of Co^{+2} to Co^{+3}, the latter being a powerful oxidizing agent in the uncomplexed form and the active entity in the catalysis. This transformation occurs even when insoluble cobalt compounds such as a suspension of cobaltous acetate in toluene, or cobalt stearate or naphthenate are used. It is brought about by interaction with organic peroxides which are produced in small amounts even in thermal oxidations.

The cobaltic ion readily decomposes water by the following reaction:

$$2Co^{+3} + H_2O \longrightarrow 2Co^{+2} + \tfrac{1}{2}O_2 + 2H^+$$

Hence, an acid environment is preferable for maintaining a useful concentration of cobaltic ion. When the above reaction is suppressed, the primary reaction step is an electron transfer between the cobaltic ion and the organic compound, generating a free radical:

$$Co^{+3} + CH_3OH \longrightarrow Co^{+2} + CH_3O\cdot + H^+$$

$$Co^{+3} + HCHO \longrightarrow Co^{+2} + CHO\cdot + H^+$$

$$Co^{+3} + HCOOH \longrightarrow Co^{+2} + HCOO\cdot + H^+$$

$$Co^{+3} + RCH{=}CH_2 \longrightarrow Co^{+2} + RCH{-}CH_2\cdot$$

In some cases, the chain-initiation reaction may occur between the cobaltic ion and an intermediate peroxide; in any case, a free radical is the result. The chain-propagation reactions are of the usual type; individual steps involve oxygen or unreacted hydrocarbon. In the case of olefin oxidation, the secondary reactions giving observed products (aldehydes, ketones, acids) result from a series of reactions in which the carbonium ion reacts with water to give hydroxylic compounds that are then rapidly oxidized by Co^{+3} in successive stages until stable products are formed.

Driers

A number of cobalt compounds have been found to be excellent driers of paints, varnishes, printing inks, and the like. The function of these driers is to catalyze the oxidation-polymerization of the unsaturated glycerides used as vehicles, so that a good protective film is formed. Thus, for paints, it is possible to use semi-drying oils such as fish, soybean, and cotton-seed oils in place of the higher-priced linseed oil. For this and other reasons, cobalt driers have become almost essential to the manufacture of the products in which they are used; cobalt soaps of a number of organic acids have become important articles of commerce. They are useful in formulations based on synthetic resins as well as in the usual paints and varnishes.

The driers commonly used are cobalt oleate, naphthenate, resinate, and linoleate, the latter having largely supplanted the others. In certain cases, inorganic compounds of cobalt, such as the carbonate or sulfate, can be employed. The only promising alternates to these forms of cobalt are the class of coordinated driers, e.g., the cobalt derivatives of o-phenanthroline. Cobalt linoleate can be prepared from linseed oil by gradually adding 10 per cent sodium hydroxide to the oil at 100°C to complete saponification, diluting the clear brown solution with hot water, and adding a solution of sodium chloride. This precipitates a granular soap which is separated, re-dissolved in water, and reprecipitated with brine. The purified soap is again dissolved in water, and a 10 per cent solution of cobaltous chloride is added; the precipitated cobalt linoleate is filtered, washed, and dried at 80°.

A more complete discussion of the methods of soap manufacture is given by Elliott.[28] The above is an example of the method of preparation of precipitated soaps, and may be applied to types other than linoleates. An alternative route is to prepare the soaps by the fusion method, which involves direct reaction between the oil and cobalt oxide, or hydroxide, at an elevated temperature. Salts such as acetates are to be avoided if true soaps, not mixed acetate-fatty acids salts, are to be obtained. In making soaps by fusion, it is better to start with the fatty acids rather than the glycerides, to ensure the production of true soaps. In the fused soaps, free fatty acid is a primary impurity, the amount depending on the metal content; in precipitated soaps, mono- and diglyceride impurities are observed, again decreasing as the metal content increases.

Cobalt linoleates are solid materials, deep red in color, having 8.0–9.0 per cent cobalt. Hardness increases with cobalt content; lower concentrations of cobalt are obtained in the liquid form as solutions in linseed oil. The cobalt naphthenates are bluish-red solids containing 10–12 per cent cobalt. The fused resinates usually contain not more than 3.5 per cent cobalt, and are red, hard, friable solids; precipitated cobalt resinate will have about 7.5 per cent Co, and is a finely-divided, red-violet powder which darkens with aging.

Cobalt is the most powerful drier known; much less of it than of lead is required for the same effect. Table 14.2 gives some comparative drying time data.[41]

TABLE 14.2. DRYING TIME FOR RAW LINSEED OIL WITH VARIOUS DRIERS

Drier	Metal, %	Drying Time, (hr)
Cobalt linoleate	0.049	11.5
Cobalt resinate	0.048	10
Cobalt naphthenate	0.049	12
Manganese linoleate	0.032	18
Manganese resinate	0.044	18
Manganese naphthenate	0.050	17
Lead linoleate	0.337	66
Lead resinate	0.330	66
Lead naphthenate	0.313	49

The effect of cobalt driers is primarily to accelerate oxidation with relatively little tendency to promote polymerization.[44] As a class, they are superior to other driers not only in drying time, but also in solubility, compatibility, desirability of color, and latitude of use; they could replace all others if available.[44] In large amounts, however, they cause extremely rapid oxidation and drying at the surface of the film, with consequent wrinkling, and early cracking and splitting (the result of stresses) as the film ages; thus, not more than about 0.05 per cent cobalt should be used. For example, a varnish containing 0.02 per cent cobalt has properties superior to similar varnishes with 0.08 per cent. In general, it is desirable to hold the cobalt content to a minimum; as little as 0.01–0.03 per cent markedly decreases drying time, whereas an excess is not only expensive, but results in inferior properties.

Driers serve similar purposes in printing inks; their behavior is much the same as it is in paints. Again, cobalt is the most effective drier.[29] However, the best ink driers consist of mixtures of all three drying metals (Co, Mn, Pb), allowing uniform drying within the film in a reasonable length of time.[73] Cobalt linoleate has long been used in printing inks; the naphthenate can be used under certain circumstances.

Uyehara[69] has measured the oxidation rates of linseed oil containing cobalt, manganese, or lead naphthenates at 25–85°C, following the oxidation volumetrically. Cobalt naphthenate is the most effective in promoting oxygen absorption. From data on maximum oxygen absorption, it was suggested that peroxide links are found at specific positions of the oleate, linoleate, and linolenate constituents of the linseed oil, the number of these sites being independent of the mode of attack. An analysis of the kinetic data indicates the presence of two consecutive reactions: (1) the initiatory process in which oxygen attacks the olefin linkages to form hydroperoxides and hydroperoxide radicals; (2) the termination stage in which polymeric peroxide links are formed, resulting in the dried films. As with most oxidation systems, these stages are preceeded by an induction period, presumably related to production of the active form of catalyst. A study of the kinetics of linseed oil oxidation was also made by Lunina.[43]

Oxidation of Carbon Monoxide

A mixture of cobalt and other oxides has been employed in gas masks to promote the oxidation of carbon monoxide to carbon dioxide.[52] Similarly, supported cobalt oxide catalysts are useful for the complete combustion of automobile exhaust gases, since they minimize concentrations of various smog-producing materials in the atmosphere.[57]

FLUORINATING AGENT

The possibility of using fluorocarbons in the separation of uranium isotopes has stimulated an enormous amount of work in the synthesis of fluorocarbons. A comprehensive series of twelve papers on this subject appears in the March, 1947 issue of *Industrial and Engineering Chemistry*.

The use of CoF_3 as a fluorinating agent depends on the fact that the lower fluoride, CoF_2, is converted to CoF_3 when fluorine is passed over it at 200–250° C. CoF_3 is the fluorinating agent, e.g.,

$$C_7H_{16} + 32 CoF_3 \longrightarrow C_7F_{16} + 32 CoF_2 + 16HF$$

Temperature is a critical factor in fluorination, 250–350° C being the range usually employed. Although other fluorides have been used as agents, for general use cobalt fluoride remains the most satisfactory.

References

1. Aldridge, C. L., Fasce, E. V., and Jonassen, H. B., "Heterogeneous Character of Hydroformylation Catalysis," *J. Phys. Chem.*, **63**, 869 (1959).
2. Aller, B. V., "Raney Cobalt Hydrogenation Catalysts. I. The Preparation of the Catalyst," *J. Appl. Chem.* (London), **1**, 130 (1957); II. "The Physical and Chemical Properties of the Catalyst," *ibid*, **8**, 163 (1958); III. "Applications and Promoter Effects," *ibid*, **8**, 492 (1958).
3. Anderson, R. B., "The Thermodynamics of the Hydrogenation of Carbon Monoxide and Related Reactions," *Catalysis,** IV**, 1 (1956).
4. —, "Catalysts for the Fischer-Tropsch Synthesis," *Catalysis*, **IV**, 29 (1956).
5. —, "Kinetics and Reaction Mechanism of the Fischer-Tropsch Synthesis," *Catalysis*, **IV**, 257 (1956).
6. Anderson, R. B., Hall, W. K., Hewlett, H., and Seligman, B., "Studies of the

*"Catalysis" refers to the series of volumes on this subject, edited by P. H. Emmett and published by Reinhold Publishing Corp., New York.

Fischer-Tropsch Synthesis. II. Properties of Unreduced Cobalt Catalysts," *J. Am. Chem. Soc.,* **69,** 3114 (1947).

7. Anderson, R. B., Hail, W. K., and Hofer, L. J. E., "Studies of the Fischer-Tropsch Synthesis. IV. Properties of Reduced Cobalt Catalysts," *J. Am. Chem. Soc.,* **70,** 2465 (1948).

8. Anderson, R. B., Hall, W. K., Krieg, A., and Seligman, B., "Studies of the Fischer-Tropsch Synthesis. V. Activities and Surface Areas of Reduced and Carburized Cobalt Catalysts," *J. Am. Chem. Soc.,* **71,** 183 (1949).

9. Anderson, R. B., Krieg, A., Seligman, B., and Tarn, W., "Fischer-Tropsch Cobalt Catalysts; Influence of Type of Kieselguhrs," *Ind. Eng. Chem.,* **40,** 2347 (1948).

10. Badische Analin u. Soda Fabrik, German Patents 293,787 (1913); 295,202 (1914); 295,203 (1914).

11. Baker, M. M., and Jenkins, G. I., "The Electronic Factor in Heterogeneous Catalysis," *Advances in Catalysis,** **VII,** 1 (1955).

12. Bawn, C. E. H., "Free Radical Reactions in Solution Initiated by Heavy Metal Ions," *Disc. Faraday Soc.,* **14,** 181 (1953).

13. Bawn, C. E. H., Hobin, T. P., and Raphael, L., "The Metal-Salt-Catalyzed Oxidation of Acetaldehyde," *Proc. Roy. Soc.* (London), **A237,** 313 (1956).

14. Bawn, C. E. H., and Jolley, J. E., "The Cobalt-Salt-Catalyzed Auto-Oxidation of Benzaldehyde," *Proc. Roy. Soc.* (London), **A237,** 297 (1956).

15. Bawn, C. E. H., Pennington, A. A., and Tipper, C., "The Catalyzed Oxidation of Trimethylethylene in Solution," *Disc. Faraday Soc.,* **10,** 282 (1951).

16. Bawn, C. E. H., and Sharp, J. A., "Reactions of the Cobaltic Ion. IV. Oxidation of Olefins by Cobaltic Salts," *J. Chem. Soc.,* **1957,** 1854; V. "Oxidation of Olefins by Cobaltic Salts in Acetic Acid-Sulfuric Acid Mixtures," *J. Chem. Soc.,* **1957,** 1866.

17. Bayston, J., King, N. K., and Winfield, M. E., "Hydrogenation Catalysis by Complex Ions of Cobalt," *Advances in Catalysis,* **IX,** 312 (1956).

18. Beeck, O., "Catalysis—A Challenge to the Physicist," *Rev. Mod. Phys.,* **17,** 61 (1945).

19. —, "Hydrogenation Catalysts," *Disc. Faraday Soc.,* **8,** 118 (1950).

20. Bond, G. C., "The Addition of Hydrogen to Carbon-Carbon Triple Bonds," *Catalysis,* **III,** 109 (1955).

21. Boudart, M., "Pauling's Theory of Metals in Catalysis," *J. Am. Chem. Soc.,* **72,** 1040 (1950).

22. Burney, D. E., Weisemann, G. H., and Fragen, N., "A New Process for Oxidation of Aromatics," paper presented before the Fifth World Petroleum Congress, New York, 1959.

23. Ciapetta, F. G., and Plank, C. J., "Catalyst Preparation," *Catalysis,* **I,** 315 (1954).

24. Corson, B. B., "Catalytic Hydrogenation of Olefinic Hydrocarbons," *Catalysis,* **III,** 79 (1955).

25. Craxford, S. R., "Mechanism of the Fischer-Tropsch Reaction," *Trans. Faraday Soc.,* **42,** 576 (1946).

*"Advances in Catalysis," published by Academic Press, Inc., New York, appears yearly in book form.

26. Craxford, S. R., and Rideal, E. K., "The Mechanism of the Synthesis of Hydrocarbons from Water Gas," *J. Chem. Soc.,* **1939,** 1604.

27. Davidson, R. L., "The Petroleum Industry's Future Hydrogen Processing," *Petroleum Processing,* November 1956, p. 115.

28. Elliott, S. B., "The Alkaline-Earth and Heavy-Metal Soaps," New York, Reinhold Publishing Corp., 1946.

29. Ellis, C., "Printing Inks," New York, Reinhold Publishing Corp., 1940.

30. Fischer, F., "Kohlenwasserstoff Synthesen auf d. Gebert d. Kohlenforsch," (Vortrag A), *Ber.,* **71A,** 56 (1938).

31. Fischer, F., and Pichler, H., "Die synthese von Paraffin aus Kohlenoxyd und Wasserstoff an Kobaltkatalysatorem (mitteldrucksynthese)," *Brennstoff-Chem.,* February 1 (1939).

32. —, *et al.,* Ueber die Annäherung an die theroetisch möglichen Ausbeuten bei der Mitteldrucksynthese," *Brennstoff-Chem.,* June 15 (1939).

33. Fischer, F., Roelen, O., and Feist, W., "Synthesis of Gasoline by the Fischer-Tropsch Process," *Petroleum Refiner,* **22,** No. 12, 97 (1943).

34. Frankenberg, W. G., "The Catalytic Synthesis of Ammonia from Nitrogen and Hydrogen," *Catalysis,* **III,** 171 (1955).

35. Golumbic, N. R., "Review of Fischer-Tropsch and Related Processes for Synthetic Liquid Fuel Production," *U. S. Bureau Mines Circ.,* **7366** (1946).

36. Hall, C. C., "The Operation and Development of the Fischer-Tropsch and Similar Processes in Germany," *Chemistry and Industry,* **1947,** Feb. 1, 67.

37. Hall, C. C., and Smith, S. L., "The Life of a Cobalt Catalyst for the Synthesis of Hydrocarbons at Atmospheric Pressure," *J. Soc. Chem. Ind.* (London), **65,** 128 (1946).

38. Hofer, L. J. E., "Crystalline Phases and Their Relation to Fischer-Tropsch Catalysts," *Catalysis,* **IV,** 373 (1956).

39. Innes, W. B., "Catalyst Carriers, Promoters, Accelerators, Poisons, and Inhibitors," *Catalysis,* **I,** 245 (1954).

40. Johnson, M. F. L., and Ries, H. E., "The Structure of Cobalt Catalysts Supported on Diatomaceous Earth," *J. Phys. Chem.,* **57,** 865 (1953).

41. Koster, J. and Davis, H. W., "Uses and Possible Substitutes for Cobalt," Advisory Committee on Metals and Minerals, National Research Council, Washington, D. C., 1942.

42. Kummer, J. T., and Emmett, P. H., "Fischer-Tropsch Synthesis Mechanism Studies. The Addition of Radioactive Alcohols to the Synthesis Gas," *J. Am. Chem. Soc.,* **75,** 5177 (1953).

43. Lunina, M. A., "Catalytic Activity of the Dispersed Metals in the Oxidizing Polymerization of Oil," *Nauch. Doklady Vyssheĭ Shkoly, Khim, i Khim. Tekhnol.,* **1958,** No. 2, 275; *Chem. Abst.,* **52,** 21155 (1958).

44. Mattiello, J. J., "Protective and Decorative Coatings, Vol. I. Raw Materials for Varnishes and Vehicles," New York, John Wiley & Sons, Inc., 1941.

45. McCartney, J. T., Seligman, B., Hall, W. K., and Anderson, R. B., "An Electron-Microscopic Study of Metal Oxides and Metal Oxide Catalysts," *J. Phys. Colloid Chem.,* **54,** 505 (1950).

46. McKinley, J. B., "The Hydrodesulfurization of Liquid Petroleum Fractions," *Catalysis,* **V,** 405 (1957).

47. Mills, G. A., Weller, S. W., and Wheeler, A., "Catalytic Activation of Molecular Hydrogen by Cobalt Cyanide Solutions," *J. Phys. Chem.*, **63,** 403 (1959).

48. Mittasch, A., "Early Studies of Multicomponent Catalysts," *Advances in Catalysis*, **II,** 81 (1950).

49. Natta, G., Colombo, U., and Pasquon, I., "Direct Catalytic Synthesis of Higher Alcohols from Carbon Monoxide and Hydrogen," *Catalysis*, **V,** 131 (1957).

50. Orchin, M., "Hydrogenation of Organic Compounds with Synthesis Gas," *Advances in Catalysis*, **V,** 385 (1953).

51. Pauling, L., "A Resonating-Valence-Bond Theory of Metals and Intermetallic Compounds," *Proc. Roy. Soc.* (London), **A196,** 343 (1949).

52. Perrault, R., "Le Cobalt," Paris, Dunod, 1946.

53. Pichler, H., "Twenty-five Years of Synthesis of Gasoline by Catalytic Conversion of Carbon Monoxide and Hydrogen," *Advances in Catalysis*, **IV,** 271 (1952).

54. Richardson, J. T., and Vernon, L. W., "The Magnetic Properties of the Cobalt Oxides and the System Cobalt Oxide-Alumina," *J. Phys. Chem.*, **62,** 1153 (1958).

55. Ries, H. E., Johnson, M. F. L., and Melik, J. S., "Adsorption-Desorption Isotherm Studies of Catalysts. III. Nitrogen and Stearic Acid Adsorption by Supported Catalysts and Their Components," *J. Phys. Colloid Chem.*, **53,** 638 (1949).

56. Sabatier, P., "Catalysts in Organic Chemistry," New York, D. van Nostrand Co., 1922.

57. Schachner, H., "Cobalt Oxides as Catalysts for the Complete Combustion of Automobile Exhaust Gases," *Cobalt*, No. 2, 37 (1959).

58. Schuit, G. C. A., and van Reijen, L. L., "The Structure and Activity of Metal-on-Silica Catalysts," *Advances in Catalysis*, **X,** 242 (1958).

59. Schultz, J. F., Hofer, L. J. E., Cohn, E. M., Stein, K. C., and Anderson, R. B., "Synthetic Liquid Fuels from Hydrogenation of Carbon Monoxide," *Bull. 578,* U. S. Bureau of Mines (1959).

60. Sheridan, J., and Reid, W. D., "The Metal-Catalyzed Reaction Between Acetylene and Hydrogen. Part VI.," *J. Chem. Soc.*, **1952,** 2962.

61. Smith, H. A., "The Catalytic Hydrogenation of Aromatic Compounds," *Catalysis*, **V,** 175 (1957).

62. Storch, H. H., "The Fischer-Tropsch and Related Processes for Synthesis of Hydrocarbons by Hydrogenation of Carbon Monoxide," *Advances in Catalysis*, **I,** 115 (1948).

63. Storch, H. H., Golumbic, N., and Anderson, R. B., "The Fischer-Tropsch and Related Syntheses," New York, John Wiley & Sons, Inc., 1951.

64. Teter, J. W. (to Sinclair Refining Company), U. S. Patent 2,381,473, August 7, 1945.

65. —, U. S. Patent 2,418,562, April 8, 1947.

66. Teter, J. W., and Olson, L. E., (to Sinclair Refining Company), U. S. Patent 2,658,041, November 3, 1953.

67. Trapnell, B. M. W., "Balandin's Contribution to Heterogeneous Catalysis," *Advances in Catalysis*, **III,** 1 (1951).

68. Unzelman, G. H., and Wolf, C. J., "Refining Process Glossary," *Petroleum Processing,* May 1957, p 97.
69. Uyehara, H., "Oxidation Rate of Linseed Oil Under the Influence of Catalysts and Temperatures. I." *Official Digest of the Federation of Paint and Varnish Production Clubs,* **27,** 794 (1955).
70. Weller, S. W., "Catalysis in the Liquid-Phase Hydrogenation of Coal and Tar," *Catalysis,* **IV,** 513 (1956).
71. Weller, S. W., and Mills, G. A., "Activation of Molecular Hydrogen by Homogeneous Catalysts," *Advances in Catalysis,* **VIII,** 163 (1956).
72. Wender, I., Sternberg, H. W., and Orchin, M., "The Oxo Reaction," *Catalysis,* **V,** 73 (1957).
73. Wolfe, H. J., "Printing and Litho Inks," New York, McNair-Dorland, 1949.

Chapter 15
BIOLOGY AND BIOCHEMISTRY

In the biological sciences, cobalt occupies a unique position among the rarer heavy metals because of its essential role in ruminant nutrition and its function as a key element in vitamin B_{12}.

Ordinary weathering and disintegration of rocks on the earth's surface causes cobalt to pass into the soil either as finely-divided solid particles or as a liquid. From the soil, the element is absorbed by plants and goes, sometimes directly, at other times by circuitous paths, to animals and humans. Man-made cobalt compounds frequently are applied with pasture top-dressings to supplement a marginal content of this element in the soil; they also may be given directly as food amendments to animals and even to humans. Occasionally, with humans, there is a minute, unrealized intake of cobalt in addition to that contained in foodstuffs. The activities of microorganisms influence the rate at which cobalt becomes available to plants and animals, and in return, the element has an important effect on the metabolism of microorganisms in soils, plants, and animals. The cobalt cycle in nature differs from the familiar carbon and nitrogen cycles in that there is no gaseous phase; examination of otherwise analogous features, however, reveals many important interrelationships of this metal in the mineral, vegetable, and animal kingdoms.

COBALT IN SOILS

Igneous rocks contain only about 0.001 per cent of cobalt; the element is usually assigned the thirty-third position in order of abundance among the elements constituting the outer crust of the earth. It is little wonder that the resulting small quantities of cobalt in soils, ranging from 0.1 to 50 ppm, attracted the attention of few scientists, with the notable exception of Bertrand and Mokragnatz,[28] and McHargue,[107] until around 1934 when certain widespread deficiency diseases in ruminants were finally traced to a lack of cobalt. Since then, a large number of analyses of cobalt in soils have been reported from various parts of the world. These are summarized in Table 15.1.

The figures in Table 15.1 indicate that there are considerable differences in the cobalt content of soils from various localities. Such differences are to be expected, since they reflect parent material, and soil forming and modi-

TABLE 15.1. COBALT CONTENT OF SOILS

Soil	Cobalt, ppm	Reference
Australia		
Enzootic marasmus area, unhealthy	0.1–1.5	Underwood and Harvey
Enzootic marasmus area, healthy	0.2–32	(167)
Britain		
Moorland, unhealthy	3.9	Patterson (121,122)
Lowland, healthy	16.7	
Devon, unhealthy	4	Patterson (121,122)
Devon, healthy	19.6	
Dartmoor, "pining"	0.20	Corner and Smith (45)
Dartmoor, healthy	0.45	
Canada		
Various soils	0.8–18.2	Wright *et al.* (177)
Nova Scotia	3.6–21	Wright and Lawton (176)
France		
Derived from granite	2.2–3.8	Bertrand and
Fertile garden soil	37	Mokragnatz (28)
Germany		
Black Forest, sick farm	0.05	Riehm *et al.*
Black Forest, healthy farm	0.14	(134,135)
Braunerde soils	4–8.5	Wehrman (175)
Marsh soils	8–11.5	Seiffert and Wehrman
Podzols	0.5–1.8	(142)
Low moor soils	0.9–3.1	
Hawaii		
Various soils	5–156	Fujimoto and Sherman (61)
Holland		
Cobalt-deficient soil	0.3	't Hart and Deijs (70)
Italy		
Various soils	4.59–20	Cambi (41)
Various soils	0.13–15.6	Giovannini *et al.* (64)
New Zealand		
"Bush-sick" soil	0.05–0.23	McNaught (108)
Healthy soil	0.33–0.94	McNaught (108)
Unhealthy soil	0.4–2.5	Kidson (94,95)
Normal soil	2.8–25.4	Kidson (94,95)
Morton Mains, unhealthy	3.3–4.8	Kidson (94,95)
Morton Mains, healthy	2.8–8.3	Kidson (94,95)
Nigeria		
Black surface soil, 0–13 in.	13	Kidson (94,95)
Concretionary horizon, 25–33 in.	110	Kidson (94,95)
Mottled brown and white clay, 41–54 in.	6.3	Kidson (94,95)
Northern Rhodesia		
Dambo soil and stream sediments, unmineralized area	3–12	Webb and Tooms (174)

Soil	Cobalt ppm	References
Dambo soil and stream sediments, mineralized area	20–160	
Poland		
Peat soils	1	Strzemski and Kabata
Sandy soils	tr.-5	(160)
Loamy soils	10–20	
Grass meadow soils	0.37–19.5	Baszynski (19)
Brown clay	8.2–15.5	Kabata (85,86)
Loam soil	14.4–28.7	
Sandy soil	7	
Spain		
Various soils	0.1–20	Burriel and Gallego (40)
United States		
Kentucky, virgin soil	1.5	McHargue (107)
Kentucky, eight soil types, "available" cobalt	0.2	Seay and DeMumbrum (141)
Missouri	4.2–37	Johnson and Graham (81)
New Jersey	0.2–30.8	Hill *et al.* (74)
Gray-brown podzolic, derived from loess	1.1–1.7	Slater *et al.* (150)
Gray-brown podzolic, derived from shale	0.1–0.4	Slater *et al.* (150)
Chernozem	0.1–0.2	Slater *et al.* (150)
Prairie	0.1–2.4	Slater *et al.* (150)
Chernozem prairie	0–1.9	Slater *et al.* (150)
Lateritic, derived from limestone	0.2–0.9	Slater *et al.* (150)
Lateritic, derived from heavy clay	0.6–1.0	Slater *et al.* (150)
Rendzina	0.9–1.4	Slater *et al.* (150)
U.S.S.R.		
Latvia, ploughed layer	0.4–4	Peive and Aizupiete (124)
Cobalt-deficient, light podzolic	0.3–1.5	Berzin (30)
Cobalt-deficient, sandy light	0.4–1.5	Peive (123)
Various soils	1.7–5.4	Katalymov and Shirshov (88)
Peat podzol	1	Malyuga and Makarova (103)
Above ore deposit	1000	
Chestnut brown, Urals	20–430	Malyuga and Makarova (103)
Clays	11	Ronov *et al.* (137)
Chernozem, Ukraine	2.3	Vlazyuk (171)
Acid podzolic and forest, Ukraine	0.25	Vlazyuk (171)
Yugoslavia		
Fertile soil	28	Bertrand and Mokragnatz (28)

fying agencies. Slight variations are also due to the methods of analysis, since some workers determined cobalt by extraction with concentrated hydrochloric or hydrobromic acid, whereas others carried out a complete fusion or acid digestion of the sample.

In general, where cattle and sheep exhibit nutritional deficiencies, the cobalt content of the soil will be lower than where animals are healthy. The many variables affecting the availability of soil cobalt tend to give a lower correlation between deficiency in soils and in animals than between deficiency in ruminants and in their pastures or feedstuffs.

There is usually a relation between the distribution of cobalt and iron in soil profiles.[40] Kubota[99] reported that the distribution pattern for cobalt, iron, and clay was similar in soils of the southeastern United States. Soils derived from granite are frequently low in cobalt,[125,185] and sands generally contain less of this element than do clays or loams. Several workers have noted that lime reduces the availability of soil cobalt,[74,125,141,176] and that plants from poorly-drained soils contain more cobalt than those from well-drained areas.[74] In the coastal region of Virginia, however, cobalt was found to be higher in plants from well drained soils.[130] Walsh, Ryan, and Fleming stated that under podzolization and impeded drainage, the surface layer of soils can become deficient in cobalt. The cobalt level in the top 15 cm was higher in free draining soil than in a strongly impeded one.[172] Kabata[86] found that cobalt increased directly with the degree of fineness of the soil fraction.

Banerjee, Bray, and Melstead[17] used tracer techniques and discovered that cobalt, after its addition to soils, was present in two forms:

(1) An easily exchangeable form extractable by neutral normal ammonium acetate similar to the other exchangeable bases.

(2) A strongly adsorbed form extractable almost completely by leaching with $0.1 N$ HCl after a 1-hour pre-treatment with this reagent. The strongly adsorbed cobalt did not seem to appear immediately, but was derived, in time, from a portion of (1).

Huser[78] found that strong adsorption of soil cobalt is related to adsorption of cobalt hydroxide by kaolinite. In a suspension of calcium kaolinite in a cobalt salt solution at pH 8, cobalt occurs as adsorbed Co^{++} and $Co(OH)^{+}$ ions, and as $Co(OH)_2$ and $Co(OH)_3$, adsorbed by kaolinite and as a precipitate.

The comparative rate of solution of various forms of cobalt under natural conditions has been determined.[183] Cobalt as finely-powdered metal or oxide dissolved extemely slowly, and cobalt carbonate and phosphate slowly have become available to plants under these conditions. Cobalt added to soil as chloride, nitrate, and sulfate show a high rate of solubility. Jones, Riceman, and McKenzie[83] found that in soils of moderate exchange capacity, provided with clay or organic matter, cobalt is not readily leached from the surface, even with various dressings. In light soils of low exchange capacity, the same leaching and dressing treatment led to considerable downward movement of cobalt. Zende[186] recorded that if soil pH is not high, much of the added cobalt remains in an easily exchangeable form for several months. Although these studies were concerned with added cobalt, their findings probably can be applied to cobalt naturally released by weathering agencies.

There does not appear to be any recorded instance of a natural soil, or one treated in a normal fashion to overcome a deficiency, that possesses sufficient cobalt to induce toxicity in plants. Stewart, Mitchell, and Stewart[158] reported that 40 lb cobalt chloride per acre had no visible effect on pasture vegetation but that 80 lb markedly depressed plant growth. Fujimoto and Sherman[61] reported that up to 200 lb added cobalt per acre were not harmful to Sudan grass in Hawaii, but 2000 pounds were extremely injurious. The few results in Table 15.1 showing a cobalt content above 40 ppm are localized enrichments of cobalt in iron minerals within the soil profile, or are soils immediately above an ore deposit containing cobalt. Though the exact tolerance for cobalt of most plants is not known, it is certainly far in excess of the quantity supplied in soil amendments by even the most enthusiastic application. Recommended dosages for most deficient soils are 1–2 lb cobalt sulfate per acre. The effect will last for several years.

Interest in soil cobalt, arising from the realization of its importance in animal nutrition, has been intensified in recent years by the popularity of geochemical prospecting, which determines the occurrence of cobalt ores by the presence of this metal in soils, vegetation, and streams. There are several reasons why this technique has not proved to be as helpful to those in the biological field as one might expect. In geochemical prospecting, the primary concern is with large differences—shown by rapid, approximate procedures—between a low background figure and a high concentration of metal. Much of the work is carried out in areas where the terrain or forest cover makes them unsuitable for agriculture. Most prospecting is done by commercial organizations, many of which do not publish any information. Nevertheless, if a closer liaison could be established between geochemists and biologists, data of the former on background figures for cobalt and other metals would be of considerable value to those working with soil, plants, and animals.

COBALT IN FERTILIZERS

The cobalt contents of some fertilizers have been published and results are compiled in Table 15.2.

TABLE 15.2. COBALT CONTENT OF VARIOUS FERTILIZERS

Fertilizer	Cobalt, ppm	Reference
Farmyard manure, Britain	6	Stojkovska and Cooke (159)
Farmyard manure, Germany	0.06	Scharrer and Prun (140)
Farmyard manure, Yugoslavia	6	Stojkovska and Cooke (159)
Basic slag, U.S.S.R.	145	Katalymov and Shirshov (88)
Phosphorite meal, U.S.S.R.	54	Katalymov and Shirshov (88)
Sodium nitrate, synthetic, Britain	0	Stojkovska and Cooke (159)
Nitrate of soda, Chilean	2-6	Young (181)
Ammonium sulfate, Britain	0	Stojkovska and Cooke (159)
Cyanamide, Yugoslavia	7	Stojkovska and Cooke (159)
Potassium chloride, Britain	1	Stojkovska and Cooke (159)
Potassium sulfate, Britain	0	Stojkovska and Cooke (159)
Sewage sludge, Britain	8.5	Clark and Hill (43)
Superphosphate, Britain	4	Stojkovska and Cooke (159)
Superphosphate, Yugoslavia	9	Stojkovska and Cooke (159)
Waste lime, beet factory, Yugoslavia	1	Stojkovska and Cooke (159)

The discrepancy in the results of Stojkovska and Cooke,[159] and Scharrer and Prun,[140] regarding cobalt in farmyard manure is difficult to resolve, since in both cases the investigators determined other micronutrients and showed results having a high degree of correlation.

Fertilizers with a low concentration of cobalt (up to 10 ppm) even when applied at the high rate of several tons per acre which is customary with farmyard manure or limestone, failed to correct a deficiency. Where cobalt concentration is higher, as in basic slag, normal applications of such fertilizers are also not sufficient to overcome cobalt deficiency.

COBALT IN PLANTS

From the middle of the nineteenth century, cobalt was detected in plant material by the occasional investigator; the first systematic studies were published by Bertrand and Mokragnatz in 1922 and 1930.[29] Interest in this field was greatly intensified when it became evident that cobalt deficiencies in livestock existed in many localities throughout the world. The quantity of cobalt found in plants is dependent not only on the amount of this element in the soil but also on a number of factors influencing availability and absorption of mineral nutrients, among which are type of soil, moisture, aeration, temperature, soil reaction, variety of plant, soil microflora, colloidal content, presence of other ions in soil solution, stage of plant growth, and other variables. Table 15.3 gives data on the cobalt content of plant products.

TABLE 15.3. COBALT CONTENT OF PLANT PRODUCTS

	Cobalt, mg/kg	Reference
Alfalfa hay	0.01-0.62	10, 37, 41, 112
Aloyce clover	0.09	112
Apricot	0.03	29
Apricot, dried leaves	0.40	29
Bahia grass	0.08	25
Beans, field, seed	0.01	29
Beans, French	0.07	147
Beans, wax	0.10	77
Beech, bark	1.10	29
Beech, dried leaves	0.35	29
Beech, wood	0.01	29
Beets, roots	0.05-0.09	77
Beets, tops	0.39-0.41	77
Bermuda grass	0.04-0.15	25, 112
Brome grass	0.03-0.09	10, 25
Buckwheat, grain	0.36	29
Cabbage, edible portion	0.07-0.24	29, 77, 147
Carolina blue grass	0.04	112
Carpet grass	0.05-0.15	25, 112
Carrots, leaves	0.31	29
Carrots, roots	0.02	29
Centipede grass	0.04	112
Chard, Swiss	0.09	77
Cherries, edible portion	0.005	29
Clover, red	1.3	87
Clover, white	0.17-4.6	10, 12
Coffee bean	0.002	29
Corn, grain	0.01-0.02	29, 77, 112, 147
Cowpeas	0.06-0.31	77
Cowpea hay	0.05-0.12	112
Cress, water	0.15	29
Dallis grass	0.03-0.15	25, 112
Figs	0.20	29
Johnson grass	0.08	25
Kentucky bluegrass	0.13-0.25	10, 25
Lespedeza	0.03-0.73	112, 127
Lettuce, dried leaves	0.05-0.23	29, 77
Lime, dried leaves	0.20	29
Mangel-beet leaves	0.16-0.54	77
Natal grass	0.05	25
Oat bran	0.01	29
Oat chop	0.02	37
Oat hay	0.02-0.07	37
Oats, grain	tr	29
Oats, whole plant	0.03-0.23	112
Onions, bulb	0.13	29

TABLE 15.3. (Cont.)

	Cobalt, mg/kg	Reference
Onions, green	0.26	147
Orchard grass	0.08	25
Para grass	0.07	25
Peanut hay	0.08	112
Pear, pulp	0.18	29
Peas, green, edible portion	0.03–0.15	29, 110
Peas, Australian field	0.15	112
Potatoes, ordinary	0.04–0.06	29
Potatoes, sweet	0.02–0.03	77
Quack grass	0.09	25
Radish	0.30	147
Rape	0.10–0.12	110
Red top	0.08	25
Rice, polished	0.006–0.13	29, 66
Rice, straw	0.42–9.3	87
Sea grass	0.15–0.66	170
Seaweed	0.22–0.64	66
Slough hay	0.015	37
Soybean hay	0.05	112
Spinach, edible portion	0.07–1.20	29, 77
Spinach, New Zealand	0.09	77
Strawberries, wild	0.10–0.12	110
Timothy hay	0.01–0.08	25
Tomato, fruit	0.10	29
Turnip greens	0.03–1.07	77
Vasey grass	0.08	25
Vetch	0.3–0.35	112
Walnuts, edible portion	0.05	29
Watermelon	0.18	110
Wheat, bran	0.01	29
Wheat, flour	0.09	66
Wheat, grain	0.01–0.04	29, 147
Wheat, whole plant	0.05–0.15	112
Wire grass	0.03	112

References

Arthur, Motzok, and Branion (10)
Askew and Dixon (12)
Beeson, Gray, and Adams (25)
Bertrand and Mokragnatz (29)
Bowstead, Sackville, and Sinclair (37)
Cambi (41)
Goto (66)
Hurwitz and Beeson (77)
Kandatsu and Mori (87)
Meleshko (110)
Mitchell (112)
Pickett (127)
Skoropostizhnaya (147)
Vinogradov (170)

It is evident from these results that plant foods for animals and man vary markedly in their cobalt content. Differences occur not only between dissimilar plants but also between the same species grown in different environments. In general, leaves have a higher concentration of cobalt than fruits, seeds, or roots.[36] Tracer techniques have demonstrated that this element accumulates at the margins of leaves and between the veins.[74] Over thirty years ago, Bertrand and Mokragnatz[29] reported a high content of cobalt in the leaves and bark of beech; this has been indirectly corroborated by the recent findings of Russian workers that sheep grazing on deficient pastures chew the cobalt-rich bark of aspen, and leaves of willow and aspen.[98] Ballantine and Stephens established that *Neurospora crassa*, grown in the presence of radioactive cobalt, accumulated as much as 40 per cent of the element in stable cobalt-protein complexes.[15] Miller,[111] studying the influence of cobalt and sugars on the elongation of etiolated pea stem segments, suggested that sucrose increases cell volume, and cobalt enlarges the surface area of cell walls.

Thimann[163] corroborated the thesis that cobalt stimulates growth in pea and oat sections; he found, further, that this is not due to increased uptake of solutes and probably does not act through the formation of vitamin B_{12}. Aliev found that cobalt tends to lower the ascorbic acid content of wheat leaves and increase the activity of peroxidase.[2] Bertrand and de Wolf[27] made the interesting discovery that the root nodules of lupines and soybeans contain a much higher concentration of cobalt than the roots or aerial parts of these plants. Yamada[178] found that cobalt stimulates the growth of pollen in *Lilium longiflorum,* and suggested that this element is vital for pollination in view of its occurrence (in ppm) in the following plant organs: leaf 0.016, petal 0.133, pollen 0.070, stigma 0.506, style 1.182. Russian investigators have reported that spraying grapevines with a dilute cobalt sulfate solution improves plant growth, grape yield, and sugar content.[54] Best results were obtained by addition of $CoSO_4$ to a Bordeaux mixture.

Applications of liming materials generally reduce the availability of soil cobalt to plants.[74,176] Hill, Toth, and Bear[74] reported that alfalfa grown on soil with a pH of 5.8 had twice the cobalt content of the same plant grown on a similar soil having a pH of 7.2. It was also observed that plants from poorly-drained soils were higher in cobalt than those from well-drained areas.

Seiffert and Wehrman[142] studied the cobalt uptake in forage on two types of soil after this element had been added. The original cobalt content of the podzol was 0.8 and of the brown earth, 5.2 ppm; the cobalt content of forage grown on both soils was greatly increased in the first year over the original values of 0.02–0.38 ppm. In the second year, the forage on the podzol continued to show an increased cobalt content; that grown on the brown earth did not.

There have been a few isolated reports that cobalt is beneficial to plant growth, e.g., from Malaya for rubber,[34] and from Russia for various crop plants.[89] Kedrov-Zikhman, Rozenberg, and Protashchik[89] carried out a series of laboratory and field experiments for six years on additions of cobalt to wheat, rye, barley, red clover, flax, and sugar beets in acid podzolic and peat soils. They found that cobalt, when added to soil with lime, significantly increased crop yields and quality. Cobalt fertilization without liming has little effect and may even be harmful; liming causes partial inactivation of the soil cobalt, and a deficiency may result. Supplementing the soil with a soluble form of cobalt, however, will restore a satisfactory balance.

Most investigators studying a wide range of cobalt additions have not been able to detect a significant increase in yield of higher plants. If this element is essential for plant metabolism, the quantity required must be so low that the chance of cobalt limiting plant growth on most of the world's soils is rather remote. On the contrary, there is considerable evidence that quite minute quantities of cobalt may be detrimental to certain species, particularly in water or sand cultures.[1,23,73,180] Cobalt toxicity is characterized by a chlorosis similar to that induced by lack of iron,[168] but it has been claimed that this symptom is not accompanied by a reduction of the iron content in the plant. The levels at which cobalt in water or sand cultures causes a marked diminution in plant growth are summarized in Table 15.4.[184]

The range of toxic concentrations reported by different investigators is, in some instances, extremely wide, and is a reflection of inherent difficulties

TABLE 15.4. CONCENTRATIONS OF COBALT TOXIC TO PLANTS IN PURE CULTURES

Plant	Cobalt in Culture Solution, ppm
Barley	1–29.5
Beans	0.02–29.5
Corn	1.6–29.5
Oats	2.9
Peas	2.3–29.5
Potatoes	5.8
Rye	2.9
Sugar beets	5.8
Tobacco	5
Tomato	0.1–5.8
Wheat	2.9–7

in evaluating plant damage at different periods of growth in pure cultures. The tolerance of plants for cobalt is evidently much lower than for micronutrients like manganese, copper, boron, and zinc. The low values given in Table 15.4 for the appearance of injury in pure cultures do not necessarily conflict with the recognized cobalt contents of naturally healthy soils or those in which a deficiency has been overcome by the addition of cobalt compounds. It is an agronomic axiom that plants can tolerate very much higher concentrations of metal ions in soils than in water or sand cultures.

Since a large proportion of food for cattle and sheep is furnished by pasture herbage, realization that cobalt is essential to their health directed attention to the quantity of this element present in pastures and hays throughout the world. The results of many such studies are summarized in Table 15.5. The lower limit in most countries is below 0.1 ppm, indicating that cobalt deficiencies may be expected, which is, indeed, the case.

TABLE 15.5. COBALT CONTENT OF PASTURE HERBAGE

	Cobalt, ppm	Reference
Australia	0.02–0.43	23,58,166,167
Britain	0.01–0.40	23,113,121,122,158
Canada	0.02–0.03	37
Germany	0.02–0.38	134,135,142
India	0.20–1.60	79
Italy	0.02–0.62	35,41,49
New Zealand	0.01–1.26	11,12,13,23,108,136
Norway	0.03–0.25	23
Poland	0.04–0.26	19,67
Switzerland	0.07–0.42	71
Uruguay	0.05–0.76	156
U.S.A.	0.01–0.73	23,24,25,74,100,112, 125,127,130,141
U.S.S.R.	0.12–0.58	88,103

Geochemical prospecting, which determines minute quantities of metals in vegetation as well as in soils and waters, reveals orebodies. Studies of some Canadian trees and shrubs[173] indicated that cobalt is distributed quite evenly in the younger parts of a bough, and that cobalt content is usually lower in leaves and needles than in boughs when determined on the dry basis or, more especially when reported on ash. Table 15.6 gives the cobalt content, on the dry basis, of young bough samples of various trees and shrubs from areas where no cobalt mineralization was known. In other words, these figures represent normal background values, whereas samples from mineralized areas might contain 10–100 times these quantities. Some trees appear to concentrate cobalt more than others. The tendency is for

TABLE 15.6. COBALT CONTENT OF CANADIAN TREES AND SHRUBS[173]

	Cobalt, ppm
Alder	0.06–0.25
Balsam	0.1–0.6
Birch	0.03–0.25
Black spruce	0.15–0.7
Blueberry	0.07–0.75
Cedar	0.1
Jackpine	0.08–0.1
Labrador tea	0.04–0.75
Lodgepole pine	0.25
Maple	0.08
Mountain balsam	0.3
Pin cherry	0.02
Poplar	0.1–0.3
Tamarack	0.06–0.15
Willow	0.08–0.35

spruce and birch to concentrate more cobalt than willow and maple when all are in close association.

Lazar and Beeson[100] found that sampling the leaves of the swamp black-gum was an efficient method for estimating the cobalt content of native forage types on the Atlantic Coastal Plain. Yamagata and Murakami[179] reported that a tree, *Clethra barbinervis* Sieb et Zucc., contained more than one hundred times as much cobalt in the leaf ash as other plant species growing in the same vicinity.

Vinogradov,[170] in his data on the composition of marine organisms, refers to cobalt in the flowering plant Zostera, the so-called sea grass. Various species contained $1.5-3 \times 10^{-5}$ per cent in the dry matter, and the ratio of Co to Ni was close to 1, indicating a concentration of cobalt from sea water.

COBALT IN ANIMAL NUTRITION

A fascinating chapter in the annals of animal nutrition includes the gradual tracing of puzzling disorders in sheep and cattle from many parts of the world to a deficiency of cobalt in their diet. For a long time, farmers and ranchers all over the world knew that if cattle and sheep grazed continuously in certain areas the animals would lose appetite and weight, become weak and anemic, and finally die. The disorders, known as "bush sickness" in New Zealand, "coast disease" in Australia, "pining" in Britain, and "salt sick" in Florida, were characterized by broadly similar symptoms. The animals could be restored to normal health by being moved to other pastures on a different type of soil or overlying a different rock formation.

For many years agricultural scientists explored the possibilities of toxic elements in the soil and vegetation, parasitic infestation peculiar to the affected region, and deficiencies in the soils and forages of the major elements essential to animal nutrition. When these investigations failed to explain the cause of the diseases, workers in New Zealand and Australia where the economic importance of this problem was greatest, turned to a study of minor mineral elements such as iron. Iron therapy gave conflicting results until it was finally discovered, around 1934, that the small quantity of cobalt present as an impurity in some iron compounds was actually the curative agent. Before long, it was definitely proved that the disorders were due to insufficient cobalt, and that cattle and sheep could be kept healthy indefinitely on the formerly "unhealthy" pastures by adding small quantities of cobalt to feed, salt licks, water, or top-dressings. The pioneer investigations of Aston,[14] Askew,[11] Rigg,[136] Kidson,[94,95] Dixon,[53] McNaught,[108,109] and others in New Zealand, and of Filmer,[58] Underwood,[166,167] Marston[104,105] and co-workers in Australia, have been a tremendous aid to world agriculture. The significance of cobalt deficiency was well emphasized by Sir Theodore Rigg's statement that in New Zealand alone, as a result of work on cobalt, hundreds of thousands of acres now produce cattle and sheep where formerly it was impossible.[136]

The conclusions of those working in the Antipodes on the corrective action of cobalt have been substantiated in the following countries where similar deficiency diseases were found: Brazil,[46] Britain,[45,119,121,158] Canada,[10,26,37,176] Denmark,[143] Eire,[118,144] Germany,[134,135] Holland.[70] Kenya,[23,184] Poland,[42,67] South Africa,[8] Sweden,[55] U. S.,[16,44,63,74,84] and U.S.S.R.[30,31,32,33,98,123,124]

The results of investigations concerning the minimum quantity of cobalt required in the pasture herbage or other foodstuffs for the maintenance of health in ruminants have varied slightly. As a general rule, however, a content of less than 0.08–0.10 ppm in the forage may produce deficiency diseases in cattle and sheep.[113] The minimum level of cobalt required in the soil to yield this concentration in herbage is a subject of lesser agreement. As a rough guide, for maintaining health in ruminants, cobalt in the soil should generally exceed 5 ppm. It must be emphasized, however, that attainment of this level may not, in some cases, provide enough cobalt in the forage to overcome a deficiency, whereas in other instances, soils containing less cobalt may be capable of supporting livestock indefinitely. Some workers, when evaluating the cobalt status of a specific region, place more emphasis on soil than on vegetation, believing that variations in the latter, due to season or stage of maturity, may be misleading. Most investigators, however, feel that the cobalt content of vegetation, representing the end result of all environmental factors responsible for availability of soil cobalt, is the best indication of its sufficiency.

In cobalt-deficient areas, the element must be added to the ration, water, salt lick, fertilizer, or pasture amendment. A daily addition to the ration of approximately 0.1 mg cobalt in the form of one of its soluble salts is completely effective in maintaining the health of sheep on affected areas, whereas for cattle, a dosage of 0.3–1 mg is required. An excellent way to prevent deficiency diseases is to incorporate small quantities of cobalt salts with the fertilizers or limestone used in top-dressing pastures. The quantities required are not large; an application of 2 lb cobalt sulfate per acre is effective for 3–5 years in Britain, Australia, and New Zealand.

To apply cobalt top-dressings to some pastures in New Zealand, an aqueous solution is sprayed from an airplane.[7] Dense pellets containing 75 per cent Co_2O_3 and 25 per cent china clay, and baked at 1000°C, deposited in the fore-stomachs of cattle and sheep, were shown to prevent phalaris staggers and cobalt-deficiency diseases.[4] Such pellets administered to weaned and unweaned lambs, and to ewes on a cobalt-deficient area prevented cobalt deficiency. Treated animals gained more weight than the controls, and had normal liver-cobalt and vitamin B_{12} levels, whereas those of the controls were low.

The form of the anion is not critical in top-dressing pastures; the carbonate, phosphate, and sulfate of cobalt give equivalent results.[13] Cobaltized superphosphate has been employed quite extensively, the ratio being 1 lb cobalt salt to 100 lb superphosphate. Cobalt compounds have also been incorporated with the limestone used for top-dressing pastures. While some workers have found this entirely satisfactory, many others have reported that the uptake of cobalt is depressed by the presence of lime.[74,176] When applying this amendment, the fact should be recognized that in many soil and climatic conditions at least a part of the cobalt may be temporarily immobilized by lime.

Cobalt deficiency has long been considered a disease affecting cattle and sheep only, since horses can apparently graze indefinitely, or certainly for extended periods, on deficient pastures without ill effects. As far as is known, ruminants are the only animals that manifest specific disorders when confined to low cobalt feeds. Recently, however, the addition of small quantities of cobalt to rations of pigs and chickens was found to be beneficial. Berzins,[32] in Russia, concluded that a daily dose of 10 mg cobalt chloride was advantageous for 20-kg pigs; Dinusson, Klosterman, Lasley and Buchanan,[52] in North Dakota, announced that the rate of gain in pigs was significantly increased by cobalt supplements of the order of 885 γ cobalt per lb of feed. Similar advantages were reported by Brazilian workers.[169] Berzins and Rozenbachs[33] found that small additions of a cobalt salt gave a 20–25 per cent improvement in the weight of chickens; Tastaldi *et al.*[162] reported that the element stimulated the bacterial synthesis of vitamin B_{12} in the intestines of chicks; Burns and Salmon[39] concluded that cobalt is nutritionally important for chicks whose diets are lacking in choline and vitamin B_{12}. A positive response to cobalt was also reported for rabbits.[148,149,155] Skoropostizhnaya[148,149] found that rabbits fed on rations high in cobalt showed increased erythrocyte and hemoglobin counts, and better body weight. Addition of vitamin B_{12} to their control ration increased the cobalt content of the liver. Solun and Roizman[155] also reported an improvement in the general metabolism of rabbits receiving 0.7–1.0 mg cobalt per week. Malaishkaite[102] obtained satisfactory results with a cobalt supplement for geese.

There have been no recorded cases of livestock poisoning caused by an excess of cobalt in natural herbage or feedstuffs. Keener, Percival, and Morrow[92] state that growing cattle can consume up to 50 mg cobalt per 100 lb body weight without ill effects. Becker and Smith[21] found that sheep can tolerate up to 160 mg daily per 100 lb weight for at least eight weeks without harmful effects, but that higher dosages are injurious.

The exact function of cobalt in animal nutrition is still a matter of controversy. That the action of the element was associated with the ruminant stomach, and that rumen microorganisms played a role in cobalt metabolism[20,154] were gradual discoveries.. After it was found that vitamin B_{12} was a cobalt-containing substance,[133,152] many workers confirmed the fact that this vitamin is an important intermediary in cobalt metabolism in ruminants.[3,75,104,153] Studies to determine whether or not cobalt deficiency is solely a vitamin B_{12} deficiency have led to many conflicting results, owing to differences in the amount of vitamin B_{12} supplied,[3,91,154] to variations in absorption by oral or parenteral administration,[5,93,154] and to the fact that the designation B_{12} includes a group of related compounds only some of which exhibit biological activity.[154] The classical vitamin B_{12} is a cyano-cobalt complex, and the B_{12} molecule minus the cyano group has sometimes been termed cobalamin. Specific compounds of the B_{12} family could be termed cyano-cobalamin, hydroxo-cobalamin, etc. Hydroxo-cobalamin, formerly termed vitamin B_{12a}, is as effective for cobalt-deficient lambs as cyano-cobalamin, the original B_{12}. Some other members of the vitamin B_{12} group, termed pseudo-B_{12}, however, are not biologically active for ruminants although they may be microbiologically active.[154] Some workers have suggested that cobalt may function either through the direct action of vitamin B_{12} on the animal or the indirect action on the microflora of the rumen.[59,164] At the present time, most investigators believe that cobalt deficiency in ruminants is essentially a deficiency of vitamin B_{12}.

Andrews, Hart, and Stephenson[6] reported that the disease cobalt deficiency is associated with livers in which vitamin B_{12} concentrations are less than 0.10 γ per g. Dosing with cobalt roughly doubled the mean vitamin B_{12} concentration. All the cobalt in the livers of healthy lambs not receiving cobalt was in the form of vitamin B_{12}, whereas most of the cobalt in the livers of lambs treated with this element was in some form other than vitamin B_{12}.

Johnson, Bentley, and Moxon[82] studied the synthesis of cobalt-60-containing vitamin B_{12}-active substances by rumen microorganisms. They concluded that as much as 65 per cent of the total activity of the rumen liquor samples was contributed by substances other than vitamins B_{12} and B_{12b}.

Many studies have been made of the distribution of cobalt in the animal organism. McNaught[109] reported that healthy sheep contained more than 0.1 ppm and cattle more than 0.12 ppm cobalt in their liver. Sheep and cattle suffering from cobalt deficiency always showed lower quantities. Radioactive cobalt administered in various ways by Braude *et al.*,[38] Comar and associates,[44] Rothery and co-workers,[138] Keener and colleagues[90] indicated that the highest levels of cobalt were always found in the liver, heart, kidney, and pancreas. Cobalt salts are eliminated about 80 per cent in feces and only 0.5 per cent in urine, while a significant per cent is excreted through the bile. When injected intravenously, cobalt rapidly disappears from the blood, most being excreted in the urine. Large injections were required to show this element in the rumen. The cobalt content of cows' milk is increased if large quantities of cobalt salts are given with the feed.[9]

Similar investigations were made of the distribution of vitamin B_{12} in organisms. Rumen contents and feces of ruminants are rich sources of B_{12}, and the concentration of the latter is a function of the quantity of cobalt ingested.[47,68,75,154] The vitamin B_{12} content of milk of various animal species has been determined, but it is not clear whether the addition of cobalt or vitamin B_{12} to the feed results in an increase of the vitamin in the milk.[154] It appears that blood vitamin levels vary with cobalt intake. Kercher and Smith found 0.11 mμg B_{12} per ml for cobalt-deficient lambs against 0.62 for lambs fed 1 mg of cobalt per day.[93]

Radioactive tracer studies have indicated, provisionally, that sheep are able to absorb appreciable quantities of insoluble cobalt compounds, such as the carbonate[91] and even the oxide Co_2O_3,[115] but more work must be done in this field. It has already been mentioned that cobalt requirements for sheep are about 0.1 mg per day and for cattle probably 0.3–1 mg, and that these needs can be met by a pasture or ration containing 0.08–0.10 ppm cobalt on a dry weight basis. In cobalt-deficient areas, if additions to the pasture, water, fertilizer, or lime are not made, direct addition of 2–4 g of cobalt sulfate, chloride, or nitrate per ton of concentrate feed is usually recommended. Because of its superior mixing properties, the dry cobalt carbonate is often preferred, in which case half this amount will provide roughly the same quantity of cobalt. If cobalt is added to a general mineral mixture, the quantity is about 0.5–1 oz of the soluble cobalt salts per 100 lb of mixture.

COBALT AND MICROORGANISMS

Apart from the effect of cobalt on the bacterial flora in the rumen, there are other interesting relationships between this element and various micro-organisms. A number of reports have been made on the effects of cobalt additions to algae, bacteria, and fungi. Cobalt stimulated growth in three algal species at concentrations of 0.002–0.2 ppm, depending on the species, but exerted a toxic effect on all three with addition of 2 ppm or more.[180] It has been reported that 0.4 ppm cobalt is necessary for optimum growth of four algal species.[76] Vinogradov[170] recorded the cobalt content of various marine algae, ranging from 1.7 to 5.3 ppm in the ash or 0.08–0.28 ppm in living matter. Marine algae have a relatively high cobalt content, the ratio Co:Ni approaching 1; in sea water it is about 0.3.

Porter[129] stated that the toxicity of cobalt towards bacteria varies with the species and in general occupies an intermediate position among cations. In certain plants, cobalt markedly inhibits the formation of bacterial tumors. Tanaka et al.[161] reported that 2 ppm cobalt did not affect growth of *Streptomyces griseus* or *B. subtilis*. Sawada et al.[139] reported that tracer studies with *B. natto* showed cobalt was necessary for cell multiplication. When cobalt was added to *B. asterosporus* in various sugar media, acid production and sugar consumption were increased, and respiration co-efficients were lowered.[48] Addition of cobalt to the culture medium for *Streptococcus faecalis* increased the level of acid pyrophosphatase activity.[117] Exposure to dilute solutions of cobalt sulfate decreased the growth and virulence of both typhoid and dysentery bacilli.[131] Garibaldi et al.[62] reported that cobalt was required only for cobalamin production, but not for growth of *B. megatherium*. Cobalt increased the microbial synthesis of an unidentified growth factor in liver extract by *Streptomyces griseus*.

Several investigators found that cobalt activates antibiotics. Forni reported a 2–15-fold increase in the bacteriostatic action of several antibiotics on *Es. coli* and *Micrococcus pyogenes* var. *aureus*.[60] Trace and Edds[165] demonstrated a similar action against various bacteria with cobalt additions to penicillin, streptomycin, and bacitracin. Pital et al. noted that cobalt increases the inhibitory effect of penicillin against *Salmonella pullorum*.[128]

The effect of small quantities of cobalt on various fungi has been described several times. Beeson[23] cites early work wherein increments of cobalt sulfate up to 0.002 per cent increased the growth and weight of *Aspergillus niger* and *Penicillium glaucum*, but a concentration of 0.033 per cent reduced growth below that of the check. Steinberg[157] found that the yield of *A. niger* decreased consistently with increasing additions of 0.1–50 mg cobalt nitrate per liter of nutrient solution. Bedford[22] reported that the toxic limits of cobalt for *A. niger* were 1500–1600 ppm; the same was found for *Penicillium oxalicum* and *P. expansum*. Cobalt salts were less injurious to *Penicillium* than were mercury or silver, but more detrimental than cadmium, lead, or nickel. It was found that the presence of ferrous sulfate had a depressing effect on the yield of ascorbic acid in *Aspergillus flavus*, but this effect was more than overcome by the addition of cobalt to the medium.[132] Only 10 per cent of the cobalt assimilated by the yeast, *Saccharomyces cerevisiae*, was adsorbed on the surface, the rest being chemically combined.[18] Although not generally confirmed, it has been reported that treatment of yeasts with a small quantity of cobalt increases cell numbers, cell sizes, and proteins in the resulting yeast-containing products.[97] It has also been reported that nitrogen is higher in cobalt yeast than in the normal product.[56] Perlman and O'Brien[126] grew *Saccharomyces cerevisiae* in media containing progressively higher concentrations of inorganic cobalt. They finally produced a tolerant culture growing in media with a cobalt concentration of 750 ppm in which the yeast cells contained up to 9.9 per cent cobalt. A strain of actinomycetes has been reported to tolerate as high as 10 per cent cobalt chloride in a standard medium.[96] Cultures of actinomycetes, as well as bacteria from cobalt-bearing muds in stagnant reservoirs, have been found to produce vitamin B_{12}.[101]

Vinogradov has recorded a few cobalt analyses for marine organisms such as Coelanterata, Vermes, Echinodermata, and Tunicata.[170] In general, the Co:Ni ratio is approximately that of sea water.

COBALT IN HUMAN NUTRITION

Knowledge of the role of cobalt in human nutrition is not yet clear. Even before the physicochemical studies of recent years showed that vitamin B_{12} contained cobalt, many prominent nutritionists believed that minute quantities of this element were necessary for humans. Shohl,[146] Sherman,[145] and McCollum[106] suggested that cobalt be considered a dietary essential for man. There is no indication, however, of the amount required. Low cobalt foods (less than 0.05 ppm) include apricots, carrots, cherries, coffee, corn, oats, peas, potatoes, rice, and wheat. Foods like beet root, chard, tomato, strawberries, walnuts, and wax beans are intermediate in cobalt content. High cobalt foods (0.2 ppm and over) include beet greens, buckwheat, cabbage, figs, green onions, pears, radishes, spinach, turnip greens, and water cress. It is worthy of note that corn, potatoes, rice, and wheat—the staples for most of the world's population—are all low in cobalt.

Differences in the reported cobalt content of the same food in various countries may be quite appreciable. In addition to the variations exhibited in Table 15.3 for plant products, normal cows' milk has been reported to range from 0.02 to 1.1 γ per liter.[66,154] Many of the plant products listed in Table 15.3 are inedible; a possible area for investigation might be the cobalt content of a wider range of human foodstuffs. There are, for instance, few and conflicting references to the cobalt content of meat. For beef, Mitteldorf and Landon give 20–100 ppm, with an average of 20;[114] Goto[66] quotes a cobalt content of 0.03–0.09 ppm for "animal meat." Skoropostizhnaya[147] gives a value of 0.35 ppm cobalt in bovine liver, and states that cobalt is absent from animal fat; he also gives the cobalt content of egg yolk as 0.068 ppm, the white, 0.034 ppm.

The cobalt content of a few species of fish has been reported by Vinogradov.[170] The following table is compiled from this data.

TABLE 15.7. COBALT CONTENT OF FISHES

Species	Cobalt, ppm	
	In Ash	In Living Matter
Osmerus eperlanus	10	1.1
Whiting	10	0.28
Gadus aeglefinus	4.2	0.1
Gadus morrhua	2.7	0.07
Gadus virens	2.4	0.07

Vinogradov observed that the amount of cobalt in the tissues of fish appears to be higher than that of nickel, whereas in sea water the reverse is true. Since there are about 20,000 species of fish, and cobalt has been determined for only a dozen, there is room for either verification or refutation of this generalization.

Several figures have been recorded for Mollusca and Arthropoda.[170] Vinogradov states that the ratio of Co:Ni is the same for these species as for rocks, but that there is a larger quantity of cobalt in mollusk eggs and in the liver of young organisms. Kandatsu and Mori[87] describe a "fish meal" containing 1.51 ppm cobalt. In Japan, Goto gives the actual daily intake of cobalt from cooked foods as 61.2 γ;[65] in Norway, Ouren[120] gives it as 30 γ.

Apart from the natural cobalt content of foodstuffs, minute quantities of this element may be inadvertently added to foods in a variety of unsuspected ways. Cobalt is one of the principal pigments imparting a blue color to glass, pottery, porcelain, and china. It is the best element for promoting the adhesion of enamel to steel and is used extensively as a ground coat in kitchen enamelware. Electrolytic nickel contains a small quantity of cobalt, and traces of the latter may, consequently, be encountered in food processing operations where nickel, Monel, or stainless steel are employed in food manufacture or in kitchens. Many cobalt compounds are used as driers for paints and varnishes, and Monier-Williams[116] has suggested that tiny quantities of the metal may be derived from driers for lacquers in cans, and for paints used on the inner surfaces of fish boxes. Other sources of trace quantities of cobalt in food or dust are contaminants from industrial products such as high-speed steel, high-temperature alloys, magnets, cemented carbides, and nickel electroplating.

For countries enjoying a fair standard of living, human foodstuffs are diversified and usually come from several areas. There is, consequently, far less chance for man to suffer from a cobalt deficiency than for ruminants. In primitive communities, however, where nearly all food is obtained from crops and animals raised in the immediate vicinity, there is a possibility of cobalt deficiency.[182] It is not inconceivable that certain nutritional disorders of Africa and Asia may eventually be linked with a low cobalt intake.

Pernicious anemia has virtually been eliminated in most countries by vitamin B_{12} therapy, but the precise nature of the mechanism by which this is brought about is still unknown. In 1926, it was reported that whole liver was effective in the dietary treatment of pernicious anemia. Over twenty years elapsed before the pure anti-pernicious anemia factor, now known as vitamin B_{12}, was isolated—independently and almost simultaneously—in the United States by Folkers and colleagues,[133] and in England by Smith and associates.[151]

Vitamin B_{12} is a red crystalline solid that is fairly soluble in water and lower alcohols but not in most other organic solvents. The empirical formula is now believed to be $C_{63}H_{88}O_{14}N_{14}PCo$, and it is the first vitamin found to contain a metal. The central cobalt atom is in the trivalent state and is firmly bound to the complex.[51] The CN group directly attached to the cobalt can be removed fairly easily by photolysis or certain reducing agents. It can be replaced by the hydroxyl ion to give vitamin B_{12a} or B_{12b}, and by nitrite to give B_{12c}. The work leading up to the announcement in 1955, of the complete structure of vitamin B_{12} has been fully described.[50,80,152] The extremely complex structure suggests that the molecule is related to haem, chlorophyll, and other natural porphin derivatives.

Man requires about 1 γ per day of vitamin B_{12}; it is one of the most potent of all physiologically active compounds, apparently having some powerful catalytic effect, possibly similar to that of a co-enzyme (an activator for a number of enzymes, specifically those containing - SH groups). It is quite possible that vitamin B_{12}, with its coordinated trivalent cobalt atom, is involved in an oxidation-reduction system. Cobalt can only be reduced in the vitamin by powerful agents, but with some protein in body fluids, the reaction might occur at physiological redox potentials.[152] Vitamin B_{12} is the only vitamin that is synthesized exclusively by microorganisms. Some bacteria and protozoa cannot synthesize the vitamin; other bacteria and actinomycetes make far more than they need and are actually employed for the manufacture of this vitamin. The most concentrated natural synthesis occurs in the fore-stomach of ruminants. Bacterial synthesis of the vitamin also occurs in the gut of other species, including man. In some animals, and in man, however, the synthesis occurs too low down in the gastro-intestinal tract for the vitamin to be absorbed, thus an external dietary source is required.

There appears to be no evidence that cobalt encountered by man under normal conditions in his foodstuffs or industrial products is deleterious to his health. Harding[69] found that 5 per cent suspensions of powdered cobalt metal injected intra-tracheally into rats caused fatal pulmonary hemorrhage and edema. Such injurious action of cobalt powder is probably related to its solubility in protein-containing fluids, about 15 mg per 100 ml in human plasma. Fairhall *et al.*[57] found that cobalt in the air to which operators of the cemented carbide industry were exposed varied from 0.05 to 1.67 mg/m^3. They concluded that while the experimental work did not indicate any great danger, further investigations would be continued. Heath[72] reported that cobalt chloride produced a non-lethal disturbance of normal mitosis in chick fibroblasts. Cobalt was also allowed to act locally on an animal tissue *in vivo*. The fine metal powder, mixed with fowl serum was injected into the thigh muscles of a rat; after five months, tumors developed at the site of the injection.

References

1. Ahmed, M. B., and Twyman, E. S., "The Relative Toxicity of Manganese and Cobalt in the Tomato Plant," *J. Exptl. Bot.,* **4,** 164–72 (1953).
2. Aliev, D. A., "Effect of Molybdenum and Cobalt on the Oxidation-Reduction Processes in Plants," *Doklady Akad. Nauk S.S.S.R.,* **14,** 465–9 (1958). *Chem. Abst.,* **52,** 18666 (1958).
3. Anderson, J. P., and Andrews, E. D., "Response to Vitamin B_{12} of Grazing Cobalt-Deficient Lambs," *Nature,* **170,** 807 (1952).
4. Andrews, E. D., "Cobalt Bullets," *New Zealand J. Agr.,* **97,** 427, 429–30 (1958).
5. Andrews, E. D., and Anderson, J. P., "Responses of Cobalt-Deficient Lambs to Cobalt and Vitamin B_{12}," *New Zealand J. Sci. Technol.,* **35,** 483–8 (1954).

6. Andrews, E. D., Hart, L. I., and Stephenson, B. J., "Vitamin B_{12} and Cobalt Concentrations in Livers from Healthy and Cobalt Deficient Lambs," *Nature*, **182**, 869–70 (1958).

7. Andrews, E. D., and Pritchard, A. M., "Top-dressing Cobalt-Deficient Land from the Air," *New Zealand J. Agr.*, **75**, 501, 503–6 (1947).

8. Anonymous, "Soil Deficiency in South Africa," *Chem. Age*, **68**, 467 (1953).

9. Archibald, J. G., "Cobalt in Cow Milk," *J. Dairy Sci.*, **30**, 293–7 (1947).

10. Arthur, D., Motzok, I., and Branion, H. D., "The Determination of Cobalt in Forage Crops," *Can. J. Agr. Sci.*, **33**, 1–15 (1953).

11. Askew, H. O., "The Effectiveness of Small Applications of Cobalt Sulphate for the Control of Cobalt Deficiency in the Sherry Valley, Nelson, N. Z.," *New Zealand J. Sci. Technol.*, **28A**, 37–43 (1946).

12. Askew, H. O., and Dixon, J. K., "Influence of Cobalt Top-Dressing on the Cobalt Status of Pasture Plants," *New Zealand J. Sci. Technol.*, **18**, 688–93 (1937).

13. Askew, H. O., and Watson, J., "Effect of Various Cobalt Compounds on the Cobalt Content of a Nelson Pasture," *New Zealand J. Sci. Technol.*, **28A**, 170–2 (1946).

14. Aston, B. C., "Control of Bush Sickness in Sheep: The Atiamuri Experiments with Iron Licks," *New Zealand J. Agr.*, **44**, 367–78 (1932).

15. Ballentine, R., and Stephens, D. G., "The Biosynthesis of Stable Cobalto-proteins by Plants," *J. Cellular Comp. Physiol.*, **37**, 369–87 (1951).

16. Baltzer, A. C., Killham, B. J., Duncan, C. W., and Huffman, C. F., "A Cobalt Deficiency Disease Observed in Some Michigan Dairy Cattle," *Mich. Agr. Expt. Sta. Quart. Bull.*, **24**, 68–70 (1941).

17. Banerjee, D. K., Bray, R. H., and Melstead, S. W., "Some Aspects of the Chemistry of Cobalt in Soils," *Soil Sci.*, **75**, 421–31 (1953).

18. Bass, H., and Zizuma, A., "Assimilation of Cobalt by Yeasts. 11. Distribution of Cobalt in Yeast *Saccharomyces Cerevisiae*," *Latvijas PSR Zinatnu Akad. Vestis*, **1956**, No. 8, 109–14. *Chem. Abst.*, **51**, 9781 (1957).

19. Baszynski, T., "Trace Elements and Vitamins in Meadow Grass Association of the Pieniny National Park," *Acta Agrobotan.*, **7**, 131–42 (1958). *Chem. Abst.*, **52**, 18984 (1958).

20. Becker, D. E., and Smith, S. E., "The Metabolism of Cobalt in Lambs," *J. Nutrition*, **43**, 87–100 (1951).

21. —, *et al.*, "The Level of Cobalt Tolerance in Yearling Sheep," *J. Animal Sci.*, **10**, 266–71 (1951).

22. Bedford, C. L., "Morphological and Physiological Studies Upon a Penicillin Sp. Tolerant to Copper Sulfate," *Zentbl. Bakt. Abt. 11*, **94**, 102–12 (1936).

23. Beeson, K. C., "Cobalt. Occurrence in Soils and Forages in Relation to a Nutritional Disorder in Ruminants," *U. S. Dept. Agr. Inf. Bull.*, 7 (1950).

24. —, "Nutrient Element Control of Native Forages in Relation to Location and Land Forms in the South Carolina Coastal Plain," *Soil Sci.*, **80**, 211–20 (1955).

25. Beeson, K. C., Gray, L., and Adams, M. B., "The Absorption of Mineral Elements by Forage Plants. 1. The Phosphorus, Cobalt, Manganese, and Cop-

per Content of Some Common Grasses," *J. Am. Soc. Agron.*, **39**, 356–62 (1947).

26. Bell, J. M., "Cobalt Feeding Experiments in Western Canada," *Brit. Agr. Bull.*, **6**, 148–52 (1953).

27. Bertrand, D., and de Wolf, A., "Nickel and Cobalt in Root Nodules of Legumes," *Bull. Soc. Chim. Biol.*, **36**, 905–6 (1954). *Chem. Abst.*, **49**, 2570 (1955).

28. Bertrand, D., and Mokragnatz, M., "Sur la Présence Simultanée du Nickel et du Cobalt Dans la Terre Arable," *Bull. Soc. Chim.*, **31**, 1330–33 (1922).

29. —, *et al.*, "Sur la Répartition du Nickel et du Cobalt Dans les Plantes," *Bull. Soc. Chim.*, **47**, 326–31 (1930).

30. Berzin, Y. M., "The Effect of Cobalt and Copper in Feeding Farm Animals," *Agrobiologiya*, **6**, 111–20 (1950). *Chem. Abst.*, **45**, 5839 (1951).

31. Berzins, J., "Significance of Cobalt and Copper in Feeding of Farm Animals," *Mikroelementy v Zhizni Rastenii i Zhivotnykh, Akad. S.S.S.R., Trudy Konf. Mikroelement.*, **1950**, 473–92 (1952). *Chem. Abst.*, **49**, 456 (1955).

32. —, "The Significance of Cobalt in Feeding of Pigs," *Latvijas PSR Zinatnu Akad. Vestis*, **1951**, 415–20. *Chem. Abst.*, **47**, 12440 (1953).

33. Berzins, J., and Rozenbachs, J., "Role of Cobalt, Copper, Manganese and Zinc Salts in Chicken Feeding," *Latvijas PSR Zinatnu Akad. Vestis*, **1953**, No. 9, 39–46. *Chem. Abst.*, **48**, 12260 (1954).

34. Bolle-Jones, E. W., and Mallikarjuneswara, V. R., "Cobalt: Effects on the Growth and Composition of *Hevea*," *J. Rubber Res. Inst. Malaya Commun.*, **15**, 128–40 (1957).

35. Bosticco, A., "Cobalt, Copper and Manganese Content of Feedstuffs Grown in the Parma District," *Atti Soc. Ital. Sci. Vet.*, **10**, 205–6 (1956). *Chem. Abst.*, **51**, 18385 (1957).

36. Bottini, E., "Nutritive Micro Elements in the Soil. III. Vegetation Tests in Mitscherlich's Pots with Boron, Copper, and Cobalt," *Ann. Sper. Agrar.* [N.S.], **4**, 895–916 (1950). *Chem. Abst.*, **45**, 7735 (1951).

37. Bowstead, J. E., Sackville, J. P., and Sinclair, R. D., "The Development of Cobalt Deficiency in Sheep," *Sci. Agr.*, **22**, 314–25 (1942).

38. Braude, R., Free, A. A., Page, J. E., and Smith, E. L., "The Distribution of Radioactive Cobalt in Pigs," *Brit. J. Nutrition*, **3**, 289–92 (1949).

39. Burns, M. J., and Salmon, W. D., "Effect of Dietary Cobalt on Growing Chicks and Rats," *J. Agr. Food Chem.*, **4**, 257–9 (1956).

40. Burriel, F., and Gallego, R., "Cobalt in Spanish Soils," *Anales Edafol. Fisiol. Vegetal*, **11**, 569–600 (1952). *Chem. Abst.*, **47**, 5595 (1953).

41. Cambi, G., "Preliminary Report on the Cobalt Content of Italian Forages," *Ann. Sper. Agrar.* [N.S.], **3**, 963–73 (1949). *Chem. Abst.*, **44**, 3630 (1950).

42. Chodhowski, A., and Slaweta, L., "Cobalt Deficiency as the Cause of Fatal Diseases in Rams," *Med. Weterynar.*, **7**, 481–3 (1951). *Chem. Abst.*, **46**, 4079 (1952).

43. Clark, L. J., and Hill, W. L., "Occurrence of Manganese, Copper, Zinc, Molybdenum, and Cobalt in Phosphate Fertilizers and Sewage Sludge," *J. Assoc. Offic. Agr. Chemists*, **41**, 631–7 (1958).

44. Comar, C. L., and Davis, G. K., "Cobalt Metabolism Studies. III. Excretion and Tissue Distribution of Radioactive Cobalt as Administered to Cattle," *Arch. Biochem.,* **12,** 257–66 (1947).
45. Corner, H. H., and Smith, A. M., "The Influence of Cobalt on Pine Disease in Sheep," *Biochem. J.,* **32,** 1800–5 (1938).
46. Correa, R., "Cobalt Deficiency in Bovine Cattle in the State of Sao Paulo, Brazil," *Rev. Brasil. Biol.,* **15,** 309–13 (1955). *Chem. Abst.,* **50,** 1142 (1956).
47. Dawbarn, M. C., Hine, D. C., and Smith, J., "Determination of Vitamin B_{12} Activity in the Organs and Excreta of Sheep. V. Effect of Cobalt Deficiency on the Vitamin B_{12} Content of the Blood Plasma," *Australian J. Exptl. Biol. Med. Sci.,* **35,** 273–6 (1957).
48. Dedic, G. A., and Koch, O. G., "The Influence of Trace Elements on *Bacillus Asterosporus.* 11. The Influence of Cobalt on Carbohydrate Metabolism," *Arch. Mikrobiol.,* **23,** 130–41 (1955). *Chem. Abst.,* **52,** 18648 (1958).
49. Del Monte, R., "Cobalt Content of Feedstuffs Grown in the Parma District," *Nuova Vet.,* **33,** 161–7 (1957). *Chem. Abst.,* **51,** 18385 (1957).
50. Diehl, H., and associates, "Physicochemical Studies on Vitamin B_{12}," *Record Chem. Progress,* **13,** No. 1, 9–21 (1952).
51. Diehl, H., and Voigt, A., "The Failure of Exchange Between Vitamin B_{12} and Radioactive Cobalt Chloride," *Iowa State Coll. J. Sci.,* **32,** 471–3 (1958).
52. Dinusson, W. E., Klosterman, E. W., Lasley, E. L., and Buchanan, M. L., "Cobalt, Alfalfa, and Meat Scraps in Drylot Ration for Growing-Fattening Pigs," *J. Animal Sci.,* **12,** 623–7 (1953).
53. Dixon, J. K., "The Use of a Cobaltized Salt Lick in the Control of a Lamb-Ailment at Morton Mains, Southland," *New Zealand J. Sci. Technol.,* **18,** 892–7 (1937).
54. Dobrolyubskii, O. K., and Slavvo, A. Y., "Extraradicle Nutrition of Grape with Cobalt Trace Element," *Doklady Akad. Nauk S.S.S.R.,* **106,** 735–8 (1956). *Chem. Abst.,* **50,** 10198 (1956).
55. Ekman, P., Karlsson, N., and Svanberg, O., "Investigations Concerning Cobalt Problems in Swedish Animal Husbandry," *Acta Agr. Scand.,* **2,** 103–30 (1952). *Chem. Abst.,* **46,** 9759 (1952).
56. Erkama, J., and Enari, T. M., "The Effect of Cobalt on the Nitrogen Metabolism in Yeast," *Suomen Kemistibehti,* **29B,** 176–8 (1956). *Chem. Abst.,* **51,** 4494 (1957).
57. Fairhall, L. T., Keenan, R. G., and Brinton, H. P., "Cobalt and the Dust Environment of the Cemented Carbide Industry," *U. S. Public Health Rept.,* **64,** 485–90 (1949).
58. Filmer, J. F., and Underwood, E. J., "Enzootic Marasmus. Further Data Concerning the Potency of Cobalt as a Curative and Prophylactic Agent," *Austral. Vet. J.,* **13,** 57–64 (1937).
59. Ford, J. E., Kon, S. F., and Porter, J. W. G., "Cobalt in Ruminant Nutrition," *Chemistry and Industry,* **1952,** May 31, 495.
60. Forni, P. V., "Cobalt and Antibiotic Action," *Boll. Soc. Ital. Patol.,* **3,** 183–4 (1953). *Chem. Abst.,* **50,** 12172 (1956).

61. Fujimoto, G., and Sherman, G. D., "Cobalt Content of Typical Soils and Plants of the Hawaiian Islands," *Agron. J.*, **42**, 577–81 (1950).
62. Garibaldi, J. A., Ijichi, K., Snell, N. S., and Lewis, J. C., "*Bacillus Megatherium* for Biosynthesis of Cobalamin," *Ind. Eng. Chem.*, **45**, 838–46 (1953).
63. Geyer, R. P., Rupel, I. W., and Hart, E. B., "Cobalt Deficiency in Cattle in the Northeastern Region of Wisconsin," *J. Dairy Sci.*, **28**, 291–6 (1945).
64. Giovannini, E., Usai, R., and Dore, G., "Cobalt in Italian Soils," *Studi Sassaresi, Sez. 111*, **2**, 60–79 (1954). *Chem. Abst.*, **50**, 8114 (1956).
65. Goto, T., "Change of Inorganic Components in Food by Cooking. 11. Zinc and Cobalt," *J. Home Econ.* (Japan), **5**, No. 1, 23–32 (1954). *Chem. Abst.*, **50**, 5932 (1956).
66. —, "Food Elements and Cooking. 11. Cobalt Contents of Ordinary Foods," *Eiyo to Shokuryo*, **7**, 102–3 (1954–55). *Chem. Abst.*, **53**, 7448 (1959).
67. Grabowski, K., Rydel, S., Szewczyk, J., and Zalewska, E., "Deficiency of Microelements and Hypovitaminosis—B_{12} in Ruminants Reared in Areas of Peat-Bog Soils," *Med. Weterynar.*, **13**, 669–74 (1957). *Chem. Abst.*, **52**, 13039 (1958).
68. Hale, W. H., Pope, A. L., Phillips, P. H., and Bohstedt, G., "The Effect of Cobalt on the Synthesis of Vitamin B_{12} in the Rumen of Sheep," *J. Animal Sci.*, **9**, 414–19 (1950).
69. Harding, H. E., "The Toxicology of Cobalt Metal," *Brit. J. Industrial Med.*, **7**, 76–8 (1950).
70. t'Hart, M. L., and Deijs, W. B., "Investigations on the Cobalt Content of Grassland," *Phosphorsaure*, **12**, 370–9 (1952). *Chem. Abst.*, **47**, 4020 (1953).
71. Hasler, A., and Zuber, R., "Cobalt Content of Swiss Pasture," *Schweiz. Landwirtsch. Monatsh.*, **1955**, No. 5. *Chem. Abst.*, **52**, 16649 (1958).
72. Heath, J. C., "Cobalt as a Carcinogen," *Nature*, **173**, 822–3 (1954).
73. Hewitt, E. J., "Metal Interrelationships in Plant Nutrition. 1. Effects of Some Metal Toxicities on Sugar Beet, Tomato, Oat, Potato, and Marrowstem Kale Grown in Sand Culture," *J. Exptl. Bot.*, **4**, 59–64 (1953).
74. Hill, A. C., Toth, S. J., and Bear, F. E., "Cobalt Status of New Jersey Soils and Forage Plants and Factors Affecting the Cobalt Content of Plants," *Soil Sci.*, **76**, 273–84 (1953).
75. Hoekstra, W. G., Pope, A. L., and Phillips, P. H., "Synthesis of Certain B Vitamins in the Cobalt-Deficient Sheep, with Special Reference to Vitamin B_{12}," *J. Nutrition*, **48**, 421–30 (1952).
76. Holm-Hansen, O., Gerloff, G. C., and Skoog, F., "Cobalt as an Essential Element for Blue Green Algae," *Physiol. Plantarum*, **7**, 665–75 (1954). *Chem. Abst.*, **50**, 1138 (1956).
77. Hurwitz, C., and Beeson, K. C., "Cobalt Content of Some Food Plants," *Food Res.*, **9**, 348–57 (1944).
78. Huser, R., "Adsorption of Cobalt by Kaolinite," *Z. Pflanzenernahr. Dung. u. Bodenk.*, **80**, 56–66 (1958). *Chem. Abst.*, **52**, 12509 (1958).
79. Iyer, J. G., and Satyanarayan, Y., "Cobalt and Zinc Contents of a Few Forage Plants of Western India," *Current Sci.* (India), **27**, 220–1 (1958). *Chem. Abst.*, **53**, 4434 (1959).

80. Johnson, A. W., and Todd, Sir Alexander, "Vitamin B_{12}," *Endeavour,* **XV,** 29–33 (1956).

81. Johnson, F. R., and Graham, E. R., "Trace Elements and Missouri Soils. 1. Copper and Cobalt Contents of Twenty-Six Soil Types," *Missouri Agr. Expt. Sta. Res. Bull.,* **517** (1952).

82. Johnson, R. R., Bentley, O. G., and Moxon, A. L., "Synthesis *In Vitro* and *In Vivo* of Cobalt-60-Containing Vitamin B_{12}-Active Substances by Rumen Microorganisms," *J. Biol. Chem.,* **218,** 379–90 (1956).

83. Jones, G. B., Riceman, D. S., and McKenzie, J. O., "The Movement of Cobalt and Zinc in Soils as Indicated by Radioactive Isotopes," *Australian J. Agr. Res.,* **8,** 190–201 (1957).

84. Kaarde, I. A., "A Special Form of Disease—Bog Disease, and its Treatment with Cobalt Salts," *Microelementy v Zhizni Rastenii i Zhivotnykh, Akad. Nauk S.S.S.R., Trudy Konf. Mikroelement.,* **1950,** 493–8 (1952). *Chem. Abst.,* **49,** 456 (1955).

85. Kabata, A., "The Cobalt Content in Some Soils of the Swietokrzynski Region," *Roczniki Gleboznowcze,* **3,** 323–32 (1954). *Chem. Abst.,* **51,** 11630 (1957).

86. —, "Cobalt in Meadow and Pasture Soils of Certain Highland Regions," *Roczniki Nauk Rolniczych Ser. A.,* **70,** 609–15 (1955). *Chem. Abst.,* **49,** 16293 (1955).

87. Kandatsu, M., and Mori, B., "Reticulo-Rumen Digestion. V. Cobalt Content of Some Feeds," *Nippon Nogei-Kagaku Kaishi,* **30,** 100–5 (1956). *Chem. Abst.,* **51,** 9969 (1957).

88. Katalymov, M. V., and Shirshov, A. A. "Content of Cobalt in Plants, Soils, and Fertilizers," *Doklady Akad. Nauk S.S.S.R.,* **101,** 955–7 (1955). *Chem. Abst.,* **49,** 12615 (1955).

89. Kedrov-Zikhman, O. K., Rozenberg, R. E., and Protashchik, L. N., "The Effect of Cobalt and Molybdenum on the Yield of Agricultural Crops Grown in Acid Podzolic and Peat Soils of Byelorussia," *Mikroelementy v Sel'sk. Khoz. i Med., Akad. Nauk Latv. S.S.S.R., Otdel. Biol. Nauk, Trudy Vsesoyuz. Soveshchan., Riga,* **1955,** 51–65. *Chem. Abst.,* **53,** 10621 (1959).

90. Keener, H. A., Baldwin, R. R., and Percival, G. P., "Cobalt Metabolism Studies with Sheep," *J. Animal Sci.,* **10,** 428–33 (1951).

91. Keener, H. A., and Percival, G. P., "Function of Cobalt in Nutrition of Sheep," *J. Animal Sci.,* **9,** 404–13 (1950).

92. Keener, H. A., Percival, G. P., and Morrow, K. S., "Cobalt Tolerance in Young Dairy Cattle," *J. Dairy Sci.,* **32,** 527–33 (1949).

93. Kercher, C. J., and Smith, S. E., "The Synthesis of Vitamin B_{12} after Oral and Parenteral Administration of Inorganic Cobalt to Cobalt-Deficient Sheep," *J. Animal Sci.,* **15,** 550–8 (1956).

94. Kidson, E. B., "Cobalt Status of New Zealand Soils," *New Zealand J. Sci. Technol.,* **18,** 694–707 (1937).

95. —, "Some Factors Influencing the Cobalt Content of Soils," *J. Soc. Chem. Ind.,* **57,** 95–6 (1938).

96. Kojima, H., and Matsuki, M., "Studies on the Influence of Cobalt Chloride

on the Growth of Actinomycetes," *Tohoku J. Agr. Res.*, **7**, 175–87 (1956). *Chem. Abst.*, **51**, 10642 (1957).

97. Korshakov, P. N., "Effect of Cobalt on the Nutritive Value of Yeast-Containing Feeds," *Zhivotnovodstvo*, **1953**, No. 5, 61–3. *Chem. Abst.*, **50**, 505 (1955).

98. Koval'skii, V. V., and Chebaevskaya, V. S., "Cobalt-Rich Feed for Romanov Sheep," *Doklady Vsesoyuz. Akad. Sel'sko-Khoz. Nauk im V.I. Lenina*, **16**, No. 8, 44–8 (1951). *Chem. Abst.*, **46**, 2203 (1952).

99. Kubota, J., "Cobalt Status of Soils of Southeastern United States. 1. Cobalt, its Distribution and Relationship to Iron and Clay in Five Selected Soils," *Soil Sci.*, **85**, 130–40 (1958).

100. Lazar, V. A., and Beeson, K. C., "Mineral Nutrients in Native Vegetation on Atlantic Coastal Plain Soil Types," *J. Agr. Food Chem.*, **4**, 439–44 (1956).

101. Letunova, S. V., "Formation of Vitamin B_{12} by Various Actinomycetes and Bacteria Isolated from Muds of Cobalt-Bearing Biogeochemical Provinces," *Mikrobiologiya*, **27**, 429–34 (1958). *Chem. Abst.*, **52**, 18660 (1958).

102. Malaishkaite, B., "The Role of Cobalt in Nutrition of Geese," *Byull. Nauch. Tekh. Inform. Litovsk. Nauch. Issledovatel. Inst. Zhivotnovodstva i Vet.*, **1957**, No. 2, 15–16. *Chem. Abst.*, **53**, 1482 (1959).

103. Malyuga, D. P., and Makarova, A. I., "Cobalt Content of Soils and Plant Ashes of Tuva," *Doklady Akad. Nauk S.S.S.R.*, **98**, 811–13 (1954). *Chem. Abst.*, **49**, 4917 (1955).

104. Marston, H. R., and Lee, H. J., "Cobalt in the Nutrition of Ruminants. Response of Cobalt-Deficient Sheep to Massive Doses of Vitamin B_{12}," *Nature*, **170**, 791 (1952).

105. Marston, H. R., and Smith, R. M., "Cobalt in the Nutrition of Ruminants. Control of Cobalt-Deficiency in Sheep by Injection of Vitamin B_{12}," *Nature*, **170**, 792–3 (1952).

106. McCollum, E. V., Orent-Keiles, E., and Day, H. G., "The Newer Knowledge of Nutrition," New York, Macmillan Company, 1944.

107. McHargue, J. S., "The Occurrence of Copper, Manganese, Zinc, Nickel, and Cobalt in Soils, Plants, and Animals, and Their Possible Function as Vital Factors," *J. Agr. Res.*, **30**, 193–6 (1925).

108. McNaught, K. J., "The Cobalt Content of North Island Pastures," *New Zealand J. Sci. Technol.*, **20A**, 14–30 (1938).

109. —, "Cobalt, Copper, and Iron in the Liver in Relation to Cobalt-Deficiency Ailment," *New Zealand J. Sci. Technol.*, **30A**, 26–43 (1948).

110. Meleshko, K. V., "The Amount of Cobalt in Certain Food Products of Plant Origin," *Voprosy Pitaniya*, **15**, No. 6, 43–7 (1956). *Chem. Abst.*, **51**, 6037 (1957).

111. Miller, C. O., "Influence of Cobalt and Sugars Upon the Elongation of Etiolated Pea Stem Segments," *Plant Physiol.*, **29**, 79–82 (1954).

112. Mitchell, J. H., "Cobalt Content of Pasture Plants and Feeding Materials," *S. Carolina Agr. Expt. Sta. Bull.*, **391** (1951).

113. Mitchell, R. L., "Trace Constituents in Soils and Plants," *Research*, **1**, 159–65 (1947).

114. Mitteldorf, A. J., and Landon, D. O., "Spectrochemical Determination of the Mineral Element Content of Beef," *Anal. Chem.,* **24,** 469–72 (1952).
115. Mittler, S., "Nutritional Availability of Cobaltic Oxide, Co_2O_3," *Nature,* **174,** 88–9 (1954).
116. Monier-Williams, G. W., "Trace Elements in Food," London, Chapman and Hall, 1949.
117. Oginsky, E. L., and Rumbaugh, H. L., "A Cobalt-Activated Bacterial Pyrophosphatase," *J. Bact.,* **70,** 92–8 (1955).
118. O'Moore, L. B., "Incidence and Control of Cobalt Deficiency Under Varying Soil and Pasture Conditions in Connemar, Co. Galway," *J. Sci. Food Agr.,* **8,** supplementary issue 105–111 (1957).
119. Osborne, A. D., "Cobalt Deficiency in Sheep in Herefordshire," *J. Sci. Food Agr.,* **8,** supplementary issue 113–118 (1957).
120. Ouren, I., "Copper, Cobalt, Zinc and Manganese Content of Food in Western Norway," *Univ. Bergen Arbok Naturvitenskap. Rekke,* **1957,** No. 9, 1–16. *Chem. Abst.,* **53,** 6460 (1959).
121. Patterson, J. B. E., "Some Observations on a Disease of Sheep on Dartmoor," *Empire J. Exptl. Agr.,* **6,** 262–7 (1938).
122. —, "Cobalt as a Preventative of Pining in Cornwall and Devon," *Nature,* **157,** 555 (1946).
123. Peive, J., "Cobalt in the Soils of Latvian S.S.R. and its Significance in Agriculture," *Mikroelementy v Zhizni Rastenii i Zhivotnykh, Akad. Nauk S.S.S.R., Trudy Konf. Mikroelement.,* **1950,** 466–72 (1952). *Chem. Abst.,* **49,** 550 (1955).
124. Peive, J., and Aizupiete, I. P., "Cobalt Content in Soils of the Latvian S.S.R.," *Latvijas PSR Zinatnu Akad. Vestis,* **1949,** No. 5, 19–27. *Chem. Abst.,* **47,** 10161 (1953).
125. Percival, G. P., Josselyn, D., and Beeson, K. C., "Factors Affecting the Micronutrient Element Content of Some Forages in New Hampshire," *New Hampshire Agr. Expt. Sta. Tech. Bull.,* **93** (1955).
126. Perlman, D., and O'Brien, E., "Characteristics of a Cobalt-Tolerant Culture of *Saccharomyces Cerevisiae,*" *J. Bact.,* **68,** 167–70 (1954).
127. Pickett, E. E., "Mineral Composition of Missouri Feeds and Forages. 1. Lespedeza," *Missouri Agr. Expt. Sta. Res. Bull.,* **594** (1955).
128. Pital, A., Stafseth, H. J., and Lucas, E. H., "The Cobalt Enhancement of Penicillin Activity Against *Salmonella Pullorum,*" *Science,* **117,** 459–60 (1953).
129. Porter, J. R., "Bacterial Chemistry and Physiology," New York, John Wiley and Sons, Inc., 1946.
130. Price, N. O., Linkous, W. N., and Engel, R. W., "Minor Element Content of Forage Plants From the Coastal Region of Virginia," *Virginia Polytech. Inst. Agr. Expt. Sta. Tech. Bull.,* **123** (1955).
131. Priselkov, M. M., and Grigor'eva, V. M., "Alterations of the Properties of Typhoid and of Dysentery (Flexner's) Microbes by Solutions of Cobalt Sulfate," *Zhur. Mikrobiol. Epidemiol. i Immunobiol.,* **1955,** No. 3, 70–6. *Chem. Abst.,* **49,** 14902 (1955).
132. Ramakrishnan, C. V., and Desai, P. J., "Effect of Addition of Iron, Cobalt,

and Ascorbic Acid to the Medium on the Synthesis of Ascorbic Acid in Molds," *Current Sci.*, **25**, 189–90 (1956).

133. Rickes, E. L., Brink, N. S., Koniuszy, F. R., Wood, T. R., and Folkers, K., "Crystalline Vitamin B_{12}," *Science,* **107**, 396–7 (1948).

134. Riehm, H., and Baron, H., "Investigation and Curing of a Hinsch Farm in the Northern Black Forest. Cobalt as a Micro Nutrient," *Landwirtsch. Forsch.,* **5**, 145–58 (1953). *Chem. Abst.,* **48**, 2958 (1954).

135. Riehm, H., and Scholl, W., "Recent Investigations on Deficiency Systems of Cobalt in the Black Forest," *Landwirtsch. Forsch. Sonderh.,* No. 9, 123–9 (1957). *Chem. Abst.,* **51**, 14179 (1957).

136. Rigg, T., "Cawthron Institute," *Research,* **3**, 131–5 (1950).

137. Ronov, A. B., Malyuga, D. P., and Makarova, A. I., "Distribution of Small Amounts of Nickel, Cobalt, and Copper in the Clays of the Russian Platform," *Doklady Akad. Nauk S.S.S.R.,* **105**, 129–32 (1955). *Chem. Abst.,* **50**, 7687 (1956).

138. Rothery, P., Bell, J. M., and Spinks, J. W. T., "Cobalt and Vitamin B_{12} in Sheep. I. Distribution of Radiocobalt in Tissues and Ingesta," *J. Nutrition,* **49**, 173–81 (1953).

139. Sawada, Y., Tanaka, K., Hirano, M., Sato, M., Miyamoto, J., and Tanaka, S., "Studies of Cobalt Metabolism of Microorganisms. II. On the Cobalt Absorption of *Aspergillus Oryzae* and *Bacillus Natto,*" *Nippon Kagaku Zasshi,* **76**, 274–7 (1955). *Chem. Abst.,* **51**, 18107 (1957).

140. Scharrer, K., and Prun, H., "The Content of Micro- and Macro-nutrients in Farmyard Manure," *Landwirtsch. Forsch.,* **8**, 182–206 (1956). *Chem. Abst.,* **50**, 12378 (1956).

141. Seay, W. A., and DeMumbrum, L. E., "Minor Element Content of Eight Kentucky Soils and Lespedeza," *Agron. J.,* **50**, 237–40 (1958).

142. Seiffert, H. H., and Wehrman, J., "Copper and Cobalt Uptake of Forage as Related to Fertilization on Podzol and Brown Earth Meadows in Schleswig-Holstein," *Z. Pflanzenernahr. Dung. Bodenk.,* **79**, 142–54 (1957). *Chem. Abst.,* **53**, 7477 (1959).

143. Shambye, P., and Jacobsen, I., "Cobalt Content in Some Danish Soils, Crops, Fertilizers, and Concentrates," Kgl. Vet. og Landbohojskole Arsskr., **1955**, 53–77. *Chem. Abst.,* **49**, 11928 (1955).

144. Sheehy, E. J., "Cobalt Deficiency in Sligo," *Nature,* **160**, 873 (1947).

145. Sherman, H. C., "Chemistry of Food and Nutrition," 8th. edition, New York, Macmillan Company, 1952.

146. Shohl, A. T., "Mineral Metabolism," New York, Reinhold Publishing Corp., 1939.

147. Skoropostizhnaya, A. S., "The Cobalt Content in Most Customary Foods," *Voprosy Pitoniya,* **16**, No. 1, 59–62 (1957). *Chem. Abst.,* **51**, 1599 (1957).

148. —, "Vitamin B_{12} Content in the Liver of Animals as a Function of Quantity of Cobalt in the Food Ration," *Voprosy Pitaniya,* **17**, No. 2, 29–32 (1958). *Chem. Abst.,* **52**, 16523 (1958).

149. —, "Effect of Cobalt Concentration in Ration on Hemopoiesis," *Fisiol.*

Zhur., Akad. Nauk. Ukr.R.S.R., **4**, 537–41 (1958). *Chem. Abst.,* **53**, 2389 (1959).

150. Slater, S. C., Holmes, R. S., and Byers, H. G., "Trace Elements in the Soils from the Erosion Experiment Stations with Supplementary Data on Other Soils," *U. S. Dept. Agr. Tech. Bull.,* **552** (1937).

151. Smith, E. L., "Presence of Cobalt in the Anti-Pernicious Anaemia Factor," *Nature,* **162**, 144–5 (1948).

152. —, "The Chemistry and Functions of Vitamin B_{12}," *Chemistry and Industry,* **1957**, May 11, 572–7.

153. Smith, S. E., Koch, B. A., and Turk, K. L., "The Response of Cobalt-Deficient Lambs to Liver Extract and Vitamin B_{12}," *J. Nutrition,* **44**, 455–64 (1951).

154. Smith, S. E., and Loosli, J. K., "Cobalt and Vitamin B_{12} in Ruminant Nutrition," *J. Dairy Sci.,* **40**, 1215–27 (1957).

155. Solun, A. S., and Roizman, P. S., "The Part Played by Cobalt in the Nutrition of Fur-Bearing Rabbits," *Trudy Moskov. Vet. Akad.,* **11**, 218–35 (1956). *Chem. Abst.,* **51**, 14927 (1957).

156. Spangenberg, G. E., and Gonzalez, F. S., "Distribution of Iron, Copper, and Cobalt in Sheep Pastures," *Arch. Fitotec. Uraguay,* **5**, 213–21 (1952). *Chem. Abst.,* **50**, 10199 (1956).

157. Steinberg, R. A., "Effect of Zinc and Iron Compared with that of Uranium and Cobalt on Growth of *Aspergillus*," *Bot. Gaz.,* **70**, 465–8 (1920).

158. Stewart, J., Mitchell, R. L., and Stewart, A. B., "Pining in Sheep: Its Control by Administration of Cobalt by Use of Cobalt-Rich Fertilisers," *Empire J. Exptl. Agr.,* **9**, 145–52 (1941).

159. Stojkovska, A., and Cooke, G. W., "Micronutrients in Fertilisers," *Chemistry and Industry,* **1958**, Oct. 18, 1368.

160. Strzemski, M., and Kabata, A., "The Amount of Cobalt in Polish Soils as Found by the Department of Soil Science in Pulawy," *Med. Weterynar.,* **12**, 86 (1956). *Chem. Abst.,* **52**, 630 (1958).

161. Tanaka, S., Sawada, Y., Nozaki, Y., and Yamamoto, T., "Cobalt Metabolism of Microorganisms. 1. Cobalt Assimilation by *Streptomyces Griseus* and *Bacillus Subtilis*," *J. Chem. Soc. Japan Pure Chem. Sect.,* **75**, 252–4 (1954). Chem. Abst., **48**, 12899 (1954).

162. Tastaldi, H., Melardi, E. B., Leal, A., and Buccheri, A., "Influence of Cobalt on the Growth of Chicks," *Anais Fac. Farm. e Odontal Univ. Sao Paulo,* **12**, 172–82 (1954). *Chem. Abst.,* **50**, 9535 (1956).

163. Thimann, K. V., "Growth and Inhibition of Isolated Plant Parts. V. Effects of Cobalt and Other Metals," *Am. J. Bot.,* **43**, 241–50 (1956).

164. Tosic, J., and Mitchell, R. L., "Concentration of Cobalt by Microorganisms and its Relation to Cobalt Deficiency in Sheep," *Nature,* **162**, 502–4 (1948).

165. Trace, J. C., and Edds, G. T., "The Influence of Cobalt on the Action of Antibiotics," *Am. J. Vet. Res.,* **15**, 639–42 (1954).

166. Underwood, E. J., "Trace Elements in Human and Animal Nutrition," New York, Academic Press Inc., 1956.

167. Underwood, E. J., and Harvey, R. J., "Enzootic Marasmus: the Cobalt Content of Soils, Pastures, and Animal Organs," *Australian Vet. J.,* **14,** 183–9 (1938).

168. Vergano, O., and Hunter, J. G., "Nickel and Cobalt Toxicities in Oat Plants," *Ann. Bot.,* **17,** 317–28 (1953).

169. Viana, J. A. C., and Moreira, H. A., "Effect of Cobalt in the Diet of Pigs Kept on Concrete Floors," *Arquiv. Escola Super. Vet. Estado Minas Gerais,* **9,** 161–8 (1956). *Chem. Abst.,* **52,** 5573 (1958).

170. Vinogradov, A. P., "The Elementary Chemical Composition of Marine Organisms," New Haven, Sears Foundation for Marine Research, 1953.

171. Vlasyuk, P. A., "The Available Forms of the Trace Elements Zinc, Boron, Cobalt, and Copper in the Soils of the Ukrainian S.S.R.," *Mikroelementy v Sel'sk. Khoz. i Med. Akad. Nauk Latv. S.S.R., Otdel Biol. Nauk. Trudy Vsesoyuz Soveshchan Riga,* **1955,** 97–103. *Chem. Abst.,* **53,** 10618 (1959).

172. Walsh, T., Ryan, P., and Fleming, G. A., "Cobalt Deficiency in Relation to Weathering Processes in Soils," *Congr. Intern. Sci. Sol., 6th. Rappts. B.,* **1956,** 771–9. *Chem. Abst.,* **52,** 15811 (1958).

173. Warren, H. V., and Delavault, R. E., "Biogeochemical Prospecting for Cobalt," *Trans. Roy. Soc. Canada Third Ser.,* Section IV, **51,** 33–7 (1957).

174. Webb, J. S., and Tooms, J. S., "Geochemical Drainage Reconnaissance for Copper in Northern Rhodesia," *Trans. Instit. Min. Met.,* Part IV, **68,** 125–44 (1958–59).

175. Wehrman, J., "Manganese, Copper and Cobalt in Plants and Soils from Schleswig-Holstein," *Plant and Soil,* **6,** 61–83 (1955). *Chem. Abst.,* **49,** 7168 (1955).

176. Wright, J. R., and Lawton, K., "Cobalt Investigations on Some Nova Scotia Soils," *Soil Sci.,* **77,** 95–105 (1954).

177. Wright, J. R., Levick, R., and Atkinson, H. J., "Trace-Element Distribution in Virgin Profiles Representing Four Great Soil Groups," *Soil. Sci. Soc. Am. Proc.,* **19,** 340–4 (1955).

178. Yamada, Y., "Effect of Cobalt on the Growth of Pollen," *Kagaku* (Science), **28,** 257–8 (1958). *Chem. Abst.,* **52,** 17409 (1958).

179. Yamagata, N., and Murakami, Y., "A Cobalt-Accumulator Plant, *Clethra Barbinervis* Sieb. et Zucc.," *Nature,* **181,** 1808 (1958).

180. Young, R. S., "Certain Rarer Elements in Soils and Fertilizers, and their Role in Plant Growth," *Cornell Univ. Agr. Expt. Sta. Mem.,* 174 (1935).

181. —, "Cobalt Content of Chilean Nitrate of Soda," *Research,* **4,** 392 (1951).

182. —, "Cobalt, an Essential Element," *Nutritional Observatory,* **14,** 1–3 (1953).

183. —, "Solubility of Cobalt in Soil," *J. Soil Sci.,* **6,** 233–40 (1955).

184. —, "Cobalt in Biology and Biochemistry," *Sci. Progress,* **44,** 16–37 (1956).

185. —, "The Geochemistry of Cobalt," *Geochim. Cosmochim. Acta,* **13,** 28–41 (1957).

186. Zende, G. K., "Fate of Applied Cobalt," *J. Indian Soc. Soil Sci.,* **2,** 67–72 (1954).

Chapter 16

RADIOACTIVE COBALT

DAVID M. RICHMAN
Division of Research
U. S. Atomic Energy Commission
Washington, D. C.

and

ERNEST J. HENLEY

Professor
Dept. of Chemistry and Chemical Engineering
Stevens Institute of Technology
Hoboken, N. J.

THE ISOTOPES OF COBALT

There are ten known isotopes of cobalt.[38] Only one, cobalt-59, is stable, and is found in nature in 100 per cent abundance. Table 16.1 lists the radioactive isotopes of cobalt, their half lives and decay schemes.

The best known cobalt radioisotope is cobalt-60. Interest in cobalt-60 originally developed as the result of reactor operation. One of the problems arising from the use of fission reactors is the accumulation of highly radioactive fission product wastes. Starting in the late 1940's, programs to evaluate the usefulness of these waste materials were undertaken in the United States and other nations with advanced nuclear technology. Because large quantities of separated fission products were not available in a convenient form, a simulated fission product was sought for experimental processes. Cobalt-60 was selected for the following reasons, to serve as the simulated fission product for research and development purposes:

(1) The physical and chemical properties of cobalt, from radiation-safety, structural, and thermal points of view, are satisfactory.
(2) One hundred per cent natural abundance of cobalt-59 minimizes the problem of producing isotopes other than the desired cobalt-60 from pure cobalt starting material.
(3) The probability of neutron capture by cobalt-59 is relatively high.
(4) A high specific radioactivity per unit weight can be produced.
(5) The half life and decay scheme of cobalt-60 are, respectively, reasonably long and relatively uncomplicated (see Figure 16.1).

347

TABLE 16.1. RADIOISOTOPES OF COBALT

Isotope	Half Life	Mode of Decay
$_{27}Co^{54}$	0.18 seconds	Emission of positive electrons of energy greater than 7.4 mev; there is evidence of the existence of this isotope, but its mass is not well established.
$_{27}Co^{55}$	18.2 hours	Emission of positive electrons (60%), and capture of orbital electrons by the nucleus (40%); gamma radiation accompanies both modes of decay.
$_{27}Co^{56}$	77.3 days	Capture of orbital electrons (80%) accompanied by gamma rays; emission of positive electrons (20%) accompanied by gamma radiation. The decay scheme is rather complex; the decay product is stable iron, $_{26}Fe^{56}$.
$_{27}Co^{57}$	270 days	Orbital electron capture accompanied by gamma radiation; the decay product is stable $_{26}Fe^{57}$.
$_{27}Co^{58m}$	9 hours	Cobalt-58m (metastable) decays in two steps. First, isomeric transition through emission of gamma radiation to a less excited nuclear state identified as cobalt-58; then, decay of cobalt-58.
$_{27}Co^{58}$	71.3 days	Capture of orbital electrons (85%) accompanied by gamma radiation; also, emission of positive electrons (15%) accompanied by gamma radiation. The decay product is the iron isotope, $_{26}Fe^{58}$.
$_{27}Co^{60m}$	10.5 minutes	Isomeric transition to cobalt-60 with accompanying gamma radiation; 0.3% cobalt-60m decays directly to $_{28}Ni^{60}$ by beta emission.
$_{27}Co^{60}$	5.2 years	Emission of beta radiation accompanied by gamma rays. The decay scheme of this isotope, the best known and industrially most important radioisotope of cobalt, is illustrated in Figure 16.1
$_{27}Co^{61}$	99.0 minutes	Emission of beta particles accompanied by low energy gamma radiation; a stable nickel isotope is produced.
$_{27}Co^{62m}$	1.6 minutes	Such an isotope probably exists though its mass is not well established; it is believed to be an isomeric state of cobalt-62.
$_{27}Co^{62}$	13.9 minutes	Beta emission accompanied by gamma radiation; the decay scheme has not yet been clearly defined.
$_{27}Co^{64}$	5 minutes	This is noted in the literature, but there is insufficient evidence of its existence.

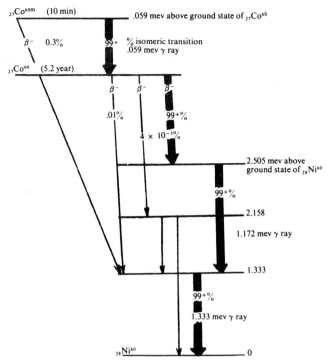

Figure 16.1. Cobalt-60 Decay Scheme.

PHYSICS OF COBALT-60 PRODUCTION

Cobalt-60 is produced from cobalt-59 by neutron bombardment of cobalt metal placed inside a nuclear fission reactor. The reaction occurring in the reactor is expressed in the following equation.

$$_{27}Co^{59} + {}_0n^1 \longrightarrow {}_{27}Co^{60} \tag{1}$$

There are several important considerations involved in the actual production of any isotope in a reactor.

(a) The product as well as the original target are subject to neutron bombardment and may be destroyed.

(b) The desired radioisotope product decays while in the reactor, with subsequent product loss.

(c) Although there is a theoretical concentration of radioactive material for any radioisotope, practical considerations of neutron intensity, time of irradiation, and impurity content of the target material prevent its attainment.

The probability of capturing neutrons is greater for cobalt-59 than for cobalt-60.[20] Also, speaking practically, cobalt-60 is present in far lower concentrations than cobalt-59, and has a nalf life greater by an order of magnitude than the time usually required for its production in a nuclear reactor. The result is that the rate of production for cobalt-60 is far greater than the rate of destruction.

The basic equation expressing the production rate of cobalt-60 is

$$\frac{d[Co^{60}]}{dt} = -\lambda[Co^{60}] + \phi[Co^{59}]\sigma_{59} - \phi[Co^{60}]\sigma_{60} \tag{2}$$

where t is time in seconds, λ is the decay constant for cobalt-60 (the reciprocal of its half life), $[Co^{60}]$ and $[Co^{59}]$ are concentrations of the isotopes in atoms/cc, ϕ is the neutron flux in the reactor in neutrons/cm^2-sec, and σ_{60}, σ_{59} are neutron capture probabilities for the denoted isotopes in cm^2/atom.

Assuming that $[Co^{60}]\sigma_{60}$ is small compared to $[Co^{59}]\sigma_{59}$, equation (2) may be integrated to give:

$$Co^{60} = \phi[Co^{59}]\sigma_{59}\frac{(1 - e^{-\lambda t})}{\lambda} . \tag{3}$$

While Co^{60} has the units of atoms/cc, it may easily be converted to a more useful unit, curies/g. A curie is a unit of power defined as 3.70×10^{10} atomic disintegrations/sec. Each disintegration is accompanied by a release of energy. The amount of energy released per disintegration is characteristic for the isotope under consideration. Consequently, for different isotopes, the curie represents a different amount of power. For cobalt-60, 1 curie equals 0.015 watts/g. Theoretically, it should be possible to obtain 1140 curies/g or 17.1 watts/g of cobalt. Practically, however, this cannot be achieved, and the specific activity of cobalt usually varies from 1–2 up to as high as 100 curies/g, depending primarily on the neutron flux level in the reactor. Of course, it is also available in lower concentrations for research and process control purposes.

COST OF COBALT-60

The cost of cobalt-60 is based on both its specific activity and the quantity purchased. Oak Ridge National Laboratory markets cobalt-60 in two forms: as a salt in solution, and as the metal.[27] In solution, the cobalt is present as $CoCl_2$ in approximately 1N HCl. It has a concentration greater than 1 millicurie/ml and a specific activity of greater than 10,000 millicuries/g of cobalt. The chemical purity of the material is better than 99 per cent. The chloride is used primarily for chemical research or tracing purposes, and is sold in millicurie quantities.

Cobalt metal for use in high level gamma sources is available at the prices given in Table 16.2.

TABLE 16.2. PRICE OF COBALT-60

Specific Activity, c/g	List Price, $/c
1–25	2.00
26–40	3.00
greater than 40	4.00

Discounts are given at Oak Ridge and Chalk River, Canada, the leading purveyors of sources, for quantities greater than 5000 curies.

Table 16.3 gives the sales from Oak Ridge of cobalt-60 as the chloride solution for a four-year period ending June 30, 1960.

TABLE 16.3. OAK RIDGE SALES OF $CoCl_2$

Time	Millicuries Sold
July 1, 1956–June 30, 1957	1,020
July 1, 1957–June 30, 1958	729
July 1, 1958–June 30, 1959	1,070
July 1, 1959–June 30, 1960	984

Table 16.4 gives the annual sales of Oak Ridge National Laboratory of cobalt-60 as cobalt metal. This is only an index of world production. The

TABLE 16.4. OAK RIDGE NATIONAL LABORATORY ANNUAL SALES OF COBALT-60

Year	Curies
1948	0
1949	85
1950	534
1951	3,991
1952	9,634
1953	6,181
1954	25,493
1955	50,532
1956	93,618
1957	146,505
1958	173,235
1959	168,817

British, Canadians, and Russians are also producing cobalt-60. Russian production, according to Soviet news releases, totaled 800,000 curies in 1959.

OTHER COBALT ISOTOPES

One of the early methods for producing radioisotopes was cyclotron bombardment of target materials. The cyclotron and other accelerators are still used extensively to make radioisotopes that cannot be prepared or obtained in a concentrated form by other methods.

Cobalt-58, the only other cobalt radioisotope available at Oak Ridge, is produced in a cyclotron by the following reaction:

$$_{28}Ni^{58} + {}_0n^1 \longrightarrow {}_{27}Co^{58} + {}_1p^1 \tag{4}$$

It is priced at $20.00 per millicurie. The chemical form for this isotope is as $CoCl_2$ in 1N HCl solution in concentrations greater than 0.1 millicurie per milliliter. The chemical purity is better than 98 per cent. Table 16.5 gives the sales of cobalt-58 of the Oak Ridge National Laboratory during the past four years.

TABLE 16.5.   OAK RIDGE SALES OF COBALT-58

Time	Millicuries
July 1956–June 1957	104
July 1957–June 1958	182
July 1958–June 1959	184
July 1959–June 1960	217

Cyclotron bombardment of iron (primarily Fe^{56}) with protons and deuterons is the basis for commercial production of Co^{56}, Co^{57}, and Co^{58}.

GROWTH OF COMMERCIAL ACTIVITIES

Cyclotron-produced cobalt isotopes, and reactor-produced cobalt-60 can be purchased from about 150 different firms. Some are actually producers, but most act as processors and retailers.

The following are published indexes and guides of the availability of radioisotopes:

(1) The Isotope Index, published yearly by Scientific Equipment Co., Publications Department 9, P.O. Box 19086, Indianapolis 19, Indiana.

(2) International Directory of Radioisotopes, Volume I. Unprocessed and Processed Radioisotope Preparations and Special Radiation

Sources, National Agency for International Publications, Inc., 801 Third Avenue, New York 22, New York. Published by the International Atomic Energy Agency, Karntner Ring, Vienna 1, Austria, as report STI/PUB No. 5a.

(3) International Directory of Radioisotopes, Volume II. Compounds of Carbon 14, Hydrogen 3, Iodine 131, Phosphorus 32 and Sulphur 35, National Agency for International Publications, Inc., 801 Third Avenue, New York 22, New York. Published by the International Atomic Energy Agency, Karntner Ring, Vienna 1, Austria, as report STI/PUB No. 7.

(4) Nucleonics Buyers' Guide, published annually; Nucleonics Products and Services Directory, published at McGraw-Hill Building, 330 West 42nd Street, New York 36, New York.

(5) Atomic Industry Directory of Products, Equipment and Services, Atomic Industrial Forum, 3 East 54th Street, New York 22, New York.

Nine concerns manufacture teletherapy machines; ten companies in the United States have announced that they are prepared to encapsulate large radiation sources; and three companies have capacity to handle up to a million curies. The United States Atomic Energy Commission withdrew from providing cobalt-60 encapsulation service in March, 1958.

In March, 1958, the United States Atomic Energy Commission discontinued providing gamma irradiation service to private groups. About 120 academic and industrial organizations in the United States have their own cobalt-60 irradiation facilities, and many offer irradiation service on a commercial basis.[3,31]

In countries other than the United States, the production, fabrication, and sales of isotopes are handled primarily by government agencies.

Two companies in the United States, Westinghouse and General Electric, have announced their intentions to produce at least some radioisotopes, such as cobalt-60, in their own reactors. Other groups are beginning to negotiate directly with private reactor facilities for purchase of commercially produced radioisotopes, including cobalt-60. There have been a number of studies on the economics of cobalt production in private reactors.[12,29,39]

COBALT-60 ACTIVATION PROCEDURES

High purity cobalt is used for isotope production, since reduction of impurities reduces the neutrons needed to produce a given amount of radioactive cobalt. However, when very thin strips are required (50 mils or less), reactor-grade cobalt metal of 97 per cent or greater purity becomes very expensive because of the difficulties encountered in rolling the strips. Research laboratories of the Haynes Stellite Company have been working on a new alloy of 92 per cent cobalt, 4 per cent iron, and 4 per cent nickel, which is more workable than reactor-grade cobalt and, consequently, much cheaper. Although using an alloy reduces the cost of thin strips, the impurities cause some neutrons to be wasted, thus added weight is required to produce the same amount of cobalt.

Depending on its ultimate use, and the source fabricators and reactor operators, fabricated cobalt is given a flash plate of some other material, such as nickel or aluminum, prior to its insertion into the reactor. This operation is necessary to minimize abrasion and consequent escape of cobalt-60 during handling between the time of activation and completion of encapsulation. Encapsulating the cobalt before activation is an alternate technique to flash coating. This is the approach generally used for the cylinder sources and some of the earlier flat plate sources. Final containers are fabricated of aluminum or stainless steel.

The cobalt, either encapsulated or flash-plated, is then placed into another container and inserted into the nuclear reactor. Calculations based on detailed knowledge of the composition of the material charged to the reactor, and the neutron flux where the cobalt is positioned, determine how long the cobalt must remain in the reactor to achieve the required specific activity. The reactor flux and nuclear properties of the cobalt itself limit the specific activity; eventually, the rate of the reactions destroying the cobalt-60 compete with the rates of formation (Equation (2)). This limits the length of time the cobalt can remain in the reactor. In a low flux reactor (10^{12} n/cm^2-sec or thereabout) this time is measured in years, perhaps 1 or 2. In a high flux reactor (10^{14} n/cm^2-sec) the activation is complete in a matter of months.

Cobalt will poison a nuclear reactor, a poison being defined as any material that reduces the number of neutrons available for maintaining the fission chain reaction process. Unless it replaces some other equally effective poison, cobalt increases the amount of fissionable material that must be used to keep the reactor operating at its specified power level. The irradiation of cobalt clad in stainless steel is particularly wasteful of neutrons since stainless steel is a rather effective poison. Also, activation of thick pieces of cobalt is ineffective because material near the center of the thicker sections see only a small fraction of the neutron flux seen by the cobalt on the surface. The neutron intensity at the middle of the cobalt is thus greatly reduced because of high neutron absorption by the surface material. This surface effect should be considered in producing high specific activity material because the flux reaching the cobalt through any thick cladding material is reduced. Also, depending on the size of the cobalt activated and its location within the reactor, it will have either a uniform or non-uniform distribution of activity; thus, the gamma flux emitted from its surface will not be uniform but may have a large variation.

After being removed from the reactor, encapsulated cobalt must also be removed from the carrier container, cleaned, and tested for leaks. If the tests are satisfactory, it is then transferred for use either as an individual source, or installed in an irradiator. Problems of shielding and heat transfer arise during these steps.

The unencapsulated, flash-coated cobalt requires a great deal of treatment when removed from the reactor. Cobalt sources, still in the activation containers used in the reactor, are transferred either to the encapsulation cell or to a storage cell where they are removed from the containers. Either type of cell may be expected to become quite contaminated since the cobalt is not completely contained, and some radioactive material, cobalt, cobalt oxide, etc., may be dispersed through the cell during handling. Wherever there are a number of capsules involved, and/or several pieces of cobalt within each capsule, evaluation of the activity in each piece is necessary for checking calculations, selecting pieces to be assembled into a large uniform source, and determining a price for the material produced and sold.

After assaying and selecting or matching source pieces wherever necessary, sources are then encapsulated. The sources are either individually encapsulated or, more probably, assembled into a large convenient unit such as a plaque or long tube. This assembly is then remotely sealed to provide safe, secure encapsulation. Care must be given to the design and fabrication of the final device to permit adequate heat transfer without damaging the assembly.

The following is an example of a problem which might arise: A source to be used in air, but stored in water, is being prepared. It contains many thousands of curies and is of high specific activity. Through self-absorption of the radiation emitted in air, it may reach temperatures of several hundred degrees centigrade. Transfer of such a hot source into a water pool, with accompanying rapid cooling, creates the problem of thermal expansion and contraction which must be taken into account in design and fabrication of any assembly.

Encapsulated units may be built into complex geometrical arrays and resealed to provide double encapsulation, most desirable from a safety point of view even though increased absorber thickness adds to inefficiencies in the use of the cobalt.

RADIOLOGICAL SAFETY

There have been many measurements of the shielding necessary for reducing radiation from cobalt-60 to safe levels, and there are many references to shielding design.[9,14,30,33] Shipping containers are generally lead casks. Some typical weights for handling 1000, 10,000, and 100,000 curie sources of cobalt-60 are, respectively, three tons, seven tons, and 15 tons. Shielding used in operative research facilities include poured lead, lead brick, standard concrete, heavy concrete containing scrap iron or iron oxide aggregate, and water in water pool facilities where cobalt may be visible below a safe depth of ten or more feet of purified water.

Lead thicknesses necessary for reducing cobalt radiation to tolerance levels are about eight inches for 1000 curies, 9.5 inches for 10,000 curies, and close to one foot for 100,000 curies. Figure 16.2, taken from Handbook

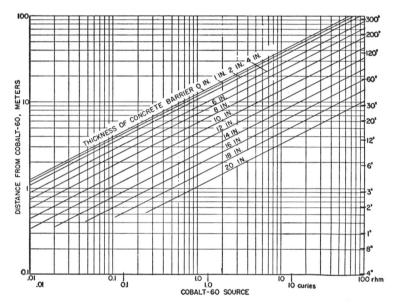

Figure 16.2. Shielding requirements for Co-60.

54, U. S. Dept. of Commerce, gives the relationship between curiage, distance, and shielding for forty-eight hour occupancy of a concrete-shielded cobalt-60 facility. In Figure 16.2, rhm denotes roentgens per hour at one meter. The roentgen is a unit of absorbed energy, about 83 ergs per gram of air and 93 ergs per gram of water.

Safety standards regarding maximum permissible amounts of radioisotopes in the human body, water, and air are to be found in the appropriate Bureau of Standards Handbooks.[26]

HIGH-LEVEL COBALT-60 IRRADIATION FACILITIES

Existing cobalt-60 gamma radiation facilities may be categorized as follows:

(1) Fixed source and fixed irradiation volume.
(2) Movable source and fixed irradiation volume.
(3) Fixed source and variable irradiation volume.
(4) Movable source and variable volume.

Design Criteria

Each type of irradiator has advantages and shortcomings which make it more or less desirable depending on the objectives of the design. There are, however, several design criteria and general considerations that are applicable to all installations:

(a) *Safety.* For any location, this factor transcends all others.

(b) *Cost.* A cobalt facility must compete, dollar-wise, with X-ray units and electron accelerators.

(c) *Irradiation Volume.* Large volumes may be obtained if dollars and shielding are sacrificed. Here, as everywhere else, a compromise referred to as "optimum design" must be achieved.

(d) *Dose Rate.* At higher dose rates, more experiments can be undertaken, and more design information collected. On the other hand, high dose rates are often incompatible with large volumes and uniform field intensities.

(e) *Flexibility.* This is a catch-all word for factors such as temperature control, ease of handling, interchangeability of isotopes, ease of dismantling and transporting, ability to run flow experiments with and without agitation, etc.

(f) *Availability of Cobalt.* Oak Ridge and Atomic Energy of Canada usually fabricate the isotope in the form of small pellets. In addition, wafers one and two centimeters in diameter and one mm thick are available from Oak Ridge; slugs $\frac{3}{8}$ in. × 1 in. are made at Chalk River; and pipes $2\frac{1}{2}$ in. O.D. by 13 in. long, as well as sheets $\frac{1}{8}$ in. × 2 in. × 13 in., can be purchased from Brookhaven National Laboratory.

Cobalt Source Designs

Having established design criteria and source availability, one can proceed to examine the four types of existing sources.

Fixed Source and Fixed Irradiation Volume. These sources are of greatest value in fundamental chemical and physical research. There are two general categories of existing sources: the small (less than 400 curie) ones fueled with capsules, and the larger (500–1000 curie) ones containing slabs or pipes.

A variety of most unorthodox source concepts and designs exists in the under 400 curie bracket. In an attempt to be economic, many designers have relied on earth, mineral oil, water, and concrete shielding.[2,7,28,35] Other designs, utilizing more conventional materials of construction, are also reported in the literature.[5,11,13,32,34] The smallest of these[34] contains 3 curies and delivers 6,000 r/hr to a few cc of material.

The largest, in terms of curies, is Eastwood's hot spot.[11] This unit, quite typical in many respects, weighs 2200 pounds, and is 20 inches in diameter and 17 inches high. Its six 70-curie cobalt-60 capsules deliver a dose of 1.5×10^6 r/hr to a one-inch long sample 0.5-inch in diameter which is lowered, by hand, into an annulus surrounded by the six cobalt slugs. The source can be shipped back to an isotope refueling center for reloading. This is in contrast to the fixed, earth-, water-, concrete-, or oil-shielded sources which must be loaded from a carrying container supplied by an isotope vendor.

A larger version of the fixed volume-fixed radiation source is typified by

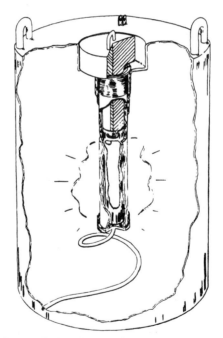

Figure 16.3.* Hollow cylinder design of fixed volume-fixed radiation cobalt source.

*Figures 16.3–16.8 were drawn by Mr. William Karn and furnished through the courtesy of Radiation Applications, Inc., New York, N. Y.

the hollow cylinder or slab units[4,17,23,25] which are able to accommodate 1,000–1,500 curies and, depending on the specific design, will deliver 200,000–800,000 r/hr to a 1–5 liter sample. The source consists of cobalt pipe or slabs set into a 1–2-ton lead shield. Samples are put into cans or baskets and lowered into the radiation cavity, usually by a hand winch. Figure 16.3 is a schematic presentation of this kind of source.

The hollow cylinder design offers a uniform radiation field, simplicity, ease of operation, and mobility for shipping. There are also a number of limitations:

(1) *Lack of flexibility.* It is very difficult, for example, to set up flow experiments, or to operate at very high temperatures. Furthermore, variations in dose rate can be achieved only if extra access holes are added which causes shield enlargement.

(2) *Poor utilization of isotope.* Less than one per cent of the radiation is intercepted by the sample; the other 99 per cent is dissipated in the shield.

(3) *High cost.* A simple, uninstalled model source costs $4500, without isotope.

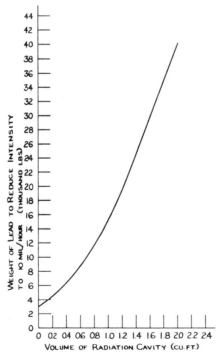

Figure 16.4. Amount of lead required to shield a point 100,000 curie cobalt source.

(4) *Point of diminishing return.* If the hollow cylinder concept is extended to large irradiation volumes, a point is quickly reached where extraordinary quantities of lead shielding are required. A crude calculation of the amount of lead required to shield a point 100,000 curie source is given in Figure 16.4. As the usable radiation volume around the source is increased, so is the amount of shielding required.

(5) *Safety.* Figure 16.5 is a survey of the radiation field above a 200 curie cobalt source with the cover removed. The access hole is 1.75 inches in diameter, and the source is recessed.[25]

Intermediate in design between the hollow cylinder and hot spot irradiators are a few large volume, low isotope sources for specialized work, particularly in the fields of genetics and biology.[9,15]

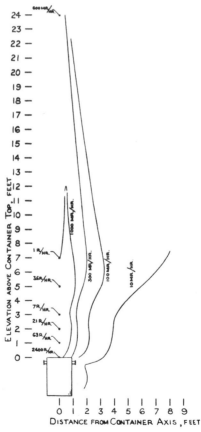

Figure 16.5. Radiation field above a 200 curie cobalt source.

Movable Source—Fixed Radiation Volume. A most economic version of this type of source is one in which the shipping container is used as the isotope holder. The cobalt is generally attached to a rod that moves axially through the storage cylinder, pushing the cobalt into a concrete- or earth-shielded enclosure. Johnson[22] built the first of these units, and the concept has been extended.[37] Figure 16.6 is a cutaway drawing of such

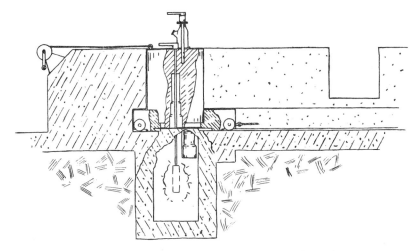

Figure 16.6. Movable cobalt source-fixed radiation volume.

an installation. The cobalt-60 shipping container is mounted on wheels and rolled over the irradiation volume. The cobalt may then be lowered.

Although cave and pool units may also be of the movable source-fixed volume type, they are more logically classified as movable source, variable volume installations, since the volumes, for all practical purposes, are infinite.

Fixed Source—Variable Volume. Small sources of this type are costly to build and difficult to operate. Two have been built,[16,21] primarily for studying reaction mechanisms. In both, the sample is rotated in and out of the radiation field by means of a device similar to the well-known rotating sectors apparatus used in photochemistry.

Movable Source—Variable Volume. This describes installations in which isotopes are moved in and out of the radiation zone, and the radiation zone itself is unrestricted or expandable. Two types of facilities are in general use—water pits and caves, and shielded rooms.

The shielded room is ordinarily built above a deep, water-filled well or a shipping container in which isotopes are stored. Remote control manipulators (of the type found in hot cells), viewing windows, and a labyrinth entrance are usually employed. For economy, the window and remote control manipulators may be eliminated.

Figure 16.7 is a plan of Esso's radiation cave. This installation was reported to cost $250,000.

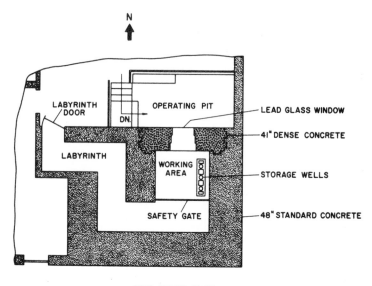

CAVE FLOOR PLAN

Figure 16.7. Movable cobalt source-variable volume installation. Radiation cave of the Esso Laboratory.

Water pools have also found some measure of popularity. The pool should be a minimum of 12 feet deep, with a deep well for storing the source during drainage and repair. Figure 16.8 illustrates a water pit.

A few of the disadvantages of water pools—ones which have made their owners, on occasion, quite unhappy—are:

(1) *Difficulty of under-water work.*

(2) *Maintenance problems.* Vegetation and corrosion can be avoided only by strenuous and expensive measures.

(3) *Attenuation.* One centimeter of water is as effective in gamma ray absorption as 770 cm of air. Although this is favorable from a shielding standpoint, it reduces materially the amount of available radiation.

The units described all contain 20,000 curies or less. During the past two years, construction of a number of pilot plant and production irradiators

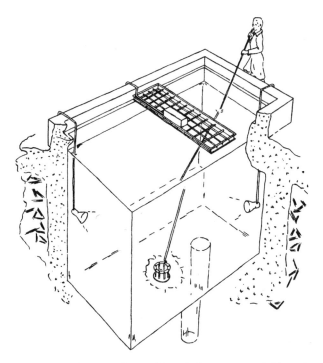

Figure 16.8. Water pit type of movable cobalt source-variable volume installation.

has commenced. These are all of the fixed source, movable volume type, having conveyor systems and reinforced concrete shielding. The total curie equivalence of the installations now being built in America, Australia, Canada, England, France, and Russia is over 5 million curies. A partial description of these units has been published by Henley.[18]

APPLICATIONS OF COBALT-60 AND OTHER COBALT ISOTOPES AS ISOTOPIC TRACERS

Cobalt-60 and other cobalt isotopes have been used in chemical, physical, and biological research. Cobalt-60 was, for instance, used by Drs. T. B. Lee and C. N. Yang in their Nobel prize-winning study which resulted in disproving the parity concept. Minute quantities of isotopes are, of course, used extensively for tracing complex reactions and processes. The great sensitivity of radioisotope techniques is illustrated by the fact that for isotopes having half lives ranging from hours to years, the theoretical amount of radioactive element necessary for analysis is of the order of 10^{-16}–10^{-19} g.

Physical and Chemical Research Utilizing Cobalt-60

The applications of radioisotopes in experimental and applied physics, and general, physical, and organic chemistry, are extensive. One review of the uses of radioisotopes in the field of analytical chemistry for the years 1955–1957 lists 1,279 papers covering that field alone.

Thicknesses down to a trillionth of an inch are measured by a calibrating technique similar to that used in electron microscopy. Specimens to be viewed are frequently sprayed at an angle with chromium or other heavy metal atoms so that shadows are formed which reveal varying depths of surface. Atoms are evaporated in vacuum from a heated metal and deposited on the specimen. The resulting film must be thick enough to produce good shadows but not so thick that they blur specimen details. Radioactive cobalt is used to determine the thickness of a film laid down at a given time in a particular place. A standard area of the film is counted, and comparisons are made between standard samples and the specimens.

Cobalt isotopes have also been applied to the study of surface phenomena in such fields as metal plating, detergent action, mirror formation, corrosion prevention, catalysis, adhesion of protective coatings, degassing of surfaces, and classification of minerals.

Autoradiography is another field of isotope application. Here, radioactive cobalt is introduced into molten metal before the specimens are prepared. In one technique, sections of three to four millimeters in thickness are cut from the ingot plate. They are planed to a thickness of 2 mm, further ground to a thickness of 0.1–0.07 mm, and finished to the desired thickness of 20–25 microns by a grinding process involving two parallel glass plates, and extremely fine abrasive powders and paste. The plates having been prepared, a nuclear photographic emulsion is placed next to the section, either by direct contact or by use of a stripping film, and the film is developed after suitable exposure. The location of the radioactivity may then be directly determined.

Industry has demonstrated the usefulness of radioactive tracer techniques for determining the wear of tool bits in machine operations. In the standard technique, non-radioactive cobalt is incorporated in the piece, and the finished tool is irradiated by neutrons to produce the cobalt-60 isotope. Tool wear may then be accurately assessed by standard counting techniques.

Activity analysis and radiometric analysis are two different types of analytical procedures. The term "activity analysis" often refers to a simple determination of the amount of radioactive material in a sample which has undergone some reaction, physical change, or perhaps material transfer. Radiometric analysis is used to determine a given nonradioactive substance by addition of a radioactive tracer. For example, radiometric analysis might be used to measure cobalt directly in a sample by precipitating some insoluble salt with a radioactive anion; or, cobalt might be determined by direct measurement of the radioactive cobalt in a sample. Two instances of work that would be difficult, if not impossible, without such tracers are studies of alterations that take place in chemical precipitates, and studies of vapor pressure.

The mechanisms by which organic materials adhere to soil particles are extremely difficult to determine. Clay minerals and other fine particles have a high capacity to absorb organic and inorganic cations. Many complexing or "chelating" organic chemicals have been reported from natural waters and sediments. For example, aspartic acid may chelate with cobalt. Although there has been a substantial amount of research on the exchange capacity of various clays and soils, information is far from complete. Cobalt isotopes are proving useful in this area.

Other analytical techniques that depend primarily on nuclear phenomena are activation analysis and isotope dilution. Activation analysis makes use of the radioactivity produced in a sample by nuclear radiation. Measurement of the activity produced is a highly sensitized means of determining impurities. Isotope dilution, a method for determining the quantity of an element present, involves measuring the change in the concentration or the specific activity of isotopes of the same element.

Biological Research

Animals require many elements in small amounts. Numerous nutritional studies have been made with radioisotopes. Metabolism in animals can be determined by tracing intake of food in the form of elements, and inorganic and organic compounds; intake and incorporation of food into various regions of the body; breakdown of food; and excretion of waste. Tracer techniques are extremely useful in nutritional studies. An element that occurs in only a few parts per 100,000,000 parts of feed can be traced through the digestive tract to its location in the tissues of a 1,000 pound animal without disturbing its normal physiology.

It has been found that a lack of cobalt in the diet inhibits the formation of vitamin B_{12}. Vitamin B_{12}, labeled with cobalt-60, may be transferred from the body of a cow to its milk during lactation; the vitamin content of the milk may then be used to indicate the extent of cobalt nutrition.

Important diagnostic applications for cobalt-60 as a trace element have developed. Radioactive vitamin B_{12}, labeled with cobalt-60, is used in the diagnosis of pernicious and other types of anemia. A test using radio-vitamin B_{12} is also being developed for measuring liver cell damage occurring in hepatitis.

RADIATION EFFECTS

Cobalt-60, as well as other radioisotopes, is useful not only for studying physical, chemical, and biological phenomena, but also for causing them. Radiation stimulates chemical change by producing ionized molecules or free radicals which, in turn, react to produce new molecules. Cobalt-60 is a unique source of such ionizing radiation.

Uses for Medical Treatment

It was first proposed in 1948 that cobalt-60 be used as a concentrated source of gamma rays for distant therapy treatment of malignancies.[1] This is a direct outgrowth of the use of radium and X-ray machines for this same purpose.

The first teletherapy unit, designed in 1950, was built by General Electric Co. Since then, over 200 individual sources have been produced in the United States, and cobalt-60 has assumed an important role in the radiotherapy departments of many leading hospitals and medical centers throughout the country. Teletherapy has been a world-wide development, and progress within the past few years has been significant.

Single compact sources with a gamma ray output equivalent to thousands of grams of radium are obtainable. Cobalt-60 having a specific activity of 50 curies per gram, permits kilocurie source dimensions of 1–2 centimeters. In comparison with X-ray equipment giving comparable depth dose patterns, teletherapy units are more compact and have greater maneuverability for field therapy, making possible a wider variety of dosage patterns.

Implantation therapy is another important therapeutic use of cobalt-60. Radioisotopes may be physically placed, both in solid form and as a liquid, in an appropriate carrier or solution. As solids, they are placed on a body surface, inserted into cavities, or implanted into the tissues. As liquids, they are injected into cavities, mingled with body fluids for transport to inaccessible parts, injected into tissues as a dispersed source in the extracellular spaces, or placed in containers, such as plastic envelopes or tubing, to give easily controlled, localized irradiation.

These methods of therapy involving the physical placement of radioisotopes may be listed in three categories: (1) intracavitary, (2) interstitial, and (3) external.

Cobalt-60 has been used as an intracavitary source for the treatment of both uterine and bladder cancer. In the latter, a small, nearly point source is introduced through a catheter into a bag which is distended to form a sphere in the bladder. Cobalt used in this way is closely related to the use of radium with which radiologists have had a good deal of experience. Compared with radium, radiocobalt has a number of advantages, including reasonable cost and easy containment. Cobalt may be used as a nickel or chromium alloy encapsulated in gold or silver, or plated with nickel or chrome.

A survey performed in 1957 showed that cobalt-60 is considered, medically, to be an important isotope, and is expected to be given greater and greater routine hospital use for diagnostic and research work.[6] This is exclusive of its unique use as a teletherapy source. On September 1, 1959, there were 271 licensed cobalt-60 teletherapy installations in the United States and 9 private companies manufacturing such machines.[24]

Sterilization

Gamma rays from cobalt-60 can be used to destroy microorganisms and thus offer a means for sterilizing medical and surgical supplies and instruments, and foodstuffs. Ionizing radiation causes chemical reactions, and consequent biological effects, independent of system temperature. Therefore, gamma-ray sterilization provides the following advantages when compared to steam sterilization: elimination of special packaging now necessary to resist high temperature and moisture effects of steam processing; adaptability of sterilization to a continuous process rather than a batch process; ability to process heat-sensitive products which hitherto have been unsuccessfully treated or for which treatment results in a high rejection rate; possible elimination of expensive aseptic handling procedures currently used for many medical products.

As part of a national program for radiation preservation of foods, a multimegacurie cobalt irradiation facility called High Intensity Food Irradiator (HIFI) was designed in the United States.[10,36,41] This facility, or a modification of it, is expected to be constructed during 1960–61 to provide necessary developmental information regarding radiation processing of foods.

In Australia, a facility using 140,000 curies of cobalt-60 (produced in Great Britain) will be in operation in 1960; its specific function will be to sterilize the goat hair used for rugs, thus reducing the possibility of transporting the dread disease, anthrax. A large effort is also being directed toward sterilization uses for cobalt-60 in Great Britain; a 150,000 curie source has been built at Wantage. Similar units are under construction in France and Russia.

Considerable interest has developed in the use of less than sterilizing doses, especially for food treatment. Called substerilization, or pasteurization, doses of 100,000–200,000 rads can be used to increase food storage life—not indefinitely, but for short, commercially advantageous periods. While sterilization is akin to canning or freezing, pasteurization reduces the need for rapid marketing of perishables.

Radiation offers promise of extending the shelf life of such highly perishable fruits as strawberries, grapes, and peaches, while only insignificantly affecting their quality.[40] Fish, since it spoils so readily, is another possible item for commercial pasteurization.

Cobalt also prevents potatoes and onions from sprouting. The Russians and the Canadians have announced an 80,000 and a 15,000 curie cobalt-60 pilot-plant potato irradiator, respectively.

An even lower dose application (10,000 rads) has successfully deinfested grain, and has aroused great interest as a means of preventing large quantities of stored grain from spoiling. Radiation deinfestation has several advantages: it can cope with problems of chemically resistant insect strains; it does not leave any residue, thus there is no problem of chemical toxicity if grain is fed to humans; radiation is penetrating rather than surface.

Genetics and Insect Eradication

Cobalt-60 research irradiators have been used successfully in genetic research. New species, such as tough-shelled peanuts, have been created, resulting in less crop loss during harvesting.

The most noteworthy genetic application, however, and one of the most important applications of cobalt-60, has been insect eradication. Levels of radiation sufficient to cause sterility in male insects has permitted virtual eradication of the screw worm fly[8] in many parts of the southeastern United States. Studies conducted for several years by the Department of Agriculture indicated a method, and one season's experimentation on the Island of Curacao, Netherland West Indies, proved that by such a method an isolated insect population could be wiped out.

The method involves releasing sexually sterile male flies to mate with normal females. Since the females mate only once, they lay eggs that never hatch. Cobalt-60 produced at Brookhaven National Laboratory was used for sterilizing the males.

Initiation of Chemical Reactions

When a 1.25 million volt photon interacts with a molecule having bonding energies of a few electron volts, one can expect almost every type of known chemical reaction to occur. This, at first, is actually what happens. Ultimately, however, the energy is degraded to the thermal levels, and one finds that the reaction products are not inconsistent with what one might predict on the basis of classical thermodynamics and kinetics. The intermediate reactive species produced by the radiation are usually postulated to be free radicals, with the exception of gases at low pressures, where ion-molecule reactions are thought to occur.

Cobalt-60 has been used extensively in investigations involving the effects of ionizing radiation on chemical systems. In particular, polymerizations, halogenations, oxidations, isomerizations, decompositions, and disproportionation reactions have been most extensively studied. The magnitude of the research effort can be judged by the fact that a 1958 *Review of Radiation Chemistry* lists over 200 references.[19]

References

1. Aebersold, P. C., "The Development of Nuclear Medicine," *Am. J. Roentgenol. Radium Therapy Nuclear Med.,* **75**, 1027–39 (1956).
2. Aitken, P. B., Dyne, P. J., and Trapp, E. C., "Two Small Cobalt Facilities," *Nucleonics,* **15**, No. 1, 100–101 (1957).
3. Anonymous, "Gamma Irradiation Facilities in the United States," *Nucleonics,* **16**, No. 7, 108–9 (1958); *Supplement,* **17**, No. 7, 88 (1959).
4. Bauman, R. G., "Goodrich Facility," *Nucleonics,* **15**, No. 1, 96–9 (1957).
5. Blomgren, R. A., Hart, E. J., and Markeim, L. S., "Radioactive-cobalt Laboratory for Chemical Research," *Rev. Sci. Instr.,* **24**, 298–303 (1953).
6. Brucer, M., Harmon, J. H., and Gude, W. D., "Radioactive Isotopes in the United States Hospitals," ORINS 21, March, 1957, Oak Ridge Institute of Nuclear Studies Inc., Oak Ridge, Tenn. (1957).
7. Burton, M., Ghormley, J. A., and Hochanadel, C. J., "Design of an Inexpensive High-intensity γ-source," *Nucleonics,* **13**, No. 10, 74–7 (1955).
8. Bushland, R. C., "Insect Eradication by Release of Sterilized Males," International Atomic Energy Agency Conference on Application of Large Radiation Sources in Industry, Warsaw, Poland, Sept. 8–12, 1959.
9. Darden, E. B., Maeyens, E., and Bushland, R. C., "A Gamma-Ray Source for Sterilizing Insects," *Nucleonics,* **12**, No. 10, 60–2 (1954).
10. Donovan, J. L., Amundson, P. I., and Rooney, K. L., "Experimental and Computational Results on Source Design for a Multimegacurie Irradiation Facility," Third Industrial Nuclear Technology Conference, Chicago, Ill., Sept. 22–24, 1959.
11. Eastwood, W. S., "The Little Hotspot-miniature Cobalt γ-irradiator," *Nucleonics,* **13**, No. 1, 52–3 (1955).
12. General Nuclear Engineering Corp., "A Study of Reactor Systems for the Production of Tritium and Radioactive Cobalt," GNEC-98, obtainable from Office of Technical Services, U. S. Dept. Commerce, Washington 25, D. C., June 8, 1959.
13. Ghormley, J. A., and Hochanadel, C. J., "A Cobalt γ-Ray Source Used for Studies in Radiation Chemistry," *Rev. Sci. Instr.,* **22**, 473–5 (1951).
14. Goldstein, H., "Fundamental Aspects of Reactor Shielding," Reading, Mass., Addison-Wesley Publ. Co., 1959.

15. Greenfield, M. A., Silverman, L. B., and Dickinson, R. W., "Cobalt[60] Irradiation Chamber," *Nucleonics,* **10,** No. 12, 65–7 (1952).
16. Hart, E. J., and Matheson, M. S., "Mechanism and Rate Constants of the γ-ray-induced Decomposition of Hydrogen Peroxide in Aqueous Solutions," *Disc. Faraday Soc.,* No. 12, 169–88 (1952).
17. Henley, E. J., "Measurement of γ-ray Dosage in Finite Absorbers," *Nucleonics,* **11,** No. 10, 41–3 (1953).
18. —, "Warsaw Atomic Energy Conference," *Chem. Eng. Progr.,* **55,** No. 11, 190–8 (1959).
19. Henley, E. J., and Chandler, H. W., "Radiation Processing," *Ind. Eng. Chem.,* **51,** No. 11, 1395–1402 (1959).
20. Hughes, D. J., and Harvey, J. A., "Neutron Cross Sections," BNL-325, Brookhaven National Laboratory, Upton, N. Y. (revised yearly).
21. Hummel, R. W., Freeman, G. R., Van Cleave, A. B., and Spinks, J. W. T., "Rotating-sector Method Applied to Reactions Induced by Cobalt[60] γ-rays," *Science,* **119,** 159–60 (1954).
22. Johnson, E. R., Bruce, R., Steinmann, R., and Cagnati, V., "Economical and Versatile Co[60] Gamma-Ray Source," *Nucleonics,* **14,** No. 11, 119–120 (1956).
23. Loeding, J. W., Petkus, E. S., Yasui, G., and Rodger, W. A., "Fission Product Kilocurie Source: Preparation, Radiation Intensity," *Nucleonics,* **12,** No. 5, 15–17 (1954).
24. Maddox, J. N., "Teletherapy Installations in the United States," Office of Isotopes Development, U. S. Atomic Energy Commission, Washington, D. C., Sept. 1, 1959.
25. Manowitz, B., "Use of Kilocurie Radiation Sources," *Nucleonics,* **9,** No. 2, 10–13 (1951).
26. National Bureau of Standards Handbooks 48, 51, 52. Nat. Bur. Standards, Washington, D. C.
27. Oak Ridge National Laboratory, Radioisotopes Catalogue and Price List, 2nd Revision, 1959.
28. Obrycki, R. R., Ball, R. M., and Davidson, W. C., "Economical Shielding for Multicurie Sources," *Nucleonics,* **11,** No. 7, 52–3 (1953).
29. Phillips Petroleum Co., Atomic Energy Division, "Cobalt-60 Production Reactor," IDO-16421, available from Office of Technical Services, U. S. Dept. Commerce, Washington 25, D. C., Oct. 20, 1957.
30. Price, B. T., Horton, C. C., and Spinney, K. T., "Radiation Shielding," New York, Pergamon Press, 1957.
31. Radiation Effects Information Center, "Survey of Irradiation Facilities," ASTIA AD 157174, May 31, 1958, and addendum ASTIA AD 210767, Feb. 15, 1959. Battelle Memorial Institute, Columbus, O.
32. Robertson, J. S., and Sanders, A. P., "An 800,000-Rontgen-per-hour Cobalt[60] Source," BNL-1330, Technical Information Service, Oak Ridge National Laboratory Studies 12, Oak Ridge, Tenn. (1952).
33. Rockwell, T., "Reactor Shielding Design Manual," New York, McGraw-Hill Book Co., 1956.
34. Saunders, D. F., Morehead, E. F., and Daniels, F., "A Convenient Source of γ-Radiation," *J. Am. Chem. Soc.,* **75,** 3096–8 (1953).

35. Schwarz, H. A., and Allen, A. O., "Economical Water- and Earth-Shielded Cobalt^{60} γ-Ray Source," *Nucleonics,* **12,** No. 2, 58–9 (1954).
36. Shivers, R. W., "High Intensity Food Irradiator Facility," Third Industrial Nuclear Technology Conference, Chicago, Ill., Sept. 22–24, 1959.
37. Silverman, J., Personal Communication, Radiation Applications Inc., New York, N. Y., 1959.
38. Strominger, D., Hollander, J. M., and Seaborg, G. T., "Table of Isotopes," *Rev. Modern Physics,* **30,** 585–90, 629–32 (1958).
39. U. S. Atomic Energy Commission, "Estimated Unit Cost of Cobalt from a Cobalt-60 Production Reactor," IDO-10034, obtainable from Office of Technical Services, U. S. Dept. Commerce, Washington 25, D. C., Oct. 20, 1957.
40. U. S. Dept. Agriculture, Personal Communication, 1959.
41. Voyvodic, L., "Design Approach for Optimized High Level Gamma Sources," Third Industrial Nuclear Technology Conference, Chicago, Ill., Sept. 22–24 (1959).

Chapter 17

ANALYSIS OF COBALT

In minerals, ores, and concentrates, cobalt is usually associated with arsenic, copper, iron, manganese, nickel, sulfur, and less frequently with lead, silver, zinc, and a few other elements. Cobalt is an important constituent in high temperature alloys, magnets, cemented carbides, high-speed steels, catalysts, electroplating solutions, driers, and coloring agents for the glass and ceramic industries. It is found in vitamin B_{12}; as a dietary essential for sheep and cattle, cobalt must be added to feedstuffs or pasture in many areas throughout the world. Many procedures have been developed to meet the requirements ranging from a few ppm of the element in biological materials to the high percentages in many cobalt alloys. The general methods outlined in this chapter have proved successful for many years with a wide variety of products, and in the absence of interfering elements can be considerably shortened. Advances in recent years in the analytical chemistry of cobalt have been summarized in a review paper.[74]

Cobalt can be separated from members of Groups 1 and 2 by removal of these in acid solution with hydrogen sulfide. If copper is the only member of these groups present, as frequently occurs, it may be advantageously removed by electrolysis in acid solution. The important separations of cobalt from other members of Group 3, and from succeeding groups, involve aluminum, beryllium, iron, nickel, chromium, manganese, vanadium, zinc, titanium, and tungsten. Although cobalt salts are soluble in excess ammonia, separation from any considerable quantity of iron by this means is seldom practiced owing to the tenacious adsorption of cobalt on ferric hydroxide and the large number of re-precipitations required. Iron can be conveniently removed by precipitation with zinc oxide or sodium phosphate, or by extraction with ether. Nickel and cobalt are separated from each other by means of dimethylglyoxime or α-nitroso β-naphthol, or by ion exchange resins. Chromium and vanadium can be precipitated with zinc oxide, or cobalt precipitated from these with sodium hydroxide and sodium peroxide. Chromium can be volatilized as chromyl chloride by several additions of HCl to a perchloric acid solution of the sample. Tungsten can be removed by precipitation with zinc oxide, or by solution with KOH followed by a cupferron separation. After the usual acid decomposition of samples and dehydration of silica, tungsten, niobium, and tantalum remain with the silica precipitate and can thereby be separated from cobalt. Aluminum, titanium, zirconium, uranium, niobium, and tantalum can be separated from cobalt by a zinc oxide separation; manganese, zinc, and uranium can be isolated by α-nitroso β-naphthol. Beryllium can be removed from cobalt by a sodium hydroxide precipitation or mercury cathode separation. Details of these may be found in analytical reference books.[30,54,77]

Qualitative determinations for cobalt are given in Chapter 2 in the section on identification of cobalt minerals. Rapid, approximate methods used in geochemical prospecting for determining the small quantities of cobalt in soils, vegetation, or streams are also discussed in Chapter 2.

Gravimetric Determination as Co_3O_4 after Precipitation with α-Nitroso β-Naphthol

The steady trend toward instrumentation in analysis has lessened the relative importance of gravimetric determination of cobalt. There are still many occasions, however, such as standardizations or infrequent analyses, where reliability over a wide range of cobalt concentrations makes it a preferred procedure. The principle of this method is that after prior removal of Cu, Bi, Ag, Sn, Fe, Cr, V, Ti, and Zr, cobalt is precipitated by the reagent α-nitroso β-naphthol, sometimes called 1-nitroso 2-naphthol, in the presence of nickel and all remaining metals. Precipitation with H_2S will remove Cu and other members of Groups 1 and 2, and a zinc oxide separation will eliminate all elements of Group 3 which interfere in the α-nitroso β-naphthol determination.

Separation of Iron with Zinc Oxide. Weight out 0.5–10 g, depending on the cobalt content of the sample, and take into solution with 10–25 ml HNO_3, 10–25 ml HCl, 10 ml 1:1 H_2SO_4, and a few drops of HF, if necessary. For high sulfide products, initial treatment with a little bromine or potassium chlorate is advisable, to avoid the inclusion of undissolved particles in a bead of sulfur. Certain high-cobalt alloys, such as Stellites, are best decomposed by prolonged treatment with perchloric acid. Evaporate to strong fumes of SO_3, cool, dilute with water, and boil. Adjust the volume of solution to give 5–10 per cent H_2SO_4 or HCl, and gas out all Group 2 metals with H_2S. Filter off the precipitated sulfides and silica, and wash thoroughly with acidulated H_2S water.

Boil the filtrate for 15 minutes to remove all H_2S, oxidize the iron with H_2O_2, and boil to remove the excess of peroxide. Almost neutralize with a strong solution of sodium carbonate, and boil to remove all CO_2. Add a thick suspension of zinc oxide until the precipitate assumes the color of coffee containing cream. Boil and filter, washing several times with hot water. Transfer the precipitate back to the original beaker, just dissolve with HCl, and re-precipitate with zinc oxide emulsion. Filter through the original paper and wash 7–8 times with hot water. The filtrate will contain cobalt, nickel, manganese, and a few other elements not affecting the precipitation with α-nitroso β-naphthol. A turbidity in the filtrate caused by colloidal zinc oxide may be disregarded, since subsequent acid treatment will dissolve it. For very accurate work on small quantities of cobalt in the presence of large amounts of iron, aluminum, etc., a third precipitation may be necessary to set free the last traces of cobalt; this is rarely required, however.

Add HCl at the rate of 20 ml/500 ml solution to dissolve the colloidal zinc oxide and hold the nickel in solution, heat to boiling, and cautiously add sufficient α-nitroso β-naphthol in 1:1 acetic acid to precipitate all the cobalt. Use 0.5 g α-nitroso β-naphthol for each 0.01 g cobalt. Allow the brick-red precipitate of cobaltinitroso β-naphthol to boil several minutes, remove from hot plate, and set aside in a warm place for several hours.

Filter on a Whatman No. 42 paper (using pulp), wash several times with hot water, ten times with hot 5 per cent HCl, and finally with hot water, until free of chlorides. Place paper and precipitate in a weighed porcelain crucible. Dry, and ignite carefully in a muffle at a temperature not exceeding 800°C. Cool in a desiccator, and weigh as Co_3O_4.

$$Co_3O_4 \times 0.7342 = Co$$

For routine work, the precipitate may be ignited in a fireclay crucible or annealing cup and brushed onto the counterpoised watch glass of the balance.

The efficiency of the zinc oxide precipitation as outlined above has been confirmed by tracer work with Co^{60}.[17] Sometimes it is recommended that a suspension of zinc oxide be added to the sample, that the flask be shaken and the contents allowed to settle, and that an aliquot portion of the supernatant liquid be withdrawn for a cobalt determination. Our results have indicated that this practice is unsatisfactory for accurate work.[78]

Uranium is precipitated with α-nitroso β-naphthol in the presence of acetic acid, but if HCl is present, uranium (like nickel) remains in solution. When great accuracy is desired, if the final residue of Co_3O_4 is very bulky and has originated from a high nickel solution, it may be dissolved in HCl and cobalt reprecipitated with α-nitroso β-naphthol. If iron contamination is suspected, dissolve the cobalt oxide in acids, take to fumes of SO_3, and electrolyze as described below in the section on electrolytic determination. A chromatographic separation in a cellulose column has been proposed as an alternative to the usual separations of cobalt from iron before precipitation with α-nitroso β-naphthol.[63]

The reactions for the zinc oxide and α-nitroso β-naphthol precipitations are:

$$3ZnO + Fe_2(SO_4)_3 + 3H_2O \longrightarrow 2Fe(OH)_3 + 3ZnSO_4$$

$$CoCl_3 + 3C_{10}H_6(NO)OH \longrightarrow [C_{10}H_6(NO)O]_3Co + 3HCl$$

Separation of Iron with Sodium Phosphate. When iron is precipitated as ferric phosphate from a solution containing cobalt, there is remarkably little occlusion of the latter.[47,78] Even in the presence of large quantities of iron, one precipitation is sufficient for routine work. Unlike the zinc oxide separation, a filtrate is obtained which is suitable for direct electrolysis of cobalt. Accordingly, the phosphate separation of iron and aluminum is useful for some samples where the quantity of cobalt renders a final electrolysis preferable to gravimetric determination as oxide. It has one disadvantage, however: although U, Ti, and Zr are wholly removed as phosphates, Cr and V divide, and Ca remains with the solution of cobalt, nickel, and manganese to give a precipitate of calcium phosphate in the ammoniacal electrolytic solution.

Carry out the sample decomposition and removal of Group 2 elements, as described in the previous section, to the stage where the sample is boiled after addition of hydrogen peroxide. Add sufficient trisodium phosphate to precipitate all the iron, aluminum, etc., plus a small excess. Ten ml of a phosphate solution containing 34.05 g $Na_3PO_4 \cdot 12H_2O$ in 1 liter will precipitate 0.05 g Fe. To reduce the bulk of the sample solution, a more concentrated phosphate solution may be used for materials high in iron. Carefully add NH_4OH, stirring vigorously until purple cobaltous phosphate is formed. If the sample is low in cobalt, it may be difficult to see the cobaltous phosphate, and red litmus should be used as an indicator. When the litmus turns blue, a pH of approximately 5.6 has been reached; this is sufficient to ensure that cobaltous phosphate has been precipitated at pH 5.3.

Add exactly 10 ml glacial acetic acid and stir vigorously to dissolve the cobaltous phosphate; this will give a pH of 3–3.5. Add 5–20 ml H_2O_2 and stir thoroughly to oxidize the solution. The iron will be precipitated as white ferric phosphate:

$$2Na_3PO_4 + Fe_2(SO_4)_3 \longrightarrow 2FePO_4 + 3Na_2SO_4.$$

Bring the sample to a boil on a hot plate, stirring to prevent bumping if a heavy iron precipitate is present. Filter through a Whatman 531 or 541 paper on a fluted funnel, using paper pulp. If a very heavy precipitate of ferric phosphate is present, filter through a Buchner funnel. Wash the precipitate 8–10 times with hot acetic acid wash solution containing 25 ml glacial acetic acid in 1 liter of water. Proceed with the determination of cobalt by precipitation with α-nitroso β-naphthol; or add 10 ml 1:1 H_2SO_4, neutralize with NH_4OH, add about 40 ml excess, and electrolyze directly.

This method of first raising and then lowering the pH of the solution has been found to minimize occlusion of cobalt. The excess addition of phosphate should be kept to a minimum, otherwise a little cobalt may be precipitated as phosphate when ammonia is added before electrolysis.

Separation of Iron with Ether. Iron may be satisfactorily removed in cobalt analyses by means of an ether separation. This procedure is particularly suitable for low cobalt steels or slags, since several 10-g portions may be conveniently combined in a low volume after their ether extractions. Aluminum is not removed with iron, but it does not interfere in a subsequent α-nitroso β-naphthol separation. Chromium and vanadium also accompany cobalt in the lower aqueous layer of the ether separation, and must be removed at a later stage with $NaOH$-Na_2O_2 separation or with zinc oxide.

After the sample has been completely decomposed by acid treatment with HNO_3, thus converting all iron to the ferric condition, and fumed to dryness with H_2SO_4, add a small quantity of HCl and carefully evaporate it to a syrupy consistency. Transfer the beaker contents to a 250 or 500 ml separatory funnel; rinse the beaker thoroughly with small quantities of HCl of sg 1.10 and then several times with ether. Add more ether to bring the concentration up to 30 ml/g of iron in 20 ml HCl of sg 1.10. The latter is made by mixing 526 ml concentrated HCl with 474 ml water.

Shake the funnel vigorously under a cold water tap, allow to settle, and draw off the lower layer into a 400 ml beaker. This contains the cobalt, together with Cu, Ni, Mn, etc., while the upper layer contains nearly all the iron. Extract the upper and lower layers again with ether and HCl of sg 1.10 to make a complete separation. The partition coefficient of iron is approximately 50. With 1 g of iron, the first ether extraction removes all but 0.02 g; the second leaves only 0.5 mg. It is usually advisable to let the separatory funnel stand for a minute or two after shaking. Then, swirl gently several times to collect the last droplets of acid from the upper ether layer.

Place the upper fractions from the separatory funnel, containing ferric chloride and ether, in a Winchester, add water, and shake the bottle. The ferric chloride will go into the lower aqueous layer, and ether will remain on top. This lower layer can be removed by siphoning and discarded, while the ether is recovered.

Place the beaker containing the cobalt and other elements from the lower layer of the ether separation on the edge of the hot plate on thick asbestos until all ether has been driven off. Add 5 ml HNO_3, 10 ml 1:1 H_2SO_4, and take to fumes of SO_3. Cool, take up in water, adjust volume to give 5–10 per cent H_2SO_4, and remove all Group 1 and 2 elements with H_2S. Remove H_2S from the filtrate by boiling, and oxidize with H_2O_2; if Cr, V, etc. are absent, add 4 ml HCl for every 100 ml of solution and proceed with the α-nitroso β-naphthol precipitation. If chromium, vanadium, and other elements affecting the naphthol precipitation are present, remove with a sodium hydroxide-peroxide separation, or with zinc oxide.

Electrolytic Determination

For large quantities of cobalt, electrolytic determination is the most satisfactory procedure. Electrolysis is carried out in ammoniacal solution after removal of copper and nickel, which would be deposited, and iron, aluminum, etc., which would impede the electrolysis. Depending on the sample, electrolysis may be preceded by separation of iron with zinc oxide or ether and precipitation of cobalt by α-nitroso β-naphthol, or removal of iron and aluminum with phosphate. In some instances, cobalt and nickel may be electrolyzed together, with subsequent separation, or cobalt may be electrolyzed in the presence of iron.

In all cobalt electrolytic work it must be remembered that cobalt and nickel, unlike copper, are not easily dissolved off a platinum cathode in cold nitric acid. Cathodes should be boiled vigorously for five minutes in nitric acid to remove cobalt. The latter can also be readily removed in the cold if a few drops of hydrogen peroxide are added to nitric acid. If a black coating persists after adequate treatment of the cathode with hot HNO_3, it is almost certainly carbon and may be removed by heating for a few seconds in the hottest zone of a bunsen flame.

The following solutions are useful in spot tests for completion of cobalt electrolysis:

(1) *Nitroso-R-salt, $C_{10}H_4OH \cdot NO(SO_3Na)_2$.* To a few drops of the cobalt solution add several drops of 50 per cent sodium acetate, acidify with HNO_3, and add several drops of a 0.5 per cent solution of nitroso-R-salt in water. A permanent red color indicates the presence of cobalt.

(2) *Phenylthiohydantoic acid, $C_9H_{10}O_2NS$.* When a few drops of a solution of 1 g phenylthiohydantoic acid in 100 ml ethyl alcohol are added to an ammoniacal cobalt solution, a pink color is produced.

(3) *Potassium thiocarbonate, K_2CS_3.* This is prepared by saturating one half of a solution of 5 per cent KOH with H_2S, adding the other half, and heating moderately with 1/25 of its volume of carbon disulfide. The dark red liquid is decanted from the undissolved carbon disulfide and kept in a well-closed flask. With this reagent, small quantities of cobalt in ammoniacal solution give a yellow color, larger quantities a brown or black.

The sensitivity of some reagents, such as nitroso-R-salt, makes the interpretation of spot tests a little difficult for the inexperienced. It is, therefore, a good plan to have on hand a stock cobalt solution of such concentration that a few tenths of a milliliter addition to the spot plate from a small capacity pipette represents about the limit of precision desired. For instance, when analyzing a 1-g sample containing 20 per cent cobalt, a quantity not over 0.5 mg left in the electrolyte volume of 200 ml may be considered satisfactory, and if so, 0.5 ml of this solution would contain 0.0012 mg cobalt. An equivalent quantity for checking the proper color of the spot test would be given by 0.25 ml of a standard solution containing 0.0238 g $CoSO_4 \cdot 7H_2O$ in 1 liter.

Electrolysis After Isolation of Cobalt by α-Nitroso β-Naphthol. If the procedure outlined in the first section has been followed, the cobalt oxide resulting from the ignition of a cobaltinitroso β-naphthol precipitate will contain only traces of impurities. Dissolve in HCl, add 10 ml 1:1 H_2SO_4, and take to fumes of SO_3. Cool, dilute with water, neutralize with NH_4OH, and add 40 ml excess. If the sample fumes to dryness, add more H_2SO_4 or ammonium sulfate to ensure the presence of the latter after making ammoniacal. Electrolyze overnight on a stationary assembly at 0.5–1 ampere or on a rotating type electrolytic apparatus at 2 amperes and 6 volts for 45–60 minutes. Unlike the electrolytic copper determination, it is difficult to tell by dilution when deposition of cobalt is complete, owing to the similarity in appearance of cobalt and platinum in the cloudy ammoniacal solution. The latter may be tested for complete deposition by withdrawing a few drops with a pipette, transferring to a spot plate, and testing with potassium thiocarbonate, phenylthiohydantoic acid, or nitroso-R-salt.

Wash the cathode quickly but thoroughly, rinse in alcohol, dry over a hot plate or in a stream of warm air from a hair-drier, and weigh the previously-tared cathode. It has been recently shown, using tracer techniques, that small quantities of cobalt are left in solution after electrodeposition, usually as a result of washing and not from metal that was never deposited.[51] In practice, however, it has been confirmed many times that the cobalt remaining in solution after electrodeposition is below the normal limit of precision for such analyses.

Electrolysis After Removal of Iron with Phosphate. Large quantities of cobalt are readily determined electrolytically following removal of iron with phosphate,[78] either by direct electrolysis of the cobalt and nickel in the filtrate, or by separation of cobalt with α-nitroso β-naphthol before plating.

Evaporate the filtrate from the phosphate separation of iron to a conveniently low volume, add 10 ml 1:1 H_2SO_4, 5 g borax, and NH_4OH to neutralization, followed by 30–40 ml excess. Electrolyze on a rotating assembly with a current of 3 amperes and 6 volts. Do not prolong the electrolysis after cobalt is deposited, particularly in the presence of manganese, or a black cathode deposit will be obtained and results will be slightly high. The addition of borax to the electrolyte is optional; many chemists prefer an ammonia-ammonium sulfate medium only.

In the presence of nickel, the combined deposit of cobalt and nickel may be dissolved in HNO_3, and cobalt or nickel determined by α-nitroso β-naphthol or dimethylglyoxime, respectively. If large quantities of both these metals are present, making appreciable co-precipitation possible, minimum co-precipitation of cobalt will occur with a slow addition of ammonia to the acid solution of Ni, Co, and dimethylglyoxime, followed by a 30-minute digestion at 25° C.[53]

Electrolysis in the Presence of Iron. For routine analyses, it is possible to determine cobalt electrolytically in the presence of iron. If only small quantities of iron are present, a little ferric hydroxide in the ammoniacal electrolyte will not require any change in technique other than the precaution that no particles of ferric hydroxide adhere to the inside meshes of the cathode after the latter are washed.

In samples with a high iron content, the adsorption of cobalt by ferric hydroxide necessitates a slight change in procedure. Electrolyze the cobalt solution containing suspended ferric hydroxide in a tall 600 ml beaker for 45 minutes at 2 amperes and 6 volts with vigorous agitation. Lower the beaker from the cathode, washing the latter; just dissolve the ferric hydroxide with 1:1 H_2SO_4, and re-precipitate with NH_4OH, adding 30 ml excess. Continue the electrolysis for 30 minutes, lower the beaker, dissolve the ferric hydroxide, and reprecipitate as before to set free any occluded cobalt. Continue the electrolysis for another 30 minutes. This should result in complete deposition of cobalt, indicated by a negative test for this element when a small portion of the solution is withdrawn with a pipette, filtered, and tested on a spot plate.

Since a little iron is occluded with the deposited cobalt on the cathode, it is necessary, in accurate work, to dissolve the plating and re-electrolyze. The second electrolysis at 2 amperes with vigorous agitation requires only 1 hour or less. There are two ways of carrying out the second electrolysis. The cathode deposit may be removed with HNO_3, H_2SO_4 added and the solution taken to fumes of SO_3, cooled, and NH_4OH added to the usual excess of 30–40 ml. Or, the first cobalt deposit may be dissolved in HCl, neutralized directly with NH_4OH (an excess of 60 ml and 15 ml of a saturated SO_2 solution being added), and electrolyzed at 2 amperes and 10 volts for 1 hour or less.

The above procedures have been employed successfully on material containing about 40 per cent Co and 45 per cent Fe by Union Minière du Haut Katanga and others for many years on thousands of routine samples.

Other Electrolytic Procedures. Methods have been described in which cobalt is determined electrolytically in high temperature alloys[25] and cobalt platinum alloys[73] after removal of interfering elements by an anion exchange column using Dowex 1 or 1–X10. A procedure has been published for the determination of cobalt by an anodic electrodeposition-isotope dilution technique.[50,51]

Volumetric Determination

With Potassium Cyanide. In the absence of nickel, cobalt may be determined by cyanide titration in a manner similar to the procedure used for nickel.[26,46] When bivalent cobalt is converted to the cobaltic state by an oxidizing agent like potassium chlorate, one atom of cobalt reacts quantitatively with five molecules of potassium cyanide to form a complex cobalt cyanide. The end point of the reaction is determined by an indirect indicator, silver iodide, which gives a turbidity to the solution until a slight excess of potassium cyanide is present. Silver iodide is formed *in situ* by the action of $AgNO_3$ on KI.

$$6Co(NH_3)_6Cl_2 + KClO_3 + 6NH_4Cl + 3H_2O \longrightarrow$$

$$6Co(NH_3)_6Cl_3 + KCl + 6NH_4OH$$

$$CoCl_3 + 5KCN \longrightarrow K_2Co(CN)_5 + 3KCl$$

or, as sometimes represented:

$$Co_2(SO_4)_3 + 10KCN \longrightarrow 2\{2KCN \cdot Co(CN)_3\} + 3K_2SO_4$$

$$AgNO_3 + KI \longrightarrow AgI + KNO_3$$

$$AgI + 2KCN \longrightarrow KAg(CN)_2 + KI$$

Since it is generally easier to detect the appearance of a turbidity than its disappearance, a slight excess of KCN is usually added and back titrated with $AgNO_3$ until a faint opalescence is again visible.

Decompose the sample with 10 ml HNO_3, 10 ml HCl and a few drops of HF, if necessary; add 10 ml 1:1 H_2SO_4 and fume strongly to dehydrate silica. Dissolve the soluble salts in water, remove copper and other Group 2 elements with hydrogen sulfide, and filter off the silica with the precipitated sulfides. If copper is the only member of preceding groups present, it may be conveniently determined or eliminated by the usual nitric-sulfuric acid electrolysis in place of H_2S separation. Boil out all H_2S; oxidize thoroughly by adding 10 ml HNO_3, 1-2 g potassium or sodium chlorate, and boiling gently for 15 minutes. Cool in a water bath, add NH_4OH just to the neutral point, and for each 0.1 g of iron present add 10-20 ml ammonium citrate-sulfate buffer solution. The latter consists of 200 g citric acid, 270 g ammonium sulfate, and 200 ml ammonia per liter of solution.

Place a piece of red litmus against the side of the beaker and carefully add NH_4OH until the paper turns blue. Add exactly 2 ml NH_4OH and boil gently for 2-5 minutes. Cool in a water bath, add 5 ml 10 per cent KI and 2-3 ml standard $AgNO_3$ solution from a burette. Add standard KCN until the cloudiness produced by silver iodide disappears. Finally, add standard $AgNO_3$ solution, drop by drop, stirring constantly over a black background until a persistent cloudiness is again produced. The total number of ml of standard $AgNO_3$ solution used is then subtracted from the number of ml of standard KCN to give the percentage of cobalt. After the addition of silver nitrate to the samples, keep them out of direct sunlight, since the latter has a tendency to reduce AgI to metallic silver, thus giving erratic results.

Standardize the cyanide solution against the silver nitrate, and titrate the cyanide against a solution containing a known quantity of cobalt. It is useful to have two standard KCN solutions, one for low cobalt samples with a value approximating 1 ml = 0.001 g Co, and another for high cobalts possessing a titre of 1 ml = 0.005 g Co. These solutions are made up to contain 5.6 g KCN and 28 g KCN per liter, with the addition of 1 and 5 g, respectively, KOH as a stabilizer. The cyanide solutions are titrated against silver nitrate solutions containing 7.2060 g and 36.0300 g $AgNO_3$ per liter, respectively. One g $CoSO_4 \cdot 7H_2O$ contains 0.2097 g cobalt, and a 25 ml aliquot from a liter of solution containing one g of this salt gives a convenient quantity for titration against dilute KCN. Standardization of these solutions should be carried out at least once a week. The following equivalents are useful: 1 g Co = 5.5234 g KCN. 1 g Co = 7.2060 g $AgNO_3$. 1 g KCN = 1.3046 g $AgNO_3$.

With the exception of copper and, of course, nickel, very few elements interfere with the cyanide titration of cobalt. Mercury interferes, but is eliminated with copper in the H_2S separation. Zinc forms a compound with KCN, leading to high results. Increasing the ammonium citrate decreases interference of zinc for quantities of the latter below 5 mg. Accurate results for cobalt are only obtained in the presence of manganese if not more than 5 mg of the latter are present, if there is a fair amount of iron in the sample, and if the manganese is not oxidized beyond the manganic state. The following are without effect: Fe, Al, Pb, Bi, Cd, As (ic), Sb, Sn, Se, Te, Mo, Cr (ate), Ti, W, U, V (ate), Zr.

Sometimes cobalt is determined indirectly from a cyanide titration of combined nickel + cobalt by subtracting the quantity of nickel found in a separate analysis using dimethylglyoxime. In this calculation, since 1 atom of Ni reacts with 4 molecules of KCN and 1 atom of cobalt with 5 molecules of cyanide, percentage cobalt = 80 per cent (per cent Ni + Co by KCN method – per cent Ni by dimethylglyoxime method).

With Other Titrants. In recent years, the application of ethylenediaminetetraacetate (EDTA) as a titrant for metal ions and as a metal-complexing agent in analysis has led to the publication of hundreds of papers in this field. Two recent monographs provide a general survey of this subject.[15,72] In practice, disodium ethylendiaminetetraacetate dihydrate, a white, water-soluble powder having a molecular weight of 372.25, is used to prepare a standard EDTA solution for titrations. EDTA and related compounds are valuable as titrants because of their strong bonding with metal ions with consequent formation of complexes or chelate structures of great stability. The end point in the titration is marked by the disappearance of the last trace of free or unbound metal ion, or by its appearance in a back-titration. Detection of this disappearance of metal ions which are not complexed with EDTA is commonly effected by the use of a metal indicator. The latter forms metal complexes which differ in color from that of the free indicator, marking the end point by a sudden color change. The end point may also be determined by procedures other than visual, such as potentiometric, amperometric, and photometric.

EDTA will complex with nearly all metals; its selectivity must be altered by pH control or by the formation with the elements present, of some complexes having even greater stability than those formed with EDTA. A number of EDTA procedures for cobalt have been reviewed,[15,16,72] many of which give good results in special applications. As a general rule, however, difficulties are encountered unless the cobalt has been isolated from other metals. EDTA methods, following a chromatographic separation of cobalt, have proved very successful.

Another approach to the volumetric determination of cobalt is furnished by the reaction between cobalt and iodine in ammoniacal solutions of ammonium nitrate to form iodopentamminecobalt (III) nitrate.[75] Though the end point in the back titration of excess iodine, using a standard arsenious acid solution, can be determined by starch indicator, it is preferably detected potentiometrically. Cu and Ni do not interfere, nor do Al, Fe, or Cr in the presence of tartrate.

Colorimetric Determination

Ammonium Thiocyanate. Cobalt forms a complex with ammonium thiocyanate which can be extracted with amyl alcohol and ether to give a beautiful blue color of ammonium cobaltothiocyanate, a sensitive test for cobalt long known by the designation "Vogel's reaction." This test has been adapted for quantitative colorimetry, its reliability and sensitivity making it extremely useful for low-cobalt products.[79] The basic reaction is $CoCl_2 + 4NH_4CNS \rightarrow (NH_4)_2 [Co(CNS)_4] + 2NH_4Cl$.

Decompose 0.5–2 g sample with 10 ml HNO_3 and 10 ml HCl, adding a few drops of bromine initially for sulfide materials, and HF for silicates, if necessary. Evaporate the sample to dryness but do not bake, since traces of HNO_3 do not affect the formation of the thiocyanate complex. Dissolve the sample in 25 ml water, and add 1 ml HCl for every 50 ml of subsequent dilution of the sample so that the resulting pH is 1. Boil, cool, and transfer to appropriate volumetric flasks. This procedure is intended for materials containing 0.01–4 per cent cobalt. The weight of the original sample, usually 0.5–2 g, and the dilution, generally 50–200 ml, should be adjusted so that a 5 ml aliquot will contain 0.02–0.5 mg cobalt for the extraction and color measurement.

Measure out the following reagent solutions into a separatory funnel: 5 ml sodium thiosulfate, 3 ml sodium phosphate, 10 ml ammonium thiocyanate, 2 ml ammonium acetate, and a few drops of tartaric acid. Add the 5 ml aliquot from the sample flask, agitate, and add 10 ml of amyl alcohol-ether mixture. Shake under a cold water tap, allow to settle, and discard the lower aqueous layer. Transfer the blue solution of cobaltothiocyanate to a cell in a photoelectric colorimeter or spectrophotometer and measure the color intensity. With the reagent additions above, no common element will give colored complexes which are soluble in amyl alcohol-ether. Large quantities of copper are without effect; iron is inactivated by thiosulfate, phosphate, and acetate; vanadium would form a blue complex extractable by alcohol but in the presence of ammonium acetate and tartaric acid this is obviated; Cr, Mn, Ni, Ti, Mo, and U do not give colored solutions which are extracted into the upper alcohol-ether layer. Elements such as Al, Si, Mg, Ca, P, Hg, Bi, As, Pb, and alkalies are without effect.

A pH of 1 for the solution of the sample is optimum for the formation of the cobalt complex. At a higher pH, the color is not so strongly developed; at a lower value, it is difficult to suppress with small quantities of phosphate the color due to iron. A final pH of 3.5–4 in the solution of sample and added reagents is well below the precipitation pH of cobalt phosphate (about 5.3). A concentration of 24–26 per cent ammonium thiocyanate is sufficient to produce the maximum color intensity for amounts of cobalt from 0.02 to 0.5 mg.

Reagents:

Ammonium acetate. Dissolve 700 g of $NH_4C_2H_3O_2$ in 1 liter of water.
Ammonium thiocyanate. Dissolve 600 g of NH_4CNS in 1 liter of water.

Amyl alcohol-ether. Mix 3 parts by volume of amyl alcohol with 1 part of ethyl ether.

Sodium phosphate. Dissolve 83.3 g of $Na_3PO_4 \cdot 12H_2O$ in 1 liter of water.

Sodium thiosulfate. Dissolve 200 g of $Na_2S_2O_3 \cdot 5H_2O$ in 1 liter of water.

Tartaric acid. Dissolve 50 g of $C_4H_6O_6$ in 1 liter of water.

This procedure can be adapted for rapid plant control purposes by visually comparing the blue color in a test tube with a series of standards. The latter can be conveniently prepared in a permanent form from copper sulfate, a solution containing 8 g $CuSO_4 \cdot 5H_2O$ per liter matching an extract containing 0.02 mg cobalt per 10 ml.

Kinnunen, Merikanto, and Wennerstrand,[35] modifying the method for certain metallurgical products, mask the effect of iron with ammonium bifluoride and of copper with thiourea, extract with methyl isopropyl ketone, and measure the optical density of the extract at 625 mμ.

Nitroso-R-salt, $C_{10}H_4OH \cdot NO(SO_3Na)_2$. This determination is based on the fact that the colored complexes formed with nitroso-R-salt by most of the common elements (except cobalt) are destroyed by nitric acid. The full development of the color with cobalt is attained in the presence of sodium acetate, and for most samples, such variables as quantity of nitric acid and of nitroso-R-salt, boiling time, etc., exert an influence. This procedure is deservedly one of the most popular for small quantities of cobalt, having general applications for a wide variety of materials. With suitable aliquoting, even medium to high cobalt concentrations can be satisfactorily determined.[5,14,28,81]

For samples containing 0.01–0.2 per cent cobalt, weigh out 0.25 g. With higher grade materials, take a 0.5 g sample and, after decomposition, withdraw for analysis an aliquot containing 0.01–0.5 mg cobalt. For very low concentrations of cobalt, larger samples of 2–25 g may be employed. Decompose with HNO_3, HCl, and a few drops of HF, if necessary; add 5 ml 1:1 sulfuric acid, and evaporate to strong fumes of SO_3. Cool, dilute to about 30 ml, add 2 ml HCl, and boil to solution of soluble salts. Pass hydrogen sulfide through the solution for 10 minutes and filter through Whatman 40 paper, washing well with acidulated H_2S water. Boil off H_2S, add 5 ml HNO_3, and take to fumes of SO_3.

If copper is the only Group 2 metal present, it may be alternatively removed by electrolysis. For products like concentrates, mattes, or blister copper, cobalt may be determined on the solution after the electrolysis of copper. Evaporate this solution to fumes of SO_3 and continue heating until only a small amount of H_2SO_4 remains. Cool, dilute to about 25 ml with water, and boil. Cool, and carefully neutralize with 20 per cent NaOH to a point where the solution becomes a deep wine red. Should there be little or no iron present, add 2 drops phenolphthalein and take to the first faint pink. Add 2 ml phosphoric-sulfuric acid, 10 ml nitroso-R-salt solution, and 10 ml sodium acetate solution. Bring to a vigorous boil for 1 minute, add 5 ml HNO_3, and boil for at least 1 minute but not more than 2 minutes. Cool, and dilute to 100 ml in a measuring cylinder or volumetric flask. Measure the optical density of this solution by standard procedures in any type of photoelectric colorimeter or spectrophotometer.

Small quantities of copper, for example 10 mg for each 0.1 mg of cobalt, do not interfere when additions of nitroso-R-salt, sodium acetate, and nitric acid are increased.[27] In this case, when copper is the only Group 2 element present in more than trace quantities, the procedure can be shortened for routine work as follows. Dissolve the sample in HNO_3, HCl, and HF, if necessary; add 5 ml phosphoric-sulfuric acid, take to fumes of SO_3, and fume strongly for 5 minutes. Cool, add 20 ml water, and boil. Add 30 ml sodium acetate and 10 ml nitroso-R-salt; boil for 1 minute. Add 10 ml of HNO_3; if all the flocculent precipitate does not dissolve, add 2–5 ml more HNO_3. Continue boiling for another minute, remove from hot plate, cool, and make up to 100 ml in a measuring cylinder. Mix well and filter about half the sample through dry paper into a dry Erlenmeyer flask. Measure the color of this solution by any appropriate equipment. In this shortened procedure, the samples are not filtered until after the color has been developed. Residual insoluble matter usually has no influence on color development. With 5 ml phosphoric-sulfuric acid added originally to a 0.25 g sample, it is not necessary, in routine work, to neutralize with NaOH or to add 2 ml of the Spekker acid. Fuming the sample strongly for about 5 minutes will give an acid concentration of 1–4 ml, which is not critical for most material when standardizations are carried out in the same manner.

Ten ml of nitroso-R-salt solution are only sufficient to form the cobalt complex with about 0.6 mg cobalt. If copper and nickel are present in the sample, they will consume the reagent, and further additions of nitroso-R-salt should be made at the rate of about 3 ml for each 5 mg Cu and 1.5 ml for every 5 mg Ni in the original sample. The sodium acetate additions should be increased to 30 ml, nitric acid to 10 ml.

Quantities of manganese in excess of 50 times the cobalt present, nickel 25 times, and chromium 15 times, interfere and should be removed. At least 25 times as much vanadium can be tolerated. The color comparison can be made in the presence of over 1000 times as much iron, and the following elements are without effect in quantities over 100 times that of the cobalt: Al, Zn, Ti, Th, U, Zr, W, Ba, Sr, Ca, Mg.

The calibration curve for the absorptiometer is drawn up using standard cobalt sulfate with the same reagent quantities and procedures employed in the determination of the unknowns.

Reagents:

Cobalt sulfate. Dissolve 0.2383 g $CoSO_4 \cdot 7H_2O$ in water and make up to 1 liter. One ml = 0.05 mg Co. Alternatively, dissolve 0.1000 g electrolytic cobalt in nitric acid, add 10 ml 1:1 H_2SO_4 and evaporate to fumes. Cool and dilute to 2 liters in a volumetric flask. One ml = 0.05 mg Co.

Nitroso-R-salt. Dissolve 1 g in water and make up to 500 ml.

Phosphoric-sulfuric acid. To 600 ml of water add 150 ml concentrated H_3PO_4 and 150 ml concentrated sulfuric acid; cool, and dilute to 1 liter. This solution is sometimes called Spekker acid.

Sodium acetate. Dissolve 500 g of $NaC_2H_3O_2 \cdot 3H_2O$ in water and make up to 1 liter.

The wide applicability of the nitroso-R-salt procedure has led to the publication of a number of modifications which have increased its field of usefulness. The British Iron and Steel Research Association has recommended procedures for this industry.[5] Guerin[24] has described the differential technique of color measurement with the Spekker absorptiometer for cobalt in ores. Various workers have eliminated certain interfering elements and extended the lower limit of quantitative determination by prior isolation of cobalt with dithizone,[2,52] α-nitroso β-naphthol,[49] or by chromatography.[12,18,34] Shipman and associates[45,55] reported that if magnesium acetate is used, large amounts of fluorides can be added to remove interferences without fear of etching the absorption cells. They oxidized excess nitroso-R-salt with potassium bromate, eliminated chloride and sulfate ions, and determined the absorbance in a spectrophotometer at 425 mμ.[56]

2-Nitroso-1-Naphthol. This reagent, formerly called β-nitroso-α-naphthol, forms a complex with cobalt which has been extracted with CCl_4,[1] chloroform,[9] and isoamyl acetate[10] for the determination of very small quantities of cobalt in materials such as soils. The recommendations of Clark[10] for this sensitive procedure in the presence of Cu, Fe, Ni, Mn, Pd, and Sn are outlined here. Following the standard decomposition methods for soils or rocks, transfer an aliquot representing 0–10 γ Co to a separatory funnel. Add bromine water, ammonium citrate, sodium thiosulfate, phenolphthalein, and NH_4OH to a pink color. Add 2-nitroso-1-naphthol and isoamyl acetate; shake, allow to stand for an hour, and discard the lower aqueous layer. Wash the acetate phase in HCl, NaOH, and HCl again, discarding the washings, and measure the transmittance of the cobalt complex at a wave length of 530 mμ. The citrate prevents the precipitation of Fe, Al, and Ca in the alkaline medium; bromine water and $Na_2S_2O_3$ obviate interference from tin; $Na_2S_2O_3$ prevents the formation of a complex with Pd and the inhibiting effect of Mn on color formation of cobalt.

Washing the acetate phase with HCl and NaOH removes the interferences of Cu and Ni. The isoamyl acetate extracts of cobalt-2-nitroso-1-naphtholate complex show excellent color stability.

Other Colorimetric Procedures. Many other colorimetric methods have been proposed. Gagnon[20] utilized the pink color of cobalt sulfate for a spectrophotometric determination of cobalt in ores at 500–520 mμ.

The reagent 1-(2 pyridylazo)-2-naphthol, or PAN, forms a chelate with cobalt which is extractable with chloroform, giving a solution on which the absorbance at 640 mμ can be measured.[22] Cobalt is previously separated from Th as are most interfering elements, such as Fe, Ni, Zn, Cd, by anion exchange on Dowex 1-X10; except for copper, the remaining elements either do not react with PAN, or can be masked by addition of citrate.

Smith and Hayes[59] separate copper and cobalt diethyldithiocarbamates chromatographically on an activated silica adsorbent, convert them to the corresponding diphenylthiocarbazone complexes, and determine cobalt photometrically.

Potentiometric Determination

A most satisfactory procedure for determining cobalt for a wide range of products is the potentiometric one, based on the oxidation of cobalt in ammoniacal solution by potassium ferricyanide. In the cold, and in the presence of ammonium citrate, the only common element that interferes is manganese which can be removed by prior separation with nitrochlorate. The potentiometric procedure is applicable in the presence of large quantities of copper, nickel, and iron—the elements which interfere most frequently in other methods of determining cobalt. The details given below are applicable to most mining and metallurgical products[26] and can be modified slightly for irons and steels.[3] The method has given excellent results for cobalt in cemented carbides[19,70] and in glass-to-metal seals.[8]

Decompose the sample with HNO_3, HCl, and a few drops of HF, if necessary. Boil the acid solution thoroughly to drive off nitrous fumes; it is not necessary to evaporate to low bulk. If manganese is present, evaporate the mixed acid solution just to dryness, add 40–50 ml HNO_3, and carefully add several successive small portions of sodium chlorate, boiling gently after each addition. Dilute slightly, and filter off the MnO_2 through a Whatman 42 paper or through asbestos on a Gooch crucible. Insoluble matter other than MnO_2 need not be filtered off unless large quantities are present.

Cool the samples, and carefully add NH_4OH until iron commences to precipitate. Redissolve the iron by the addition of a drop or two of 1:1 HNO_3. Cool the sample again. From a standard burette into a 600 ml beaker, measure out sufficient excess potassium ferricyanide solution to give a back titration of 10–15 ml of cobalt nitrate solution. Add to the ferricyanide solution 10–20 ml ammonium citrate for every 0.1 g iron present in the sample, followed by 80 ml NH_4OH. Stirring constantly, slowly pour the sample into the beaker containing potassium ferricyanide, etc. There must be no heating effect produced at this stage or some of the cobalt will be oxidized, and low results will be obtained. If the sample has been almost neutralized and cooled beforehand, no heat will develop.

Place the beaker containing the sample on the potentiometer assembly and switch on the current and stirrer. Back titrate the excess potassium ferricyanide with standard cobalt nitrate solution until the end point is shown by a large and permanent deflection of the galvanometer beam.

If chromium and vanadium are present, the samples should be decomposed with HNO_3 and HCl, and taken to strong fumes of a low volume of perchloric acid. The sample should then be poured directly into the beaker containing excess ferricyanide, ammonium citrate, and 80 ml ammonia, without preliminary neutralization. Vanadium is in the vanadate state and will not interfere with the titration.

From 5 to 150 mg cobalt in complex materials can be accurately and rapidly determined in this manner. The following do not interfere: Hg (ic), Pb, Fe, Ni, Cu, Bi, Cd, As (ic), Sb, Sn (ic), Se, Te, Mo, Cr (ate), Be, Al, Zn, Ti, W, U, V (ate), Zr.

Reagents:

Ammonium citrate solution. Dissolve 200 g citric acid in water and slowly add 270 ml ammonia. Cool and make up to 1 liter. If desired, tartaric acid may be used in place of citric acid.

Cobalt nitrate solution. Weigh out 5.00 g Co $(NO_3)_2 \cdot 6H_2O$; dissolve in water and make up to 1 liter. One ml of this solution should contain 1 mg Co. Standardize by determining the cobalt electrolytically.

Potassium ferricyanide solution. Weigh out 11.17 g $K_3Fe(CN)_6$; dissolve in water and make up to 1 liter. This solution should be kept in a brown bottle since it decomposes if exposed to light. As 329.24 g $K_3Fe(CN)_6$ react with 58.94 g Co, 1 ml of a solution containing 11.17 g $K_3Fe(CN)_6$ should be equivalent to 2 mg Co. This solution in standardized by measuring out 10 ml ferricyanide from a burette into a 600 ml beaker, adding 20 ml ammonium citrate and 80 ml ammonia, making a volume of about 400 ml with water, placing the solution on the potentiometric titration assembly, and switching on the current and stirrer. Standard cobalt nitrate is run in from a burette until the end point is indicated on the galvanometer scale. Ten ml potassium ferricyanide should be equivalent to 20 ml standard cobalt nitrate.

It has been recommended[76] that in potentiometric determination of cobalt, the reactants should be covered with a layer of light petroleum of bp 100–120° C to exclude air, and to shield the operator and equipment from the strongly ammoniacal vapors.

Replacement of ammonia by ethylenediamine has been suggested for cobalt-bearing stainless steels and bronzes, and Stellites.[13] Potentiometric determination of cobalt, either directly or by back titration, is successful if ethylenediammonium sulfate is present as well as ethylenediamine, and if oxygen is rigidly excluded.

Polarographic Determination

The polarograph has furnished another useful tool for the determination of small concentrations of cobalt, particularly in the presence of large amounts of nickel and only minor quantities of most other metals. Discussion of the principles and applications of polarography are given in the books by Kolthoff and Lingane,[37] and Meites.[41]

Polarographic determinations of cobalt have been published by Lingane and Kerlinger,[38] Jones,[31] Stromberg and Zelyanskaya,[65] Souchay and Faucherre,[61] Watters and Kolthoff,[71] Kolthoff and Watters,[37] Suchy,[66] Symthe and Gatehouse.[60] Meites,[41,42] Kobarelova and Trifonov,[36] and Saraswat.[48] A typical example of these methods is given below.[42]

Weigh 2.5 g nickel nitrate containing about 1 mg cobalt into each of two 100 ml calibrated flasks, and to each add 50 ml water, 2.5 g NH_4Cl, and 10 ml ammonia. To one of the flasks add 2 ml saturated $KMnO_4$ solution and allow to stand for one minute to ensure complete oxidation of cobalt. A brown turbidity of MnO_2 will form. Add 2 ml saturated hydroxylammonium sulfate and 1 ml Triton X-100 to each flask, and dilute to the mark. Allow a few seconds for the excess permanganate and MnO_2 in the oxidized solution to react completely and the vigorous evolution of nitrogen to cease; then stopper and shake thoroughly. Transfer a portion of the oxidized solution to a polarograph cell, de-aerate it with hydrogen or nitrogen, and record its polarogram for –0.2–0.8 volt *vs.* S.C.E. The half wave potential of the cobalt wave is approximately –0.40 volt *vs.* S.C.E. Discard this solution and replace it with a portion of the sample which was not treated with permanganate. De-aerate this and record its polarogram under the same conditions as the first solution. Measure the vertical distance between the two curves on the plateau of the cobalt wave, roughly –0.70 volt *vs.* S.C.E. Compare the diffusion current thus measured with the values obtained when solutions containing known amounts of cobalt are treated in the same way. With this sample containing 2.5 g nickel nitrate and about 1 mg Co, the following do not interfere: As, Sb, Sn, Cd, and Zn.

The approximate milligram amounts of the following can be tolerated: Bi 100, Cu 25, Fe 50, Mn 30, and Mo 50. Pronounced interference is shown by Cr, Pb, V, and W.

In common with other analytical methods for determining minute quantities of cobalt, the polarographic determination may be preceded by one or more concentrating steps. Suchy[66] precipitated with α-nitroso β-naphthol before dissolving in pyridine and determining cobalt polarographically. In the work of Smythe and Gatehouse,[60] 50–400 ppm cobalt and other heavy metals in rocks were collected as rubeanates, the cobalt isolated with α-nitroso β-naphthol, decomposed with perchloric and HCl, made alkaline with ammonia, and added to the supporting electrolyte of ammonium chloride-ammonia for polarography.

Spectrographic Determination

Spectrographic procedures were originally developed for very small quantities of metals. This is still their greatest area of usefulness, but in recent years various techniques and equipment have been developed to extend the range of concentrations which can be profitably determined by spectrography.

Measurement of the cobalt content of animal tissue, where amounts are in the millimicrogram range, poses unusual problems. Cobalt in human blood, about 1 part per billion, has been determined by ashing, removing iron and alkali chlorides, separating cobalt on the anion exchange resin Dowex 1–X8, eluting, and determining spectrographically.[69] Another procedure for determining cobalt in animal tissue involves ashing; separation of cobalt with α-nitroso β-naphthol; collection in a mixture of aluminum oxide, lithium chloride, and graphite as a constant base material for direct current arc spectrography.[33]

Strasheim and Camerer[64] found that the cathode layer arc excitation method was more suitable than the anode arc method for determining 0.1–2.9 ppm cobalt in plant materials. The concentration procedure proposed by Mitchell was employed.

Investigations on the spectrographic analysis of residual cobalt in steel,[6] and stainless steel[23] have been reported. In the analysis of high purity iron,[29] cobalt was determined spectrographically on the aqueous layer after separation of iron by an ether extraction. Standen[62] has given the concentration of many elements which may interfere with the spectrographic determination of traces of cobalt.

From 0.005 to 0.1 per cent cobalt in nickel salts have been determined with the lines Co 2378.6 Å and Ni 2379.7 Å.[11] The cobalt lines 3044.005 and 3061.819 are recommended when iron and nickel are present in the sample,[4] but in the presence of much manganese and chromium, the

3044.005 line can be masked. The 3405.120 cobalt line, often recommended, cannot be used with a graphite electrode, since it is masked by the carbon spectrum. In cobalt alloys, line pairs of cobalt and other metals have been recommended for Cr, Mn, Si, Fe, Ni, and W.[67] A spark method for the analysis of Vitallium alloys has been published.[57] Spectrographic determination of up to 0.5 per cent cobalt in beryllium copper has been described.[21] The spectrochemical analyses of impurities in cobalt oxide[40] and metallic cobalt[43] have also been outlined.

Determination of 0.2–6 per cent cobalt in concentrates containing 5–40 per cent Cu and 5–40 per cent Fe has been given by Mason and de Beer.[39] Digestion with Br, HNO_3, HCl, HF, and $HClO_4$ brings everything into solution. Five ml HCl are added and the solution made up to 25 ml. For 1–6 per cent Co, 5 ml of this solution are mixed with 1 ml 0.05 g/ml Ni solution; for 0.15–1 per cent Co, 10 ml of sample solution are used with 1 ml of this Ni solution. The spectrum is excited by using a condensed spark and 0.1 ml prepared solution in a Feldman porous cup. Calibration solutions are prepared from spectrographically pure metals with the inclusion of CaO, Al_2O_3, MgO, and NaCl.

Other Methods

Cobalt may be precipitated from a solution containing nickel as potassium cobaltinitrite $(2K_3Co(NO_2)_6 \cdot 3H_2O)$ by adding a hot solution of potassium nitrite to an acetic acid solution of cobalt and allowing it stand overnight. The precipitate is not weighed as such, nor is it titrated. So many substances interfere—such as oxidizing agents; free mineral acids; Group 2 elements; appreciable quantities of Fe, Al, Cr; alkaline earths; ammonium salts—that for most materials, cobalt and nickel must be isolated by electrolysis before carrying on with the potassium cobaltinitrite procedure. Details are given by Scott and Furman,[54] and Kallman.[32]

A novel chromatographic parting of nickelous and cobaltous ions has been proposed:[44] a solution is passed at pH 9–10 through a column charged with wet, solid dimethylglyoxime; the column is washed until free of cobalt, then eluted with 0.1 N HCl.

FORMS OF COBALT

The diverse processes now employed in the extractive metallurgy of cobalt have made it necessary, at times, to determine metal, sulfide, or oxides when these forms occur together. Frequently, other metals are present in similar states so that an analysis for sulfur or oxygen will not reveal the form of cobalt present.

Metallic Cobalt

With Mercuric Chloride Solution. The following procedure, based on the report of Smirnov and Mishin,[58] has been very useful in the study of cobalt mattes and slags at Rhokana Corporation. The results of these determinations showed close agreement with the volume percentages of metallic cobalt or cobalt-iron alloy estimated by careful microscopic studies.[68,77]

To 2 g –200 mesh slag, add 50 ml 7 per cent mercuric chloride solution. Boil 1 minute, filter through Whatman 42 paper, and wash thoroughly with hot water. The following reaction will occur: $Co + HgCl_2 \longrightarrow CoCl_2 + Hg$. Metallic cobalt passes into the filtrate as the chloride and can be determined by any suitable procedure. The α-nitroso β-naphthol and ammonium thiocyanate methods can be applied directly, as can the potentiometric procedure if an excess of ammonium chloride is used. Electrolytic or nitroso-R-salt determinations must be preceded by elimination of mercury with H_2S.

The following, if present in metallic form, will be extracted along with the cobalt: Bi, Cr, Cu, Fe, Mn, and Ni. Cobalt sulfide, cobalt silicate, and cobaltosic oxide (Co_3O_4) are virtually insoluble in the mercuric chloride solution. Cobaltic oxide (Co_2O_3) is only soluble to the extent of 0.1–0.3 per cent, but cobaltous oxide is slightly soluble. The extent of the solubility of CoO is difficult to determine, since it is invariably mixed with Co_3O_4 and Co_2O_3.

With Chlorine-Alcohol Solution. A differentiation of metal and sulfide from oxide in roasted and reduced ores and concentrates, based on leaching with a chlorine-alcohol solution, is sometimes employed in the base metal industries. For cobalt, however, in the presence of sulfide, this procedure has a limited value since the time required to leach all the sulfide also results in considerable solution of the higher oxides. For example, for the same mesh size and experimental techniques used with a 0.25 g sample, 1 ten-minute leach will dissolve 99 per cent of the metallic cobalt, about 80 per cent of the cobalt sulfide, 0.2 per cent of the CoO, and 1–3 per cent of the Co_2O_3 and Co_3O_4. To attain 99 per cent extraction of the sulfide, 3 ten-minute leaches are required; the solubility of the oxides then increases to 2–3 per cent for CoO, 10–20 per cent for Co_2O_3 and 8–11 per cent for Co_3O_4.

In the absence of cobalt sulfide, the method separates metallic cobalt from its oxides; if the higher oxides of cobalt are not present, cobaltous oxide can be differentiated from the metal and sulfide by this means.

Weigh out a suitable quantity of –200 mesh sample, depending on the analytical procedure to be employed for cobalt; transfer to a dry 400 ml tall beaker. Add 10 times the sample weight of anhydrous methyl alcohol, stir, and place in fume cupboard. Introduce a vigorous stream of gaseous chlorine from a cylinder into the dilute pulp for 10 minutes. Cobalt in metallic form, and most of the sulfide cobalt, will dissolve in the chlorine-alcohol solution, leaving the oxides virtually unattacked. Filter, and wash the residue with anhydrous methyl alcohol; carefully evaporate the filtrate to dryness and acidify with HNO_3. Make up to a definite volume and determine cobalt in a suitable aliquot.

If cobalt sulfide is present, a second or third ten-minute leach may be required to dissolve all this compound; in this case, the procedure is suitable only when cobaltous oxide is the sole form of cobalt oxide present.

Oxide Cobalt in Ores and Concentrates

In the extractive metallurgy of cobalt, it is sometimes necessary to differentiate the oxidized from the sulfide state in natural forms of the element. For instance, it may be required to obtain a measure of the ratio of oxidized minerals, such as asbolite, heterogenite, sphaerocobaltite, and stainierite, to the cobalt sulfides, carrollite, linnaeite, and siegenite. The following procedure, based on the selective solvent action of dilute H_2SO_4 or HCl on oxidized cobalt minerals in the presence of the reducing agent sulfurous acid, is applicable to ores and concentrator products.[80]

Depending on the quantity of oxide cobalt present in the material and the analytical method used, select a weight of –200 mesh sample that will enable an accurate determination of cobalt to be made on the leached portion. For instance, in a mill feed or tailing containing 0.02 per cent oxide cobalt, at least 25 g must be taken for the initial sample if cobalt is to be precipitated by α-nitroso β-naphthol and weighed as oxide, or determined electrolytically. If the colorimetric nitroso-R-salt procedure is employed on the same sample, a weight of 0.25 g will suffice.

The ratio of leach solution to sample may vary considerably, depending on the quantity of oxide cobalt present and the other acid-consuming constituents of the ore. In general, add 15–25 ml of 10 per cent by volume HCl saturated with SO_2, or 5 per cent by volume H_2SO_4 saturated with SO_2, to each g of material in a stoppered Erlenmeyer flask or covered beaker. When the initial effervescence and attack has subsided, add 0.1–0.3 ml HF/g of sample. For large samples, these quantities of HF can be proportionally reduced.

Shake the flask or beaker for 10–15 seconds every 10 minutes for 1 hour; allow to stand for another hour, and agitate again at intervals of 10 minutes for the third hour. A useful timer for controlling such intermittent mechanical shaking has been described.[83] Filter the sample through a Whatman 40 paper (using pulp), and wash thoroughly with hot water. Add

10 ml 1:1 H_2SO_4 to the filtrate, boil out SO_2, and evaporate to fumes of SO_3. Cool, dilute, boil to solution of salts, and remove copper and other Group 2 metals with H_2S.

Filter off copper and other sulfides, washing well with acidulated H_2S water. Boil out H_2S from the filtrate and proceed with the determination of cobalt by any standard method.

Differentiation of Cobalt Oxides

The proportions of cobaltous oxide and the higher oxides Co_2O_3 and Co_3O_4 in a mixture resulting from refining operations can be determined in the following manner.[7] Place one gm of –200 mesh sample in a 250 ml Erlenmeyer flask with 20 ml water and shake well until all particles are thoroughly wetted. Add 30 ml glacial acetic acid and attach a reflux condenser to the flask. Boil gently for one hour. Pour the contents of the flask on to a tared sintered glass crucible and wash well with hot water. Dry to constant weight in a 105° C oven.

Under these conditions, cobaltous oxide is soluble in acetic acid, whereas the higher oxides, Co_2O_3 and Co_3O_4, are not. This treatment leaves cobalt sulfide virtually insoluble,[82] and consequently affords a procedure for separating sulfide from cobaltous oxide in metallurgical products.

References

1. Almond, H., "Determination of Traces of Cobalt in Soils," *Anal. Chem.,* **25,** 166–7 (1953).
2. Arthur, D., Motzok, I., and Branion, H. D., "The Determination of Cobalt in Forage Crops," *Can. J. Agr. Sci.,* **33,** 1–15 (1953).
3. Bagshawe, B., and Hobson, J. D., "A Study of the Cobalt Ferricyanide Reaction with Relation to the Determination of Cobalt in Steels," *Analyst,* **73,** 152–7 (1948).
4. Bakhmutov, L. A., "Analytical Spectral Lines of Cobalt When Iron and Nickel are Present in the Sample," *Zavodskaya Lab.,* **22,** 1321–2 (1956). *Chem. Abst.,* **51,** 11164 (1957).
5. British Iron and Steel Research Association, "Absorptiometric Determination of Cobalt in Iron and Steel," *J. Iron Steel Inst.,* **176,** Part 1, 63–6 (1954).
6. —, "Spectrographic Determination of Residual Elements in Steel," *J. Iron Steel Inst.,* **181,** 316–8 (1955).
7. Bryant, P. S., "Cobalt Refining at Rainham Works of Murex, Ltd.," Inst. Mining Met. Symposium on Refining of Non-Ferrous Metals, 259–79 (1950).
8. Chirnside, R. C., Cluley, H. J., and Proffitt, P. M. C., "The Analysis of Nickel-Cobalt-Iron Alloys Used in Glass-to-Metal Seals," *Analyst,* **72,** 351–9 (1947).
9. Claassen, A., and Daamen, A., "The Photometric Determination of Cobalt by Extraction with β-nitroso-α-naphthol," *Anal. Chim. Acta,* **12,** 547–53 (1955).

10. Clark, L. J., "Cobalt Determination in Soils and Rocks with 2-nitroso-1-naphthol," *Anal. Chem., 30*, 1153–6 (1958).
11. Cuta, F., and Rauscher, K., "Spectrographic Determination of Small Amounts of Cobalt in Nickel Salts," *Chem. Listy, 48*, 1616–22 (1954). *Chem. Abst., 49*, 4446 (1955).
12. Dean, J. A., "Isolation and Determination of Cobalt as Nitroso-R-salt Complex by Chromatographic Ion Exchange," *Anal. Chem., 23*, 1096–7 (1951).
13. Diehl, H., and Butler, J. P., "Ferricyanide Titration of Cobalt Using Ethylenediammine," *Anal. Chem., 27*, 777–81 (1955).
14. Edwards, J. C., "Report on Mineral Constituents of Mixed Feeds. Cobalt Determination in Mineral Feeds," *J. Assoc. Offic. Agr. Chem., 35*, 559–65 (1952).
15. Flaschka, H. A., "EDTA Titrations," London, Pergamon Press Ltd., 1959.
16. Flaschka, H. A., Barnard, A. J., Jr., and Broad, W. C., "The EDTA Titration: Applications," *Chemist-Analyst, 47*, 22–8 (1958).
17. Fortunatov, N. S., Nazarenko, Y. P., and Mikhailovskaya, V. I., "Separation of a Small Quantity of Cobalt from Solutions," *Zhur. Obschei Khim., 25*, 656–62 (1955). *Chem. Abst., 49*, 14546 (1955).
18. Fujimoto, M., "Microanalysis By Means of Ion Exchange Resins. XIII. Detection of Cobalt in 0.001 γ Amounts with Nitroso-R-salt," *Bull. Chem. Soc. Japan, 30*, 274–8 (1957). *Chem. Abst., 51*, 17579 (1957).
19. Furey, J. J., and Cunningham, T. R., "Analysis of Simple and Complex Tungsten Carbides," *Anal. Chem., 20*, 563–70 (1948).
20. Gagnon, J., "Spectrophotometric Determination of Cobalt in Ores," *Chemist-Analyst, 43*, 15–17 (1954).
21. Gallaher, J., "Collected Papers on Metallurgical Analysis by the Spectrograph," British Non-Ferrous Metals Research Assoc., 135–9 (1945).
22. Goldstein, G., Manning, D. L., and Menis, O., "Spectrophotometric Determination of Cobalt with 1-(2-Pyridylazo)-2-Naphthol," *Anal. Chem., 31*, 192–5 (1959).
23. Gordon, N. E., Jacobs, R. M., and Rickel, M. C., "Spectrographic Analysis of 18-8 Stainless Steel for Cobalt, Manganese, and Stabilizing Elements," *Anal. Chem., 25*, 1031–4 (1953).
24. Guerin, B. D., "The Nitroso-R-Salt Method for the Determination of Cobalt in Ores," *Analyst, 81*, 409–16 (1955).
25. Hague, J. L., Maczkowske, E. E., and Bright, H. A., "Determination of Nickel, Manganese, Cobalt, and Iron in High Temperature Alloys Using Anion Exchange Separations," *J. Res. Nat. Bur. Standards, 53*, 353–9 (1954).
26. Hall, A. J., and Young, R. S., "The Volumetric Determination of Cobalt," *Chemistry and Industry, 1946*, Nov. 2, 394–5.
27. —, et al., "Colorimetric Determination of Cobalt with Nitroso-R-Salt in the Presence of Copper," *Anal. Chem., 22*, 497 (1950).
28. Haywood, F. W., and Wood, A. A. R., "Metallurgical Analysis by Means of the Spekker Photoelectric Absorptiometer," Second Edition, London, Hilger and Watts, Ltd., 1956.
29. Heffeldinger, R. E., Chase, D. L., Rengstorff, G. W. P., and Henry, W. M., "Analysis of High Purity Iron," *Anal. Chem., 30*, 112–4 (1958).

30. Hillebrand, W. F., Lundell, G. E. F., Bright, H. A., and Hoffman, J. I., "Applied Inorganic Analysis," New York, John Wiley and Sons, Inc., 1953.
31. Jones, R. H., "Application of Polarographic Analysis to the Estimation of High Purity Selenium, Nickel and Cobalt Compounds," *Analyst,* **71,** 60–5 (1945).
32. Kallmann, S., "Precipitation of Cobalt as Potassium Cobaltinitrite," *Anal. Chem.,* **22,** 1519–21 (1950).
33. Keenan, R. G., and Kopp, J. F., "Spectrochemical Determination of Trace Quantities of Cobalt in Animal Tissues," *Anal. Chem.,* **28,** 185–9 (1956).
34. King, R. P., Bolin, D. W., Dinusson, W. E., and Buchanan, M. L., "A Chromatographic Method for the Determination of Cobalt in Feeds," *J. Animal Sci.,* **12,** 628–34 (1953).
35. Kinnunen, J., Merikanto, B., and Wennerstrand, B., "Determination of Cobalt in Metallurgical Products," *Chemist-Analyst,* **43,** 21–2 (1954)
36. Kobarelova, S., and Trifonov, A., "Polarographic Determination of Cobalt in Ores and Concentrates," *Godishnik Khim.-Tekhnol. Inst.,* **3,** No. 1, 261–70 (1956). *Chem. Abst.,* **52,** 13529 (1958).
37. Kolthoff, I. M., and Lingane, J. J., "Polarography," Volumes 1 and 11., New York, Interscience Publishers, Inc., 1952.
38. Lingane, J. J., and Kerlinger, H., "Polarographic Determination of Nickel and Cobalt," *Ind. Eng. Chem. Anal. Ed.,* **13,** 77–80 (1941).
39. Mason, G. L., and de Beer, Z., "Spectrochemical Solution Method for the Determination of Copper, Cobalt, and Iron in Copper and Cobalt Concentrates," *Analyst,* **83,** 129–35 (1958).
40. McClure, J. H., and Kitson, R. E., "Spectrochemical Determination of Impurities in Cobalt Oxide," *Anal. Chem.,* **25,** 867–8 (1953).
41. Meites, L., "Polarographic Techniques," New York, Interscience Publishers, Inc., 1955.
42. —, "Polarographic Determination of Cobalt in Presence of Nickel," *Anal. Chem.,* **28,** 404–6 (1956).
43. Mikhailov, P. M., and Velichko, O. C., "Determination of Nickel, Copper, Iron, Manganese, and Silicon in Metallic Cobalt by Spectral Analysis," *Zavodskaya Lab.,* **22,** 1307–10 (1956). *Chem. Abst.,* **51,** 11170 (1957).
44. Oschapovskii, V. V., "Chromatographic Parting of Nickelous and Cobaltous Ions," *Zhur. Anal. Khim.,* **11,** 606–12 (1956). *Chem. Abst.,* **51,** 7229 (1957).
45. Pascual, J. N., Shipman, W. H., and Simon, W., "Rapid Photometric Determination of Cobalt in the Presence of Iron," *Anal. Chem.,* **25,** 1830–2 (1953).
46. Pigott, E. C., "Ferrous Analysis. Modern Practice and Theory," London, Chapman and Hall, Ltd., 1953.
47. Pinkney, E. T., Dick, R., and Young, R. S., "The Entrainment of Cobalt and Sulfur in Iron Separations," *J. Am. Chem. Soc.,* **68,** 1126–8 (1946).
48. Saraswat, H. C., "Volumetric Estimation of Cobalt by Potassium Ferrocyanide," *J. Sci. Ind. Research,* **17B,** 45–6 (1958). *Chem. Abst.,* **52.** 18080 (1958).
49. Saltzman, B. E., "Microdetermination of Cobalt in Biological Materials," *Anal. Chem.,* **27,** 284–7 (1955).
50. Salyer, D., and Sweet, T. R., "Determination of Small Amounts of Cobalt in Steels and Nickel Alloys," *Anal. Chem.,* **29,** 2–4 (1957).

51. —, et al., "Cathodic Electrodeposition Methods for Cobalt," *Anal. Chem.*, **30**, 1632–5 (1958).
52. Scharrer, K., and Taubel, N., "Determination of Smallest Quantities of Cobalt in Biochemical Substances and Soils," *Landwirtsch. Forsch.*, **7**, 105–12 (1955). *Chem. Abst.*, **49**, 8541 (1955).
53. Schweitzer, G. K., and McDowell, B. L., "Co-precipitation of Cobalt with Nickeldimethylglyoxime," *Anal. Chim. Acta*, **14**, 115–20 (1956).
54. Scott, W. W., and Furman, N. H., "Standard Methods of Chemical Analysis," New York, D. Van Nostrand Co., 1939.
55. Shipman, W. H., Foti, S. C., and Simon, W., "Nature and Elimination of Interferences in the Determination of Cobalt with Nitroso-R-Salt," *Anal. Chem.*, **27**, 1240–5 (1955).
56. Shipman, W. H., and Lai, J. R., "General Photometric Microdetermination of Cobalt with Nitroso-R-Salt," *Anal. Chem.*, **28**, 1151–2 (1956).
57. Sihvonen, Y. T., Fry, D. L., Nusbaum, R. E., and Baumgartner, R. R., "Spectrographic Analysis of High Cobalt (Vitallium) Alloys," *J. Optical Soc. Am.*, **39**, 257–60 (1949).
58. Smirnov, V. I., and Mishin, V. D., "Analysis of Industrial Products for Cobalt Compounds," *Zavodskaya Lab.*, **11**, No. 1, 35–8 (1945). *Chem. Abst.*, **39**, 4020 (1945).
59. Smith, D. W., and Hayes, J. R., "Trace Determination of Copper and Cobalt by Chelate Chromatography and Dithizone Photometry," *Anal. Chem.*, **31**, 898–902 (1959).
60. Smythe, L. E., and Gatehouse, B. M., "Polarographic Determination of Traces of Copper, Nickel, Cobalt, Zinc, and Cadmium in Rocks," *Anal. Chem.*, **27**, 901–3 (1955).
61. Souchay, P., and Faucherre, J., "Polarographic Determination of Cobalt and Iron with the Aid of New Base Solutions of Trilon," *Anal. Chim. Acta*, **3**, 252–61 (1949).
62. Standen, G. W., "Qualitative Spectrographic Analysis," *Ind. Eng. Chem. Anal. Ed.*, **16**, 675–80 (1944).
63. Stern, D. G., "The Determination of Cobalt in Ferrous Alloys Using a Chromatographic Separation," *Metallurgia*, **55**, 207–8 (1957).
64. Strasheim, A., and Camerer, L., "The Spectrographic Analysis of Trace Elements in Plant Materials," *J. S. African Chem. Inst.* [N.S.], **8**, No. 1, 28–38 (1955).
65. Stromberg, A. G., and Zelyanskaya, A. I., "Polarographic Determination of Cobalt in the Presence of Nickel. Catalytic Evolution of Hydrogen in the Presence of Cobalt Complexes with Dimethylglyoxime," *J. Gen. Chem.* (U.S.S.R.), **15**, 303–18 (1945). *Chem. Abst.*, **40**, 3361 (1946).
66. Suchy, K., "Determination of Traces of Cobalt in the Mineral Water from Uratislavice," *Vestnik Ceskoslov, Fysiat. Spolecnosti*, **30**, 14–27 (1952). *Chem. Abst.*, **49**, 11920 (1955).
67. Sukhenko, K. A., Mladentseva, O. I., and Yakovleva, N. P., "Spectral Analysis of Complex Alloys of Nickel, Cobalt, and Aluminum," *Izvest. Akad. Nauk S.S.S.R., Ser. Fiz.*, **12**, 436–8 (1948). *Chem. Abst.*, **44**, 3838 (1950).

68. Talbot, H. L., and Hepker, H. N., "Investigations on the Production of Electrolytic Cobalt from a Copper-Cobalt Flotation Concentrate," *Trans. Inst. Mining Met.*, **59**, 147–79 (1949–50).

69. Thiers, R. E., Williams, J. F., and Yoe, J. H., "Separation and Determination of Millimicrogram Amounts of Cobalt," *Anal. Chem.*, **27**, 1725–31 (1955).

70. Touhey, W. O., and Redmond, J. C., "Analysis of Cemented Carbide Compositions," *Anal. Chem.*, **20**, 202–6 (1948).

71. Watters, J. I., and Kolthoff, I. M., "Polarographic Procedure for Determination of Cobalt as Cobalt (111) Ammine," *Anal. Chem.*, **21**, 1466–9 (1949).

72. West, T. S., and Sykes, A. S., "Analytical Applications of Diamino-Ethane-Tetra-Acetic Acid," Poole, Dorset, The British Drug Houses, Ltd., 1959.

73. Wilkins, D. H., and Hibbs, D. E., "Determination of Cobalt in Cobalt Platinum Alloys," *Anal. Chim. Acta*, **16**, 449–51 (1957).

74. Williams, W. J., "Analytical Chemistry of Cobalt," *Talanta*, **1**, 88–104 (1958).

75. Yalman, R. G., "New Iodometric Determination of Cobalt Based on Formation of Iodopentamminecobalt (111) Nitrate," *Anal. Chem.*, **28**, 91–3 (1956).

76. Yardley, J. T., "The Accurate Determination of Cobalt," *Analyst*, **75**, 156–9 (1950).

77. Young, R. S., "Industrial Inorganic Analysis," London, Chapman and Hall, Ltd., 1953.

78. Young, R. S., and Hall, A. J., "Determination of Cobalt in High-Cobalt Products," *Ind. Eng. Chem. Anal. Ed.*, **18**, 262–4 (1946).

79. —, *et al.*, "Colorimetric Determination of Cobalt with Ammonium Thiocyanate," *Ind. Eng. Chem. Anal. Ed.*, **18**, 264–6 (1946).

80. Young, R. S., Hall, A. J., and Talbot, H. L., "The Determination of Oxide Cobalt," *Am. Inst. Min. Met. Eng. Tech. Publ.*, 2050 (1946).

81. Young, R. S., Pinkney, E. T., and Dick, R., "Colorimetric Determination of Cobalt in Metallurgical Products with Nitroso-R-Salt," *Ind. Eng. Chem. Anal. Ed.*, **18**, 474–6 (1946).

82. Young, R. S., and Simpson, H. R., "Differentiation of Cobalt Oxides," *Metallurgia*, **45**, 51 (1952).

83. Young, R. S., Snaddon, R., and Tullett, V. A., "A Laboratory Timer for Intermittent Operations," *J. Sci. Instr.*, **29**, 266–7 (1952).

AUTHOR INDEX

SUBJECT INDEX